PRACTICAL ACCOUNTING

and

COST KEEPING

for

CONTRACTORS

A TREATISE ON MODERN BUSINESS METHODS

PRACTICAL ACCOUNTING

AND

COST KEEPING

FOR

CONTRACTORS

Illustrating and Describing
In Easy, Understandable Language, Bookkeeping and Accounting Systems
for Contractors, Giving Complete Instructions and Examples of
the Proper Methods of Keeping Time and Compiling
Costs on all Classes of Construction Work

By
FRANK R. WALKER COMPANY
Publishers of
The Building Estimator's Reference Book

Eighth Edition
Illustrated

FRANK R. WALKER COMPANY, PUBLISHERS
CHICAGO

ISBN-0-911592-08-3

PRINTED IN THE U. S. A.

Table of Contents

CHAPTER 1

INTRODUCTION

Contractors to-day need accurate business records more than ever before, not only for their personal information but to be able to prepare the reports and pay the taxes imposed by many State Sales and Use Taxes, Old Age Pensions, Unemployment Compensation, Income and Profit Taxes, etc.

To be practical and workable, bookkeeping, accounting and cost keeping methods for contractors must take into consideration the unusual conditions surrounding the industry, if the information is to be of value to the contractors for whom it is intended.

This would be an easy task if mercantile and factory accounting methods could be applied to the construction business—but the contractor's business is different. The contractor takes contracts, lets contracts, purchases materials and employs labor on a number of jobs at one time and if he is to know whether his business is being conducted at a profit or loss, it is essential that accurate records be kept of every contract. Preparation of financial statements are an essential need for credit and bonding requirements.

This book deals primarily with the accounting procedures for contractors. The accounting and bookkeeping principles are fundamental to any type of business. Chapter 14 is an introduction to bookkeeping leading to the preparation of interim and year end financial statements.

Briefly, there are three classes of contractors and each of them requires a different system of accounts:

First, the small contractor who operates a shop or conducts a jobbing business will require a very simple system—a system that will not take much of his time because in most instances the contractor will keep his own records.

Second, the medium size contractor who constructs residences, small apartment and business structures, will require a system that will furnish detailed information regarding his business, but the system must be simple and the number of entries reduced to minimum because this contractor seldom employs a bookkeeper, and the books are usually kept in spare time.

Third, all contractors who want a modern double-entry bookkeeping system that will furnish detailed information regarding every phase of the business, contracts on hand, sub-contract accounts, job cost accounts, work in progress, etc., but the system must be free of "red-tape" and easy to keep.

This also applies to methods of keeping time on the job and compiling costs because the contractor who keeps his own time or has it kept by the job foreman will require an altogether different system than the contractor who employs a timekeeper on his different jobs.

Keeping time and compiling costs and the methods described in this book are simple enough for the smaller contractors yet elaborate enough for the largest.

Costs, to be of value to the contractor and estimator, should state the quantity of work a man will perform per day or the number of hours required to complete a certain unit of work. The costs should always be stated in the same units as new work is estimated in order that comparisons may be made between estimated and actual costs and in order that the costs may be of value in preparing future estimates.

Complete labor and material cost schedules are included which describe how costs on each class of work should be kept and how they should be designated. It also contains illustrations giving practical examples of how the costs should be reported from the job. All steps necessary to gather and compile the data from checking the workmen's time, distributing the labor hours, and working the costs into suitable units is given in each instance.

It is the purpose of this book to impart to contractors, timekeepers, superintendents, foremen, accountants and bookkeepers the essentials of accurate cost keeping, describing the methods by which maximum results may be obtained with a minimum amount of labor. For this reason the book should be of especial interest to bookkeepers and timekeepers just starting in the construction business because it contains information regarding methods and their results that would take them years to acquire if left to their own resources.

This book also contains illustrations and descriptions of other forms required on the job and in the office, such as Social Security Records, Expense Sheets, Construction and Material Reports, Progress Reports, Extra Work Forms, Purchase Orders, Estimate Sheets, Proposals, Contract and Sub-Contract Forms, and in fact, practically everything required in the construction business.

It is the intention of this book to assist the contractor in conducting his business so that he will have complete records, from the preparation of the estimate to completion of the job, showing all steps necessary, together with a description of the various methods available and illustrations of different record forms to obtain the desired results.

For that reason, we begin by giving methods of preparing estimates, purchasing materials, letting sub-contracts, organizing the job for construction, and on through to the methods used in keeping a complete set of books.

The inexperienced contractor may also find it most helpful in preparing his estimates to refer to the "Building Estimator's Reference Book," also published by Frank R. Walker Co., which presents a detailed study of estimating procedures in over 1200 pages of detailed analyses and examples.

Several methods are described for performing every operation so the contractor may select the one that best meets his particular requirements.

CHAPTER 2

PREPARATION OF THE ESTIMATE

One of the most important parts of a contractor's business is his estimating. If your estimates are too high you lose the job—if they are too low, you lose your money.

Poor estimating is responsible for as many failures among contractors as any other cause.

The contractor who uses "averages" or "short cut" methods of estimating is asking for trouble. They usually result in estimates that are so low the contractor must assume a loss before the job is even started or they are so high you not only lose the job but may even appear ridiculous.

For these reasons every contractor should insist on estimates prepared with the utmost care.

You may ask, "What constitutes a good estimate?"

A good estimate is one with accurate quantities, intelligently priced, good covering on sub-bids, adequate allowance for general conditions based on a thorough and expert analysis of the job, allowances to cover taxes and insurance, overhead expenses plus a reasonable profit.

A good estimate does not mean that the contractor will get the job, as a competitor may make a mistake too—or needing a job, may figure a smaller profit—or feel that he can perform the work at a lower cost.

It does mean however, that with a well prepared estimate, the contractor knows where he stands; can negotiate with confidence, and if awarded the contract, the job probably will be profitable.

In order to obtain consistently good estimates, it is essential the contractor set up a sound estimating procedure and insist on it being followed to the letter.

Estimating Procedure

Estimating procedure varies considerably among contractors, but any method that will produce good estimates without taking excessive time may be used. The following procedure is being successfully used by many estimators:

1. Plans and specifications are inspected and a list made of all major items in the job, such as General Conditions, Excavation, Concrete Foundations, Reinforced Concrete, Masonry, Rough Carpentry, Millwork, Roofing, Sheet Metal, Glass and Glazing, Plastering, etc. If a blank summary sheet is used, these items are entered in the description or classification column.

2. All classifications of work which the contractor does not do with his own crews are noted as sub-contract items and "Request for Bid Cards" are sent to a number of contractors specializing in each classification. Good sub-bid coverage is absolutely essential to successful bidding. At the same time, requests are made for quotations on vendor items, such as reinforcing steel, millwork, etc.

3. Site of the proposed work is visited and all information necessary to estimate the job is obtained. This need not be done until later as many estimators prefer to take off the concrete work first, in order to become familiar with the job.

4. Quantities of work to be done by the contractor's own crews are accurately taken from the plans and listed on a General Estimate Sheet where they will be priced, or on a Quantity sheet and summarized on a Recapitulation sheet for pricing.

5. Quantities are priced, extended and totaled.

6. The job is analyzed to determime the job overhead and general condition items required. These items are listed, priced and totaled.

7. Fees for the building permit, street obstruction bond, etc., are estimated. State sales taxes on materials, if required, are computed. Payroll taxes and insurance, based on labor are figured.

8. Plant and equipment requirements are listed, priced and totaled.

9. All sub-bids are carefully analyzed to determine the lowest complete and acceptable quotation for each classification of sub-work.

10. All general item totals and low sub-bids are entered in their proper places on the Summary Sheet and the columns are totaled and cross totaled to arrive at the estimated job cost.

Steps 1 to 10 being completed, the possibilities of contingencies are considered and the job cost adjusted with provisions for same if required. Contractor's profit is then determined and added. If a Surety Bond is required, the premium is added at the very end and is based on the total amount of the estimate, including cost of bond.

At this point it should be mentioned that all operations in preparing the estimate should be carefully checked, especially extensions and totals, and preferably by a person other than the one doing the original work. The most common arithmetical errors are misplaced decimal points and mistakes in Summary Sheet additions.

A brief discussion of each step in the preparation of an estimate is given on the following pages.

Inspection of Plans and Specifications

Before starting to prepare an estimate, the estimator should slowly leaf through the plans and specifications to become acquainted with the job.

The plans are usually inspected first to learn the scope of the job. It is surprising how much information can be fixed in the mind by a casual perusal of the floor plans, elevations, sections and details and this knowledge makes the subsequent steps of preparing the estimate easier.

In leafing through the specifications, all of the different classifications of work included, should be listed. To save duplication of effort, this should be done on the summary sheet which will be used in making up the bid. If a blank summary sheet is used, the various classifications are listed in the column provided for that purpose. If a printed summary sheet is used, the classifications which apply to the particular job being figured are checked off and the balance of the items are marked out. (See Figures 1 and 2.)

When listing the classifications of work on the summary sheet, some contractors prefer to list their own work first and then the items they intend to sub-let, while others list the various items in the same order as they appear in the specifications. Either method is satisfactory, as long as care is taken to insure against open items, that is, classifications of work which are specified or shown on the plans but through oversight are not included in the estimate.

It is not enough to just list each section heading of the specifications, as many architects make a practice of lumping several items under one heading. For example: Under "Miscellaneous Metals," some architects include such items as Miscellaneous Iron, Steel Sash, Metal Doors, Steel Stacks, Flagpoles, Metal Casework, Metal Lockers, etc., all items which are usually bid and purchased separately and therefore should be listed separately on the summary sheet. Other specification headings may be similarly composite, so when checking the specifications, more than a casual glance is necessary to be sure each classification of work is listed on the summary sheet.

Requesting Sub-Bids

When the listing of the various job items has been completed, the contractor or estimator can readily determine which part of the work he will do with his own crews and the classifications for which he must obtain sub-bids. He can also determine the various vendor items, i.e., materials which require fabrication but are installed by the contractor's own crews, for which he must also obtain quotations.

The usual procedure in asking for bids on sub and vendor items is to send our "Request for Bid Cards" to a number of sub-contractors or suppliers specializing in each of the various classifications required. Most contractors send ordinary postal cards which give the pertinent information of the job, such as, Name of Work, Location, Architect, where plans may be seen, date bids are due, etc. (See Figure 3.) If the response to the cards seems slow, follow-up telephone calls may be necessary. It is important to let a sufficient number of concerns know you desire their quotations so that when the time comes to make up your bid you will have an adequate number of proposals for each classification of work.

SUMMARY OF ESTIMATE

PRACTICAL
PRACTICAL FORM 115

BUILDING *STORE BUILDING* LOCATION *S.E. CORNER MAIN & OAK STS.* ESTIMATE NO. *429*

ARCHITECT *JOHNSON & ANDERSON* OWNER *MR. JOHN H. SMITH* DATE *APRIL 7, 19--*

CUBICAL CONTENTS *19,830 CF* NO. OF STORIES *AND BSMT.* COST PER CUBIC FOOT *$2.98* ESTIMATOR *EFZ*

FLOOR, AREA, SQUARE FEET *(INCL BSMT)* *2000 SF* COST PER SQUARE FOOT *$26.61* CHECKER *JMB*

CLASSIFICATION	TOTAL ESTIMATED MATERIAL COST	TOTAL ESTIMATED LABOR COST	TOTAL SUB-BIDS	TOTAL	ADJUSTMENTS
1. GENERAL CONDITIONS AND OFFICE OVERHEAD	300	2400		2700	
2. JOB CONDITIONS AND JOB OVERHEAD	3157			3157	
3. CONSTRUCTION PLANT, TOOLS AND EQUIPMENT	575			575	
4. DEMOLITION AND SITE CLEARANCE					
5. EXCAVATION, GRADING AND DEWATERING	938	413		1351	
6. SHEETING, SHORING AND BRACING					
7. PILING AND CAISSON WORK					
8. SITE DEVELOPMENT					
9. CONCRETE FORM WORK	1210	3026		4236	
10. CAST IN PLACE CONCRETE	2772	2447		5219	
11. PRECAST CONCRETE AND CEMENTITIOUS DECK					
12. BRICK, TILE, CONCRETE & GLASS UNIT MASONRY	2281	6402		8683	
13. UNIT MASONRY PARTITIONS & FIREPROOFING					
14. CUT, ROUGH, NATURAL & SIMULATED STONE					
15. STRUCTURAL METALS			800	800	
16. OPEN WEB JOISTS AND METAL DECKING					
17. MISCELLANEOUS METALS		288	1287	1575	
18. ORNAMENTAL METALS					
19. ROUGH CARPENTRY AND ROUGH HARDWARE	2753	2525		5278	
20. FINISH CARPENTRY		369	1275	1644	
21. CUSTOM MILLWORK					
22. WATERPROOFING AND DAMP-PROOFING					
23. BUILDING INSULATION					
24. SHINGLE AND ROOFING TILE					
25. MEMBRANE ROOFING			1675	1675	
26. PREFORMED ROOFING AND SIDING					
27. ROOFING ACCESSORIES					
28. SHEET METAL FLASHINGS					
29. SEALANTS AND CAULKING			300	300	
30. METAL DOORS AND FRAMES			175	175	
31. WOOD AND PLASTIC DOORS			500	500	
32. SPECIAL DOORS					
33. METAL WINDOWS					
34. WOOD AND PLASTIC WINDOWS			750	750	
35. FINISHED HARDWARE & WEATHER STRIPPING					
36. GLASS, GLAZING AND MIRRORS			325	325	
37. CURTAIN WALL AND STORE FRONT SYSTEMS			1250	1250	
38. LATHING AND FURRING					
39. PLASTERING AND STUCCO WORK			2315	2315	
40. GYPSUM DRYWALL					
41. CERAMIC, MOSAIC, QUARRY, MARBLE & SLATE TILE					
42. TERRAZZO AND SEAMLESS FLOORING					
43. WOOD FLOORING					
44. RESILIENT FLOORING					
45. ACOUSTICAL TILES AND PANELS					
46. SPRAY ON FIRE PROTECTION					
47. PAINTING AND SPECIAL FINISHES			1375	1375	
48. SPECIAL BUILDING PARTITIONING					
49. BUILDING SPECIALTIES, EQUIP. & FURNISHINGS					
50. ELEVATORS & MECHANICAL TRANSPORT					
51. PLUMBING			2200	2200	
52. FIRE PROTECTION & SPRINKLER SYSTEMS					
53. HEATING, VENTILATION & AIR CONDITIONING			4200	4200	
54. ELECTRICAL WORK			3560	3560	
55. COMMUNICATION SYSTEMS					
56. TOTALS	13986	17185	22672	53843	

57.	TOTAL COST	53843
58.	PROFIT 10%	5384
59.	SURETY BOND NOT REQ'D	
60.	AMOUNT OF BID	59227

MFD. IN U.S.A.

FRANK R. WALKER CO., PUBLISHERS, CHICAGO

Fig. 1. Summary of Estimate, With or Without Printed Classifications. Size 9¼ x 11⅞ Inches. Form 115.

PRACTICAL FORM 515

SUMMARY OF ESTIMATE

BUILDING **RESIDENCE**   ADDRESS **419 ELM ST., SKOKIE, ILL.** ESTIMATE NO. **216**

OWNER **T. O. SMITH**   ADDRESS **5407 N. WAYNE, CHGO.** DATE **JUNE 19, 19--**

ARCHITECT **JONES & HOWARD**   ADDRESS **I N. LaSALLE ST., CHGO.** ESTIMATOR **E.F.Z.**

CLASSIFICATION	TOTAL ESTIMATED MATERIAL COST	TOTAL ESTIMATED LABOR COST	TOTAL SUB-BIDS	TOTAL ESTIMATED COST	TOTAL ACTUAL COST
1. GENERAL CONDITIONS AND JOB OVERHEAD EXPENSE		250		250	294 80
2. BUILDING AND STREET PERMITS, INSURANCE, TAXES	590			590	562 18
3. SUPERINTENDENT, FOREMAN, WATCHMEN		500		500	542 09
4. CONSTRUCTION PLANT, TOOLS AND EQUIPMENT	100			100	75 26
5. WRECKING, REMOVING TREES, CLEARING SITE			300	300	300 00
6. EXCAVATING AND BACKFILLING		32		32	35 47
7. GRADING, ROUGH AND FINISH, TOP SOIL	388	304		692	652 15
8. FOUNDATIONS AND PIERS, AREAWAYS, ETC.			60	60	60 00
9. WATER AND DAMPPROOFING, DRAIN TILE, GRAVEL	144	122		266	279 39
10. CEMENT FLOORS, WALKS, PAVEMENTS					
11. REINFORCED CONCRETE, BEAMS, JOISTS, FLOORS, STAIRS					
12. BRICK, TILE AND CONCRETE MASONRY	1418	2121		3539	3219 21
13. CUT STONE, CAST STONE, GRANITE, ETC.					
14. ROUGH CARPENTRY, FRAMING LUMBER, ETC.	996	687		1683	1715 09
15. INSULATING BOARD, WALL BOARD, PLYWOOD, ETC.			360	360	325 00
16. INSULATION, SOUND DEADENING					
17. MILL WORK AND INTERIOR FINISH. FINISH CARPENTRY		701	1265	1966	1899 21
18. GARAGE DOORS, WOOD OR METAL. OPERATORS			212	212	200 00
19. WOOD OR METAL CASES AND CABINETS		52	600	652	660 78
20. FLOORS, WOOD. LAYING, SANDING, FINISHING			772	772	750 00
21. STAIRS, WOOD. ROUGH AND FINISH	21	26	280	327	329 85
22. ROUGH HARDWARE	152			152	162 94
23. FINISH HARDWARE			120	120	120 00
24. WEATHER STRIPS			88	88	85 00
25. CAULKING	30	50		80	82 43
26. LATHING AND PLASTERING			1680	1680	1650 00
27. SHEET METAL, GUTTERS, DOWNSPOUTS, FLASHING, ETC.			160	160	160 00
28. ALUMINUM OR SHEET SASH AND WINDOWS					
29. ROOFING, ASBESTOS, ASPHALT, BUILT-UP, SLATE, TILE, WOOD			224	224	210 00
30. STRUCTURAL IRON AND STEEL		50	128	178	181 14
31. MISCELLANEOUS IRON, STEEL AND ALUMINUM					
32. TILE FLOORS, WALLS AND MANTELS, MARBLE			740	740	725 00
33. PLASTIC OR METAL WALL TILE AND BASE					
34. ASPHALT, CORK, RUBBER OR VINYL TILE, LINOLEUM			44	44	40 00
35. GLASS AND GLAZING, VITROLITE OR CARRARA GLASS			168	168	168 00
36. PAINTING, EXTERIOR			520	520	475 00
37. PAINTING AND DECORATING, INTERIOR			500	500	500 00
38. PLUMBING, SEWERAGE AND GAS FITTING			1800	1800	1800 00
39. HEATING AND AIR CONDITIONING			1400	1400	1400 00
40. ELECTRIC WIRING, LIGHT AND POWER			600	600	600 00
41. LIGHTING FIXTURES			120	120	152 65
42. SCREENS, DOOR AND WINDOW					
43. STORM DOORS AND WINDOWS			460	460	460 00
44. ELEVATOR, DUMB-WAITER					
45. KITCHEN AND LAUNDRY EQUIPMENT, INCINERATOR			975	975	975 00
46. CURTAIN RDS., WINDOW SHDS., VENETIAN BLDS., AWNINGS			85	85	75 00
47.					
48.					
49.					
50.					
51.					
52. **TOTALS**	3839	4895	13661	22395	21922 64
53. TOTAL COST				22395	21922 64
54. PROFIT				2200	2672 36
55. SURETY BOND					
56. AMOUNT OF BID				24595	24595 00

MFD. IN U.S.A.   FRANK R. WALKER CO., PUBLISHERS, CHICAGO

Fig. 2. Summary of Estimate, Designed Especially for Houses and Apartment Buildings. Size 8½ x 11 Inches. Form 515.

ANDREWS CONSTRUCTION COMPANY
209 East Elm Street
Arlington, Illinois

Please send us your bid for all work in your line on the ....19.............
....
....
....
Plans may be seen at our office and..Architects
Bids to be in our office not later than...
Send your bid promptly to insure consideration; if not figureing, please so advise.
Thank you.

ANDREWS CONSTRUCTION COMPANY

Fig. 3. Request for Bid Card. Size 3¼ x 5½ Inches.

Visiting the Site

Visiting the site is of great importance and the information gained is absolutely essential to the preparation of an accurate estimate. Never submit a bid on a job without first visiting the site and determining the actual existing conditions under which the work will have to be performed.

This may be done at any time prior to the submission of bids. Many estimators prefer to take off the quantities of concrete foundation work first in order to become familiar with the job and then visit the site before taking off the earthwork.

While at the site, all existing conditions should be checked and those which will affect the construction work and influence the amount of the bid, should be listed so they may be considered when pricing the estimate. The following list of conditions, by no means complete, will serve as an example of the things to look for when at the site.

1. General Site Conditions. Look for obstructions which will have to be removed, such as, trees, brush, existing buildings, foundations or slabs, etc. Also check location of public utilities, condition of existing walks, curbs, streets, etc.

2. Soil Conditions. Determine the thickness of top soil to be removed and the nature of the sub soil to be excavated. Is the site dry and is there natural drainage in the event of wet weather? Will the banks of excavations stand safely or will it be necessary to brace them or use sheet piling? If there is other construction work in progress in the vicinity, a visit to these jobs may answer most of the questions as to soil conditions.

3. Location, Accessibility and Size of Site. Is the job readily accessible to construction traffic or will a road have to be built and maintained? How far is job from material yards, railroad siding, ready-mix concrete plant, etc.? Is the site large enough to store material and equipment or will the job be congested? Distance from job to disposal area for excess excavated materials, rubbish, etc.

4. Nature of Neighborhood and Availability of Labor. From the looks of the neighborhood, what precautions should be taken to safeguard the job? Is there much work going on in the vicinity which will affect manning the job? A visit to local labor union headquarters and material yards will help answer the question on labor conditions. Check availability of water and electric power for construction use. Check permit cost and local regulations concerning building operations, such as, requirements for protection of public, inspections required, bonds required, etc.

The above list contains a few of the many items you may find at a job site which will influence your bid so keep your eyes open and learn all you can about the conditions you will have to contend with and it will pay off in the long run.

Taking Off Quantities

The most laborious and tedious operation in estimating is taking off quantities of work from the plans and specifications, which the contractor intends to do with his own crews. To measure and list quantities for estimating purposes requires a great deal of time and effort which the contractor often prefers to spend in the more interesting manner of overseeing the construction work in the field. However, he must realize that good estimating is just as important to his business as good building and an accurate quantity take-off is one of the requisites of good estimating. He should take the time to accurately take off quantities on jobs he is going to bid or if he does not have time to do it himself he should hire a qualified estimator.

The task of taking off quantities can be made easier if the estimator will adopt a system of listing the quantities which will, in general, be the same for all jobs he figures. To accomplish this he can use any of the standard estimating forms available as shown in the accompanying illustrations. After using these forms for a short while, the actual listing of dimensions becomes almost automatic and leaves the mind free for the more exacting task of determining which dimensions to list. These forms are available in several styles, namely, the General Estimate sheet, which is used for both taking off and listing quantities and pricing; the Quantity sheet, which is used for taking off and listing quantities only, and the Recapitulation sheet, which is used for listing and pricing the quantities obtained from the Quantity sheets.

Figures 4 to 7, illustrate the General Estimate sheets with the method of listing quantities and pricing shown. This is an excellent estimating sheet as if provides space for both quantities and pricing and is adaptable to any size job. After the heading, which gives ample space to enter information to properly identify the estimate, the sheet is divided into twelve clearly headed columns which guide the estimator, as to the proper entries. The first column is for a brief description of the item being listed. The next four columns are for the number of pieces and dimensions of the quantity. There are then two columns for quantity extensions, which make it possible to perform double extensions from one set of dimensions for such items as concrete footings, walls, columns, slabs or beams and the necessary forms, thus reducing the time required to list dimensions without detracting from the accuracy of the estimate. Some estimators also use the second column to list deductions for openings separate from the rest of the take-off for such items as masonry, flooring, plastering, etc. The next column is for total estimated quantities, after they have been reduced to working units, and it is these figures to which the unit prices will be applied. The last four columns are for pricing and consist of a unit price column and a total estimated cost column for both material and labor, thus keeping material and labor costs separate. This is a time saver as it facilitates computing sales taxes on materials and insurance premiums and social security taxes on labor costs.

An estimate prepared in this manner can be readily checked both as to accuracy of take-off as well as pricing by anyone familiar with estimating. In addition, as the job progresses, the contractor can readily check his actual costs against his estimated costs, thus giving better control of the work and increasing the possibilities for greater profits.

The General Estimate form is also available in a double width sheet, as shown in Figure 8, containing twelve extension columns and a three column space for total estimated quantities, consisting of one column each for the name of the item, the quantity and unit of measurement. In addition, it contains a total column for listing the sum of the material and labor cost for each item and when totaled, serves as a check on the totals of material and labor costs. This sheet, is letter size when folded, and can be filed with the regular size General Estimate sheets. This form fills the need for an estimating sheet for taking off quantities on the most complex work where a large number of items are encountered, such as, concrete combination floor slabs where the item headings in addition to concrete, might be solid slab forms, pan slab forms, beam bottom forms, beam side forms, trowel finish, float or screed finish under terrazzo or similar floor finish, forms for boxed openings, etc., all of which could be computed from the same set of dimensions used for the concrete calculations.

Some contractors and estimators prefer to take off quantities on a Quantity sheet as shown in Figure 9, and then summarize and list all the items of work on a Recapitulation sheet for pricing, as shown in Figures 11 or 12. This method is more generally used by contractors figuring a large volume of work and having several take-off men who split up the quantity take-off among themselves, each taking one or more classifications of work, such as, Earthwork, Concrete, Masonry, Rough Carpentry, Erection of Millwork, etc., thus turning out an individual estimate in less time. The quantities are then summarized and listed on a Recapitulation sheet, usually being done by the chief estimator or the person who is to do the pricing.

The Quantity sheet differs from the General Estimate sheet in that it contains no columns for pricing but instead has four columns for extensions plus columns for the estimated quantity and the unit of meas-

GENERAL ESTIMATE

BUILDING: STORE BUILDING
LOCATION: S.E. CORNER MAIN & OAK
ARCHITECTS: JOHNSON & ANDERSON
SUBJECT: GENERAL

ESTIMATOR: E. F. Z.
CHECKER: J. M. B.
DATE: APRIL 7, 19--

DESCRIPTION OF WORK	NO. PIECES	L	W	D	EXTENSIONS	EXTENSIONS	TOTAL ESTIMATED QUANTITY	UNIT PRICE M'T'L	TOTAL ESTIMATED MATERIAL COST	UNIT PRICE LABOR	TOTAL ESTIMATED LABOR COST
EXCAVATION											
GENERAL		46-6	31-6	9-0	13183 CF		489 CY	1 50	734		
TRENCH & PIT		126-0	2-0	1-0	252		11 CY			9 50	105
(CUT NEAT)		2-4	2-4	1-0	5						
		4-0	4-0	1-0	16	273 CF					
BACKFILL - PUDDLED		143-0	3-3	9-0	4183 CF		155 CY	.35	54		
PUMPING WATER							ALLOW		150		100
GRADING, EXT. ROUGH		85-0	25-0		2125		2080 SF			.10	208
OUT FOR WALK		15-0	3-0		DED. 45	2080 SF					
									938		413
CONCRETE FOUNDATIONS - 3000# CONC. - READY-MIX											
COLUMN FOOTING		4-0	4-0	1-0	16 CF		1 CY	38 00	38	25 00	25
WALL "		126-0	2-0	1-0	252		10 CY	38 00	380	25 00	250
ADDL. AT STACK		2-4	2-4	1-0	5	257 CF					
FOUNDATION WALLS					CF CONCRETE	SF FORMS	44 CY	38 00	1672	27 00	1188
F 2 S		122-4	1-0	9-4	1142	2284	2421 SF	.50	1210	1 25	3026
"		7-4	0-8	9-4	46	137					
					1188	2421					
SET 12"X 12" CAST IRON CLEAN OUT DOOR IN FORMS (FURN. BY MISC. IRON CNTR.)											10
SET 8" DIAM. SMOKE PIPE THIMBLE IN FORMS (FURN. BY HEATING CNTR.)											10
									3300		4509
CONCRETE FLOORS AND WALKS - 2500# CONC. - READY-MIX											
BASEMENT FLOOR - 4" CONC. ON 6" CINDER FILL - MONOLITHIC TROWEL FIN.											
		38-0	23-0				874 SF	.30	262	.50	437
SIDEWALK - 5" CONC. ON 6" CINDER FILL MONOLITHIC FINISH							981 SF	.40	392	.50	490
		156-0	6-0		936						
		15-0	3-0		45	981 SF					
CURE AND PROTECT CEMENT FINISH ON FLOOR & WALK							1855 SF	.015	28	.02	37
									682		964
MASONRY											
FACE BRICK - FULL HEADERS EVERY 6TH C. 3/8" TOOLED JOINTS							5 M	90 00	450	262 50	1310
		66-0	X	12-0	792						
LESS OUTS					DED 183						
					609 SF X 8 BRK/SF =	4872					
(SEE NEXT PAGE)											

MFD. IN U.S.A.

FRANK R. WALKER CO., PUBLISHERS, CHICAGO

Fig. 4. General Estimate. Size 9¼ x 11⅞, 8½ x 11 or 8½ x 14 Inches. Form 514.

PRACTICAL
FORM 514

GENERAL ESTIMATE

BUILDING STORE BUILDING
LOCATION S.E. CORNER MAIN & OAK
ARCHITECTS JOHNSON & ANDERSON
SUBJECT GENERAL

ESTIMATOR E.F.Z.
CHECKER J.M.B.
DATE APRIL 7, 19--

DESCRIPTION OF WORK	NO. PIECES	L	W	D	EXTENSIONS	EXTENSIONS	TOTAL ESTIMATED QUANTITY	UNIT PRICE M'T'L	TOTAL ESTIMATED MATERIAL COST	UNIT PRICE LABOR	TOTAL ESTIMATED LABOR COST
OUTS OPNGS - STORE WIN.	3	8-0	X	5-6		132	F. BRK 75⁰⁰				
" ENTRANCE		3-6	X	7-0		24	MORTAR 15⁰⁰				
" SIDE WIN.		3-0	X	5-0		15	MTL UNIT 90⁰⁰				
OUT FOR STONE SILLS		28-4	X	0-5		12					
							183				
COMMON BRICK		100-8	1-0	12-0	1208		21 M 80⁰⁰		1680	200⁰⁰	4200
		21-8	1-0	10-0	217						
STACK		6-8	0-8	16-0	71	OUTS	C BRK = 65⁰⁰				
OPNGS STORE WIND.	3	8-0	1-0	5-6		132	MORTAR = 15⁰⁰				
" ENTRANCE		3-6	1-0	7-0		24	MTL UNIT 80⁰⁰				
" REAR DOOR		3-0	1-0	7-0		21					
" SIDE WIND.	2	3-0	1-0	5-0		30					
" REAR WIND.	2	2-0	1-0	4-0		16					
OUT FOR STONE SILLS		36-4	0-4	0-5		5					
" " FACE BRK VOL	1/6	609 S.F. X		0-4		237					
					1496	465					
LESS OUTS			DED.	465							
					1031 CF X 20	BRK / C.F. =					
							20620				
13"x13" CLAY FLUE TILE LINING							16 LF	1⁷⁰	27	1⁶⁵	26
12" DBL SLANT VIT. TILE COPING							38 LF	2⁰⁰	76	1⁵⁰	57
SET CUT. STONE (MAT. BY SUB) 5"x7' SILLS							37 LF	.05	2	3⁰⁰	81
14½"X7 COPING							64 LF		3	2⁸⁰	179
2'6"x2'6"x0'6" CHIMNEY CAP							ALLOW		2		15
CLEAN & POINT F. BRK & STONE 609 + 37 + 160 + 11 P.P. SILLS COPING CAP							817 SF	.05	41	.50	409
SET LOOSE STEEL LINTLES 3-4"X 4" ANGLES 3' TO 4' L.							6 OPNGS.			1⁸⁰	11
- 10" CHANNEL & ½" PLT. - 10' L.							3 OPNGS.			20⁰⁰	60
SET BAR GRATINGS IN MASONRY JAMBS 3'0"x5'0"							2 OPNGS.			15⁰⁰	30
2'0"x4'0"							2 OPNGS.			12.	24
									2281		6402
SET STEEL COL. & BEAM (FURN. BY MISC. IRON CNTR.)											
LALLY COL 5" DIA. X 8'4"							ALLOW				15
12" - 35 lb. I BEAM 39 L.F.							1365 lbs			20	273
											288

MFD. IN U.S.A.

FRANK R. WALKER CO., PUBLISHERS, CHICAGO

Fig. 5. General Estimate. Size 9¼ x 11⅞, 8½ x 11 or 8½ x 14 Inches. Form 514.

GENERAL ESTIMATE

BUILDING __STORE BUILDING__

LOCATION __S.E. CORNER MAIN & OAK__

ARCHITECTS __JOHNSON & ANDERSON__

SUBJECT __GENERAL__

ESTIMATE NO. __429__

SHEET NO. __3 OF 4__

ESTIMATOR __E. F. Z.__

CHECKER __J. M. B.__

DATE __APRIL 7, 19--__

DESCRIPTION OF WORK	NO. PIECES	L	W	D	EXTENSIONS	EXTENSIONS	TOTAL ESTIMATED QUANTITY	UNIT PRICE M'T'L	TOTAL ESTIMATED MATERIAL COST	UNIT PRICE LABOR	TOTAL ESTIMATED LABOR COST
ROUGH CARPENTRY - ORDINARY WORKMANSHIP											
1ST FL. FRAMING	62	2x10's	14-0				1447 FBM	.26	376	.16	232
CROSS BRIDGING		1"x4"					60 SETS	.20	12	.85	51
ROUGH FLOORING 1"x6" D&M	38-0	23-0			874		985 FBM	.25	246	.15	148
OUT FOR STAIR		4-0	11-6		DED. 46						
					828 SF x 1.19 FBM/SF = 985 FBM						
FIN. FLRG 25/32" x 2¼" HARD MAPLE = 828 SF x 1.33 FBM/SF =							1101 FBM	1.00	1101	.60	661
SANDING & FINISHING MAPLE FLOOR							828 SF	.10	83	.35	290
ROOF FRAMING	31	2x12's	24-0				1488 FBM	.27	402	.19	283
CROSS BRIDGING		1"x4"					90 SETS	.20	18	.85	77
ROOF SHEATHING 1"x6" D&M	38-0	23-0			874 SF x 1.19 FBM/SF		1040 FBM	.25	260	.22	229
RGH. WD. STAIRS & STRINGS	3	2x12's	16-0		96		229 FBM	.28	64	.55	126
TREADS	14	2x10's	4-0		93						
RAILING	5	2x4's	12-0		40						
					229 FBM						
HAND RAIL - WALL HUNG							15 L.F.	.50	8	1.50	23
METAL BRACKETS FOR HAND RAIL							4 PCS.	.75	3		
STUD PARTITIONS - PLTS	6	2x4's	10-0		40		241 FBM	.24	58	.20	48
"	6	2x4's	12-0		48						
STUDS	23	2x4's	10-0		153						
					241 FBM						
1"x2" FURRING STRIPS ON INT. OF MAS. WALLS							875 L.F.	.05	44	.25	219
1"x2" GROUNDS FOR TRIM AT DOORS, WDWS, BASE, ETC.							550 L.F.	.05	28	.25	138
ROUGH HARDWARE							ALLOW		50		
									2753		2525
FINISH CARPENTRY - MATERIAL BY SUB											
FRONT ENTRANCE	3-0	7-0	2¼	SASH DOOR, PLK FR., TRIM INSIDE, BRK M							100
REAR "	2-8	7-0	1¾	" " " " " "							65
INT. DOORS	2-4	7-0	1¾	FL. DRS, HEAD, JAMBS, STOPS, TRIM 2 SIDES - 3 OPNGS						16.00	48
SCREEN DOORS				2 OPNGS						20.00	40
BASE - 2 MEMBER	5/8" x 5¼	& ½" x ¾" SHOE					203 L.F.			.40	81
WINDOW STOOLS	3/4"	7¼"					37 L.F.			.65	24
WINDOW APRON	5/8"	3⅝"					37 L.F.			.30	11
											369

Fig. 6. General Estimate. Size 9¼ x 11⅞, 8½ x 11 or 8½ x 14 Inches. Form 514.

GENERAL ESTIMATE

BUILDING _STORE BUILDING_

LOCATION _S.E. CORNER MAIN & OAK_

ARCHITECTS _JOHNSON & ANDERSON_

SUBJECT _GENERAL_

ESTIMATE NO. _429_

SHEET NO. _4 OF 4_

ESTIMATOR _E. F. Z._

CHECKER _J. M. B._

DATE _APRIL 7, 19--_

DESCRIPTION OF WORK	NO. PIECES	DIMENSIONS		EXTENSIONS	EXTENSIONS	TOTAL ESTIMATED QUANTITY	UNIT PRICE M'T'L	TOTAL ESTIMATED MATERIAL COST	UNIT PRICE LABOR	TOTAL ESTIMATED LABOR COST
GENERAL CONDITIONS AND JOB OVERHEAD										
SUPERINTENDENT (1/3 TIME ONLY)		3 MONTHS @ 1200.00 ÷ 3								1200
TIMEKEEPER (1/3 TIME ONLY)		3 MONTHS @ 600.00 ÷ 3								600
RUBBISH REMOVAL - PERIODIC & FINAL		5 @ 50.00/LOAD								250
JOB OFFICE & TOOL HOUSE								300		350
								300		2400
PERMITS INSURANCE & TAXES										
BUILDING PERMIT								150		
PLUMBING INSPECTION FEE								25		
STREET OBSTRUCTION BOND								100		
STATE SALES TAX- 5% OF TOTAL EST. MAT. ($10,254)								513		
SOCIAL SECURITY TAXES										
FED'L INSURANCE CONTRIBUTION 5.85% OF TOT. EST. PAYROLL ($17,189)								999		
UNEMPLOYMENT COMPENSATION 4% " " " " "								687		
INSURANCE										

No. CLASSIFICATION	WORKMENS COMP.	PUBLIC LIABILITY	PROPERTY DAMAGE	TOTAL RATE	ESTIMATED PAYROLL					
14. EXCAVATION EARTH	5.10/c	0.41/c	1.00/c	6.51/c	413			27		
8. CONCRETE - GEN'L.	2.70/c	0.20/c	0.22/c	3.12/c	5473			171		
26. MASONRY	3.40/c	0.17/c	0.16/c	3.82/c	5717			218		
23. STEEL ER. - 2 STY.	13.00/c	0.23/c	0.18/c	13.41/c	288			39		
3. CARPENTRY - 3 STY.	4.00/c	0.14/c	0.12/c	4.26/c	2894			123		
36. SUPERVISION	5.10/c	0.47/c	0.27/c	5.84/c	1800			105		
								3157		
PLANT & EQUIPMENT										
VIBRATOR	1 MONTH @ 100.00							100		
MORTAR MIXER	1 MONTH @ 125.00							125		
SMALL TOOLS, FUEL, LUBRICATING MAT'LS., ETC					ALLOW			350		
								575		

Fig. 7. General Estimate. Size 9¼ x 11⅞, 8½ x 11 or 8½ x 14 Inches. Form 514.

Fig. 8. General Estimate. Size 17 x 11 Inches. Form 519.

ure. The Quantity sheet is also available in a double width sheet containing fifteen extension columns and can be used for the most complex take-off work, such as structural glazed tile, 2" furring and partitions, with all special shapes being listed, as shown in Figure 10.

The Recapitulation sheet (See Figure 11) is divided into seven columns headed: Description, Quantity, Unit (of measure), Unit Price (for material), Total Estimated Material Cost, Unit Price (for labor), and Total Estimated Labor Cost. The Recapitulation sheet is also available with an additional column in which may be entered the total of the material and labor costs for an additional check. (See Figure 12.)

From a study of the accompanying illustrations, the contractor or estimator should readily see the advantage of adopting a standard form and method for taking off and listing quantities in the preparation of his estimates and can choose the one best suited to his needs. Assuming the plans and specifications are clear and complete, there is less possibility for an inaccurate quantity take-off, when one of these methods is employed.

Before starting to take off quantities on a job, the estimator may be confused as to the amount of detail required to produce a good estimate. Taking off volumes or areas of the different classes of construction and then pricing these quantities with a unit price designed to cover all of the operations necessary to produce the finished work is not detailed enough to use as a basis for making up a firm bid. On the other hand, a practical limit exists in the other direction also. An estimator cannot take into consideration every saw cut, nail driven or bolt tightened, because if he did, it would take as long to figure the job as to build it.

In general, each classification of work should be divided into the major items of which it is composed, and then quantities for these items should be taken off from the plans and specifications. For example: the classification of Concrete may be divided into column footings, wall footings, foundation piers, foundation walls, columns, slabs, beams, floors on ground, walks, driveways, etc. These items may be further divided into the actual concrete to be placed, the forms required to contain the concrete and the type of finish the concrete is to receive. In addition, there are always items to be built into the concrete, such as anchor bolts,

QUANTITY SHEET

PROJECT **NEW HIGH SCHOOL**   ESTIMATOR **E. F. Z.**   ESTIMATE NO. **252**

LOCATION **GARY, INDIANA**   EXTENSIONS **J. M. B.**   SHEET NO. **1**

ARCHITECT ENGINEER **SMITH & WILSON**   CHECKED **H. J. B.**   DATE **APRIL 22, 19--**

CLASSIFICATION **GENERAL**

DESCRIPTION	NO.	L	W	D						ESTIMATED QUANTITY	UNIT
EXCAVATION											
GENERAL		429-0	70-0	10-6	315315					13751	CY
		74-0	72-0	10-6	55944						
					371259	CF					
TRENCH & PIT		1106-0	2-6	1-0	2765					223	CY
		296-6	2-0	1-0	593						
COL. FTGS.	49	6-0	6-0	1-6	2646						
					6004	CF					
CONCRETE FOUNDATIONS - 3000# CONCRETE					CONCRETE → OUTS		FORMS → OUTS				
WALL FOOTINGS		1106-0	2-6	1-0	2765					125	CY
		296-6	2-0	1-0	593						
					3358	CF					
COLUMN FOOTINGS	49	6-0	6-0	1-6	2646	CF				98	CY
							2LD	2LD			
FOUNDATION WALLS		1106-0	1-0	11-0	12166		24332			556	CY
"		304-0	1-0	10-6	3192		6384			30006	SF
DOOR OPNGS.	10	3-2	1-0	7-2		227		454			
WDW OPNGS.	3	8-0	1-0	5-4		128		256			
					15358	355	30716	710			
LESS OUTS					355		710				
					15003	CF	30006	SF			
BOXING FORMS FOR OPENINGS IN FOUNDATION WALLS										287	SF
	10	20-8	X	1-0	207						
	3	26-8	X	1-0	80						
					287	SF					
BASEMENT FLOOR - 2500# CONCRETE - 4 1/4" ROUGH CONCRETE - 3/4" TOP 1:2										29748	SF
		419-0	60-0		25140						
		72-0	64-0		4608						
					29748	SF					
REINFORCED CONCRETE - 3000# CONCRETE					CONCRETE		(2L x 2W) D FORMS				
COLUMNS - BSMT.	49	1-6	1-6	10-6	1158	3087				154	CY
1ST	108	1-3	1-3	10-0	1688	5400				13671	SF
2ND	108	1-0	1-0	12-0	1296	5184					
				(CF)	4142	13671	SF				

Fig. 9. Estimate Quantity Sheet. Size 8½ x 11 or 8½ x 14 Inches. Form 516.

FORM 520

QUANTITY SHEET

PROJECT: NEW HIGH SCHOOL	ESTIMATOR: E.F.Z.
LOCATION: GARY, INDIANA	EXTENSIONS: J.M.B.
ARCHITECT ENGINEER: SMITH & WILSON	CHECKED: H.J.B.
CLASSIFICATION: PARTITIONS, FURRING & COLUMN COVERING	ESTIMATE NO. 252 — SHEET NO. 11 — DATE APRIL 25, 19--

GLAZED TILE PARTITIONS & FURRING - 6T SERIES (3"x12" FACE) - CERAMIC GLAZED

DESCRIPTION	NO.	L	W	D	2" SOAPS BY MASONRY	OUTS	2" SOAPS ON CONCRETE	OUTS	4" STRETCHERS GL.1 SIDE	OUTS	4" STRETCHERS GL.2 SIDES	OUTS	LF BULLNOSE CORNERS	PCS HORIZONTAL BULLNOSE	PCS MITER CORNERS	PCS 2" COVE BASE	PCS 4" COVE BASE	PCS COVE BASE STRETCHERS	PCS COVE BASE CORNERS	QUANTITY	UNIT
2" FURRING ON MASONRY		216-0	X	10-3	2214											216				2" on Mas.	
WDW. OPNGS	10	8-0	X	6-8		533							133	160	40					7643	Pcs.
2" FURRING ON CONCRETE	12	3-0	X	10-3			369						246			48				2" on Conc.	
"	21	8-8	X	10-3			1867						861			168		24		5715	Pcs.
"	3	14-0	X	8-0			432									54		84		4" Gl.1 Side	
WDW. OPNGS		22-0						128					32							14857	Pcs.
4" PARTITIONS - GL.1 SIDE		526-0	X	10-3					5392				32	48	12					4" Gl.1 Sides	
DOOR OPNGS	11	3-4	X	7-1						260			156	-33	22		481	40		4804	Pcs.
" "	4	3-0	X	7-1						85			57	12	8			22		Bull. Cor.	
BOR. LT. OPNGS	5	6-0	X	5-4						160			53	60	20		8			3992	Pcs.
4" PARTITIONS- GL.2 SIDES		205-0	X	10-3							2101					410				Horiz. Bull.	
"		22-0	X	8-0							176					8				375	Pcs.
DOOR OPNGS - No Specs	6	3-4	X	7-1								142								Miters	
6" PARTITIONS - GL.2 SIDES		182-0	X	10-3	1866						1866	142	21		167	167		24		142 2" Cove Base	
DOOR OPNGS	5	3-4	X	7-1		118					118		142	3.0	20			20		1071	Pcs.
PASS WDW. OPNGS.	2	4-0	X	4-0		32					32		32	32	16					4" Cove Base	
LESS OUTS					4080	683	2668	128	7258	655	2277	142	1774	375	198	1071	648	74	162	648	Pcs.
					683		128		655		142		1774 PCS	PCS	PCS	PCS	Pcs	Pcs	Pcs	74	Pcs.
					3397 SF		2540 SF		6603 SF		2135 SF		3992 pcs							Base Stretchers	
					2.25 ft²/pc		2.25 ft²/pc		2.25 ft²/pc		2.25 ft²/pc									74	Pcs.
					7643 Pcs		5715 Pcs		14857 Pcs		4804 Pcs									Base Corners 162	Pcs.

Fig. 10. Estimate Quantity Sheet. Size 17 x 11 Inches. Form 520.

curb angles, floor frames, sleeves, inserts, etc., which must be located and set before the concrete is placed. All of these items should be included in the estimate and quantities measured and listed.

In taking measurements from the plans, dimensions as given on the plans should always be used in preference to measuring with a scale rule. In listing dimensions, they should be adjusted to keep the take-off on a practical basis, especially in the case of fractional dimensions. It would be ridiculous to list the dimensions of a general excavation as 46'-3½" x 31'-3¾" x 8'-11¾" because it could not be dug that accurately even though it may be exactly the dimensions required by the plans. The experienced estimator would list it as 46'-6" x 31'-6" x 9'-0". On the other hand a beam width of 11½" or a slab thickness of 6½" can be constructed without any trouble and the dimensions should be listed as called for.

All quantities of work should be measured and listed, as far as practical, in the same manner and order as the construction is carried on in the field, although this may be varied by the individual estimator, who may prefer to take off the concrete foundations before the earthwork in order to become familiar with the job.

Figures 4 to 7 illustrate the estimate sheets used in preparing an estimate for a small store building. In this case the General Estimate forms have been used for the entire estimate.

Note how the quantities have been listed and identified by entries in the columns headed Description of Work, No. Pieces and Dimensions. The usual procedure in taking off quantities, is to first list all items of one classification of work, together with their description and dimensions, and then go back later and make the extensions. This method is faster and more accurate quantities are obtained as there is no break in the take-off operation to disturb the estimator's concentration. In the larger contractors' offices, extensions are often done entirely by personnel hired especially for this purpose and the estimator is relieved of this chore.

Note how the sequence of item listings in each classification closely parallels the order in which the work will be done in the field. Setting up an estimate in this manner aids the estimator in visualizing the job in his mind and decreases the possibility of omitting any item.

RECAPITULATION

FORM 517

PROJECT *NEW HIGH SCHOOL*	ESTIMATE NO. *252*
LOCATION *GARY, INDIANA*	SHEET NO. *1*
ARCHITECT ENGINEER *SMITH & WILSON*	DATE *APRIL 30, 19--*
SUMMARY BY *E.F.Z.* PRICES BY *E.F.Z.*	CHECKED BY *H.J.B.*

DESCRIPTION	QUANTITY	UNIT	UNIT PRICE	TOTAL ESTIMATED MATERIAL COST	UNIT PRICE	TOTAL ESTIMATED LABOR COST
EXCAVATION - GENERAL (SUB)	13,751	CY	.70	9626	.50	6876
TRENCH & PIT	223	CY	.55	123	1.20	268
				9749		7144
CONCRETE FOUNDATIONS						
3000# CONCRETE WALL FOOTINGS	125	CY	37⁰⁰	4625	25⁰⁰	3125
COLUMN "	98	CY	37⁰⁰	3626	25⁰⁰	2450
FOUNDATION WALLS	556	CY	35⁰⁰	19460	15⁰⁰	8340
FORMS - FOUNDATION WALLS	30,006	SF	.75	22505	1⁰⁰	30006
BOXED OPNGS IN WALLS	287	SF	.60	172	1⁹⁰	545
				50388		44466
BSMT. FLOOR 4¼" - 2500# CONC & ¾" TOP	29,748	SF	.30	8924	.50	14874
REINFORCED CONCRETE						
3000# CONCRETE - COLUMNS	154	CY	65⁰⁰	10010	115⁰⁰	17710
SLABS + BEAMS - 1ˢᵗ FL	576	CY	40⁰⁰	23040	45⁰⁰	25920
" " 2ⁿᵈ FL	561	CY	40⁰⁰	22440	50⁰⁰	28050
" " ROOF	508	CY	40⁰⁰	20320	50⁰⁰	25400
STAIRS & PLATFORMS	45	CY	40⁰⁰	1800	130⁰⁰	5850
FORMS - COLUMNS	13,671	SF	.35	4785	.80	10937
SOLID SLAB FORMS	3,362	SF	.95	3194	1.10	3698
OPEN DECK SLAB FORMS	74,648	SF	.48	35831	1.05	78380
BEAMS - SPANDREL - BOTTOMS	2,217	SF	.45	998	2.05	4545
" " - SIDES	3,426	SF	.40	1370	1.20	4111
" INTERIOR - BOTTOMS	3,922	SF	.38	1490	1.60	6275
" " - SIDES	2,435	SF	.34	828	1.10	2679
STAIRS & PLATFORMS	2,760	SF	.65	1794	3.50	9660
FINISHES - MONOLITHIC TROWEL	60,812	SF	.03	1824	.15	9122
FLOAT ROOF	30,814	SF	.03	924	.13	4006
STAIRS & PLATFORMS	2,097	SF	.05	105	.30	629
				130753		236972
MASONRY						
FACE BRICK ⅜" TOOLED JOINTS - FLEMISH BOND	169	M	92⁰⁰	15548	330⁰⁰	55770
COMMON BRICK - BACK-UP	26	M	65⁰⁰	1690	275⁰⁰	7150
8" INTERIOR WALLS	72	M	65⁰⁰	4680	210⁰⁰	15120
CONCRETE BLK. BACK UP - LT. WT. 8"X8"X16"	21,830	PCS	.38	8295	1.20	26196
FORWARD				30213		104236

MFD. IN U.S.A.   FRANK R. WALKER CO., PUBLISHERS, CHICAGO

Fig. 11. Estimate Recapitulation Sheet. Size 8½ x 11 or 8½ x 14 Inches. Form 517.

PRACTICAL
STANDARDIZED FORMS FOR CONTRACTORS

RECAPITULATION

PROJECT **NEW HIGH SCHOOL**   ESTIMATE NO. **252**

LOCATION **GARY, INDIANA**   SHEET NO. **1**

ARCHITECT ENGINEER **SMITH & WILSON**   DATE **APRIL 30, 19--**

SUMMARY BY **E.F.Z.**   PRICES BY **E.F.Z.**   CHECKED BY **H.J.B.**

DESCRIPTION	QUANTITY	UNIT	UNIT PRICE	TOTAL ESTIMATED MATERIAL COST	UNIT PRICE	TOTAL ESTIMATED LABOR COST	TOTAL
EXCAVATION - GENERAL	13,751	CY	.70	9626	.50	6876	16502
TRENCH & PIT	223	CY	.55	123	1.20	268	391
				9749		7144	16893
CONCRETE FOUNDATIONS							
3000# CONCRETE - WALL FTGS.	125	CY	37.00	4625	25.00	3125	7750
COL. "	98	CY	37.00	3626	25.00	2450	6076
FOUNDN. WALLS	556	CY	35.00	19460	15.00	8340	27800
FORMS - FOUNDATION WALLS	30,006	SF	.75	22505	1.00	30006	52511
BOXED OPNGS IN WALLS	287	SF	.60	172	1.90	545	717
				50388		44466	94854
BASEMENT FLOOR 4¼" 2500#C + ¾" TOP	29,748	SF	.30	8924	.50	14874	23798
REINFORCED CONCRETE							
3000# CONCRETE - COLUMNS	154	CY	65.00	10010	115.00	17710	27720
SLABS & BEAMS - 1ST FL	576	CY	40.00	23040	45.00	25920	48960
" " 2ND FL	561	CY	40.00	22440	50.00	28050	50490
" " ROOF	508	CY	40.00	20320	50.00	25400	45720
STAIRS & PLATFORMS	45	CY	40.00	1800	130.00	5850	7650
FORMS - COLUMNS	13,671	SF	.35	4785	80	10937	15722
SOLID SLAB FORMS	3,362	SF	.95	3194	1.10	3698	6892
OPEN DECK SLAB "	74,648	SF	.48	35831	1.05	78380	114211
BEAMS - SPANDREL - BOTTS	2,217	SF	.45	998	2.05	4545	5543
" " SIDES	3,426	SF	.40	1370	1.20	4111	5481
" INTERIOR - BOTTS	3,922	SF	.38	1490	1.60	6275	7765
" " SIDES	2,435	SF	.34	828	1.10	2679	3507
STAIRS & PLATFORMS	2,760	SF	.65	1794	3.50	9660	11454
FINISHES - MONOLITHIC TROWEL	60,812	SF	.03	1824	.15	9122	10946
FLOAT ROOF	30,814	SF	.03	924	.13	4006	4930
STAIRS & PLATFORMS	2,097	SF	.05	105	.30	629	734
				130753		236972	367725
MASONRY							
FACE BRICK ⅜" TOOL JTS - FLEM. BOND	169	M	92.00	15548	330.00	55770	71318
COMMON BRICK - BACK UP	26	M	65.00	1690	275.00	7150	8840
8" INTERIOR WALLS	72	M	65.00	4680	210.00	15120	19800
CONC. BLK. BACK UP LT. WT. 8"x8"x16"	21,830	PCS	.38	8295	1.20	26196	34491
GL'D TILE - 5"x12" CER. GL. 2" FURR.	13,358	PCS	.48	6412	1.05	14026	20438
4" STRETCHERS - GL 1 SIDE	14,857	PCS	.60	8914	1.10	16343	25257
4" " - GL 2 SIDES	4,804	PCS	.80	3843	1.10	5284	9127
EXTRA COST - BULLNOSE CORNERS	3,992	PCS	.25	998	.30	1198	2196
FORWARD				50380		141087	191467

FRANK R. WALKER CO., PUBLISHERS, CHICAGO

Fig. 12. Estimate Recapitulation Sheet. Size 8½ x 11 or 8½ x 14 Inches. Form 518.

After the extensions have been completed and reduced to working units, the quantity and its unit of measure are entered in the column headed Total Estimated Quantity, ready for pricing. The factors applied to obtain the quantities in working units may be found along with more complete information on estimating in "The Building Estimator's Reference Book," a sister publication to this text.

Finally, when the take-off is complete and ready for pricing it should contain the quantities for every item necessary to complete the work the contractor intends to do with his own crews.

For lack of space in the illustrations, several classifications of work appear on the same sheet. This is contrary to general practice except on very small work, as most contractors start each classification on a new sheet. This applies to both quantity take-off and summarizing and is necessary to correctly estimate the insurance premiums as each class of work has a different premium rate. This also permits rough checking the estimate, such as, cost per cubic yard of concrete, cost per thousand brick, etc., and is useful in making up budgets and breakdowns, should the bid be successful. In listing quantities, allow plenty of room on the sheet, leaving several lines between items. There is less possibility of errors of omission and mistakes in computation when the figures stand out without being crowded.

All quantities should be reduced to the same working units as are used in the field, so that when actual costs are obtained from the job, they can be compared with the estimate, enabling the contractor to compare his estimated and actual costs and giving him the opportunity to make any changes in personnel or methods of operation he may deem necessary.

Pricing the Quantities

Pricing the quantities is one of the most variable factors in estimating. In most cases, pricing involves two sets of unit prices, one for material and one for labor.

Material unit prices are the easiest to determine, as they are usually based on quotations obtained from various material supply companies. Quite often the quotations may be guaranteed for the life of the job. The material prices are then combined in the proper ratios to obtain unit prices to be used in pricing the estimate.

In computing a material unit, the estimator must take the prices of all materials required to produce the finished item and apply them to the formula of the finished material. For example: In the estimate illustrated in Figure 4, to work up the material unit for face brick, the following steps are taken: First, the face brick quotation of $75.00 per thousand, delivered to the job, is noted. Second, it is determined that it will take 14 cubic feet of masonry cement mortar to lay up 1,000 brick with ⅜" cross joints and a ½" back joint. Third, it is also determined that 14 cubic feet of masonry cement mortar is composed of 4⅔ sacks of masonry cement and 14 cubic feet of sand. Fourth, applying the material quotations obtained from the supplier, 4⅔ sacks of masonry cement @ $1.65 per sack and 14 cubic feet of sand @ $5.25 per cubic yard equals $7.00 for the 14 cubic feet of mortar required, which when added to $80.00 for the brick gives a material unit of $90.42 per thousand face brick. Similarly all other material units should be computed and entered in their proper places in the estimate.

Labor units are much less tangible in their composition and consist of labor rates applied to the estimated labor production which the estimator thinks will be attained on the job.

Of the two component parts of a labor unit, only the labor rates are positively known at time of figuring, and these may change during the course of the job. Labor production is the big variable in estimating and is affected by practically any change in job conditions. One of the most effective factors influencing labor production, is the economic situation. It is an established fact that men will work harder and produce more when jobs are scarce than when jobs are abundant. Another important factor is the seasons of the year during which the men will have to work. Here again, men will produce more when the weather is ideal than when it is wet and cold or very hot. The type of job also influences labor production. On large, simple jobs with a good percentage of repetition, high production may usually be expected, whereas small, cut-up jobs, will be penalized by much lost motion and have a low overall production.

Considering all of the above conditions, and others which will influence the job, the estimator must exercise his best judgment in determining the values to be used to price the labor in the estimate. This should be backed by a thorough working knowledge of the production of men, of the multitude of operations encountered and of the most up-to-date methods which can be used to construct the job. He should be able to build the job in his mind and to visualize it at any stage of the operation. Estimators are not born with this knowledge, it can only be acquired by a careful study of construction methods and cost records of many jobs.

The best source of information the estimator has on which to base his figuring, is the cost records of previous jobs, the more recent the better. This amounts to predicting what will occur in the future by what has happened in the past and is really the only tangible information he has to work with. How to keep cost records will be discussed later but it should be stated here that cost records, to be of lasting value, should be kept in terms of production as well as money. Taking "production" records, adjusting them to suit the job being figured and then applying prevailing labor rates are steps which the estimator must take in working up labor units. Much of this is done mentally but some notes or computations are usually required to aid the figuring and these should be filed with the rest of the estimate for future reference.

In working up labor units, it must be remembered that a mechanic seldom works alone, usually having helpers to bring material, build and remove scaffolds, etc., thus adding to the cost of the item being priced. For example: In Figure 4, the estimator has priced the labor of laying face brick at $90.00 per thousand brick. In arriving at this unit, he has estimated that a mason will take 17.8 hours to lay a thousand brick and that it will also take 12 hours labor time, to mix the mortar, keep the mason supplied with brick and mortar, and build and remove the "horse" scaffold per thousand brick. Applying the prevailing labor rates for both mason and laborer we get, 17.8 hours @ $9.95 equals $177.11 and 12 hours @ $7.10 equals $85.20, or a total unit labor cost of $262.31 per thousand face brick, which has been rounded out to $262.00 per thousand brick and entered in its proper place in the estimate. In like manner, all other labor units should be figured and entered in the estimate.

The usual procedure followed by many estimators is to figure and enter all material and labor units before making any extensions for total estimated material and labor costs. It is also general practice to make money extensions only in whole dollars and if an extension ends in 50 cents or over it is raised to the next whole dollar, if below 50 cents the pennies are dropped. For example: $14.50 would be raised to $15.00 and $14.49 would be lowered to $14.00. After the extensions are made, they are totaled, keeping each classification separate, and are then ready to be entered on the summary sheet.

Job Overhead and General Conditions

The next step in preparing an estimate is to determine the Job Overhead and General Condition items required to do the job properly and economically. These items are often more or less ignored or overlooked, but since they are a definite part of the job cost, they should be included in the estimate or their cost will have to come out of the contractor's profit.

One of the governing factors in the costs of these items is the length of time it will take to complete the job. By now, the estimator should be familiar with the scope of the job and able to judge the amount of time required without too much difficulty. Another factor is the seasons of the year through which the job will run and what weather to expect. The size of the job will also influence the amounts estimated for the various items both as to the time required to build the job and the personnel and job office facilities necessary for efficient operation. In addition, the specifications should be closely checked for items of general conditions the architect specifically calls for. The entire job must be carefully analyzed to determine adequate, but not excessive, provisions for Job Overhead and General Conditions to be used in the estimate.

The Job Overhead should be considered first and all non-productive personnel required to properly run the job, should be listed, together with the length of time they will be needed and the salary they will receive. This should include all supervisory personnel, job office employees, such as, timekeeper, cost clerk, material clerk, stenographer, etc., and watchmen, waterboys, etc. Included with the supervisory personnel should be superintendent, construction engineer and all non-working foremen. If any foremen will work part time with their tools, that portion of their time should be included in the various labor units of work they will do. Also, if a superintendent or any other personnel is figured as only spending part time on the job, this should be reflected by the amount included in the estimate.

After the Job Overhead has been determined, all General Condition items which the estimator anticipates will be required should be listed. This should include construction or provisions of a temporary nature, such as job office, tool house and other sheds; temporary sanitary facilities; temporary water installation, including charges for water used; temporary light and power installation, including charges for energy consumed; temporary ladders and stairs; temporary heating of the building, if the job will run during the winter, including installation of equipment, fuel and operating labor; heating of construction materials and protecting the work from freezing; and temporary provisions for the protection of the public, such as, barricades, warning lights, sidewalk bridges, outrigger platforms, etc. Also allowances for job office supplies and equipment, including stationery, postage, office furniture, typewriters, adding machines, etc.; telephone and telegraph; progress photographs of job, if required; surveys and blueprints; material tests and samples; traveling and living expenses for key personnel; etc. In addition, allowances for periodic and final cleaning of building, cleaning windows, cleaning floors and removing rubbish accumulated during construction. All of the items listed should be priced for material and/or labor and, in the case of temporary construction and provisions, should include the cost of removal after the job is completed.

When the Job Overhead and General Conditions items have been listed and priced, extensions should be made and totaled.

Permits, Taxes and Insurance

Most jobs will require permits and all jobs will have to pay several kinds of taxes and insurance premiums. These items are also job costs and must be included in the estimate. The various items should be listed, priced and totaled on an estimate sheet like any other part of the structure. (See Figure 6 and 7.)

To determine whether permits, licenses or special bonds will be required for the job, the estimator should contact the local authorities and obtain all information necessary to figure their costs, such as, method of charging for permit, rates applicable, etc. This information should be obtained when the site is visited.

There are a number of taxes the contractor must pay, the most common being the state sales or use tax on materials and the Social Security taxes based on the total labor cost.

Many states have sales or use taxes which apply to building construction and the method of determining and collecting them varies with the different states. Some charge a tax on all the materials in a job which is paid to the dealer supplying the materials. Other states charge a tax on the total cost of the materials incorporated into the building and is paid by the contractor direct to the state. Still others charge a tax based on the entire amount of the contract plus extras and is paid by the contractor direct to the state. Information as to the type and cost of these taxes may be obtained from the local contractor's association, material dealers or sub-contractors when visiting the site.

All contractors must pay the taxes imposed by the Social Security Laws, consisting of the Federal Insurance Contribution and the Unemployment Compensation Tax. Both of these taxes are applied to the total estimated labor cost. The tax rates are fixed by law and may change from time to time. In the case of Unemployment Compensation Tax, the rates vary slightly in the different states and upon the experience rating of the contractor.

Every contractor should be adequately covered with insurance to protect himself and the owner from any claims arising from injuries to the workmen or the public or property damage occasioned by some phase of the building operation. In many states this is a statutory requirement. The premium rates for this insurance varies both as to the locality of the job and the classification of the work and may be determined by contacting an insurance broker. In addition, the owner and contractor should be protected against losses to material and completed construction work, from fire, tornado, explosion, riot, vandalism, etc., with comprehensive insurance coverage. Rates for this type insurance may also be obtained from the insurance broker. On many jobs the specifications state this insurance will be taken out and paid for by the owner.

The contractor should also acquaint himself with the new Article 4:18 of the General Conditions of the Contract for Construction, published by the American Institute of Architects, if this document is made a part of any of his contracts. This article, entitled "Indemnification," requires the contractor to hold harmless both the architect and owner against all claims, damages, expenses, etc., resulting from the contractor's operation as detailed therein.

Premiums for insurance which the contractor should carry on his own tools and equipment are generally considered as part of the cost of ownership of the equipment.

Plant and Equipment

When considering allowances for Plant and Equipment, the estimator should list on an estimate sheet, all the major pieces of equipment, which he anticipates will be required to build the job. This should include such equipment as, concrete mixers, vibrators, power buggies, hoisting engines and towers, mortar mixers, saw rigs, etc. Tools and equipment such as, hammers, sledges, shovels, picks, water hose, small power tools, wheelbarrows, etc., are usually lumped under the heading of small tools.

Along with the items listed, include the length of time each piece of equipment will be required and the rental rate to be charged to the job, except in the case of small tools, a lump sum allowance is usually made.

Another item which should be included in the Plant and Equipment listing is fuel and lubricating materials required.

Provision should also be made for transporting the equipment to and from the job.

Analyzing Sub-Bids

After the contractor's own work has been taken off and priced and the general conditions have been determined, the estimator can turn his attention to the sub-bids received in answer to the requests sent out when starting to figure the job. All bids should be separated according to classifications of work and each one should be carefully read and thoroughly analyzed, especially those which are apparently the low bidders.

In analyzing a sub-bid, the first thing to determine is whether the bid is complete, i.e., does it cover all of the work in its classification, called for on the plans and in the specifications. This is doubly important where the architect has lumped several classifications of work under one section heading of the specifications. Special attention should also be paid to those sub-bids which the subcontractor has qualified by either listing the items he has or has not included.

There are a number of classifications of work which may be quoted either on a "material only" basis or as a complete job, including erection or installation, such as structural steel, metal windows, metal doors, etc. In comparing the quotations on these items, the estimator must make sure what each bid includes and it may be necessary to obtain separate erection figures to complete the estimate or to compare them with any complete bids received. Also, in the case of "material only" quotations, the estimator should determine how the material will be delivered and whether or not the quotation includes transportation charges.

Some jobs may contain classifications of work which are critical due to a shortage of either material or labor or both. For these items, the estimator should determine in addition to the amounts of the bids, the delivery date for the materials involved or the sub-contractor's ability to properly man the job, in the case of labor shortages. The estimator must know this as it may revise his estimate of the time it will take to complete the job. In some cases, it may be necessary to use a quotation that is not the low one, in order to obtain a critical material or get certain work done at an earlier date, so that no delays will be experienced on the job.

Another important factor in analyzing sub figures, is the reputation of the sub-contractor, as to the quality of his work, his spirit of cooperation and his general reliability. Most sub-contractors are sincere and conscientious in their efforts to produce a good job, but, as in every business, there are a few who either lack the qualifications to do good work or don't care whether or not they produce a workmanlike job. Before using a sub-contractor's bid in your estimate, be sure he is reliable and will do a good job.

It sometimes occurs that a sub-contractor will submit a bid that is extraordinarily low. In such cases, the right thing is to contact the sub-contractor, advise him of this condition and ask him to check his quotation. This will give him a chance to either retain, revise or withdraw his figure from the bidding. Whatever the sub-contractor decides to do, he should take the same action with all other general contractors who have his bid. In notifying a sub-contractor that his bid seems too low, the estimator is really protecting himself because if he uses the bid in making up his final figure and the sub-contractor discovers a serious mistake in his estimate he may refuse to take the job at the price quoted, and then the estimate will contain a losing item before the work is even started. On the other hand, if the sub-contractor accepts the job at the low figure and then finds an error in his estimate, in many cases he will try to get more money for his work and, if he does not succeed, will probably make every effort to reduce his costs by cutting every corner he can, using cheap materials, doing poor work and in general turning out an inferior job, thereby penalizing the whole operation. This frequently leads to controversy between the general contractor, sub-contractor, architect and owner and may seriously damage the general contractor's reputation. In addition to protecting his own interests, and incidentally those of the sub-contractor, the estimator will gain many friends in the business, friends which every contractor needs to be successful.

Sub-contract bids form the largest part of the estimate, usually ranging from two-thirds to three-fourths of the total cost of the job, and this fact alone should impress the estimator as to the importance of good sub coverage and an accurate analysis of each quotation. To be a successful contractor, having a good following of reliable sub-contractors in all classifications of work, is absolutely essential and the only way to gain this is to deal fairly with them and get a reputation for doing so. Let them make money and they will help you too.

Very often last minute sub-bids are received over the telephone. An efficient form for recording these quotations is the Telephone Bid sheet. (See Figure 13.)

Contains space for Name and Location of Job, Name, Address and Telephone Number of Bidder, Class of Work, together with plenty of space for writing details of bid, exclusions, amount, etc. Also contains space for names of persons giving and receiving the bid.

Summary of Estimate

When all of the preceding steps are finished, the next step is the completion of the Summary Sheet set up at the beginning of the estimate. The estimator now enters on the Summary Sheet the material and labor totals for each classification of work the contractor intends to do with his own crews. He also enters the amounts figured for Job Overhead and General Conditions; Permits, Taxes and Insurance; and Plant and Equipment. In addition, he enters the amount of each sub-bid he is going to use. All columns are then totaled and cross totaled to arrive at the estimated job cost.

Illustrated in Figures 1 and 2, is a method of filling out the Summary Sheet. Note how each figure has its place and how the material, labor and sub-bids are kept separate. Also note the Total column, where all cross totals of each item are entered, which provides an additional check on the other three column additions. In addition, note the column for Adjustments, where any last minute revisions may be noted and the final figure changed without rewriting the entire summary.

This method of summarizing the estimate is used by many successful contractors and is adaptable to any size job.

Contingencies

Some contractors make a practice of adding a percentage of the total estimated cost to cover contingencies, claiming that they do not have to be as careful in estimating the job and that this amount will take care of any items that may have been overlooked. This practice is not recommended and is not necessary, if the job is properly estimated. If the contractor feels the estimate is inadequate to do the job profitably, without adding for this sort of contingency, he should either re-figure the job or not bid it at all.

However, there is one contingency the contractor is justified in providing for and that is expected increases in either material prices or wage rates. In this case, he should list on an estimate sheet, quantities of materials or the percentage of estimated payroll which he anticipates will be affected and apply the amount of the increases to them. Also remember that, if the cost of the materials increases, so will the sales tax, if required, and in the case of labor increases, the Social Security taxes and insurance premiums will be affected.

After all computations are made, the contingency item should be entered on the Summary Sheet and a new total estimated cost obtained.

Profit

Having arrived at a total estimated cost, the contractor must decide what profit to add to his estimate. There are no hard and fast rules dictating what percentage to add, so he must use his best judgment and knowledge of current market conditions. This amount varies with the times, when jobs are abundant, profits are high; when jobs are scarce, profits are low. It is therefore not a matter of what the contractor wants for a profit, but how much he can get.

Every contractor is in business to make money and to do this each job should produce its share, to help pay the cost of maintaining his office, to reimburse him for his own services, to give him a fair return on his investment and to provide working capital for his business. Deciding what to add for profit is a most perplexing problem. If he adds too much, he loses the job, if he adds too little, he may not even make his actual expenses. The only way he can keep pace with his competition is to actively participate in the bidding market, being satisfied with a small estimated profit and endeavoring to increase his profits by economical buying and striving for greated efficiency and production in the field.

TELEPHONE BID

ESTIMATE NUMBER _429_

DATE _APRIL 24, 19--_

JOB _SMITH STORE BUILDING_

LOCATION _S.E. CORNER MAIN & OAK, ARLINGTON_

FIRM _HUGHES HEATING Co._   BY _A.T. HUGHES_

ADDRESS _175 N. HICKORY ST., ARLINGTON_   PHONE _276-2857_

CLASS OF WORK

WORK INCLUDED	AMOUNT OF BID
HEATING WORK PER PLANS & SPECS	$4200.00
CONFIRMATION TO FOLLOW BY MAIL	
TOTAL BID	$4200.00

EXCLUSIONS AND QUALIFICATIONS

ELECTRICAL CONNECTIONS BY OTHERS

ACKNOWLEDGEMENT OF ADDENDA: _NONE_

DELIVERY:

TAX	
EXCLUDED	
INCLUDED	

RECEIVED BY: _Phil Andrews_

Fig. 13. Telephone Bid Sheet. Size 8½ x 11 Inches. Form 512.

Certain types of jobs, such as alteration or remodeling jobs, which usually contain a certain element of risk, are entitled to and usually can get a higher percentage of profit than new work which can be estimated with a good degree of accuracy. Also the size of the job seems to influence the percentage of profit a job can carry in an inverse ratio, that is, the larger the job, the smaller the percentage of profit. Most contractors would be satisfied to add profits of 15 to 25 per cent on alteration and remodeling jobs, depending on their difficulty, and 10 per cent on new work, but in today's market this is impossible, with only about half these percentages being obtainable and on jobs in the million dollar class the profit added may run as low as 4 to 5 per cent.

Surety Bond

Some jobs require the contractor to furnish a performance bond to insure the owner that he will faithfully fulfill the terms of the contract and in most cases, he is also required to furnish a bid or proposal bond guaranteeing that he will enter into contract if he is awarded the job for the amount of his proposal. This is most common on jobs built with public funds for municipal, state or federal governments, but is occasionally requested by individual owners.

When Surety Bonds are called for, the specifications or bid form usually state this requirement and the contractor should contact his bonding company in sufficient time for them to prepare the necessary documents which must accompany his bid.

For those who have had no previous bonding experience and who wish to bid a job with this requirement, it is advisable to contact the bonding company before any work is done on the estimate, to see if they are eligible for a bond. Bonding eligibility is dependent not only on the contractor's financial statement but also upon his reputation as a builder and business man. This usually requires a little time for investigation on the part of the bonding company.

The charge for a performance bond frequently runs from three quarters of one per cent to one per cent of the full amount of the contract, including the bond premium. There is also a small charge for the bid or proposal bond which will be quoted by the bonding company and usually costs about $5.00. These charges are part of the job cost and are added at the very end of the estimate resulting in the amount to be quoted in the proposal.

Other bonds may be required such as bid bonds, perfomance and maintenance bond, license or permit bonds, and subdivision bonds.

Final Checking the Estimate

Before submitting the proposal, the estimate should receive a final check. The quantity take-off should be examined and the pricing reviewed. All extensions and additions should be checked and particular attention paid to checking each extension that has been made to see that there are no open quantities. Following this, comparisons should be made between the total material and labor costs for concrete and masonry work. Under ordinary conditions, the concrete labor cost should run slightly higher than the material and the masonry labor cost should be from 50 to 75 per cent higher than the material.

An additional method of rough checking the estimate is by comparing the unit price per square foot of floor area and per cubic foot of building with the same units of similar jobs previously estimated or constructed. This is not an accurate check, but will serve to show up any large errors. All calculations, for total floor area, cubical contents and unit price computations, should be made on an estimate sheet and the results entered in the spaces provided on the Summary Sheet. This information may also be a valuable aid in preparing preliminary estimates for proposed jobs and can be used to rough check finished estimates of future similar jobs but should never be used as the basis for submitting a proposal. In addition, this check should only be used to supplement the other checking operations and not to supplant them.

Finally, consult a check list such as is given on the reverse of the Summary Sheet, to discover any possible open items or classifications of work which have been left out of the estimate and then check the additions on the Summary Sheet.

Following the above procedure in checking the estimate, the contractor should be able to satisfy himself as to the accuracy of the estimate and is then ready to write the proposal.

CHAPTER 3

SUBMITTING THE BID

The degree of formality required in submitting the proposal varies with the type of job being bid. Most small to medium sized jobs may be bid informally with the proposal written on the contractor's letterhead or on standard forms, such as illustrated in Figures 14, 15 and 16. Larger jobs usually require a more complex proposal and for these the architect or owner generally furnish the contractor with special bid forms.

In preparing simple proposals, the easiest method is to use a standard form as illustrated. Most of the information usually written into the bid is already printed on these forms and all that is necessary is to write or type in the specific information pertaining to the job, such as, description of work to be done, list of documents or information upon which the bid is based, any particular qualifications which the contractor wishes to establish or emphasize, the amount of the bid and the desired terms of payment. With this information inserted, the proposal is ready for submission.

In addition, on small work these proposal forms may serve as a contract, requiring only the owner's signature and date of signing in the acceptance clause at the bottom of the form to make it a legal and binding contract between the contractor and the owner.

For the contractor who does small repairs, remodeling work or who conducts a jobbing business, the pocket-size Proposal illustrated in Figure 14 will prove adequate. The contractor may carry these forms in his pocket and be prepared to submit on-the-spot proposals at all times, retaining an exact copy for his files.

For contractors who prefer to submit their proposals on a letter-size sheet, the Proposal illustrated in Figures 15 and 16 is satisfactory. Inasmuch as these proposals are usually submitted by mail, they should be prepared in triplicate with the original and duplicate submitted for consideration and the third copy retained by the contractor so that he has an exact copy of the proposal at all times.

On larger jobs, where special bid forms are furnished the contractor, these are usually accompanied by instructions to guide the contractor in preparing the proposal. These instructions must be followed to the letter, as any deviation from them constitutes an informality in the bid, which may be the basis for the proposal being rejected. Quite often, the instructions will call for the contractor to furnish a financial statement along with his bid and may even request that he furnish a list of the major pieces of equipment he has available for use on the job. He may also be asked to give unit prices to be used in determining additions or deductions to the contract in the event of changes or to quote on alternate methods of construction involving either different materials or a change in the design as a whole. In addition, he may be required to list the sub-contractors he has used in making up his bid and the amounts of their proposals; also to list the manufacturer's name, brand name, size, capacity, etc., for certain items of equipment to be incorporated in the job. These are some of the items of information the contractor may have to furnish in order to have a complete bid. The owner usually reserves the right to waive any or all informalities in the bids but don't depend on it. Give all the information requested and your bid should receive full consideration. Many bids of this type will require notarization, which also must not be overlooked to avoid having an incomplete proposal.

One of the most important factors in submitting a proposal on a job, is to get it delivered within the specified time limit. This is absolutely essential if the bids are to be opened publicly, as is usually the case for any of the several branches of government. This is one informality which can rarely be waived without the presiding officer inviting severe criticism of his action. Many a contractor has had his bid returned unopened because it arrived too late, and had all the work and expense of figuring the job for nothing. It may sometimes occur that a bid mailed in time to arrive at its destination before the expiration of the time limit is delayed due to circumstances beyond the contractor's control. If it can be proven, through the postmark, that it should have arrived in time with normal postal handling, the informality may then be waived and

PROPOSAL

APRIL 14   19 — —

TO MR. WILLIAM AVERY
416 N. MAIN ST., ARLINGTON, ILL.

WE propose to furnish all materials and perform all labor necessary to complete the following:

WORK ON THE WILLIAM AVERY
RESIDENCE AT 231 E. WOODLANE DR.
MAKE AND INSTALL SCREENS AND
SCREEN DOORS IN BREEZWAY
BETWEEN HOUSE AND GARAGE IN
ACCORDANCE WITH SKETCH
PREPARED BY YOU.

All of the above work to be completed in a substantial and workmanlike manner for the sum of

THREE HUNDRED TWENTY FIVE Dollars ($ 325.00)

Payments to be made each_____ as the work progresses to the

value of_____per cent (_____%) of all work completed. The entire amount

of contract to be paid within THIRTY (30) days after completion.

Any alteration or deviation from the above specifications involving extra cost of material or labor will only be executed upon written orders for same, and will become an extra charge over the sum mentioned in this contract. All agreements must be made in writing.

Respectfully submitted,
ANDREWS CONSTRUCTION COMPANY

Phillip H. Andrews

ACCEPTANCE

You are hereby authorized to furnish all materials and labor required to complete the work mentioned in the above proposal, for which _____agree to pay the amount mentioned in said proposal, and according to the terms thereof.

"STANDARDIZED" FORMS FOR CONTRACTORS
PRACTICAL

FORM P-135   FRANK R. WALKER CO., PUBLISHERS, CHICAGO

Fig. 14. Proposal and Acceptance. Size 4¼ x 6¾ Inches.

PROPOSAL

April 24 _____ 19 --

Johnson and Anderson, Architects

Room 922, First National Bank Building, Arlington, Ill.

Dear Sir:

    The undersigned proposes to furnish all materials and perform all labor necessary to complete the following:

Construct, for Mr. John H. Smith the Store Building at the Southeast Corner of Main and Oak Streets, Arlington, Illinois, in accordance with the Plans, Sheets 1 to 6 inclusive, and Specifications, Pages 1 to 33 inclusive, as prepared by you and all dated April 2, 19--.

The following quotation is based on the understanding that Fire and Extended Coverage Insurance will be taken out and paid for by the Owner and will cover materials on the site as well as completed construction.

    All of the above work to be completed in a substantial and workmanlike manner for the sum of Fifty-Nine Thousand Two Hundred Twenty-Seven and No/100---------------- ($ 59,227.00) Dollars

Payments to be made each___month___as the work progresses to the value of Ninety-Five (95 %) per cent of all work completed. The entire amount of contract to be paid within Thirty (30) days after completion.

    Any alteration or deviation from the above specifications involving extra cost of material or labor will only be executed upon written orders for same, and will become an extra charge over the sum mentioned in this contract. All agreements must be made in writing.

    The Contractor agrees to carry Workmen's Compensation and Public Liability Insurance, also to pay all Sales Taxes, Old Age Benefit and Unemployment Compensation Taxes upon the material and labor furnished under this contract, as required by the United States Government and the State in which this work is performed.

Respectfully submitted,

ANDREWS CONSTRUCTION COMPANY
Contractor

By

ACCEPTANCE

    You are hereby authorized to furnish all materials and labor required to complete the work mentioned in the above proposal, for which the undersigned agrees to pay the amount mentioned in said proposal, and according to the terms thereof.

Date_____ 19_____

PRACTICAL Form 147
MFD. IN U. S. A.

FRANK R. WALKER CO., PUBLISHERS, CHICAGO

Fig. 15. Proposal and Acceptance. Size 8½ x 11 Inches. Form 147.

PROPOSAL

May 15,   19 --

Mr. Fred L. Williams

1605 E. Maplewood Ave., Arlington, Ill.

Dear Sir:
    The undersigned proposes to furnish all materials and perform all labor necessary to complete the following:

Install half screens on all first floor double hung windows, (22) and full screens on all basement windows, (8).

Install wood combination storm and screen doors, as selected, at front and rear entrances.

Repair overhead garage door and adjust to operate properly.

Repair windstorm damage to asphalt shingle roofs of house and garage.

No painting work included.

All of the above work to be performed at your residence and garage located at 1605 E. Maplewood Ave., Arlington, Illinois

    All of the above work to be completed in a substantial and workmanlike manner for the sum of ------------
Two Hundred Twenty Five and --------------No/100-----------($ 225.00) Dollars
    Payments to be made each ------------- as the work progresses to the value of ------------- (--- %) per cent of all work completed. The entire amount of contract to be paid within --Thirty--- days after completion.
    Any alteration or deviation from the above specifications involving extra cost of material or labor will only be executed upon written orders for same, and will become an extra charge over the sum mentioned in this contract. All agreements must be made in writing.
    The Contractor agrees to carry Workmen's Compensation and Public Liability Insurance, also to pay all Sales Taxes, Old Age Benefit and Unemployment Compensation Taxes upon the material and labor furnished under this contract, as required by the United States Government and the State in which this work is performed.

                      Respectfully submitted,

                      Walter E. Wirtz Construction Co.
                      Contractor

                                   Sole Owner
                      By

ACCEPTANCE

    You are hereby authorized to furnish all materials and labor required to complete the work mentioned in the above proposal, for which the undersigned agrees to pay the amount mentioned in said proposal, and according to the terms thereof.

Date_____ 19____   _____

PRACTICAL   Form 147
MFD. IN U.S.A.

FRANK R. WALKER CO., PUBLISHERS, CHICAGO

Fig. 16. Proposal and Acceptance. Size 8½ x 11 Inches. Form 147.

the bid considered. The best way to submit the bid is to deliver it personally, if at all possible, and witness the opening of the bids, if it is performed publicly. In this way, the contractor or his representative can make a tabulation of the bids as they are read and thus gain valuable information about his competition and the current market trend, for use in estimating future jobs.

The completion of the bid form and the preparation of any accompanying documents, should be started in sufficient time before the bid is due so that it may be done carefully and not left until the last few hours, when the work will have to be rushed, thus increasing the possibilities for errors. Usually, much of the information may be entered in the bid form prior to the actual determination of the final bid amount and in many instances, contractors have telephoned the final bid amount to a representative attending the bid opening who enters the figure before submitting the proposal.

Methods of Filing the Estimates

After the proposal has been submitted, all papers pertaining to the estimate, including take-off sheets, material quotations, sub-bids, summary sheet, copy of proposal, copy of bid bond, scratch sheets with computations, correspondence and any other information concerning the bid, should be gathered together for filing. In order to keep all papers together in the file, they should be contained in either a heavy manila envelope or in an expanding file pocket, the latter being particularly adaptable to larger estimates. In both cases, the container should be properly identified with the name of job, its location, name of owner, name of architect or engineer, estimate number and date the bid was submitted. These envelopes or file pockets may then be filed in a regular file cabinet.

There are several systems which may be followed in filing the estimates. Some contractors prefer to file them according to number while others file them alphabetically according to the architect's or engineer's name, etc. In any case, the file should be indexed so as to permit a ready reference to any particular estimate.

Plans and specifications, from which the job was estimated, should be safely stored until the contract is awarded. If the contractor is not the successful bidder, the plans and specifications should be returned to the architect or owner. If the contractor is awarded the contract, they become part of the bidding documents and should be labeled "Estimating Set" and should be kept in good condition for the life of the job, as they are the basis of the proposal.

CHAPTER 4

AFTER PROPOSAL HAS BEEN ACCEPTED

After the contractor has been notified that his proposal has been accepted and he is to be awarded the contract, there are a number of steps to be taken to get the job started right.

First, negotiations leading to the signing of the contract must be started and carried to a conclusion as quickly as possible.

Next is the building permit. If a permit, licenses, or special bonds are required, they must be applied for immediately and obtained in the shortest possible time. Many communities will not allow a job to start until a permit has been issued to a licensed contractor.

Insurance certificates and Surety Bond, if required, must be obtained and delivered to the architect or owner. At the same time, if the owner is to furnish any insurance coverage for the job, he should provide the contractor with certificates verifying this fact.

A breakdown of the contract price and a proposed progress schedule for the job will usually have to be prepared for the architect and owner.

The contractor should make up a budget containing all the classifications of work in the job, as a guide in letting sub-contracts, purchasing materials and setting up a schedule of costs on his own work, for his crews to shoot at.

Material requirements for the contractor's own work, must be compiled from the estimate, in the order they will be needed and their purchases begun.

A list of sub-contract and vendor items should be made, in the order they will be required. An effort should be made to obtain additional quotations and negotiations started for their purchases.

Most of these operations will have to be carried on simultaneously, so the contractor's office will be a very busy place until the job gets under way. The following pages contain a brief discussion of each of the above details.

Negotiating the Contract

The contractor should begin contract negotiations immediately upon being advised that his bid has been accepted. These negotiations will vary with the type of job and with whom the contractor is dealing.

On small jobs where the contractor deals directly with the owner, and the owner prefers a formal contract, the usual procedure is for the contractor to prepare the contract documents and submit them to the owner for his acceptance and signature. To accomplish this quickly and still assure himself and the owner of complete protection, the contractor should use one of several standard contract forms available. (See Figures 18 and 19.)

The short from is suitable for residential and small to medium-size commercial and industrial work and contains all of the "fine print" usually required for jobs of this size. In addition, there is ample space to enter a complete description of the work to be performed, a listing of the documents and any qualifications upon which the contractor has based his bid, the proposed date of completion, contract amount, terms of payment, etc.

The long form will give complete protection and coverage to both contractor and owner for any size job and includes all of the clauses usually required for larger jobs such as, the manner of performance to eliminate delays, liquidated damages for delays, basis for extension of time, protection of owner against claims due to patent infringements, etc., periodic and final clean up and rubbish removal, insurance coverage to be furnished by the owner, Surety Bond, etc.

Contract Agreement

THIS AGREEMENT, made this <u>twenty-seventh</u> day of <u>April</u> A.D. 19<u>--</u>, by and between <u>Mr. John H. Smith</u> Owner, and <u>Andrews Construction Company</u> hereinafter called the hereinafter called the Contractor.

For the consideration hereinafter named, the said Contractor covenants and agrees with said Owner, as follows:

FIRST. The Contractor agrees to furnish all material and perform all work necessary to complete the <u>General Contract, including excavation, foundations, cement floors and walks, masonry, iron work, rough and finish carpentry, aluminum doors and windows, sheet metal work, roofing, lathing, plastering, glass and glazing, painting, plumbing, heating and electrical work for the one-story and basement store building to be erected at 656 North Main Street, Arlington, Illinois, in accordance with Plans, Sheets 1 to 6 inclusive, dated April 2, 19--, and Specifications, Pages 1 to 33 inclusive, dated April 2, 19--.</u>

for the above named structure, xxxxxxxxxxxxxxxxxxxxxxxxxxxxxxxxxxxxxx (details thereof to be furnished as needed) xx <u>prepared by Johnson and Anderson,</u> Architect, and to the full satisfaction of said Architect or Owner.

SECOND. The Contractor agrees to promptly begin said work as soon as notified by said Architect or Owner, and to complete the work as follows: <u>Commence work within forty-eight (48) hours after receiving notice from the Owner or Architect that the site is cleared and ready for contractor to start work, and carry same on to completion as rapidly as possible. The entire structure to be completed and ready for occupancy not later than August 1, 19--.</u>

THIRD. The Contractor shall take out and pay for Workmen's Compensation and Public Liability Insurance, also Property Damage and all other necessary insurance, as required by the Owner, Architect or by the State in which this work is performed.

FOURTH. The Contractor shall pay all Sales Taxes, Old Age Benefit and Unemployment Compensation Taxes upon the material and labor furnished under this contract, as required by the United States Government and the State in which this work is performed.

FIFTH. No extra work or changes under this contract will be recognized or paid for, unless agreed to in writing before the work is done or the changes made.

SIXTH. This contract shall not be assigned by the Contractor without first obtaining permission in writing from the Architect or Owner. All Sub-contracts shall be subject to the approval of the Architect or Owner.

IN CONSIDERATION WHEREOF, the said Owner agrees that he will pay to the said Contractor, in <u>monthly</u> payments, the sum of <u>--- FIFTY NINE THOUSAND TWO HUNDRED TWENTY SEVEN -----</u> <u>---------($59,227.00)--</u> Dollars for said materials and work, said amount to be paid as follows: <u>--Ninety-five--------</u> per cent (<u>-95-</u>%) of all labor and material which has been placed in position by said Contractor, to be paid on or about the <u>--Tenth--(10th)-----</u> of the following month, except the final payment, which the said Owner shall pay to the said Contractor within <u>---------- --Thirty--(30)-------</u> days after the Contractor shall have completed his work to the full satisfaction of the said Architect or Owner.

The Contractor and the Owner for themselves, their successors, executors, administrators and assigns, hereby agree to the full performance of the covenants of this agreement.

IN WITNESS WHEREOF, they have executed this agreement the day and date written above.

Witness:

JOHN H. SMITH

ANDREWS CONSTRUCTION COMPANY ^{Owner.}

Contractor.

FRANK R. WALKER CO., PUBLISHERS, CHICAGO

Fig. 18. Contract Agreement, Short Form. Size 8½ x 11 Inches. Form 158.

Contract Agreement

THIS AGREEMENT, made this_____day of_____A. D. 19_____,
by and between_____
hereinafter called the Contractor and_____
_____hereinafter called the Owner:

For the consideration hereinafter named, the said Contractor covenants and agrees with the said Owner as follows:

FIRST. The Contractor shall and will furnish, construct, set in place, finish and deliver to the Owner, free from all claims, liens and charges, and in a good substantial, thorough and workmanlike manner perform and in every respect complete_____

_____

_____

_____

_____

_____

_____

_____

_____

_____

_____

_____

_____

_____

_____

_____

for the above named structure, according to the plans and specifications (details thereof to be furnished as needed) of _____, Architect, and to the full satisfaction of said Architect.

SECOND. The Contractor will promptly begin said work as soon as he is notified by the Architect that the ground is clear or the structure far enough advanced to allow the beginning of that portion included hereunder, and will carry forward and complete said work as rapidly as said Architect may judge that the progress of the structure will permit, unless detained by other contractors; in which event he will promptly notify the Architect in writing, who (if satisfied that said delay is caused by others than said Contractor hereunder) will allow additional time sufficient in his judgment to make up the time so lost. This paragraph shall cover any extra work done or materials furnished under this contract.

THIRD. The Contractor will furnish said materials, including all necessary scaffolding, and prosecute said work with due diligence, without delay, and will not in any manner, by delay or otherwise, interfere with the work of any other Contractors, and should the said Architect conclude that the said Contractor is delaying said work, he shall so notify said Contractor, who shall, within_____days thereafter, furnish whatever materials are required by said Architect, and employ additional men, as required by said Architect, and in case said Contractor fails to comply with said demand, the said Owner shall have the right to (but without any obligation to do so, and without prejudice to any other right or remedy the Owner may have hereunder or otherwise) furnish said materials and employ said additional men and charge the expense thereof against the said Contractor and deduct same from this contract, and should the amount or balance due on said contract be insufficient, to collect said deficiency by legal process.

FOURTH. The Contractor shall, from time to time, as directed by the Architect, remove all debris, dust and rubbish incidental to or resulting from said Contractor's work; and shall, upon completion of the work required by this Agreement, remove all scaffolds, material, machinery, implements, debris, rubbish and dust connected with, incidental to, or resulting from said work, and leave said work and the premises clean, neat, complete and perfect, without any cost or expense in that behalf to the Owner.

Fig. 19. Page 1. Contract Agreement. Form 160.

FIFTH. The Contractor shall provide sufficient, safe and proper facilities at all times for the inspection of the work by the Architect, the Owner or his authorized representatives. He shall, at once, remove all materials and take down and rebuild all portions of the work condemned by the Architect, upon receiving notice in writing of such condemnation.

SIXTH. The Contractor shall not employ any workmen whose employment on the building or improvement may be objected to by the Architect or Owner.

SEVENTH. No extra work or changes under this contract will be recognized or paid for, unless agreed to in writing before the work is done or the changes made; in which writing shall be specified in detail the extra work or changes desired, the price to be paid or the amount to be deducted, should said change decrease the amount to be paid hereunder.

EIGHTH. The Contractor hereby covenants and agrees to indemnify and save harmless the Owner from all and all manner of claims or suits for infringements of patents or violation of patent rights, including all costs and expenses to which the Owner may be put in defending any actions that may arise under this clause of the contract.

NINTH. The Contractor shall comply with all applicable laws, ordinances, rules, regulations and orders of any public authority having jurisdiction for the safety of persons or property or to protect them from damage, injury or loss.

_____
_____
_____
_____
_____
_____
_____
_____

TENTH. The Contractor shall protect and indemnify said Owner against any loss or damage suffered by any one arising through the negligence of the Contractor, or those employed by him or his agent or servants; he shall bear any expense which the Owner may have by reason thereof, or on account of being charged therewith; and if there are any such injuries to persons or property unsettled for, when the work herein provided for is finished, final settlement between the Owner and Contractor shall be deferred until such claims are adjusted or suitable special indemnity acceptable to the Owner is provided by the Contractor.

ELEVENTH. The Contractor shall, as soon as obtainable after signing the contract, secure and pay for Employers' Liability or Workmen's Compensation, also Public Liability and Property Damage Insurance, in amounts and in Companies acceptable to the Owner, and in accordance with the laws (now or hereafter in force), of the State in which this work is performed.

The Contractor also agrees to indemnify and save the Owner harmless from any and all damages, losses, costs and expenses of every kind and nature sustained, borne or coming to the Owner by reason or on account of his liability under the laws (now and hereafter in force), of the State in which this work is performed.

TWELFTH. The Contractor shall pay all Sales Taxes, Excise Taxes, Old Age Benefit and Unemployment Compensation Taxes upon the materials and labor furnished under this contract, as required by the Statutes of the United States Government and the State in which this work is performed.

THIRTEENTH. The Owner shall, as soon as obtainable from reliable Companies, during the progress of the work, secure policies of insurance on said work, against loss or damage by fire, lightning, earthquake, cyclone, explosion or other casualty not the fault of the contractor; the policies to cover all work incorporated in the building, and all materials for the same in or about the premises, and shall be made payable to the various parties in interest, as their interest may appear; but the provisions of this article shall in no wise be construed as imposing or fastening any liability on the Owner, other than to secure said insurance, as aforesaid, or as lessening or affecting the liability of the Contractor, or as altering or modifying in any way the rights or responsibilities of the parties in respect of the said work or otherwise.

FOURTEENTH. This contract shall not be assigned by the Contractor. Any attempt to assign the contract shall operate as an instant forfeiture and repudiation thereof by the Contractor and the rights of the parties shall be determined in the same manner as though the Contractor had at the time of such attempted assignment failed and refused to continue to perform the contract. All sub-contracts shall be subject to the appproval of the Architect.

FIFTEENTH. It is expressly UNDERSTOOD AND AGREED by and between the parties hereto that time is and shall be considered the essence of the contract on the part of the said Contractor, and in the event that the said Contractor shall fail in the performance of the entire work to be performed under this contract, by and at the time or times herein mentioned or referred to, the said Contractor shall pay unto the said Owner, as and for liquidated damages, and not as a penalty, the sum of_____Dollars per day, which said sum of $_____per day, in view of the difficulty of estimating such damages with exactness, is hereby expressed, fixed, computed, determined and agreed upon as the damages which will be suffered by the Owner by reason of such default; and it is understood and agreed by the parties of this contract that the liquidated damages hereinbefore mentioned are in lieu of the actual damages arising from such breach of this contract, which said sum the said Owner shall have the right to deduct from any moneys otherwise due or to become due to the said Contractor, or to sue for and recover compensation or damages for the non-performance of this contract at the time or times herein stipulated or provided for.

Fig. 19. Page 2. Contract Agreement. Form 160.

The Contractor shall prosecute the work diligently to completion, and shall complete the several portions, and the whole of the work comprehended in this Agreement, by and at the time or times hereinafter stated, to-wit: _____

_____
_____
_____
_____
_____
_____
_____
_____
_____
_____
_____
_____
_____
_____
_____
_____

No allowance for time will be made Contractor for delay in preparing his drawings or in securing approval of Architect hereto when such drawings are not properly prepared for approval of Architect.

SIXTEENTH. Should the Contractor be delayed in the prosecution or completion of the work by the act, neglect or default of the Owner, of the Architect, or of any other contractor employed by the Owner upon the work, or by any damage caused by fire, lightning, earthquake, cyclone or other casualty, not the fault of the Contractor, or by strikes or lock-outs caused by acts of employees, then the time fixed herein for the completion of the work shall be extended for a period equivalent to the time lost by reason of any or all of the causes aforesaid, which extended period shall be determined and fixed by the Architect; but no such allowance shall be made unless a claim therefor is presented in writing to the Architect within forty-eight (48) hours of the occurrence of the cause or commencement of such delay.

SEVENTEENTH. The Contractor further agrees that he will within ten days from date, at the option of the Owner, provide the Owner with a bond in the sum of $_____conditioned for the faithful performance of this contract in all its particulars, duly executed with Surety company acceptable to the Owner, as surety, and in form and contents acceptable to the Owner.

IN CONSIDERATION WHEREOF, the said Owner agrees that he will pay to the said Contractor, in monthly payments, the sum of_____
_____for said materials and work, said amount to be paid as follows: _____per cent. (_____%) of all labor and material, or both, on the premises, to be paid on or about the_____of the following month, except the last payment, which the said Owner shall pay to said Contractor within_____days after said materials and labor installed by said Contractor have been completed and approved by the said Architect.

It is further understood and agreed that no payment on account shall operate as an approval of said work or materials, or any part thereof.

All negotiations and agreements prior to the date of this memorandum are merged herein. We have read and fully understand this agreement.

The Owner and the Contractor for themselves, their successors, executors, administrators and assigns, hereby agree to the full performance of the covenants of this agreement.

IN WITNESS WHEREOF, they have executed this agreement the day and date written above.

Witness:

_____   _____
                                                          Contractor.

_____   _____
                                                          Owner.

Fig. 19. Page 3. Contract Agreement. Form 160

CONTRACT
AGREEMENT

between

_____

_____

and

_____

_____

for

_____

_____

_____

_____

Dated_____19____

ARCHITECTS

_____

Contract Amount_____$_____

Fig. 19. Page 4. Contract Agreement. Form 160.

The use of these contract forms will enable the contractor to draw up a contract in less time than it takes to write a letter and yet maintain consistency in having contracts which afford complete and just coverage for both himself and the owner.

On larger jobs, however, the architect and owner usually prefer to draw up the contract and present it to the contractor for his acceptance and signature. This reduces the control the contractor has over both the initial contents of the agreement and the speed with which it is drawn up and may prolong the negotiations. In these cases, the contractor should read the document very carefuly and also seek the advice of his attorney before approving and signing it, to be sure he is not assuming obligations which have not been figured. He should also be sure that a list of plans and specifications, describing the work to be performed, are included in the contract agreement and the dates given for them agree with those of the "Estimating Set" in his possession. Briefly, he should not sign the contract until he is in complete agreement with all of the terms contained therein.

At the time of signing any contract, a duplicate set of plans and specifications, with dates agreeing with those listed in the agreement and also those of the "Estimating Set" should be designated as the "Contract Set" and should be initialed or signed by both parties to the contract, on each sheet of the plans and each page of the specifications, thereby incorporating them into the contract documents. Each party should retain a "Contract Set" and any deviation from them in the actual construction, should be preceded by negotiations resulting in a Change Order which may or may not revise the contract amount.

Obtaining the Building Permit

In many communities, obtaining the building permit simply involves paying a visit to the local building department, showing the plans and specifications, answering a few questions and paying the required fee.

In some communities and most of the larger cities, obtaining a permit is more difficult and takes much more time. Usually the contractor must be licensed and registered with the building department before he can file an application for a permit.

In most cases, the first step the licensed contractor must take to obtain a building permit is to fill out an application form and submit it, along with several sets of plans and specifications, for approval. It is generally required that the plans and specifications bear the seal of registration and the certification of the architect or engineer who prepared them. Once these documents are submitted, there is very little the contractor can do to speed up the operation and usually must wait his turn for consideration. In addition to being checked for structural and mechanical design by the construction department, they are also considered by various other municipal departments, such as, zoning, health, fire, public works, etc., adding up to a very lengthy operation.

Furthermore, there are a number of other conditions which may delay the issuance of the building permit, such as, plans being rejected and needing correction by the architect to meet ordinance requirements, obtaining special permits for driveways crossing public sidewalks and parkways, obtaining an indemnifying bond to protect the city from any claims arising out of the construction work, etc. Usually these conditions must be satisfactorily cleared up before the permit is issued.

An additional permit may be required, where the street or sidewalk will be obstructed or its construction disturbed, and usually will be issued upon depositing an amount sufficient to cover restoration of the work to its orginal condition. This deposit is returned at the end of the job, after all repairs or construction work has been completed, less an amount charged for occupying the space.

Some communities permit limited construction activity during the time the application for permit is being considered, but others will not. It is therefore essential to the progress of the work that the permit be applied for promptly and that all conditions required for its issuance be met without delay.

Insurance Certificates and Surety Bond

After the contract is signed, the contractor will probably be requested to furnish the owner with certificates indicating that he has taken out all insurance called for in the specifications. These may be obtained from the insurance company following application for insurance and payment of the first premium, which should be done promptly to insure full coverage for the job.

At the same time, the contractor should request the owner to furnish him with insurance certificates for any insurance the owner is to provide.

If a surety clause is contained in the contract, the owner may exercies his option and request the contractor to furnish one within the specified time limit. In this case, the contractor must make the bond application to the surety company promptly, as the processing of the application will take several days, especially if this is the first time the contractor is being bonded.

Breakdown of Contract Amount

On many jobs, especially where an architect is involved, the contractor will be requested to furnish a breakdown of the contract price into the individual amounts for each of the various classifications of work contained in the job. The main purpose of this breakdown is to enable the architect and owner to more easily check the contractor's monthly requests for payment and to see where the money is being spent.

If the architect and owner request that the breakdown be prepared before any sub-contracts are let or vendor items purchased, the breakdown may be prepared on the contractor's letterhead or on a Summary of Estimate form. The classifications of work listed should be the same as those listed on the estimate summary sheet and the amounts used for each classification should be the same as used in the estimate with each being increased by its proportionate share of the anticipated profits. Most contractors, however, upset this proportion and add the entire profit to their own work and list the sub-contract and vendor items at their net amounts. The upsetting of the proportion is only feasible when the contractor is going to perform, at least, the usual general classifications of work, consisting of excavation, concrete, masonry and carpentry. The contractor may break down the contract price in any manner he chooses, as long as the total of the figures equals the amount of the contract and the architect and owner approve it. Where a work classification has separate amounts for labor and material in the estimate, these are added together and listed as one figure in the breakdown.

If the architect and owner are willing to wait until the sub-contracts are let and the vendor items purchased, the listing may then include the name of the sub-contractor or supplier for each classification. In these cases, most contractors enter the actual amounts of the sub-contracts and purchase orders first and then spread the remainder of the contract amount over the classifications of work they will do themselves. It is a good idea to prepare this breakdown in the same manner and on the same form which will be used for the monthly payment request. An example of one form specifically requested by many architects is shown in Figure 20.

Progress Schedule

Another request the contractor will likely receive from the architect and owner is to prepare a progress schedule showing the anticipated starting and completion date for each classification of work in the job. The main purpose of this time table is to enable all parties involved to more accurately judge the progress of the construction work. In addition, it serves as a valuable aid to the contractor in determining when each sub-contractor or vendor item will be needed on the job and on which items to concentrate in letting sub-contracts and issuing purchase orders.

Most contractors and architects prefer the bar graph type of progress schedule, as shown in Figure 21. This type of schedule is not difficult to prepare and gives a quickly and easily understood picture of how all the various operations must dovetail to keep the job moving. This schedule should be designed and drawn up special for each individual job.

As may be seen in the illustration, the sheet is divided into as many horizontal spaces as are required for the major operations of the job. It is also divided into vertical columns which provide space for a description of the work, the deadline date for letting the sub-contract or purchase order, the anticipated starting date, the estimated completion date and enough monthly columns, divided into payroll periods, to cover the estimated length of the job, plus one or two extra for any overrun.

After the form is drawn up, the next step is to enter in the description column, all of the major operations required to complete the job. These entries should be made in approximately the same order as the operations will take place on the job, except that operations belonging to the same classification of work should be grouped together regardless of when they will occur and the mechanical trades are usually entered last. Following this, the bars indicating that a certain operation will be in progress, may be drawn in

FORM 591
MFD IN U.S.A.

SWORN STATEMENT FOR CONTRACTOR AND SUBCONTRACTOR TO OWNER

State of ILLINOIS   } ss.

County of COOK

The affiant -----PHILLIP H. ANDREWS --------------------- being first duly sworn, on oath deposes and says that he is (1) Sole Owner of the Andrews Construction Company of Arlington, Illinois, who has entered into a ---

contract with (2) ---------John H. Smith, Arlington, Illinois----------------------------owner____for (3)__ the General Contract work on a one-story and basement store building------------------ on the following described premises in said County, to-wit: property known as 656 North Main Street, Arlington, Cook County, Illinois

That, for the purpose of said contract, the following persons have been contracted with, and have furnished, or are furnishing and preparing materials for, and have done or are doing labor on said improvement. That there is due and to become due them, respectively, the amounts set opposite their names for materials or labor as stated. That this statement is made to said owner____for the purpose of procuring from said owner____ (4) Partial—Final Payment on said contract, and is a full, true and complete statement of all such persons, and of the amounts paid, due and to become due them.

(1) A member of the firm of, or officer of the corporation of, naming same. If a subcontractor so state and name the contractor. (2) Name of the owner or owners. (3) What the contract or subcontract is for. (4) Partial or Final Payment.

NAME AND ADDRESS	CONTRACT FOR	AMOUNT OF CONTRACT		TOTAL PREVIOUS REQUESTS	AMOUNT OF THIS REQUEST	BALANCE TO COMPLETE	
Andrews Construction Co.	General Cond.	$ 3584	00				
Andrews Construction Co.	Permits, Ins. & Taxes	3657	00				
Andrews Construction Co.	Const. Plant & Equip.	1075	00				
Andrews Construction Co.	Excavation	1851	00				
Andrews Construction Co.	Foundations	8309	00				
Andrews Construction Co.	Cem.Fls. & Walks	2146	00				
Andrews Construction Co.	Masonry	8498	00				
McCarthy Stone Co.	Cut Stone Mat'l.	1300	00				
Andrews Construction Co.	Rough Carpentry	5778	00				
Andrews Construction Co.	Fin. Carpentry-Lab.	869	00				
Arlington Millwork & Lumber	Millwork	1275	00				
Weatherseal Co.	Weatherstrips & Caulking	175	00				
Clark & Son Plastering Co.	Lath & Plaster	3000	00				
Modern Window Co.	Aluminum Doors & Windows	1250	00				
Simpson Sheet Metal Co.	Sheet Metal Work	300	00				
Anderson Roofing Co.	Roofing	1675	00				
Arlingotn Glass Co.	Glass & Glazing	1250	00				
Cook Painting & Decorating Co.	Painting	1375	00				
Adams Iron Works	Misc. Iron & Stl.	1575	00				
Link Bros. Hardware Co.	Finish Hardware	325	00				
Arlington Plumbing Co.	Plumbing	2200	00				
Hughes Heating Co.	Heating	4200	00				
Kester Electric Co.	Electrical	3560	00				
		$ 59227	00				

AMOUNT OF ORIGINAL CONTRACT	$59,227.00	TOTAL AMOUNT REQUESTED	$	
EXTRAS TO CONTRACT	$	LESS % RETAINED	$	
TOTAL CONTRACT AND EXTRAS	$	NET AMOUNT EARNED		
CREDITS TO CONTRACT	$	AMOUNT OF PREVIOUS PAYMENTS	$	
NET AMOUNT OF CONTRACT	$	AMOUNT DUE THIS PAYMENT	$	
		BALANCE TO COMPLETE	$	

It is understood that the total amount paid to date plus the amount requested in this application shall not exceed _____% of the cost of work completed to date.

I agree to furnish Waivers of Lien for all materials under my contract when demanded.

Signed_____

_____

Subscribed and sworn to before me this_____day of_____19___

PRACTICAL

© FRANK R. WALKER CO., PUBLISHERS.
CHICAGO

The above sworn statement should be obtained by the owner before each and every payment.

Notary Public

Fig. 20. Method of Listing Breakdown of Contract Amount on Contractor's Sworn Statement Form. Form 591.

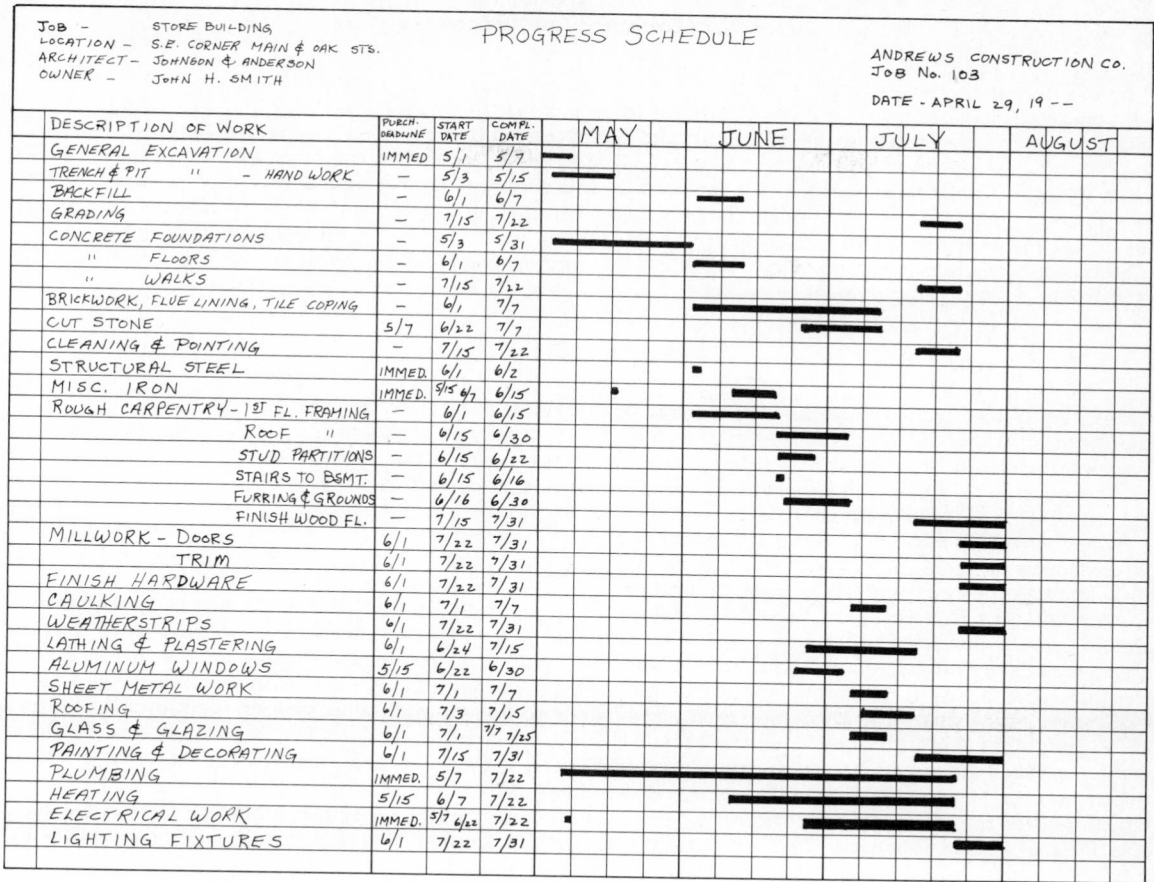

Fig. 21. Design for Progress Schedule.

their respective spaces in the monthly columns. If this is done progressively, starting with the first operation to take place and then drawing bars for each subsequent operation, in its proper order, the schedule can be drawn up with a minimum of effort.

With all the bars drawn, it is then a simple matter to enter the starting and completion date of each operation, as these may be taken directly from the graph. As to the deadline dates for buying the sub and vendor items, these must be worked back from the starting date and time allowances made for those operations which will involve shop drawings and fabrication.

The progress schedule, illustrated, applies to the store building job previously mentioned, a job which, because of its size, would hardly need one, and is therefore extremely simple. Most jobs, requiring a progress schedule are larger and the schedule would be larger, containing more items of operation and also more monthly columns for the length of the job. Most contractors prepare a master schedule on a heavy grade of paper, from which copies are made and distributed to the architect, owner, job office, etc., where they are posted on a bulletin board for reference.

Walker's Construction Progress Report, Form 112, is shown in Figure #31, page 57.

The Critical Path Method is popular with many contractors which provides graphically the scheduling of each activity of a project. A chapter describing this method is found in Walker's Building Estimator's Reference Book.

Contractor's Job Budget

In an effort to increase profits, many contractors, before doing any serious buying for their jobs, make up a budget consisting of a list of all the classifications of work they intend to sub-let or purchase, together with an amount, discounted somewhat from the figure used in the estimate, for which they will try to buy the item. This does not mean they will be able to buy at these figures but only serves as a target to shoot at when negotiating with the various sub-contractors and suppliers. If, through economical buying, induced by striving to stay within the budget, the contractor can pick up an additional four or five per cent of job profit, the few minutes spent in making up the budget will probably be the most profitable of the job.

Some contractors even set up a similar budget for their own work, discounting the unit prices used in the estimate and then trying to meet these lower cost figures in the field.

Purchasing Materials

Before purchasing any materials, the contractor must first determine the quantity of each kind of material required to do the job. This information may be obtained from the estimate and a list of material requirements should be made without delay. He should also have all the material quotations received when he figured the job, which can be used to begin negotiations. Now that he has the job the contractor may be able to obtain somewhat better prices in dealing with the various suppliers.

Materials which will be needed first should receive first attention, such as, concrete materials or ready-mixed concrete, form lumber for foundations, wall ties, nails, etc. Following this, the balance of the materials, such as, masonry materials, framing lumber, etc. should be purchased.

After all terms of purchase have been agreed upon by both contractor and supplier, the contractor should issue a purchase order covering the transaction. Most contractors use a standard purchase order form, such as are illustrated in Figures 22, 23 and 24. These forms contain all the information necessary for the purchase of any construction materials and may be completed with a minimum of effort and time. They are usually written in triplicate, the original going to the supplier, one copy retained for the files and the other copy going to the job. The small form, size 4¼ x 6¾ inches (Figure 22), is a convenient purchase order for the small contractor as a book may be carried in the pocket, enabling the contractor to write orders wherever he may be. Figure 23 is a larger purchase order form, one-half letter size 5½ x 8½ inches, which is ideal for job use in confirming telephone orders and making other job purchases. The large form, size 8½ x 11 inches, illustrated in Figure 24, may be used for any size work either in the office or on the job.

Letting Sub-Contracts and Purchasing Vendor Materials

In letting sub-contracts and purchasing vendor materials, the contractor will probably spend at least two thirds of the total amount of his estimated job cost and it will be the best opportunity he will have to increase the amount of job profit. After the contractor has the job, the subs and vendors will usually compete a little harder to obtain a share of the work, thus permitting the purchase of some items at a saving from the amounts used in the estimate.

If the contractor has prepared a progress schedule, he can tell at a glance, which items should be purchased first. If not, he should analyze his requirements and determine the sequence in which they must be purchased, considering the fact that some items will require time for the preparation and approval of shop drawings, and fabrication before being incorporated into the job.

Usually one or more classifications of work must be purchased immediately to start the job, such as, excavation, reinforcing steel, etc., and these items should be bought with a minimum amount of negotiation. The balance of the job requirements may be handled in a different manner. All subs and vendors who submitted quotations should be contacted and given the opportunity to re-figure their portion of the work. Also, an effort should be made to obtain additional quotations from sub-contractors and suppliers who did not bid originally.

At this stage of the operation, it is not unusual to receive a large number of bids and to facilitate their analysis, a tabulation should be made for each classification, of all quotations received, listing along with the price, any conditions, exceptions, etc., by which they may be qualified. These negotiations may be kept open until the very deadline for letting the work, knowing exactly how each bid stands as to completeness and price. This is especially helpful where combinations of bids must be compared, or where some bids are

Job No.		Order No

Job *FRED H. HILLES RES.* Date *SEPT 10, 19--*

To *CITY LUMBER & SUPPLY CO.*

Address *212 E. MAIN ST.*

PLEASE DELIVER THE FOLLOWING ORDER TO:
*FRED H. HILLES RESIDENCE
176 WAYNE AVE.*

QUAN.	DESCRIPTION	PRICE
2500	FBM 2x6 -16'0" @ $250.00 MBF	625.00
40	BBLS PORTLAND CEMENT @ 8.00/BBL	320.00
13	CY #2 TORPEDO SAND @ 4.80/CY	62.40
25	CY GRAVEL @ 5.00/CY	125.00
		1132.40

**INVOICES MUST STATE ORDER NUMBER AND POINT OF DELIVERY.
PRICES ON THIS ORDER NOT SUBJECT TO CHANGE.**

PRACTICAL
"STANDARDIZED" FORMS FOR CONTRACTORS

PURCHASER

FORM P-113   FRANK R. WALKER CO., PUBLISHERS, CHICAGO   MFD. IN U. S. A.

Fig. 22. Purchase Order. Size 4¼ x 6¾ Inches. Form P-113.

more complete than others. It will also help prevent individual items being purchased more than once or overlooked entirely.

When the contractor decides who he wants for the work, he may advise the successful bidder verbally, but should immediately follow up with a confirming purchase order, or sub-contract. Where the work involves job labor or both material and job labor, a sub-contract should be prepared and signed by both parties. If material only is involved, as in the case of cut stone, millwork, etc., the amount of the purchase usu-

PURCHASE ORDER

TO Arlington Hardware & Supply Co.
414 So. Main Street
Arlington, Ill. 60053

ORDER NUMBER F-103-3

DATE 5/5/--

JOB Smith Store Bldg.

PLEASE DELIVER THE FOLLOWING ORDER TO:

SHIP TO Andrews Const. Co.
656 N. Main St.
Arlington, Ill. 60053

JOB NO. 103

F.O.B. Job Site

TERMS 2% - 10th of month

SHIP VIA

DELIVERY TO BE MADE ON X̶X̶X̶X̶ X̶X̶X̶X̶X̶X̶ at once OR RIGHT IS RESERVED TO CANCEL ORDER

In Accepting Verbal Orders, Purchase Order Number Must be Obtained Before Making Delivery.

QUANTITY	DESCRIPTION	PRICE	AMOUNT
200 lbs.	16d Common Nails	14.50	29.00
100 lbs.	12d Common Nails	14.50	14.50
			43.50
	Sales Tax		2.18
			45.68
	CONFIRMING PHONE ORDER		

INVOICES MUST STATE ORDER NUMBER AND POINT OF DELIVERY.

PRICES ON THIS ORDER NOT SUBJECT TO CHANGE.

Andrews Construction Co.

Supt.

BY _____

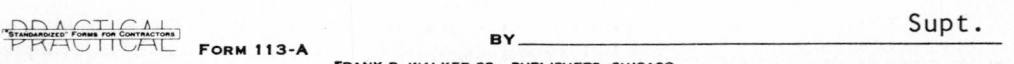

FORM 113-A
STANDARDIZED FORMS FOR CONTRACTORS
FRANK R. WALKER CO., PUBLISHERS, CHICAGO

Fig. 23. Purchase Order. Size 5½ x 8½ Inches. Form 113-A.

PURCHASE ORDER

ORDER NO. O-103-9

DATE   May 12, 19--

JOB   Smith Store Building

JOB NO.   103

F.O.B.   Job Site

TERMS   2% - 10th of month

TO   Arlington Builders Supply Co.
961 Railroad Avenue
Arlington, Illinois 60053

PLEASE DELIVER THE FOLLOWING ORDER TO:

SHIP TO   Andrews Construction Co.   VIA   Truck
656 N. Main St.
Arlington, Ill. 60053

IT IS AGREED THAT DELIVERY WILL BE MADE ON OR BEFORE   June 1, 19--   OR RIGHT IS RESERVED TO CANCEL ORDER

IN ACCEPTING VERBAL ORDERS, PURCHASE ORDER NUMBER MUST BE OBTAINED BEFORE MAKING DELIVERY

JOB REQUIREMENTS OF THE FOLLOWING

Approximately 21,000 Common Brick   @ $65.00 per M
16 Lin Ft., 13" x 13" Clay Tile Flue Lining   @   1.70 per LF
38 Lin. Ft., 12" Dbl. Slant Vitrified Tile Coping   @   2.00 per LF

RECEIPTS FOR ALL DELIVERIES MUST BE OBTAINED AND MAILED WITH INVOICE IN DUPLICATE TO MAIN OFFICE

TERMS: ON OR BEFORE THE.........TH OF THE MONTH FOLLOWING SATISFACTORY DELIVERY, UNLESS OTHERWISE NOTED

INVOICES MUST STATE ORDER NUMBER AND POINT OF DELIVERY

PRICES ON THIS ORDER NOT SUBJECT TO CHANGE

Andrews Construction Company

PRACTICAL
STANDARDIZED Forms for Contractors
MFD. IN U.S.A.   Form 113-C   FRANK R. WALKER CO., PUBLISHERS, CHICAGO

By _____

Sole Owner

Fig. 24. Purchase Order. Size 8½ x 11 Inches. Form 113C.

Sub-Contract Agreement

THIS AGREEMENT, made this ------Second------------ day of -----May-------- A.D. 19 --,
by and between ---------Andrews Construction Company--------------------- hereinafter called the
Contractor, and ----------Arlington Plumbing Company---------------------- hereinafter called
the Sub-contractor.

For the consideration hereinafter named, the said Sub-contractor covenants and agrees with said Contractor, as follows:

FIRST. The Sub-contractor agrees to furnish all material and perform all work necessary to complete the Plumbing,
Sewerage and Gas Fitting work for the one-story and basement store building to be
erected for Mr. John H. Smith, at 656 North Main Street, Arlington, Illinois, in
accordance with Plans, Sheets 1 to 6 inclusive, dated April 2, 19--, and Specifications
Pages 1 to 33 inclusive, dated April 2, 19--.

for the above named structure, according to the plans and specifications (details thereof to be furnished as needed) as
prepared by Johnson and Anderson, Architect, and to the full satisfaction of said Architect.

SECOND. The Sub-contractor agrees to promptly begin said work as soon as notified by said Contractor, and to complete
the work as follows: Commence work on May 7, 19-- and carry same to completion as rapidly
as possible, the entire work to be completed by July 22, 19--.

THIRD. The Sub-contractor shall take out and pay for Workmen's Compensation and Public Liability Insurance, also
Property Damage and all other necessary insurance, as required by the Owner, Contractor or by the State in which this work
is performed.

FOURTH. The Sub-contractor shall pay all Sales Taxes, Old Age Benefit and Unemployment Compensation Taxes upon the
material and labor furnished under this contract, as required by the United States Government and the State in which this
work is performed.

FIFTH. No extra work or changes under this contract will be recognized or paid for, unless agreed to in writing before
the work is done or the changes made.

SIXTH. This contract shall not be assigned by the Sub-contractor without first obtaining permission in writing from
the Contractor.

IN CONSIDERATION WHEREOF, the said Contractor agrees that he will pay to the said Sub-contractor, in -------
monthly------payments, the sum of ------------Two Thousand Two Hundred-------------------
-------------------------($2,200.00)--- Dollars
for said materials and work, said amount to be paid as follows: Ninety-Five------- per cent (95 %) of all labor
and material which has been placed in position by said Sub-contractor, to be paid on or about the ---Tenth (10)------
of the following month, except the final payment, which the said Contractor shall pay to the said Sub-contractor within
Thirty (30)--------- days after the Sub-contractor shall have completed his work to the full satisfaction of the said
Architect or Owner.

The Contractor and the Sub-contractor for themselves, their successors, executors, administrators and assigns, hereby agree
to the full performance of the covenants of this agreement.

IN WITNESS WHEREOF, they have executed this agreement the day and date written above.

Witness:
_____

       Arlington Plumbing Company
_____
Sub-Contractor

By _____ President

_____
    Andrews Construction Company
Contractor

By _____ Sole Owner

PRACTICAL   FORM 133   FRANK R. WALKER CO. PUBLISHERS, CHICAGO
MFD. IN U.S.A.

Fig. 25. Sub-Contract Agreement, Short Form. Size 8½ x 11 Inches. Form 133.

Sub-Contract Agreement

THIS AGREEMENT, made this..day of .... A. D. 19........,
by and between...
hereinafter called the Sub-contractor and...
....hereinafter called the Contractor.

For the consideration hereinafter named, the Sub-contractor covenants and agrees with the said Contractor as follows:

FIRST. The Sub-contractor will furnish all materials and labor, including all necessary scaffolding, and fully construct
and in a good substantial, thorough and workmanlike manner perform and in every respect complete...............................
....
....
....
....
....
....
....
....
....
....
....
....
....
....
....
....
....
....

for the above named structure, according to the plans and specifications (details thereof to be furnished as needed) of
...., Architect, and to the full satisfaction of said Architect.

SECOND. The Sub-contractor will promptly begin said work as soon as he is notified by the Contractor that the
ground is clear or the structure far enough advanced to allow the beginning of that portion included hereunder, and
will carry forward and complete said work as rapidly as said Contractor may judge that the progress of the structure
will permit, unless detained by other Sub-contractors; in which event he will promptly notify the Contractor in writing,
who (if satisfied that said delay is caused by others than said Sub-contractor hereunder) will allow additional time
sufficient in his judgment to make up the time so lost. This paragraph shall cover any extra work done or materials
furnished under this contract.

THIRD. The Sub-contractor will furnish said materials, including all necessary scaffolding, and prosecute said work
with due diligence, without delay, and will not in any manner, by delay or otherwise, interfere with the work of the
Contractor, or other Sub-contractors, and should the said Contractor conclude that the said Sub-contractor is delaying
said work, he shall so notify said Sub-contractor, who shall, within.....................................days thereafter, furnish whatever materials are required by said Contractor, and employ additional men, as required by said Contractor, and in
case said Sub-contractor fails to comply with said demand, the said Contractor shall have the right to furnish said
materials and employ said additional men and charge the expense thereof against the said Sub-contractor and deduct
same from this contract, and should the amount or balance due on said contract be insufficient, to collect said deficiency
by legal process.

Fig. 26. Page 1. Sub-Contract Agreement. Form 144.

FOURTH. Should said Sub-contractor fail to begin, continue and complete the work as hereinbefore provided and should the Contractor suffer or permit said Sub-contractor to occupy more time than required under this agreement, in that event the said Sub-contractor hereby covenants and agrees to indemnify and save harmless the said Contractor from any loss or damages which he may be compelled to make good to the owner of said building, under or by virtue of the contract with the owner, for or on account of delay in the completion thereof, insofar as said delay was caused by the said Sub-contractor.

FIFTH. The Sub-contractor shall provide sufficient, safe and proper facilities at all times for the inspection of the work by the Architect, the Contractor or his authorized representatives. He shall, at once, remove all materials and take down and rebuild all portions of the work condemned by the Architect or Contractor, upon receiving notice in writing of such condemnation.

SIXTH. The Sub-contractor shall not employ any workmen whose employment on the building or improvement may be objected to by any of the other Sub-contractors, the Contractor, the Architect, or the Owner.

SEVENTH. No extra work or changes under this contract will be recognized or paid for, unless agreed to in writing before the work is done or the changes made; in which writing shall be specified in detail the extra work or changes desired, the price to be paid or the amount to be deducted, should said changes decrease the amount to be paid hereunder.

EIGHTH. The Sub-contractor hereby covenants and agrees to indemnify and save harmless the Contractor from any and all manner of claims or suits for infringements of patents or violation of patent rights, including all costs and expenses to which the Contractor may be put in defending any actions that may arise under this clause of the contract.

NINTH. The Sub-Contractor shall comply with all applicable laws, ordinances, rules, regulations and orders of any public authority having jurisdiction for the safety of persons or property or to protect them from damage, injury or loss. _____
_____
_____
_____
_____
_____
_____
_____
_____

TENTH. The Sub-contractor agrees to indemnify and save harmless the Owner and General Contractor against loss or expense by reason of the liability imposed by law upon the Owner or General Contractor for damage because of bodily injuries, including death at any time resulting therefrom; accidentally sustained by any person or persons or on account of damage to property arising out of or on account of or in consequence of the performance of this contract, whether or not such injuries to persons or damage to the property are due or claimed to be due to any negligence of the Sub-contractor, his employees, his agents or servants.

ELEVENTH. The Sub-contractor shall protect and indemnify said Contractor against any loss or damage suffered by any one arising through the negligence of the Sub-contractor, or those employed by him or his agent or servants; he shall bear any expense which the Contractor may have by reason thereof, or on account of being charged therewith; and if there are any such injuries to persons or property unsettled for, when the work herein provided for is finished, final settlement between the Contractor and Sub-contractor shall be deferred until such claims are adjusted or suitable special indemnity acceptable to the Contractor is provided by the Sub-contractor.

TWELFTH. The Sub-contractor shall take out and pay for Employers' Liability or Workmen's Compensation insurance as required by the State in which this work is performed, also Public Liability and Property Damage insurance, in amounts to be agreed upon by the Contracting parties. Upon signature of this contract the Sub-contractor must submit certificate of insurance to include Owners' or Contractors' Protective Liability.

THIRTEENTH. The Sub-contractor shall pay all Sales Taxes, Use Taxes, Excise Taxes, Old Age Benefit and Unemployment Compensation Taxes upon the material and labor furnished under this contract, as required by the Statutes of the United States Government and the State in which this work is performed.

FOURTEENTH. This contract shall not be assigned by the Sub-contractor. Any attempt to assign the contract shall operate as an instant forfeiture and repudiation thereof by the Sub-contractor and the rights of the parties shall be determined in the same manner as though the Sub-contractor had at the time of such attempted assignment failed and refused to continue to perform the contract.

FIFTEENTH. It is expressly UNDERSTOOD AND AGREED by and between the parties hereto that time is and shall be considered the essence of the contract on the part of the said Sub-contractor, and in the event that the said Sub-contractor shall fail in the performance of the entire work to be performed under this contract, by and at the time or times herein mentioned or referred to, the said Sub-contractor shall pay unto the said Contractor, as and for liquidated damages, and not as a penalty, the sum of_____
Dollars per day, which said sum of $_____ per day, in view of the difficulty of estimating such damages with exactness, is hereby expressed, fixed, computed, determined and agreed upon as the damages which will be suffered by the Contractor by reason of such default; and it is understood and agreed by the parties of this contract that the liquidated damages hereinbefore mentioned are in lieu of the actual damages arising from such breach of this Contract, which said sum the said Contractor shall have the right to deduct from any moneys otherwise due or to become due to the said Sub-contractor, or to sue for and recover compensation or damages for the non-performance of this contract at the time or times herein stipulated or provided for.

Fig. 26. Page 2. Sub-Contract Agreement. Form 144.

The Sub-contractor knows that the Contractor must have his contract performed on or before the_____ _____day of_____; and it is therefore understood and agreed that the work provided for herein shall be entirely completed on or before _____ and to that end the Sub-contractor will perform not less than the following average amount of work:_____

_____
_____
_____
_____
_____
_____
_____
_____
_____
_____
_____
_____
_____

No allowance for time will be made Sub-contractor for delay in preparing his drawings or in securing approval of Architect hereto when such drawings are not properly prepared for approval of Architect.

When extension of time for strikes or fire casualties has been granted Contractor by Architect or Owner, the same extension will be granted said Sub-contractor.

SIXTEENTH. The Sub-contractor further agrees that he will within ten days from date provide the Contractor with a bond in the sum of $_____conditioned for the faithful performance of this con-tract in all its particulars, duly executed with Surety company acceptable to the Contractor, as surety, and in the form and contents acceptable to the Contractor.

IN CONSIDERATION WHEREOF, the said Contractor agrees that he will pay to the said Sub-contractor, in monthly payments, the sum of_____ _____for said materials and work, said amount to be paid as follows:_____per cent. (_____%) of all labor and material which has been placed in position and for which payment has been made by said "Owner" to said Contractor, to be paid on or about the_____of the following month, except the last payment, which the said Contractor shall pay to said Sub-contractor immediately after said materials and labor installed by said Sub-contractor have been completed, approved by the said Architect, and final payment received by the Contractor and satisfactory evidence furnished to Contractor by Sub-contractor that all labor and material accounts for use on this particular work have been paid in full.

It is further understood and agreed that no payment on account shall operate as an approval of said work or materials, or any part thereof.

All negotiations and agreements prior to the date of this memorandum are merged herein. We have read and fully understand this agreement.

The Contractor and the Sub-contractor for themselves, their successors, executors, administrators and assigns, hereby agree to the full performance of the covenants of this agreement.

IN WITNESS WHEREOF, they have executed this agreement the day and date written above.

Witness:

_____   _____
                                          Sub-Contractor.

                                          _____
                                          By

_____   _____
                                          Contractor.

                                          _____
                                          By

Fig. 26. Page 3. Sub-Contract Agreement. Form 144.

SUB-CONTRACT AGREEMENT

between

_____

_____

and

_____

_____

for

_____

_____

_____

Dated_____19____

ARCHITECTS

_____

_____

Contract Amount_____$_____

Fig. 26. Page 4. Sub-Contract Agreement. Form 144.

ally governs whether a sub-contract or purchase order is used. Many contractors issue purchase orders for these materials, if the amount is under five thousand dollars, and sub-contracts if over this amount. In the case of reinforcing steel, the suppliers usually insist that the acceptance clause of their proposal be signed, which in itself is sufficient to bind both parties, but most contractors send their own purchase order along with the signed acceptance, in order to keep their purchase records uniform and complete. A purchase order is usually sufficient, for such items as, finish hardware, etc., regardless of the amount.

Much of the time and effort required to draw up subcontract documents may be eliminated by the use of standard sub-contract forms, such as illustrated in Figures 25 and 26. The short form will be sufficient for small to medium sized work and the long form may be used for any size job. The purchase order forms previously mentioned under "Purchasing Materials", will serve just as well for the purchase of vendor items. Sub-contracts are usually prepared in duplicate, with each party retaining a copy and in these cases the job is issued memorandums advising who received a sub-contract and the type of work covered. Purchase orders should be prepared in triplicate, with the original going to the supplier, one copy being retained for the files and the other going to the job.

CHAPTER 5

STARTING THE JOB

The manner in which a contractor starts a job, creates a lasting impression on the architect, owner and other interested observers which may influence the entire course of the work and definitely will affect his reputation. The contractor, who makes a practice of starting his jobs promptly, usually enjoys the fullest cooperation from the architect and owner and also establishes a job morale, which is indispensable to its successful conclusion. This must be the product of thorough planning on the part of the contractor and his staff and cannot be accomplished simply by waving a magic wand. As a result of this planning, decisions should be made as to key personnel to supervise the work; what equipment will be used; location and method of building all temporary construction, such as, job office, shed, etc.; the manner in which the job will be laid out; etc.

Prompt starting of a job will pay dividends in better business relations, better reputation and better profits and is usually the trademark of a successful contractor.

Job Organization

One of the first moves the contractor must make in starting the job, is to set up his job organization. Every job needs competent supervision and if the contractor is too busy to do this himself, he should employ capable men to do it for him. It often happens that the man selected to supervise the work is not immediately available, and in this case, a temporary arrangement should be made so that the job will have competent supervision from the very start. This may be accomplished by using a foreman for a temporary superintendent or the contractor may take over these duties himself until the right man is available.

Most jobs will also need competent foremen for each classification of work the contractor intends to do with his own crews. These men must be expert in their own field and be able to work together in harmony with each other and the rest of the trades.

All jobs will require someone to keep the men's time, make up the payroll and distribute the workmen's time to the various operations for the purpose of keeping costs. On small jobs this may be done by the various foremen, each man taking care of his own crew and the work they perform, with the balance of the clerical work done in the office. Larger jobs may require the services of a timekeeper and good sized jobs will usually require a complete staff of timekeepers, cost clerks, material clerks, etc.

Some jobs will require the services of a watchman for protection after working hours and for tending warning lights, barricades, etc. Many jobs employ stenographers, additional clerical help, errand boys, porters, etc., to advantage. The size of the job organization is usually dependent on the scope of the job. Every job should be adequately, but not excessively, staffed to insure efficient prosecution of the work.

Job Layout

Before any actual work can be started on a job, it must be laid out so that it will be properly located. On many jobs, this is a simple operation, requiring a few measurements and the setting of some stakes to permit the excavator to start digging. Some jobs are more difficult to lay out and may require a construction engineer and assistants to establish base lines and benchmarks from which the building may be located. Still others may require one or more surveying parties to establish and maintain the basic reference points which control the location of the work. What ever the requirements, they must be anticipated and planned for, during the estimating and bidding period, so that arrangements may be made to lay out the job without delay, should the bid be successful.

Starting Work

Every owner and architect likes to see the actual work get under way. This means getting the excavator on the job with his equipment and starting clearing, stripping and digging operations. This also means that temporary construction, such as job office, sheds, tool house, etc., should be started and pushed to completion. Material deliveries should begin as soon as possible and a crew of men started on the installation of foundation work. If all these operations get under way without delay, the job will have a healthy aspect, morale will be high and everyone concerned will be satisfied.

To properly proceed with the work, the contractor must obtain from the architect or owner, enough sets of plans and specifications to distribute to his supervisory personnel, so that they may be thoroughly informed as to the details of the job. He must also furnish each sub-contractor and vendor with plans and specifications. All of these demands need not be met at once, but their ultimate need should be kept in mind and furnished as required, so there will be no excuse for delays.

CHAPTER 6

PERFORMING THE WORK

It is not the intention here to advise the contractor as to the methods to be employed in the field to perform the actual construction work, as a step by step discussion of each operation would fill many volumes. The main purpose is to stimulate the contractor's awareness of some of the essential factors to bring the job to a profitable conclusion, within the stipulated time limit.

Job Progress

The following steps should be considered:
    Planning the job
        Getting all essential data.
        Making decisions
    Directing the job
        Organizing the working plans
        Communicating the working plans
        Directing and supervising personnel
    Controlling the job
        Comparing the job's progress with the original job plan
        Evaluating the performance of the job

Together in importance with satisfying the demands of the architect and owner for quality construction, is the progress of the work. The job that drags along in a lackadaisical manner is seldom profitable and is never a credit to the contractor's reputation. On the other hand, the job which proceeds at a brisk pace usually will repay the contractor handsomely for his efforts and will elicit favorable comment from most observers. A construction job is usually open to public view and its progress the object of intense interest to the "sidewalk superintendents", some of which may become future clients.

No job can progress satisfactorily unless it has competent supervision. The contractor or his representative, in addition to knowing how to construct the job, must be aggressive and literally push the job to completion. They must plan each move of the work far in advance, anticipate what materials or services will be required and procure them at the proper time to avoid congestion or delay. This is especially true on jobs which are confined to a site with little or no room for storing materials.

Another requisite for speedy job progress is the cooperation of all parties concerned. Everyone must work together in harmony toward the common goal of getting the job done and this means, not only the contractor's organization, but the owner, architect, sub-contractors, vendors, etc., as well. To maintain this cooperation which is so essential, many contractors conduct job meetings at regular intervals, usually daily, weekly or monthly, during the course of the work and at which all interested parties are represented. These meetings serve as a clearing house for all job problems and it is here that all present difficulties are ironed out, disputes are settled and plans made for future operations so that all efforts are coordinated in the right direction.

On some jobs, usually the larger ones, the progress may be jeopardized by the threatened inability of one or more suppliers to furnish their materials at the proper time. This usually occurs in materials requiring fabrication at a shop or mill, such as structural steel, millwork, etc., and may be due to a shortage of material, a shortage of labor, too much work or for a number of other reasons. When this condition exists, the contractor should make an effort to expedite the work by sending a representative to the point of delay and thus be able to gain an eye-witness account of the reasons for same. Quite often, just the appearance of an expediter in a mill or shop is enough to persuade the supplier to put forth more effort to get the work finished and delivered to the job. Many companies doing a large volume of work, experience this sort of thing constantly and have a department in their organization which devotes its entire time to expediting.

Construction and Material Reports

Most contractors performing a large volume of work or executing contracts away from the home office keep in touch with the jobs by means of daily construction reports. These reports should contain a complete statement of each day's activities and should include such information as weather conditions, temperature, number of men of all different trades employed on the work, where they were working, and what they were accomplishing. They should also contain comments as to the general progress, reasons for delay, if any, memorandum of visits made to the job by the owner, architect, engineer, or their representatives, together with any comments made regarding the work. In fact, they should contain a complete history of the events occurring on the job. See Figure 27.

This is especially desirable on Municipal, County, State or Government work or on any contracts with time penalty clauses, as notations regarding changes from original plans may be made each day, together with delays caused by weather, strikes, lack of information, etc., so that in the event of disputes or litigation the facts may be ascertained by referring to the Daily Construction Reports.

This is a very important form of report and one that could be used to advantage by many contractors, as it keeps conditions on every job at the finger tips.

Many contractors also require the job to submit a daily report on the materials received, stating just what materials have been received, from whom, quantities, etc., and for convenience this should be done on the reverse of the Daily Construction Report as illustrated in Figure 28. From these reports the bookkeeper in the office is able to check invoices as they are received from the material concerns and it eliminates the necessity of sending all delivery tickets to the main office, except in cases of discrepancy or where the material reports and invoices do not tally.

Figures 29 and 30 illustrate a small or pocket-size Construction and Material Report, showing just what trades were working, number of each, what they were doing, comments, etc. The back of the form, Figure 30, contains a record of materials received that day and for what they are to be used; also a perpetual inventory of all materials received on the job from the beginning up to the present time.

Some contractors require their timekeepers or foremen to report the quantities of materials used on the job each day. This has its advantages and disadvantages for the reason that reports made out every day giving the approximate quantities of sand, gravel, brick, cement, lumber, etc., used that day, will prove satisfactory until near the end of the job or until they reach the bottom of the pile, when they discover there is either too little or too much (usually the former) material on hand to check with the bills of material actually received. The most satisfactory method is to charge the material as it is received on the job, and not report material used daily. However, if the contractor desires a report of the materials used daily, either of the Material Reports illustrated will prove efficient and easy to keep.

Some contractors prefer to use a weekly Construction Progress Report of the bar graph type, as shown in Fig. 31. This form may be used singly or as a summary in conjunction with the daily reports previously mentioned.

As may be seen in the illustration, each major operation of the work is listed together with its cost allowance and its percentage of the total cost. In addition, the planned starting and completion dates for each item is entered in the spaces provided. These entries will be constant for all of the weekly reports during the entire job, unless the contract is revised due to changes in the work.

As the work progresses, the actual starting date for each operation is entered in its proper space and its bar graph begun. The graph consists of two bars, the upper bar indicating the planned progress and the lower bar representing the actual progress with the current weeks progress shown cross hatched. When an operation has reached completion, the date of completion should be entered in the 100% column. The last column is for the percentage of materials which have been delivered to the job.

If this report is used singly, the reverse of the sheet contains space for comments or remarks regarding the progress of the work, reasons for delays, materials required and any other information relevant to the job. If the report is used in conjunction with daily reports, it is unnecessary to include this information as it would be only a duplication of effort.

PRACTICAL
FORM 110
MFD. IN U.S.A.

DAILY CONSTRUCTION REPORT

BUILDING	SMITH STORE BUILDING		DATE	JUNE 6, 19--
LOCATION	656 N. MAIN ST., ARLINGTON, ILL.		WEATHER	CLEAR
ARCHITECTS	JOHNSON & ANDERSON		TEMPERATURE	62 7 A.M. 83 2 P.M.

CLASS OF WORK	Fore-men	Mech-anics	Labor-ers	Misc.	REMARKS
1. WRECKING—SHORING					2. BULLDOZER OPERATOR AND 2 LABORERS
2. EXCAVATING—PUMPING		1	2		BACKFILLING AROUND FOUNDATION WALLS.
3. PILING OR CAISSONS					
4. FOUNDATIONS—RETAINING WALLS					6. 2 CEMENT MASONS AND 2 LABORERS
5. WATER—DAMPPROOFING					PLACING CEMENT FLOOR IN BASEMENT.
6. CEMENT FLOORS—WALKS—PAVEMENTS		2	2		
7. BRICK, TILE, CONCRETE MASONRY	1	4	6		7. LAYING FACE BRICK AND COMMON BRICK
8. CAST STONE—CUT STONE—GRANITE					BACK-UP ON EAST ELEVATION. LAYING
9. TERRA COTTA					SOLID COMMON BRICK SOUTH WALL.
10. FIRE-PROOFING, TILE—GYPSUM					
11. ARCHITECTURAL CONCRETE					13. FRAMING AND PLACING JOISTS FOR
12. REINFORCED CONCRETE					FIRST FLOOR.
(a) Forms					
(b) Reinforcing Steel					
(c) Mix and Deposit Concrete					30. 2 IRONWORKERS FINISHED ERECTION
13. ROUGH CARPENTRY	1	3	2		OF LALLY COLUMN AND GIRDERS.
14. FINISH CARPENTRY					
15. WOOD FLOORS					31. 2 PLUMBERS WORKING ON CONNECTION
16. INSULATION, SOUND DEADENING					TO WATER MAIN.
17. WEATHER STRIPS—CAULKING					2 LABORERS BACKFILLING SEWER
18. LATHING					TRENCHES.
19. PLASTERING					
20. FIRE DOORS—WINDOWS					OWNER VISITED JOB TODAY. SEEMS
21. STEEL DOORS—WINDOWS					WELL SATISFIED WITH PROGRESS.
22. SHEET METAL WORK					
23. ROOFING					MUST HAVE 1"x6" D&M FOR ROUGH
24. TILE AND MOSAIC					FLOORING IMMEDIATELY. LUMBER YARD
25. ASPHALT, CORK, LINOLEUM FLOORS					SAYS THEY ARE TRACING A CAR OF
26. ART MARBLE—SCAGLIOLA					THIS MATERIAL WHICH WAS DUE IN
27. MARBLE—SLATE Exterior Interior					TWO DAYS AGO. BETTER CHECK
28. GLASS AND GLAZING					WITH THEM.
29. PAINTING AND DECORATING					
30. STRUCTURAL IRON—STEEL Erection Riveting		2			ALSO CHECK WITH HEATING
31. MISC. IRON AND STEEL					CONTRACTOR. SHOULD HAVE STARTED
32. ORNAMENTAL IRON—STEEL					TODAY.
33. PLUMBING—SEWERAGE—GAS FITTING		2	2		
34. HEATING AND VENTILATING					
35. AIR CONDITIONING					
36. ELECTRIC WIRING					
37. LIGHTING FIXTURES					
38. ELEVATORS—ESCALATORS					
39. SPRINKLER SYSTEM					

FRANK R. WALKER CO., PUBLISHERS, CHICAGO

Fig. 27. Daily Construction Report. Size 9¼ x 11⅞ Inches. Form 110/111.   Front

PRACTICAL
FORM 111
MFD. IN U.S.A.

STANDARDIZED FORMS FOR CONTRACTORS

DAILY MATERIAL REPORT

JOB NO. _103_ DATE _JUNE 6, 19--_

NAME OF WORK _SMITH STORE BUILDING_ WEATHER _CLEAR_

LOCATION _656 N. MAIN ST., ARLINGTON, ILL._ TEMPERATURE _62_ 7 A.M. _83_ 2 P.M.

RAILROAD AND CAR NO.	CLASS OF WORK	MATERIALS RECEIVED AND FROM WHOM	QUANTITY
	CEM. FLOORS	READY-MIXED CONCRETE – ARLINGTON READY-MIX CO.	9 CY
	MASONRY	COMMON BRICK – ARLINGTON BUILDERS SUPPLY CO.	8000
	ROUGH CARPENTRY	62 PCS. – 2 X 10 – 14'0" ⎫ FROM	1447 FBM
		31 " – 2 X 12 – 24'0" ⎬ BILLINGS LUMBER CO.	1488 "
		25 " – 1 X 4 – 12'0" ⎭	75 "

SUMMARY OF MATERIALS RECEIVED AND USED

KIND OF MATERIAL	Concrete Sand	Gravel	Crushed Stone	Portland Cement	Brick Sand	Lime	Cement for Mortar	Common Brick	Hollow Brick	Press Brick	Enamel Brick
PREVIOUS					10 CY		25 BBLS	5 M		5 M	
TO-DAY					—		—	8		—	
TOTAL					10		25	13		5	

KIND OF MATERIAL	Fire Brick	Special Brick	Reinforcing Steel	2-Inch Furring Tile	3-Inch Hollow Tile	4-Inch Hollow Tile	6-Inch Hollow Tile	8-Inch Hollow Tile	10-Inch Hollow Tile	12-Inch Hollow Tile	Back-Up Tile
PREVIOUS											
TO-DAY											
TOTAL											

KIND OF MATERIAL	Conc. Form Lumber	Framing Lumber	READY-MIX CONCRETE								
PREVIOUS	2500 FBM	—	56 CY								
TO-DAY	—	3010 FBM	9								
TOTAL	2500	3010	65								

FRANK R. WALKER CO., PUBLISHERS, CHICAGO

Fig. 28. Daily Material Report. Size 9¼ x 11⅞ Inches. Form 110/111.

Back

CONSTRUCTION REPORT

JOB SMITH STORE BLDG. DATE JUNE 6, 19--

WEATHER CLEAR   TEMP. 62 A.M. 83 P.M.

NO. MEN	TRADE	REMARKS
1	SUPT.	BULLDOZER & 2 LABORERS
1	CARP. FOREMAN	BACKFILLING AROUND FOUNDATION
3	CARPENTERS	WALLS.
1	MASON FOREMAN	
4	MASONS	2 CEMENT MASONS & 2
	CONC. FOREMAN	LABORERS PLACING CEMENT
2	CEMENT FINISHER	FLOOR IN BASEMENT
	LABORERS	
	ENGINEER	MASONS LAYING FACE BRICK
	TILE-MARBLE SETTERS	& COMMON BRICK BACK-UP
	HELPERS	ON EAST WALL & SOLID
	LATHERS	COMMON BRICK SOUTH WALL
	PLASTERERS	
14	LABORERS	CARPENTERS FRAMING &
	GLAZIERS	PLACING 1ST FLOOR JOISTS
	PAINTERS	IRON WORKERS FINISHED ERECTION OF
2	IRON WORKERS	LALLY COLUMNS & GIRDERS
	ROOFERS	PLUMBERS & HELPERS WORKING ON
2	PLUMBERS	WATER MAIN CONNECTION & BACK-
	GAS FITTERS	FILLING SEWER TRENCHES
	STEAM FITTERS	
	ELECTRICIANS	OWNER VISITED JOB SEEMS WELL
	TEAMS- TRUCKS	SATISFIED WITH PROGRESS
1	BULLDOZER OPR.	NEED 1"x6" D&M FOR ROUGH
		FLOORING IMMEDIATELY
		CHECK WITH HEATING CONTRACTOR
		SHOULD HAVE STARTED TODAY

FRANK R. WALKER CO., PUBLISHERS, CHICAGO   FORM P-111

Fig. 29. Construction Report. Size 4¼ x 6¾ Inches. Form P-111.

MATERIAL REPORT

JOB SMITH STORE BLDG.   DATE JUNE 6, 19--

CHARGE TO	MATERIAL RECEIVED AND FROM WHOM	QUANTITY
CEM. FL.	READY-MIXED CONCRETE FROM ARLINGTON READY-MIX	9 CY
MASONRY	COMMON BRICK FROM ARLINGTON BLDRS. SPLY.	8000
RGH. CARP.	62 PCS 2X10-14'-0" ⎫ FROM	1447 FBM
	31 " 2X12-24'-0" ⎬ BILLINGS	1488 "
	25 " 1X4-12'0" ⎭ LUMBER	75 "

MATERIALS RECEIVED AND USED

KIND OF MATERIAL	CONCRETE READY-MIX	FORM LUMBER	FACE BRICK	COMMON BRICK	MASONRY CEMENT	MASONS SAND
PREVIOUS	56 CY	2500 FBM	5 M	5 M	25 BBLS	10 CY
TO-DAY	9	—	—	8	—	—
TOTAL	65	2500	5	13	25	10
KIND OF MATERIAL	FRAMING LUMBER					
PREVIOUS	—					
TO-DAY	3010 FBM					
TOTAL	3010					

FRANK R. WALKER CO., PUBLISHERS, CHICAGO   FORM P-111

Fig. 30. Material Report. Size 4¼ x 6¾ Inches. Form P-111.

By studying the various progress reports of his jobs, the contractor can get a good picture of what is going on, but he should not rely completely on the reports for his only source of information and should visit each job as often as possible. The more he knows about his jobs the more chance he will have to correct any conditions or situations which may tend to jeopardize his profits.

Job Changes

It is seldom that a job will progress to completion without some changes being made in the original plans. These changes may originate either in the office or on the job, but in both cases an agreement should be reached between the contractor and the architect or owner, before any work is performed, as to the change in the contract price or the method of determining same.

Office changes usually have their inception with the contractor receiving revised plans and specifications from the architect or owner with a request for a quotation, either extra or credit, for the changes involved. Upon receipt of the revised plans, they should be inspected immediately to determine whether any of the work actually in progress will be affected which would necessitate a stop order being issued to the job for that portion of the work. Following this, the change amount should be determined by whatever method specified or requested.

In the event of changes to the work, various methods may be employed to arrive at the amount to be added to the contract price, and on the larger jobs this is usually set forth in the specifications or included with the change information.

FORM 112

JOB NO. 103	CONSTRUCTION PROGRESS REPORT		REPORT NO. 8
PROJECT SMITH STORE BUILDING	LOCATION 656 N. MAIN ST ARLINGTON, ILL.		SHEET 1 OF 1
CONTRACTOR ANDREWS CONSTRUCTION CO.	ADDRESS 209 E. ELM ST. ARLINGTON, ILL.		WEEK ENDING JUNE 26, 19--

NO.	DESCRIPTION	COST ALLOWANCE	PER CT TOTAL	START	COMPLETE	DATE STARTED	Bar graph dates	% MT'L ON JOB
1	G.C., PERMIT, INS.	8316 00	14.0	5-1	7-31	5-1		X
2	EXCAVATION	1481 00	2.5	5-1	5-15	5-1	5-14	X
3	BACKFILL	92 00	0.1	6-1	6-7	6-2	6-7	X
4	GRADING	278 00	0.5	7-15	7-22			X
5	FOUNDATION CONC.	3803 00	6.4	5-5	5-27	5-4	6-1	100
6	FDTN. FORMWORK	4506 00	7.6	5-3	5-31	5-5	6-2	100
7	CONCRETE FLOORS	979 00	1.7	6-1	6-7	6-3	6-6	100
8	CONCRETE WALKS	1167 00	2.0	7-15	7-22			0
9	MAS. & CUT STONE	9798 00	16.5	6-1	7-22	6-1		100
10	ROUGH CARPENTRY	5778 00	9.8	6-1	7-31	6-3		67
11	FIN. CARP. MILLWORK	2469 00	4.2	7-22	7-31			0
12	CAULKING	125 00	0.2	7-1	7-7			0
13	WEATHERSTRIPS	50 00	0.1	7-22	7-31			0
14	LATH & PLASTERING	3000 00	5.1	6-24	6-26	6-26		40
15	ALUM. WIND. & DOORS	1250 00	2.1	6-22	6-30	6-22	6-30	100
16	SHEET METAL WORK	300 00	0.5	7-1	7-7			0
17	ROOFING	1675 00	2.8	7-3	7-15			0
18	GLASS & GLAZING	1250 00	2.1	7-1	7-25			0
19	PAINTING	1375 00	2.3	7-15	7-31			0
20	MISC. IRON & STEEL	1575 00	2.7	6-1	6-2	6-1	6-2	100
21	PLUMBING	2200 00	3.7	5-7	7-22	5-5		85
22	HEATING	4200 00	7.1	6-7	7-22	6-7		75
23	ELECTRICAL	3560 00	6.0	6-22	7-31	6-22		40

TOTAL OR CARRY FORWARD 59227 00

PERCENT COMPLETE THIS WEEK 12.8 PREVIOUS 33.9 TOTAL TO DATE 56.7

WORK ORDER ISSUED MAY 1 19--
CONTRACT COMPLETION DATE JULY 31 19--

TOTAL PROGRESS PLANNED: 5-1 5-15 6-3 6-6 6-12 6-21 7-1 7-8 7-15 7-20 7-31
ACTUAL: 5-1 5-15 6-1 6-4 6-11 6-23

USE OTHER SIDE FOR REMARKS

Fig. 31. Construction Progress Report. Form 112. Size 8½ x 11 Inches. Also available in 17'' x 22 size. Form 112L.

One method of determining change amounts is on a Time and Material plus a Fee basis and involves keeping separate costs of both material and labor on all work included in the change. See figure 33A. These costs should be kept daily and should be submitted to the architect, owner or their representatives for approval at the end of each day. When the extra work is completed, these costs are totaled, the fee agreed upon is added and the contract price changed accordingly. This method is especially adaptable where the extent of the change cannot be determined accurately and little or none of the original work is omitted which would involve credits.

Another method for determining change amounts, and the one most frequently used is the Lump Sum method. The contractor prepares an estimate of the change in the same manner as estimating a new job, except that certain portions of the original work may be omitted and will therefore have to be figured separately as a credit and then deducted from the amount determined for the extra work. When the contractor has arrived at the net amount for the change he submits a proposal to the architect or owner for their approval and acceptance.

A third method of arriving at the amount to be added to the contract for a change is by means of unit prices which have been agreed upon at the time of signing the contract. When using this method either the quantities of extra work are computed in advance or the work is performed and field measurements are taken. The unit prices are then applied to the quantities and totaled, resulting in the change amount.

In figuring changes, the contractor should remember that other job costs may be affected in addition to the actual items of work, such as general conditions, permits, insurance, taxes, plant and equipment and the surety bond, if required. No change would be complete without these items being included in the computations, except where the Unit Price method is employed. Unit prices are usually specified and requested to be selling prices and should contain enough mark up from the bare costs to cover these items including the contractor's fee.

Field changes usually originate with the architect or owner issuing an extra work order to the job organization. A convenient and sure method for taking orders for additional work in the field is for the superintendent or foreman to write up the order on an Extra Work Order form such as illustrated in Figure 32 and

Extra Work Order

No. __1__   Date __JULY 5__   19--

Job __SMITH STORE BUILDING__

To __ANDREWS CONST. CO.__

Address __209 E. ELM, ARLINGTON, ILL.__

Please furnish all Materials and Labor necessary to complete the following work, and charge to our account as noted below:

PAVE 25'0" X 25'0" AREA AT REAR OF JOB SITE WITH A TROWEL FINISHED 5" CONCRETE SLAB ON A 4" BED OF WELL TAMPED CINDERS. ELEVATION OF SLAB TO BE SAME AS SIDEWALK.

The work covered by this order shall be performed under the same Terms and Conditions as that included in the Original Contract.

1. The above work to be paid for at actual cost of Labor and Materials, plus _____ percent (__ %).

2. All of the above work to be completed for the sum of _____

FIVE HUNDRED EIGHTY ($580.00) Dollars.

Signed __JOHNSON & ANDERSON__

'STANDARDIZED' FORMS FOR CONTRACTORS
PRACTICAL
MFD. IN U. S. A.

By __Gust C. Anderson__

FORM P-101   FRANK R. WALKER CO., PUBLISHERS, CHICAGO

Fig. 32. Extra Work Order. Size 4¼ x 6¾ Inches. Form P-101.

CONTRACT CHANGE ORDER

JOB   SMITH STORE BUILDING
CONTRACT JOB NO.   527

CHANGE
ORDER **No.** 1

FOR

DATE   July 7, 19--

TO   Andrews Construction Company
209 E. Elm Street
Arlington, Illinois 60053

REVISED **CONTRACT AMOUNT**

PREVIOUS **CONTRACT AMOUNT** $ 59,227.00

AMOUNT OF THIS ORDER $ 580.00

TOTAL CONTRACT AND EXTRAS $ 59,807.00

To cover paving of 25" - 0" x 25" - 0" area at rear of Smith Store
Building site at 656 No. Main St., Arlington, Illinois, as stated
in Extra Work Order No. 1, dated July 5, 19--, and as follows:

Elevation of concrete slab to be same as sidewalk.
Concrete slab to be placed on a well tamped bed of cinders, 4"
    thick after tamping.
Concrete slab to be 5" thick and to have a monolithic trowel
    finish.
Concrete to be same mix as for sidewalk (2500 lb. ready-mix).

The work covered by this order shall be performed under the same Terms and Conditions as that included in the Original Contract.

CHANGES APPROVED

By _____

By _____

AMOUNT OF ORIGINAL CONTRACT $ 59.227.00

CHANGE NO.   1   580.00

JOHNSON AND ANDERSON, ARCHITECTS

By _____

PRACTICAL
STANDARDIZED FORMS FOR CONTRACTORS
MFD IN U.S.A   Form L-101

FRANK R. WALKER CO., PUBLISHERS, CHICAGO

Fig. 33. Contract Change Order. Size 8½ x 11 Inches. Form L-101.

DAILY TIME AND MATERIAL SHEET
FOR EXTRA WORK ON CONTRACT JOBS

EXTRA WORK
ORDER NO. _____

JOB NO. _____ REPORT NO. _____

NAME _____ SHEET NO. _____

LOCATION _____ DATE _____

REMARKS: | LABOR CLASSIFICATIONS | WEATHER |

TEMPERATURE
8 A. M.

1 P. M.

OCCUP-ATION	EMPLOYEE'S NAME	EMP. NO.														HOURS	RATE	AMOUNT

TOTAL LABOR

LABOR TAX

MATERIAL USED

NO. PCS.	ITEM	WHERE PURCHASED	QUANTITY	UNIT PRICE	TOTAL		

TOTAL MATERIAL

TOTAL LABOR AND MATERIAL

OVERHEAD EXPENSE

PRACTICAL FORM 507   **TOTALS**

MFD. IN U. S. A.   FRANK R. WALKER CO., PUBLISHERS, CHICAGO

Fig. 33A. Daily Time and Material Sheet. Form 507.

have the person doing the ordering sign it. This order should be prepared in triplicate with the original being sent to the office, the duplicate given to whoever signs the order and the triplicate being retained for the job records. Usually on small jobs any price changes can be agreed upon at the time the order is written, leaving the contractor free to do the work with the assurance that he will be paid for the additional work. If the changes are so involved as to require a quantity survey and pricing by an estimator, the order should be forwarded to the office to be handled in the same manner as an office change.

To keep the records straight, any change in the contract amount should be covered by the architect or owner issuing to the contractor a Contract Change Order (See Figure 33) in which the nature of the extra work is described and the revision to the contract price is set forth. After receiving this, the contractor should then issue a similar order to each of the sub-contractors or vendors involved in the change, revising their contract prices in the same manner. Contract Change Orders should always be prepared in triplicate. When used by the architect, the original should be issued to the contractor, the duplicate retained for the architect's files and the triplicate sent to the owner. When used by the contractor, the original should be issued to the sub-contractor, the duplicate retained for the contractor's files and the triplicate sent to the job office to keep their records complete.

The job should be kept fully informed at all times, regarding negotiations for changes and their results, to prevent doing work which might have to be removed due to the changes.

CHAPTER 7

TIME KEEPING SYSTEMS FOR CONTRACTORS

Time keeping is an essential part of every job and its purpose is two-fold, the first being to keep an accurate record of each workman's time for pay-roll purposes, and the second to distribute that time accurately so that each class of work is charged with the proper amount of labor for the cost records.

The method used in keeping the workmen's time on the job and in making up the pay-rolls will vary according to the size of the business and the preference of the individual contractor.

The larger contractors employing a timekeeper on their different jobs will require an altogether different system than the smaller contractors who have the time kept by the job foremen, or who have each workman keep a record of his own time to be turned in each night or at the end of the pay-roll period.

In either event, a system should be used where the foreman or timekeeper can carry the time-book in his pocket on the job, as this eliminates a lot of unnecessary running from the job to the construction office every time a man is to be laid off or when any reference is to be made to the time book.

The author has had considerable experience keeping time on construction work and has always found the simplest system the most efficient.

A complete description of the various time-keeping methods for use by both large and small contractors is given on the following pages.

Method Used in Keeping the Workmen's Time
Where a Timekeeper is Employed

On jobs where a timekeeper is employed, and where the time of the men on the job is checked several times a day, it is possible to obtain a more accurate record of the different classes of work performed by them than could be secured where the foreman must keep the men's time and labor distribution in addition to his regular duties.

On jobs where a timekeeper is employed, the workmen should report at the job office in the morning before starting work, either giving their name and check or badge number or depositing their check, depending upon the system in use.

Some contractors prefer to have the men deposit their brass checks at the office in the morning before starting work and call for them in the evening after the day's work is completed. Either of these methods is satisfactory.

From this record the timekeeper makes his entries opposite each man's name on the time sheet, making a small dot or notation, indicating that the man has reported for work. This enables the timekeeper to know which men to look for when checking their time on the job during working hours. If the men report for work late in the morning, a small "L" should be entered on the left side of the square provided for that day's time. If the men leave work early in the day, a small "E" is placed at the right side of the square provided for that day's time.

The workmen should be checked not less than four times a day, and at least two or three times while at work on the job. The oftener they are checked on the job the more accurate the distribution of the labor hours and costs will be. This will vary somewhat depending upon the duties of the timekeeper and the amount of time at his disposal, but to be reasonably accurate, the time should be checked at two-hour intervals.

As the timekeeper goes over the job checking the men at work, a small symbol designating the particular class of work being done by each man, is placed in the square allotted for that purpose. See Figures 34 and 36 for method used. For example, the symbol E-22 signifies that the man is working on common brick.

These symbols are repeated each time the workmen's time is checked during the day. From these checkings the timekeeper is able to charge the workmen's time to the different classes of work performed on the job that day, which is essential if correct labor costs are to be obtained.

At the close of the day, the workmen report at the job office again before leaving work, where they either give their name or collect their check as the case may be. From this record the timekeeper is able to enter the workmen's time on the pay-roll sheets for the permanent record.

Symbols Used in Checking the Workmen's Time
On the Job

When checking the workmen's time on the job, it is advisable to use symbols to designate the various classes of work performed, as it is often possible to say as much with one symbol as would ordinarily take several lines to write in longhand.

The method of using symbols is fully described on the following pages where a complete cost schedule is given, covering all classes of construction work. The advantage of symbols will be readily seen where there are several lines of descriptive matter taken care of by the use of one small symbol.

This cost schedule can be carried in the pocket time-book for reference when checking the workmen's time on the job.

From the original check marks on the time sheets or time check reports, Figure 34 or 36, the timekeeper goes through the different sheets and totals the number of hours worked by each trade on the same kind of work during the day. These items are totaled and the total number of hours worked by the different trades, such as common laborers, masons, carpenters, etc., are entered on the distribution report under the proper labor classification. This is illustrated and described in detail in Chapter 9.

Check Systems in Use By Different Contractors

Most contractors on large construction work use some style of brass check or badge for identifying the workmen employed on each job. This may be accomplished by means of brass checks containing numbers or by the use of large buttons or pins containing numbers, that the workmen pin to their shirt or cap. This is undoubtedly the most satisfactory method to use, as it enables the timekeeper to tell at a glance each workman's number and occupation, making it unnecessary to speak to the men while checking their time on the job.

Some of the construction companies using brass checks for identifying their workmen, have the men remove the checks from the board when reporting for work in the morning and deposit them again at night when leaving work for the day. In the author's opinion, it is more satisfactory to have the workmen deposit their checks in the office or on the check board in the morning before commencing work and then call for them at night before leaving work, so that they can take their checks with them at night. This is important on large work because if the man fails to return to work for any reasons, such as illness, death, etc., he always retains his check as a means of identification, until he has been paid in full. At the time the workman is paid in full, the check is then lifted.

This same method may be used where pins, badges or buttons are used, as the workman is given a pin or button containing his number. This is carried by him on his person where it can be seen by the foreman or timekeeper and identifies him at any time. If the man is discharged, laid off, or quits for any reason, the pin or button is lifted at the time he receives his final pay check.

In giving either checks, pins or badges to the workmen, it is advisable to separate the various trades by different series of numbers, as far as possible. For instance, common laborers would have checks or pins running from 1 to 150 in number; carpenters from 151 to 200; masons from 201 to 250, etc. In this way it is possible to tell a man's trade merely by glancing at his check number.

This same method should be used when writing the workmen's names on the pay-roll sheets, as by keeping all workmen of the same trade together on the pay-roll sheets, numbered consecutively, it avoids confusion and saves time when checking the men's time on the job and when copying to the pay-roll sheets at night or at the end of each pay-roll period.

Weekly Time Check Report

The Weekly Time Check Report, as illustrated in Figure 34, is for use by contractors who employ a time-keeper on their work, and is intended for use on jobs employing from 50 to 1,000 or more men, as it is flexible enough to be used on the largest work.

This report should be pocket-size, enabling the timekeeper to conveniently carry it with him on the job. The form as illustrated is ruled so that the records of 20 men may be kept on each sheet (10 on each side) for an entire week. This form provides four spaces for checking the time each day—two for the morning and two for the afternoon. This enables the foreman or timekeeper to make the necessary notations if the men report for work late in the morning, or if they quit work early in the day.

The checking spaces are of sufficient size to permit the timekeeper or foreman making all necessary notations or symbols regarding the kind of work performed by each man when they are checked during the day. Symbols may be used in making these notations or they may be written in long hand, as preferred.

The time should be entered from the Time Check Report, Figure 34, to the pay-roll sheets each day, and at the end of each payroll period only the last day's time is inserted and the pay-rolls are complete and ready to extend.

The Labor Distribution may also be made up from the Time Check Reports, as all necessary information is contained thereon. It is only necessary to total the number of hours worked by each trade on the different labor classifications and see that they balance with the total number of hours on the pay-roll for that day. Care must be exercised to see that the total number of hours for each class of workmen on the labor distribution agree to the hour with the total number of hours appearing on the pay-roll for the same period.

These Reports may be kept by the timekeeper and the various job foremen. Each night the foremen should turn in their reports to the timekeeper for comparison so that any mistakes made in checking the time or any differences in the distribution may be rectified at once.

Fig. 34. Weekly Time Check Report. Size 4¼ x 6¾ Inches. C-118.

Foreman's Report

This is a daily report that should be kept by each crew foreman on the job. At the close of each working day the foreman should turn in a report covering the work performed by the men in his crew. For instance, if the carpenter foreman has 15 carpenters working 8 hours each, he will have to account for 120 hours carpenter time for that day. Likewise, each foreman on the job will have to account for the men working in his crew.

The foreman should not be required to report the quantity of work performed by his men, unless he is thoroughly capable of doing so, as it has been found that many very good foremen are unable to make accurate computations. This may be left for the job office to complete or the quantities may be computed and included on the Labor Distribution Report for that pay-roll period.

These reports should contain sufficient information to enable the timekeeper to make an accurate distribution report of the labor hours and costs, which should be prepared each day. Should there be a discrepancy between the timekeeper's checkings and the foremen's reports it can be rectified immediately, thus eliminating all chance of error.

When the Foreman's Report, Figure 35, is used by the smaller contractors who do not employ a timekeeper, the foreman in charge of the job should turn in his report each day, stating the number of men working in his crew or on the job, together with the number of hours worked by each trade on the different kinds of work. The total number of hours for all classes of workmen must agree with the total number of hours appearing on the pay-roll for that day.

A Combination Time Card and Pay-Roll

The time and pay-roll sheet, illustrated in Figure 36, is as simple and accurate a method of keeping the workmen's time as can be found. It contains sufficient space to write the names of 10 men, their occupation

---

PRACTICAL
Standardized Forms for Contractors

FOREMAN'S REPORT   JOB NO. 103

JOB SMITH STORE BUILDING   DATE JUNE 26, 19--

OCCUPATION	NO. OF MEN	DESCRIPTION OF WORK	QUANTITY OF WORK	HOURS	TOTAL HOURS
MASON FOREMAN	1	SETTING 13" x 13" FLUE LINING	8 LF	2	2
"	1	SETTING STONE SILLS AND CHIMNEY CAP	37 LF SILLS 3 CF CAP	3 1	4
"	1	LAYING COMMON BRICK	1100	2	2
MASON	1	" " "		8	8
LAB.	2	HELP MASONS - COMMON BRICK	—	4/8	12
"	1	" " -STONE SILLS & CHIMNEY CAP	—	3 1	4
CARP.	1	PLACING WOOD GROUNDS	275 LF	4	4
LAB.	1	HELP CARPENTER -WOOD GROUNDS	—	4	4
SIGNED Geo. Wilson			TOTAL	40	40

FORM C-107   MFD. IN U.S.A. FRANK R. WALKER CO., PUBLISHERS, CHICAGO

Fig. 35. Foreman's Report. Size 4¼ x 6¾ Inches. C-107.

WEEKLY PAY-ROLL   SHEET NO. _1_ OF ____

JOB SMITH STORE BLDG   WEEK ENDING JUNE 26, 19--   JOB NO. 103

OCCU-PATION	EMPLOYEE'S NAME (EXEMP)	M	T	W	T	F	S	S	HOURS	RATE	AMOUNT	F.I.C.A.	FEDERAL INC. TAX	STATE INC. TAX		NET AMOUNT PAID
LAB	JAMES LARSON 5	8	8	8	8	8	—	—	40	7 00	280 00	16 38	33 90	4 61		225 11
"	FRANK PARKER 1	8	8	8	8	8	—	—	40	"	280 00	16 38	54 80	6 53		202 29
"	H. KELLEY 2	—	8	8	8	4	—	—	28	"	196 00	11 47	24 30	3 95		156 28
CARP	CHAS KRESSLER 4	—	8	8	8	4	—	—	28	9 15	256 20	14 99	30 50	4 49		206 22
"	Wm JOHNSON 4	—	8	8	—	—	—	—	16	"	146 40	8 56	12 10	1 73		124 01
MAS. FORE	GEO. WILSON 2	8	8	8	8	8	—	—	40	10 00	400 00	23 40	75 10	9 02		292 48
MAS.	DAN HUGHES 4	8	8	8	8	8	—	—	40	9 50	380 00	22 23	61 50	7 56		288 71
REG. O.T. TOTALS		32	56	56	48	40	—	—	232		1938 60	113 41	292 20	37 89		1495 10

MFD. IN U.S.A.   FORM C-104   FRANK R. WALKER CO., PUBLISHERS, CHICAGO

Fig. 36. Weekly Time Card and Pay-Roll. Size 4¼ x 6¾ Inches. Form C-104.

and check numbers, together with their time for seven days. Space is also provided for inserting the total number of hours worked, the hourly rate of wage and the total amount due, together with a record of all money deducted for Federal Insurance Contributions and Income Withholding Tax.

Inasmuch as this sheet may be carried in the pocket on the job, it serves the double purpose of a time book and payroll. At the end of each day the time is entered on the sheet and on the last day of the week it is necessary to insert only the last day's time, add the total number of hours worked by each man, multiply by his hourly rate, and the result is the amount due each man for his week's work.

This eliminates the necessity of copying from a time book to a pay-roll sheet, as one operation completes the record.

If a copy of the pay-roll is desired by the foreman or timekeeper on the job, an exact copy of the original may be obtained by placing a piece of carbon paper between two pay-roll sheets.

On jobs employing a large number of men (100 or more), where it is necessary for the timekeeper to record the men's time and make notations regarding the class of work performed by them, this may be accomplished by the use of small symbols placed in the squares provided for each day's time, as illustrated. The time is filled in each day, and on the last day of the week, one day's time is inserted, the hours totaled and the pay-roll is complete.

Weekly and Semi-Monthly Pay-Roll Sheets

To comply with the requirements of the Social Security Act, it is necessary for every contractor to keep a Weekly, Semi-Monthly or Monthly Pay-Roll, showing each Employee's Name, Occupation, number of hours worked each day, total hours worked each pay-roll period, rate of pay, together with total earnings for the period. From the total wages due, it is necessary to show deductions made from each employee's pay for Federal Insurance Contributions, Income Withholding Tax and for State Unemployment Compensation, in states requiring such deductions, together with the Net Amount paid to each employee each pay-roll period.

Figure 37 illustrates a pay-roll sheet suitable for use by contractors whose employees do not receive any compensation other than wages.

You will note there is space provided for Employee's Occupation, Name, Number, Time Worked Each Day, Total Hours Worked, Rate of Pay, Total Earnings and Number of Income Tax Exemptions. It also provides space for deductions for Federal Insurance Contributions, Income Withholding Tax, State Unemployment Compensation, Other Deductions, Total Deductions, Net Amount paid to each Employee and Check Number.

Where the contractor desires to have each employee sign the pay-roll as a receipt for wages, the pay-roll sheet illustrated in Figure 38 furnishes the necessary information.

The Semi-Monthly Pay-Roll sheet illustrated in Figure 39 is similar to the one illustrated in Figure 37, except it provides for semi-monthly payments instead of weekly payments.

WEEKLY PAY-ROLL

JOB NO. 103
NAME OF WORK SMITH STORE BUILDING LOCATION ARLINGTON, ILL.
PAY ROLL SHEET NO. 1 OF
WEEK JUNE 20, 19-- TO JUNE 26, 19--
FORM SS-104
FRANK R. WALKER CO., PUBLISHERS, CHICAGO

OCC.	NAME OF EMPLOYEE	EMP. NO.	M	T	W	T	F	TOTAL HOURS	HOURLY RATE	TOTAL EARNINGS	NO. OF EX.	F.I.C.A.	FEDERAL INCOME TAX	STATE INCOME TAX		TOTAL DEDUC-TIONS	AMOUNT	CHECK NO.
LAB.	JAMES LARSON	102	8	8	8	8	8	40	7.00	280 00	5	16 38	33 90	4 61		54 89	225 11	5021
"	FRANK PARKER	103	8	8	8	8	8	40	7.00	280 00	1	16 38	54 80	6 53		77 71	202 29	5022
"	H. KELLEY	104	–	8	8	8	4	28	7.00	196 00	2	11 47	24 30	3 95		39 72	156 28	5023
CARP.	CHAS. KRESSLER	151	–	8	8	8	4	28	9.15	256 20	4	14 99	30 50	4 49		49 98	206 22	5024
"	WM. JOHNSON	152	–	8	8	–	–	16	9.15	146 40	4	8 56	12 10	1 73		22 39	124 01	5025

Fig. 37. Weekly Pay-Roll. Size 9¼ x 11⅞ Inches. Form SS-104.

WEEKLY PAY-ROLL

JOB NO. 103
NAME OF WORK SMITH STORE BUILDING LOCATION ARLINGTON, ILL.
WEEK JUNE 20, 19-- TO JUNE 26, 19--
PAY ROLL SHEET NO. 1
FORM SS-104-R
FRANK R. WALKER CO., PUBLISHERS, CHICAGO

	OCCUP.	NAME OF EMPLOYEE	EXEMP.	M	T	W	T	F	TOTAL HOURS	HOURLY RATE	TOTAL EARN-INGS	F.I.C.A.	FED. INCOME TAX	STATE INCOME TAX		TOTAL DEDUC-TIONS	NET AMOUNT PAID	RECEIVED PAYMENT IN FULL OF WITHIN AMOUNT	
1	LAB	JAMES LARSON	5	8	8	8	8	8	40	7.00	280 00	16 38	33 90	4 61		54 89	225 11		1
2	"	FRANK PARKER	1	8	8	8	8	8	40	"	280 00	16 38	54 80	6 53		77 71	202 29		2
3	"	H. KELLEY	2	–	8	8	8	4	28	"	196 00	11 47	24 30	3 95		39 72	156 28		3
4	CARP.	CHAS. KRESSLER	4	–	8	8	8	4	28	9.15	256 20	14 99	30 50	4 49		49 98	206 22		4
5	"	WM. JOHNSON	4	–	8	8	–	–	16	"	146 40	8 56	12 10	1 73		22 39	124 01		5

Fig. 38. Weekly Pay-Roll. Size 9¼ x 11⅞ Inches. Form SS-104-R.

SEMI-MONTHLY PAY-ROLL

JOB NO. 103
NAME OF WORK SMITH STORE BUILDING LOCATION ARLINGTON, ILL.
PAY ROLL SHEET NO. 1
PAY ROLL ENDING JUNE 30, 19--
FORM 33-103
FRANK R. WALKER CO., PUBLISHERS, CHICAGO

	EMPLOY-EE'S NUMBER	NAME OF EMPLOYEE	OCCUPATION	1 16	2 17	3 18	4 19	5 20	6 21	7 22	8 23	9 24	10 25	11 26	12 27	13 28	14 29	15 30	16 31	TOTAL HOURS	HOURLY RATE	TOTAL EARN-INGS	F.I.C.A.	FED. INCOME TAX	STATE INC. TAX	TOTAL DEDUC-TIONS	NET AMOUNT PAID	
1	102	JAMES LARSON	LAB.	8	8	–	–	8	8	8	8	–	8	8	8	8	–	88	7 00	616 00	36 04	71 60	10 22	117 86	498 14	1
2	103	FRANK PARKER	"	8	8	–	–	8	8	8	8	–	8	8	8	8	–	88	"	616 00	36 04	116 60	14 39	167 03	448 97	2
3	104	H. PARKER	"	8	8	–	–	8	8	8	4	–	8	8	8	8	–	76	"	532 00	31 12	74 90	11 22	117 24	414 76	3
4	151	CHAS. KRESSLER	CARP	8	8	–	–	8	8	8	4	–	8	8	8	8	–	76	9 15	695 40	40 68	93 80	13 27	147 75	547 65	4
5	152	WM. JOHNSON	"	8	8	–	–	8	8	–	–	–	8	4	–	–	–	44	"	402 60	23 55	40 70	5 89	70 14	332 46	5

Fig. 39. Semi-Monthly Pay-Roll. Size 9¼ x 11⅞ Inches. Form SS-103.

WEEKLY PAY-ROLL — JOB NO. 117 — PAY-ROLL SHEET NO. 1 OF — WEEK AUG 8, 19-- to AUG 14, 19--

NAME OF WORK: CENTRAL HOSPITAL   LOCATION: INDIANAPOLIS, IND.   FORM WH-105.

SOCIAL SECURITY NUMBER	OCC.	NAME OF EMPLOYEE	EMPL. NO.	REGULAR TIME WORKED M T W T F S S	TOTAL HOURS	HOURLY RATE	REGULAR EARNINGS	EXCESS TIME WORKED M T W T F S S	TOTAL HOURS	HOURLY RATE	EXCESS EARNINGS	TOTAL EARNINGS	NO. OF EX.	F.I.C.A.	FEDERAL INC. TAX	STATE INC. TAX			TOTAL DED.	AMOUNT	CHECK NO.
167-41-3267	LAB.	JAMES McLEAN	121	8 10 10 10 7 - -	45	7.00	315.00	- 1 1 1 - - -	3	7.00	21.00	336.00	4	19.66	49.30	6.48			75.44	260.56	121
155-42-3312	"	ROBT. GORDON	122	8 10 8 8 - - -	34	7.00	238.00	- 1 - - - - -	1	7.00	7.00	245.00	3	14.33	31.40	4.69			50.42	194.58	122
163-42-3184	CARP	SAM OLSON	215	10 8 10 10 10 - -	48	9.15	439.00	- 1 - 1 1 1 -	4	9.15	36.60	475.00	5	27.83	82.60	9.48			119.91	355.89	123
167-24-4125	"	FRED STONE	216	8 8 8 8 8 - -	40	9.15	366.00	- - - - - - -	—	—	—	366.00	4	21.40	56.50	7.21			85.11	280.89	124
165-28-3176	MASON	A. C. WILCOX	251	8 8 12 8 8 - -	44	9.50	418.00	- - 2 - - - -	2	9.50	19.00	437.00	6	25.56	67.40	8.03			100.99	336.01	125

Fig. 40. Weekly Pay-Roll. Size 11 x 17 Inches. Form WH-105.

WEEKLY PAY-ROLL — JOB NO. 112 — PAY ROLL SHEET NO. 1 OF — WEEK OCT 10, 19-- to OCT 16, 19--

NAME OF WORK: MUNICIPAL WATER TREATMENT PLANT   LOCATION: ARLINGTON, ILL.   FORM WH-106.   FRANK R. WALKER CO., PUBLISHERS, CHICAGO

OCCUPATION	NAME OF EMPLOYEE	EXEMPT	EMP. NO.		TIME WORKED M T W T F S S	TOTAL HRS.	HOURLY RATE	REGULAR EARNINGS	EXCESS EARNINGS	TOTAL EARNINGS	F.I.C.A.	FEDERAL INCOME TAX	STATE INCOME TAX			TOTAL DEDUCTIONS	AMOUNT	CHECK NO.
LAB	JOHN S. WILLIAMS	2	127	B	1 - - 1 - - 2	44	7.00	308.00	14.00	322.00	18.84	53.80	7.09			79.73	242.27	
				S	10 8 8 10 8 - -													
"	FRED ANDERSON	4	128	B	1 - - 1 - - 2	44	7.00	308.00	14.00	322.00	18.84	46.90	6.13			71.87	250.13	
				S	10 8 8 8 10 - -													
CARP	JOSEPH SMITH	3	161	B	- - - 1 - - 1	42	9.15	384.30	9.15	393.45	23.13	68.30	8.42			99.85	295.60	
				S	8 8 8 10 8 - -													
"	SAMUEL DUNBAR	4	162	B	- - - 1 - - 1	42	9.15	384.30	9.15	393.45	23.02	64.30	7.91			95.23	298.22	
				S	8 8 8 10 8 - -													
MASON	JAMES BURNS	5	207	B	- - - - - - -	40	9.50	380.00	—	380.00	22.23	57.90	7.08			87.21	292.79	
				S	8 8 8 8 8 - -													

Fig. 41. Weekly Pay-Roll. Size 9¼ x 11⅞ Inches. Form WH-106.

Where contractors are performing work in Interstate Commerce and operating under the Wage and Hour Act, also on Government work where Regular and Overtime must to kept separate, the pay-roll illustrated in Figure 40 furnishes an excellent record.

This form contains space for Social Security Number, Occupation, Name, Number, Regular Hours Worked each Day, Total Weekly Hours, Rate, Total Regular Earnings, Number of Excess Hours Worked each Day and Total for Week, Rate, Total Excess Earnings, Total Earnings and Number of Income Tax Exemptions. It also provides space for Deductions made for Federal Insurance Contributions, Income Withholding Tax, two blank spaces for Other Deductions, Total Deductions, Net Amount Paid and Check Number.

Figure 41 illustrates a Weekly Pay-Roll sheet that provides space for both straight or regular time, also for excess or overtime hours and earnings.

The form contains space for Employee's Occupation, Name, Number of Income Tax Exemptions, Number, Two spaces for time worked each day ("S" denotes straight or regular time hours, "B" denotes bonus, excess or overtime hours), Total Regular Hours, Total Excess Hours, Hourly Rate, Regular Earnings, Excess Earnings, Total Earnings, together with Deduction Columns for Federal Insurance Contributions, Income Withholding Tax, Unemployment Compensation Tax, etc., Total Deductions, Net Amount Paid and Check Number.

A Combined Weekly Pay-Roll and Labor Distribution

Illustrated, in Figure 42, is a Weekly Pay-Roll and Labor Distribution for use by contractors who desire a daily and weekly distribution of each workman's time, where the men are working on a number of different

WEEKLY PAY-ROLL AND LABOR DISTRIBUTION

JOB NO. ___ NAME OF WORK: MISCELLANEOUS WORK LOCATION ___ PAYROLL SHEET NO. 1 OF ___ WEEK AUG 15, 19— TO AUG 21, 19—

OCCUPATION	NAME OF EMPLOYEE	NO. OF EXEMP.	EMPL. NO.	SMITH RES. JOB 105 M	T	W	T	F	S	S	HOURS	AMOUNT	RUDD HDWE CO. JOB 106 M	T	W	T	F	S	S	HOURS	AMOUNT
LABORER	JOHN S. WILLIAMS	2	127	8	4	-	-	-	-	-	12	84 00	-	4	3	-	-	-	-	7	49 00
" "	FRED ANDERSON	4	128	-	-	-	-	-	-	-	—	—	-	8	-	8	-	-	-	16	112 00
CARPENTER	JOSEPH SMITH	3	161	8	8	-	-	-	-	-	16	146 40	-	-	-	-	-	-	-	—	—
" "	SAMUEL DUNBAR	4	162	-	-	-	-	-	-	-	—	—	-	8	-	8	-	-	-	16	146 40
MASON	JAMES BURNS	5	207	8	4	-	-	-	-	-	12	114 00	-	4	3	-	-	-	-	7	66 50

Left Hand Page. Fig. 42. Weekly Pay-Roll and Labor Distribution. Size 9¼ x 11⅞ Inches. Form SS-107.

WEEKLY PAY-ROLL AND LABOR DISTRIBUTION

JOB NO. ___ NAME OF WORK: MISCELLANEOUS JOBS LOCATION ___ FORM SS-107 FRANK R. WALKER CO., PUBLISHERS, CHICAGO PAYROLL SHEET NO. 2 OF ___ WEEK AUG 15, 19-- TO AUG 21, 19--

PARKER RES. JOB #107 M	T	W	T	F	S	S	HOURS	AMOUNT	UNION DAIRY Co. JOB #108 M	T	W	T	F	S	S	HOURS	AMOUNT	TOTAL HOURS	HOURLY RATE	TOTAL EARNINGS	F.I.C.A.	FEDERAL INC. TAX	STATE INC. TAX			NET AMOUNT PAID
-	-	5	-	-	-	-	5	35 00	-	-	-	8	8	-	-	16	112 00	40	7 00	280 00	16 38	44 20	6 05			213 37
-	8	8	-	4	-	-	20	140 00	-	-	-	-	4	-	-	4	28 00	40	"	280 00	16 38	37 30	5 09			221 23
-	-	-	8	-	-	-	8	73 20	-	-	8	-	8	-	-	16	146 40	40	9 15	366 00	21 41	60 00	7 69			276 90
-	8	8	-	4	-	-	20	183 00	-	-	-	-	4	-	-	4	36 60	40	"	366 00	21 41	56 50	7 21			280 88
-	-	5	-	-	-	-	5	47 50	-	-	8	8	-	-	-	16	114 00	40	9 50	380 00	22 23	57 90	7 08			292 79

Fig. 42. Weekly Pay-Roll and Labor Distribution. Size 9¼ x 11⅞ Inches. Form SS-107. Right Hand Page.

jobs during the week or where they are working on one job and a distribution of time is desired to the various classes of work on which they were engaged, such as Concrete Forms, Reinforcing Steel, Mixing and Placing Concrete, Brick Masonry, Rough Carpentry, etc.

It is a double page form (size 9¼ x 11⅞ inches) printed on two sides of the sheet—one side as shown for Left Hand Page and the other as shown for Right Hand Page. It provides space for recording the daily and weekly time on six different jobs or six different classes of work during any one week, giving the total number of hours and cost of each job or labor classification.

This form also provides space for Employee's Occupation, Name, Number of Income Tax Exemptions, Numbers, Total Hours, Hourly Rate, Total Earnings, together with Deductions for Federal Insurance Contributions, Income Withholding Tax, Unemployment Compensation Tax, Total Deductions and Net Amount Paid.

Daily Time Sheets

Where a Daily Time Sheet is desired for each workman, the form illustrated in Figure 43 furnishes a very satisfactory record. It contains space for 9 different jobs, together with a description of the work and the time spent on each. It also contains space for Total Hours, Rate, Total Pay, Social Security, Income Tax and Other Deductions, and Balance Due.

Where it is desirable to have the job foreman keep a daily time record of the various men and turn it in each night, the form illustrated in Figure 44 meets all requirements. It contains space for the Names and time of 10 workmen, a description of the work performed by each, also Total Hours, Hourly Rate and Total Pay for the day. This is turned in by the foreman each day at the close of work.

Timekeeping Methods For Small Contractors
and Those Conducting a Jobbing Business

A great many contractors performing small work or conducting a jobbing business prefer to give each workman a time card and have him keep a record of his own time and turn it in each day or at the end of the pay-roll period. The workman fills in his own card, stating where he was working each day and the length of time on each job. This card is then turned in each night or at the end of the pay-roll period and the time extended and it serves as a pay-roll sheet as well as a time card.

This method of keeping time is also preferred by a number of the larger contractors, as they like to have each man turn in a record of his own time, which is then compared with the foreman's or timekeeper's record, preventing errors and serving to check the foreman or timekeeper.

The weekly time card illustrated in Figure 45 is an excellent form for use by contractors who desire to have each workman keep a record of his own time.

You will note there is sufficient space provided for reporting in full the exact time worked on the different jobs each day, and when turned in at the end of the week it forms a complete record of each man's time.

Where it is desirable to have each workman report the amount of material used on every job, together with any miscellaneous expenses, such as carfare, telephone, cartage, etc., incurred by him, the Material and Expense Report should be printed on the back of the time card, as illustrated in Figure 46.

DAILY TIME SHEET

EMPLOYEE'S NUMBER __157__

NAME __F. J. WILLIAMS__ (4)   DATE __MARCH 31, 19 - -__

NAME OF JOB	DESCRIPTION OF WORK	HOURS	RATE	AMOUNT	
HENDERSON RES.	COMB. SCREEN & STORM DOOR	4	9.15	36	60
BURNS & CO.	REPAIR SASH	1	"	9	15
JONES RES.	REPAIR SCREENS	2	"	18	30
W. L. WAREN CO.	NEW DOOR LOCK	1	"	9	15

TIME AND JOBS CORRECT		REG.	O.T.		TOTALS	8	9.15	73	20
Carl Johnson FOREMAN	F.I.C.A. 4.28	FED. INC. TAX 16.72	STATE INC. TAX 1.54					22	54
PRACTICAL FORM P-108						BALANCE DUE		50	66

MFD. IN U.S.A.   FRANK R. WALKER CO., PUBLISHERS, CHICAGO

Fig. 43. Daily Time Sheet. Size 4¼ x 6¾ Inches. Form P-108.

DAILY TIME SHEET

SHEET NO. __1__

JOB SMITH STORE BUILDING DATE JUNE 26, 19-- JOB NO. 103

EMPLOYEE'S NAME	JOB OR DESCRIPTION OF WORK	HOURS	RATE	AMOUNT	
GEO. WILSON	SETTING 13"x13" FLUE LINING	2	9 50	19	00
" "	SETTING ST. SILLS & CHIMNEY CAP	4	"	38	00
" "	LAYING COMMON BRICK	2	"	19	00
DAN HUGHES	" " "	8	9 50	76	00
CHAS. KRESSLER	PLACING WOOD GROUNDS	4	9 15	36	60
JAMES LARSON	HELP MASON - SETTING STONE	4	7 00	28	00
" "	" " - COMMON BRICK	4	"	28	00
FRANK PARKER	" " - " "	8	7 00	56	00
H. KELLEY	" " - GROUNDS	4	7 00	28	00
TIME AND JOBS CORRECT					
	TOTALS	40		328	60

FORM P-109

MFD. IN U.S.A. FRANK R. WALKER CO., PUBLISHERS, CHICAGO

Fig. 44. Daily Time Sheet. Size 4¼ x 6¾ Inches. P-109.

Another satisfactory form of time card is illustrated in Figure 47. This time card is for use by contractors conducting a jobbing business or where the men are employed on several jobs during the pay-roll period, as it is possible to state the job on which the men are working together with the class of work performed on each. The Material Report illustrated in Figure 46 may also be used in connection with this time card, if desired.

Where the men remain on one job for the entire payroll period, the time card illustrated in Figure 48 serves the purpose satisfactorily.

The name of the job is written at the top of the card with the workman's name underneath. The workman fills in all of the different kinds of work performed by him during the pay-roll period in the column headed "Class of Work," together with the number of hours spent on each kind of work each day.

If the workman is to report the amount of material used in connection with his work, the Material Report illustrated in Figure 46 may be printed on the back of the time card.

A Combination Time Card and Job Work Ticket

This Time Card and Job Work Ticket is used by all kinds of jobbing contractors, such as Masons, Carpenters, Painters and Decorators, Plasterers, etc.

The Job and Work ticket is given to the man in charge at the beginning of the job and turned in by him at completion.

This Job and Work ticket contains space for Description of Work to be performed, Workmen's Names and Time for One Week, Amount, etc.

The back of the form contains space for listing materials used and other miscellaneous expense in connection with the job.

WEEKLY TIME CARD

PRACTICAL

STANDARDIZED FORM FOR CONTRACTORS

EMPLOYEE'S NUMBER _____ 176 _____

NAME _JOSEPH BROWN_ (3) WEEK ENDING MAY 16, 19--

DAY	NAME OF JOB	HOURS	RATE	AMOUNT	
MON	H.S. HART, 222 W 6TH	2	9.15	18	30
MON	W.H. SIMPSON, 63 ADAMS ST.	6	"	54	90
TUES	W.H. SIMPSON, 63 ADAMS ST.	2	"	18	30
TUES	F.H. PERKINS, 110 LUNT AVE. LEFT WORK AT 3:30 P.M.	5	"	45	75
WED	S.L. WALLACE, 167 MAIN	8	"	73	20
THUR	S.L. WALLACE, 167 MAIN	8	"	73	20
FRI	S.L. WALLACE, 167 MAIN	2	"	18	30
FRI	MRS. P. JONES, 208 MAIN	1	"	9	15
FRI	J.C. SMOCK, 48 JEFFERSON ST.	3	"	27	45
FRI	O.H. JOHNSON, 278 CLAY ST.	2	"	18	30
REG. O.T. TOTALS		39	9.15	356	85
F.I.C.A. 20.88 FED. INC. TAX 57.60 STATE INC. TAX 9.00				-87	48
BALANCE DUE				269.37	

MFD. IN U.S.A.   FORM C-128   FRANK R. WALKER CO., PUBLISHERS, CHICAGO

Fig. 45. Weekly Time Card. Size 4¼ x 6¾ Inches. C-128.

MATERIAL AND EXPENSE REPORT

JOB	QUANTITY	DESCRIPTION	DATE		OTHER EXPENSE	AMOUNT
				AMOUNT		
	FORM 131	TOTALS				

MFD. IN U.S.A.   FRANK R. WALKER CO., PUBLISHERS, CHICAGO

Fig. 46. Material Report. Size 4¼ x 6¾ Inches. Printed on the back of Weekly Time Cards.

WEEKLY TIME CARD

EMPLOYEE'S NUMBER 157

NAME F. J. WILLIAMS (4)

SHEET NO. 1 OF ____

WEEK ENDING APRIL 4, 19--

NAME OF JOB	DESCRIPTION OF WORK	M	T	W	T	F	S	S	HOURS	RATE	AMOUNT
HENDERSON RES	TRIM WINDOWS	8	—	—	—	—	—	—	8	9 15	73 20
" "	" "	—	2	—	-	-	-	-	2	"	18 30
" "	" DOORS	—	6	—	—	-	-	-	6	"	54 90
" "	HANG COMB. SCR & ST. DR.	—	-	4	-	-	-	-	4	"	36 60
BURNS & CO.	REPAIR SASH	—	-	1	-	-	-	-	1	"	9 15
JONES RES.	" SCREENS	—	-	2	-	-	-	-	2	"	18 30
W.L. WARREN CO.	NEW DOOR LOCK	—	-	1	—	-	-	-	1	"	9 15
JONES RES.	LATTICE PORCH	—	—	—	8	4	—	-	12	"	109 80
" "	REPAIR SCREENS	—	—	—	-	4	—	-	4	"	36 60
REG.	O.T. TOTALS	8	8	8	8	8	—	-	40	9 15	366 00

TIME AND JOBS CORRECT	F.I.C.A.	FED. INC. TAX	STATE INC. TAX			
	21.41	56.50	7.21			
FOREMAN Carl Johnson						− 85 12
					BALANCE DUE	280 88

MFD. IN U.S.A.   FORM C-130   FRANK R. WALKER CO., PUBLISHERS, CHICAGO

Fig. 47. Weekly Time Card. Size 4¼ x 6¾ Inches. C-130.

WEEKLY TIME CARD

JOB WEST SIDE H.S.
NAME FRED BOWERS (5)

WEEK ENDING APRIL 10, 19--

DESCRIPTION OF WORK	M	T	W	T	F	S	S	HOURS	RATE	AMOUNT	
TUNNEL WALL FORMS	4	—	—	—	—	—	—	4	9¹⁵	36	60
" SLAB "	4	—	—	—	—	—	—	4	"	36	60
MASON SCAFFOLD	—	2	2	2	—	—	—	6	"	54	90
FURRING STRIPS ON WALLS	—	1	—	—	—	—	—	1	"	9	15
ROOF FRAMING	—	5	4	—	—	—	—	9	"	82	35
" SHEATHING	—	—	2	—	—	—	—	2	"	18	30
SUB FLOORING	—	—	—	4	2	—	—	6	"	54	90
SET WINDOW FRAMES	—	—	—	2	2	—	—	4	"	36	60
FIT CASEMENT SASH	—	—	—	—	2	—	—	2	"	18	30
HANG " "	—	—	—	—	2	—	—	2	"	18	30
REG. O.T. TOTALS	8	8	8	8	8	—	—	40	9¹⁵	366	00

TIME AND JOBS CORRECT	F.I.C.A.	FED. INC. TAX	STATE INC. TAX				
	21.41	53.10	6.73			81	24
FOREMAN Oscar Ohlsen					BALANCE DUE	284	76

MFD. IN U.S.A.   FORM C-129   FRANK R. WALKER CO., PUBLISHERS, CHICAGO

Fig. 48. Weekly Time Card. Size 4¼ x 6¾ Inches. C-129.

JOB AND WORK TICKET

JOB NO. 582

JOB RESIDENCE
NAME JOS. J. MARTIN
ADDRESS 1576 OAK DRIVE

DATE AUG. 20, 19--
TELEPHONE 232-3456

DESCRIPTION OF WORK TO BE PERFORMED

BASEMENT: ERECT STUD PARTITION - 12'0" x 20'0" - 8'0" HIGH
COVER BOTH SIDES WITH ½" SHEETROCK
TAPE, CEMENT AND SAND JOINTS
WOOD BASE BOTH SIDES

NAME	M	T	DAY OR DATE W	T	F	S	S	HOURS	RATE	AMOUNT	
DAVID JONES	—	8	8	4	—	—	—	20	9¹⁵	183	00
FRED WILLIAMS	—	8	8	4	—	—	—	20	"	183	00
TOTALS								40		366	00

MFD. IN U.S.A.   FORM C-127   FRANK R. WALKER CO., PUBLISHERS, CHICAGO

Fig. 49. Job and Work Ticket. Size 4¼ x 6¾ Inches. C-127.

MATERIAL AND EXPENSE REPORT

DATE **AUG. 23, 19--**

NO.	SIZE			QUANTITY	DESCRIPTION	AMOUNT		OTHER EXPENSE	AMOUNT	
4	2×4	10'		27	FRAMING LUMBER	8	00	PHONE		30
2	2×4	12'		16	" " " "	4	80	GAS	4	50
26	2×4	8'		137	" " " "	41	60			
16	4×8			512	½" SHEETROCK	46	08			
70'	1×6			70	6" BASE	28	00			
70'	3/4			70	3/4" BASE SHOE	3	50			
				5#	JOINT CEMENT + TAPE	2	50			
				5#	NAILS		75			
					TOTALS	135	23		4	80

MFD. IN U.S.A.   FORM C-127   FRANK R. WALKER CO., PUBLISHERS, CHICAGO

Fig. 50. Material and Expense Report. Size 4¼ x 6¾ Inches. Printed on the Back of Job and Work Ticket. C-127.

CHAPTER 8

SOCIAL SECURITY RECORDS

To comply with the requirement of the Federal Insurance Contributions Act (Social Security), it is necessary for every contractor to keep a Weekly, Semi-Monthly or Monthly Pay-Roll, showing the Employee's Name, Occupation, number of hours worked each day, total hours worked each pay-roll period, rate of pay, together with total earnings for the period. From the total pay it is necessary to show deductions made from each employee's pay for State Unemployment Compensation (where applicable), Federal Insurance Contributions Act, Withholding Tax, etc., together with the Net Amount paid to each employee each pay-roll period. This is illustrated in the Weekly Pay-Roll sheets on the previous pages.

Application For Employment

While all the information contained on this form is not required by the Social Security Act, it contains the essential information required for making up the Record of Employment and Earnings.

Application forms should be kept on each job and filled in by each workman at the time of making application for employment.

These sheets are then sent to the office and the Record of Employment and Earnings Record sheets are made up from same.

Where a large Application for Employment sheet (8 ½ x 11 inches) is not required by the contractor, a small card form about 3x5 inches in size may be used which contains all the essential information required by the Social Security Act and for Income Withholding Tax.

This small card form should be filled out on the job by each applicant for employment, giving Registration Number, Name, Address, and other information required by the Contractor for completing his Social Security records.

Record of Employment and Earnings

The Record of Employment and Earnings form is an individual record that must be kept for each employee, showing the total hours worked each day and each pay-roll period, rate of wages, total earnings, together with deductions for Federal Insurance Contributions Act, Income Withholding Tax, Unemployment Compensation—if deductible, and any other necessary deductions.

Where a contractor operates locally or within the boundaries of one state it may not be necessary to keep separate records of overtime worked but when performing work for concerns conducting business in interstate commerce, it may be necessary to keep records of straight time and overtime separately to comply with the Wage and Hour law.

The forms illustrated show just how these records should be kept furnishing a complete record of each employee, such as full Name, Social Security Number, Address, Date Born, Sex, Starting Date, Separation Date, together with information required for the Income Withholding Tax deductions, such as Single, Married, Number of Dependents, and Income Tax Classification for ready reference.

The record also gives the number of hours worked each period, Rate, Wages, Other Compensation, Total Earnings, together with Deductions for Federal Insurance Contributions Act, Income Withholding Tax, Unemployment Compensation Insurance, where applicable, etc., together with the Net Amount Paid each pay-roll period.

At the end of each Quarter these sheets are totaled and the Government reports are made up from same.

APPLICATION FOR EMPLOYMENT

(PLEASE PRINT PLAINLY)   APPLICANT SHOULD NOT WRITE ABOVE THIS LINE

NAME   DUNBAR   SAMUEL   TRADE OR OCCUPATION   CARPENTER

ADDRESS   1622 GLENWOOD DR., ARLINGTON, ILLINOIS   60053   TELEPHONE NUMBER   ARLINGTON 6-2950

Last   First   City   Middle   State   Zip Code

UNION AFFILIATION   UNITED BROTHERHOOD OF CARPENTERS & JOINERS   SOCIAL SECURITY NUMBER   319-01-0847

OWN A CAR   YES   OWN HOME   YES   RENT   BOARD

DATE OF BIRTH   6-10-14   HEIGHT   5'11"   WEIGHT   175   COLOR OF HAIR   BROWN   COLOR OF EYES   BLUE

MALE   ✓   FEMALE   MARRIED   ✓   SINGLE   WIDOWED   DIVORCED   SEPARATED

DEPENDENTS – CHILDREN   2   DEPENDENTS – OTHER   NONE   CITIZEN OF U.S.A.   YES

LIST ANY PHYSICAL DEFECTS   NONE

IN CASE OF ACCIDENT NOTIFY   KATHLEEN DUNBAR   ADDRESS   1622 GLENWOOD, ARLINGTON   TELEPHONE   6-2950

WHAT IS YOUR PRESENT SELECTIVE SERVICE CLASSIFICATION

COMMENTS:

EDUCATION	NAME AND LOCATION OF SCHOOL	YEARS ATTENDED	DATE GRADUATED	SUBJECTS STUDIED
GRAMMER SCHOOL	JOHN P. LYONS MEMORIAL	8	19--	GENERAL
HIGH SCHOOL	ARLINGTON H.S.	4	19--	"
COLLEGE				
TRADE SCHOOL				

FORMER EMPLOYERS	OCCUPATION	TIME WORKED FROM	TIME WORKED TO	RATE OF PAY	REASON FOR LEAVING
PETERSON CONST. CO.	CARPENTER	6/55	9/55		NO MORE WORK
MID-WESTERN CONST. CO.	"	8/51	6/55		JOBS COMPLETED
NORTHWEST CONST. CO.	"	6/49	7/51		" "

REFERENCES: GIVE THE NAMES OF THREE PERSONS NOT RELATED TO YOU, WHOM HAVE KNOWN AT LEAST ONE YEAR.

NAME	ADDRESS	BUSINESS	YEARS ACQUAINTED
ARLEN F. SMOOT	1427 MORRIS DR.	ATTORNEY	11
BRIAN T. McNAMARA	2343 HARVARD	PRINTER	6
FLLOYD J. BURNS	1004 LAWLER	CARPENTER FOREMAN	4

DATE   SEPT. 19, 19--   SIGNATURE   Samuel Dunbar

PRACTICAL

MFD. IN U.S.A.
SOCIAL SECURITY FORM SS-100

Fig. 51. Application for Employment. Size 8½ x 11 Inches. SS-100.

APPLICATION FOR EMPLOYMENT
(Please Print)

Social Security Registration No. **319 - 01 - 0847**   Income Tax Classification **4**

NAME   **DUNBAR   SAMUEL**

Street Address   **1622   GLENWOOD   DRIVE**
Last   First   Middle

City **ARLINGTON**   State **ILL.**   Zip   Phone **6-2950**

Date of Birth **6-10-14**   Height **5' 11"**   Weight **176**   Married? **YES**

Trade or Occupation **CARPENTER**   Number of Dependents **3**

Previous Employer   **JOHN P. OWENS, INC.**

Grammar School ☒ High School ☒ College ☐ Trade School ☐ Other ☒ **APPRENTICE**

In case of Accident Notify **KATHLEEN DUNBAR**

Address **1622 GLENWOOD DRIVE**   Phone **6-2950**

Form SS-100C   Frank R. Walker Company, Publishers, Chicago   MFD. IN U.S.A.

Fig. 52. Application for Employment. Size 3 x 5 Inches. SS-100C.

Many smaller contractors who use an individual time card for each workman, will prefer a Social Security Record, similar to Figure 55, which provides space for daily time for each workman and serves as a payroll as well as a Social Security record.

One of the requirements of the Social Security Act is that the employer is required to furnish each employee every time he is paid, a statement showing the total amount of the employee's earnings and the amount deducted from same for Federal Insurance Contributions.

The form illustrated provides space for the necessary information and can be furnished either as a separate statement or printed on the face of a pay envelope.

Employer's Earnings Statement

The Record of Employment and Earnings sheet illustrated in Figure 57 is an individual record to be kept for each employee, and is the same size as a standard ledger sheet so that it may be filed in a regular bookkeeping ledger or post binder.

This form contains all information required for Federal Insurance Contributions Act, and Income Withholding Tax reports to the Federal Government and Unemployment Compensation reports to the various States.

Space is provided for a complete individual record of each employee, such as Name, Occupation, Social Security Number, Address, Telephone Number, Age, Starting Date, Separation Date, Single, Married, Number of Dependents, Income Tax Classification, Rate of Pay, etc.

It also shows Total Hours Worked for both Regular and Excess Earnings, Other Compensation and Total Earnings for each pay-roll period.

Under the heading "Deductions," the amounts deducted each pay-roll period for Federal Insurance Contributions, Income Withholding Tax, etc., are shown, together with the Net Amount Paid, Date Paid and Check Number. Three additional columns are provided for other deductions, such as Unemployment Compensation, U. S. Bonds, Hospitalization, Insurance, etc.

Furnishes weekly, monthly, quarterly, half-yearly and yearly totals.

At the end of each Quarter these sheets are totaled and the reports to the Government are made up from same.

A Record of Employment and Earnings and Pay-Roll Check At One Operation

Here is a method of keeping Social Security Records that will appeal to many larger contractors because the Pay-Roll check and Social Security Record are written at one operation and may be written on the typewriter or with pen.

OCCUPATION	SOCIAL SECURITY NUMBER	FULL NAME		COMPANY NO.
Carpenter	163-42-3194	Samuel James Olson		215

ADDRESS			TELEPHONE NO.
4150 North Hermitage Avenue	Chicago, Illinois 60613		SU 4-4152

DATE BORN	BECOMES 65	STARTING DATE	SEPARATION DATE	MALE ☒
July 21, 1924	July 21, 1989		Nov. 7, 19--	FEMALE ☐

HOURS FULL TIME WEEK	RATE PER HOUR	EARNINGS FULL TIME WEEK	NUMBER OF EXEMPTIONS	SINGLE ☐
40	$9.15	$366.00	2	MARRIED ☒

RECORD OF EMPLOYMENT AND EARNINGS

19 -- PAY-ROLL ENDING	TOTAL HOURS WORK-ED	RATE PER HOUR	CASH EARNINGS				DEDUCTIONS							NET PAID
			WAGES	OTHER COMP.	TOTAL EARNINGS	F.I.C.A.	FEDERAL INC. TAX	STATE INC. TAX						AMOUNT
FORWARDED														
JAN 1	32	9 15	292 80		292 80	17 13	46 60	6 34						222 73
8	32	"	292 80		292 80	17 13	46 60	6 34						222 73
15	40	"	366 00		366 00	21 41	63 90	8 17						272 52
22	40	"	366 00		366 00	21 41	63 90	8 17						272 52
29	40	"	366 00		366 00	21 41	63 90	8 17						272 52
MONTHLY TOTAL	184		1,683 60		1,683 60	98 49	284 90	37 19						1,263 02
FEB														
MONTHLY TOTAL														
MAR														
MONTHLY TOTAL														
TOTAL 1ST QUARTER														
APR														
MONTHLY TOTAL														
MAY														
MONTHLY TOTAL														
JUN														
MONTHLY TOTAL														
TOTAL 2ND QUARTER														
TOTAL 1 ST HALF														

Fig. 53. Record of Employment and Earnings. Size 8½ x 11 Inches. Form SS-102.

OCCUPATION	SOCIAL SECURITY NUMBER	FULL NAME		COMPANY NO.
BRICKLAYER	166 – 28 – 3176	ANDREW CHARLES WILCOX		351

ADDRESS		TELEPHONE NO.
222 W. PARK AVENUE, LITTLE ROCK, ARK.		439-6261

DATE BORN	BECOMES 65	STARTING	SEPARATION	MALE	
APRIL 7, 1915	APRIL 7, 1980	DATE JAN. 2, 19--	DATE	MALE ☒ FEMALE	

HOURS FULL TIME WEEK	RATE PER HOUR	EARNINGS FULL TIME WEEK	NUMBER OF EXEMPTIONS	SINGLE MARRIED
40	$ 9.50	$ 380.00	3	SINGLE ☐ MARRIED ☒

RECORD OF EMPLOYMENT AND EARNINGS

19 – –	REGULAR EARNINGS			EXCESS EARNINGS			OTHER COMP.	TOTAL EARNINGS		DEDUCTIONS						NET PAID	
PAY-ROLL ENDING	HOURS	RATE	AMOUNT	HOURS	RATE	AMOUNT				F.I.C.A.	FEDERAL INC. TAX	STATE INC. TAX				AMOUNT	
FORWARDED																	
JAN. 7	32	9 50	304	00						304	00	17 70	45 60	3 04			237	58
14	40	"	380	00	4	9 50	38	00		418	00	24 45	73 90	4 18			315	47
21	40	"	380	00	2	"	19	00		399	00	23 34	68 30	3 99			303	37
28	40	"	380	00						380	00	22 23	62 70	3 80			291	27
MONTHLY TOTAL	152		1444	00			57	00		1501	00	87 80	250 50	15 01			1147	69
FEB.																	
MONTHLY TOTAL																	
MAR.																	
MONTHLY TOTAL																	
TOTAL 1ST QUARTER																	
APRIL																	
MONTHLY TOTAL																	
MAY																	
MONTHLY TOTAL																	
JUNE																	
MONTHLY TOTAL																	
TOTAL 2ND QUARTER																	
TOTAL 1ST HALF																	

Fig. 54. Record of Employment and Earnings. Size 8½ x 11 Inches. Form WH-102.

MFD. IN U.S.A.

PRACTICAL STANDARDIZED FORMS FOR CONTRACTORS

FRANK R. WALKER CO., PUBLISHERS, CHICAGO

FORM WH-102

OCCUPATION	SOCIAL SECURITY NUMBER	FULL NAME	COMPANY NO.
CARPENTER	163-42-3194	SAMUEL JAMES OLSON	215

ADDRESS 4150 N. HERMITAGE AVENUE, CHICAGO, ILLINOIS 60613 **TELEPHONE NO.** SU-4-4152

DATE BORN	BECOMES 65	STARTING DATE	SEPARATION DATE	MALE ☒ FEMALE ☐
JULY 21, 1924	JULY 21, 1989	NOV. 7, 19--		

HOURS FULL TIME WEEK 40	RATE PER HOUR $9.15	EARNINGS FULL TIME WEEK $366.00	NUMBER OF EXEMPTIONS 2	SINGLE ☐ MARRIED ☒

RECORD OF EMPLOYMENT AND EARNINGS

19 — — PAY-ROLL ENDING	M	T	W	T	F	S	S	TOTAL HOURS WORKED	RATE PER HOUR	WAGES		OTHER COMP.		TOTAL EARNINGS		F.I.C.A.		FEDERAL INC. TAX		STATE INC. TAX				AMOUNT	
FORWARDED																									
JAN. 1	–	8	8	8	8	–	–	32	9 15	292	80			292	80	17	13	46	60	6	34			222	73
8	–	8	8	8	8	–	–	32	"	292	80			292	80	17	13	46	60	6	34			222	73
15	8	8	8	8	8	–	–	40	"	366	00			366	00	21	41	63	90	8	17			272	52
22	8	8	8	8	8	–	–	40	"	366	00			366	00	21	41	63	90	8	17			272	52
29	8	8	8	8	8	–	–	40	"	366	00			366	00	21	41	63	90	8	17			272	52
MONTHLY TOTAL								184		1683	60			1683	60	98	49	284	90	37	19			1263	02
FEB.																									
MONTHLY TOTAL																									
MAR.																									
MONTHLY TOTAL																									
TOTAL 1ST QUARTER																									
APRIL																									
MONTHLY TOTAL																									
MAY																									
MONTHLY TOTAL																									
JUNE																									
MONTHLY TOTAL																									
TOTAL 2ND QUARTER																									
TOTAL 1ST HALF																									

Fig. 55. Record of Employment and Earnings. Size 8½ x 11 Inches. Form SS-1027.

```
┌─────────────────────────────────────────────────────┐
│              EARNINGS STATEMENT                      │
│                                                      │
│   Pay-Roll                                           │
│   Period____10/17____ To__10/22/--                   │
│                         Company                      │
│                         Number____162____            │
│                                                      │
│   NAME  SAMUEL DUNBAR                                │
│                                                      │
│   Social Security                                    │
│   Account Number  319-01-0847                        │
│                                                      │
│   ___40___ HOURS AT $_9.15_  $ 366.00                │
│   ┌─────────────────────────────┐                    │
│   │          DEDUCTIONS         │                    │
│   ├─────────────────────┬───────┤                    │
│   │ F. I. C. A.         │$ 21│41 │                    │
│   │ Fed. Inc. Tax       │ 85│30 │                    │
│   │ State Inc. Tax      │  8│65 │                    │
│   │                     │   │   │                    │
│   │                     │   │   │                    │
│   │ Unemp. Comp.        │   │   │                    │
│   │ Advances            │   │   │                    │
│   │ Other Deductions    │   │   │                    │
│   └─────────────────────┴───────┘                    │
│                                   115.36             │
│      TOTAL DEDUCTIONS_____                       │
│                                                      │
│   NET AMOUNT PAID    $__250.64__                     │
│  ═══════════════════════════════════════════        │
│                 EMPLOYER                             │
│   ANDREWS  CONST.  Co.                               │
│   961 RAILROAD AVE.                                  │
│   ARLINGTON, ILL.                                    │
│                                                      │
│   Form SS-99 Frank R. Walker Company, Publishers, Chicago │
└─────────────────────────────────────────────────────┘
```

Fig. 56. Earnings Statement. Size 3⅛ x 5½ Inches. Form SS-99.

It is an individual record that must be kept for each employee and contains space for all Social Security Records, such as Name, Social Security Number, Company Number, Address, Single, Married, Number of Dependents, Income Tax Classification, Starting and Stopping Date, etc.

It also shows the Total Regular Hours Worked, Rate, Amount; Total Excess or Overtime Hours Worked, Rate, Amount; Total Earnings; together with deductions for Federal Insurance Contributions, Income Withholding Tax, State Unemployment Compensation Tax, Two Spaces for Other Deductions and Net Amount Paid.

It furnishes Weekly, Monthly, Quarterly, Half-Yearly and Yearly Totals and contains a complete record of Employment and Earnings for each employee for a year.

The front of the Record of Employment and Earnings Card contains information for the first six months of the year and the back of the card contains the same information for the last six months.

At the end of each Quarter these cards are totaled and the Government reports for Social Security and Income Tax deductions are made up from same.

The Pay-Roll check should have a carbon line on the back of the portion containing the Social Security Record, so that when entry is made on the check, and exact copy is written on the Social Security Card at

FRANK R. WALKER CO., PUBLISHERS, CHICAGO MFD. IN U.S.A. SOCIAL SECURITY AND WAGE AND HOUR FORM WH-103

RECORD OF EMPLOYMENT AND EARNINGS

OCCUPATION BRICK LAYER | COMPANY NUMBER 351 | SOCIAL SECURITY NUMBER 166-28-3176
DATE BORN APRIL 7, 1915 | BECOMES 65 APRIL 7, 1980 | TELEPHONE NUMBER 439-6261 | FULL NAME ANDREW CHARLES WILCOX | SEX [X] M F
STARTING DATE JANUARY 2, 19-- | SEPARATION DATE | STREET AND NUMBER 222 W. PARK AVE. | SINGLE ☐ MARRIED [X]
HOURS FULL TIME WEEK 40 | HOURLY RATE 9.50 | EARNINGS FULL TIME WEEK $380.00 | NUMBER OF DEPENDENTS 3 | CITY AND STATE LIME ROCK, ARK. | INCOME TAX CLASSIFICATION 3

WEEK	19 PAY-ROLL ENDING	REGULAR EARNINGS HOURS	RATE	AMOUNT	EXCESS EARNINGS HOURS	RATE	AMOUNT	OTHER COMPEN-SATION	TOTAL EARNINGS	DEDUCTIONS F.I.C.A.	FEDERAL INC. TAX	STATE INC. TAX			TOTAL DEDUCT.	NET PAID AMOUNT	DATE PAID	CHECK NUMBER
FORWARDED																		
1	JAN. 7	32	9 50	304 00	—		— —		304 00	17 78	45 60	3 04			66 42	237 58	1/10	728
2	14	40	"	380 00	4	9 50	38 00		418 00	24 45	73 90	4 18			102 53	315 47	1/17	816
3	21	40	"	380 00	2	" "	19 00		399 00	23 34	68 30	3 99			95 63	303 37	1/24	901
4	28	40	"	380 00	—		— —		380 00	22 23	62 70	3 80			88 73	291 27	1/31	986
5																		
MONTHLY TOTAL		152		1,444 00	6		57 00		1,501 00	87 80	250 50	15 01			353 31	1147 69		
1	FEB.																	
2																		
3																		
4																		
5																		
MONTHLY TOTAL																		
1	MAR.																	
2																		
3																		
4																		
5																		
MONTHLY TOTAL																		
TOTAL FIRST QUARTER																		
1	APRIL																	
2																		
3																		
4																		
5																		
MONTHLY TOTAL																		
1	MAY																	
2																		
3																		
4																		
5																		
MONTHLY TOTAL																		
1	JUNE																	
2																		
3																		
4																		
5																		
MONTHLY TOTAL																		
TOTAL SECOND QUARTER																		
TOTAL FIRST HALF																		

Fig. 57. Record of Employment and Earnings. Size 9¼ x 11⅞ Inches. Form WH-103.

the same time. This insures accuracy, saves considerable time and eliminates all copying of these important records.

The Pay-Roll check should also contain a perforated stub, which can be bent back of the Social Security Card to hold it in place while writing. A hole should also be punched at the left of the line (as a guide) containing the Social Security entries, which insures writing on the correct line.

There are also systems using the peg board method where the pay-roll sheets, Social Security record and the Workman's check are written at one operation. This system must be written in long hand and cannot be used on the typewriter. The author does not feel that this system saves any time over the traditional pay-roll sheet, as the daily time must be collected and totaled on another time sheet before the total hours can be transferred to the pay-roll sheet on the peg board. Then each workman's time and deductions must be computed separately and the entries made on the pay-roll check, which are transferred by carbon to the pay-roll sheet and the Social Security record.

This system is much better for commercial or manufacturing concerns having regular employees than for the construction business, which usually has a large number of name changes on the pay-roll each week.

FULL NAME	OCCUPATION	SOCIAL SECURITY NUMBER	COMPANY NO.
Andrew Charles Wilcox	Bricklayer	166-28-3176	351

STREET AND NUMBER	CITY AND STATE		TELEPHONE NO.
2222 West Park Avenue	Little Rock, Arkansas		6-6166

DATE BORN	BECOMES 65	STARTING DATE	SEPARATION DATE		MX / F SEX
April 7, 1915	April 7, 1980	Jan. 2, 19--			

HOURS FULL TIME WEEK	RATE PER HOUR	EARNINGS FULL TIME WEEK	INCOME CLASSIFICATION	SINGLE / MARRIED X
40	$9.50	$380.00	3	

	NUMBER OF DEPENDENTS

RECORD OF EMPLOYMENT AND EARNINGS

WEEK	19-- PAY-ROLL ENDING	REGULAR EARNINGS HOURS	RATE	AMOUNT	EXCESS EARNINGS HOURS	RATE	AMOUNT	OTHER COMPEN-SATION	TOTAL EARNINGS	DEDUCTIONS F.I.C.A.	FEDERAL INC. TAX	STATE INC. TAX		NET PAID AMOUNT
	FORWARDED													
1	JAN. 7	32	9.50	304 00	—				304 00	17 78	45 60	3 04		237 58
2	14	40	"	380 00	4	9.50	38 00		418 00	24 45	73 90	4 18		315 47
3	21	40	"	380 00	2	"	19 00		399 00	23 34	68 30	3 99		303 37
4	28	40	"	380 00	—		—		380 00	22 23	62 70	3 80		291 27
5														
	MONTHLY TOTAL	152		1,444 00	6		57 00		1,501 00	87 80	250 50	15 01		1,147 69

PAY-ROLL CHECK

PAY-ROLL CHECK

April 7, _____ 19--

PAY TO THE ORDER OF _____ ANDREW C. WILCOX _____ $ 315.47

_____ THE SUM OF $315 and 47/100 _____ DOLLARS

PAYMENT IN FULL FOR SERVICES RENDERED. PAY-ROLL PERIOD UP TO AND INCLUDING THE ABOVE DATE.

BY ENDORSEMENT, THIS CHECK IS ACCEPTED IN FULL OF THE ATTACHED ACCOUNT. IF INCORRECT, PLEASE RETURN.

DETACH ALONG THIS LINE BEFORE CASHING

PAY-ROLL ENDING	REGULAR EARNINGS HOURS	RATE	AMOUNT	EXCESS EARNINGS HOURS	RATE	AMOUNT	OTHER COMPEN SATION	TOTAL EARNINGS	DEDUCTIONS F.I.C.A.	INCOME TAX	State		NET PAID AMOUNT
4/4/--	40	9.50	380 00	4	9.50	38 00		418 00	24 45	73 90	4 18		315 47

NAME Andrew C. Wilcox

SOC SEC NUMBER 166-28-3176   COMPANY NUMBER 351

EMPLOYEE'S STATEMENT OF EARNINGS

1	MAY												
2													
3													
4													
5													
	MONTHLY TOTAL												
1	JUNE												
2													
3													
4													
5													
	MONTHLY TOTAL												
	TOTAL SECOND QUARTER												
	TOTAL FIRST HALF												

Fig. 58. Record of Employment and Earnings and Pay-Roll Check Written at One Operation. Form WH-108/CK-110.

For the contractor who can afford to spend $7,500.00 to $10,000.00 for a pay-roll system, there are machines that will tabulate the time, amount, and any number of deductions and give the net amount of the pay-roll at one operation. Some of these systems require a pay-roll sheet almost the size of an ordinary desk top but they do save considerable time in making up pay-rolls and their accompanying deduction reports.

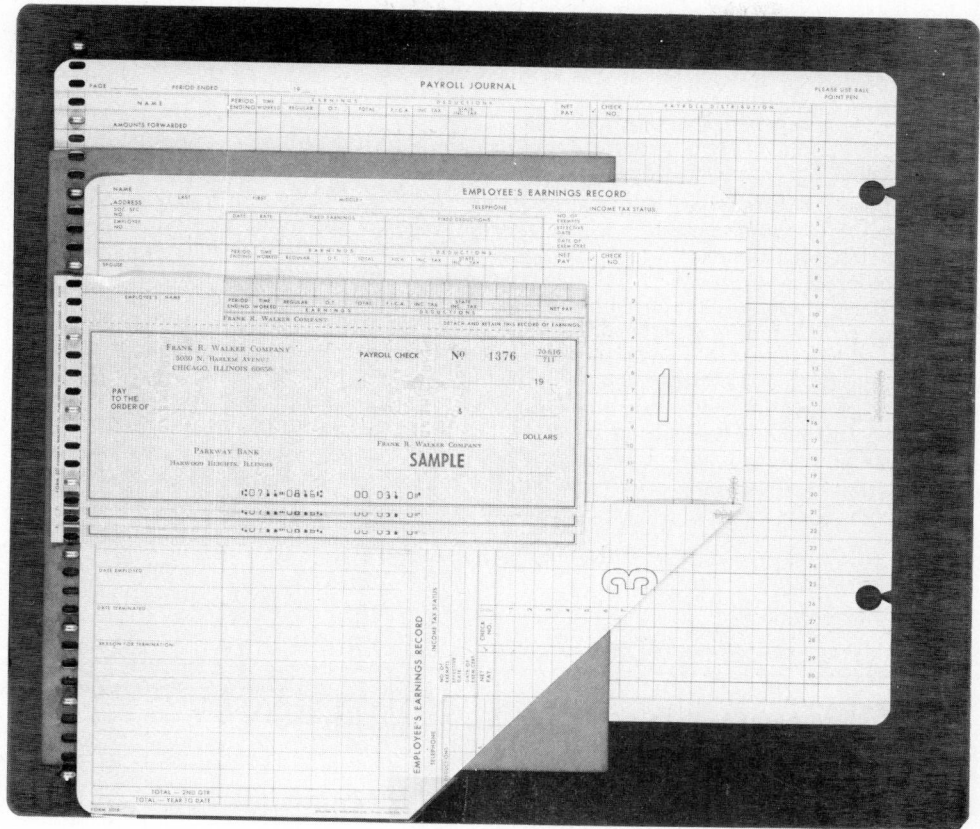

3-IN-1 PAYROLL SYSTEMS

WORK IS SIMPLE. ACCURATE, AND QUICK DOING # RECORDS AT ONCE!

1. Merely write in the amount of earnings, deductions, and net pay in the allotted columns at the top of each check, which is carbon backed, and you simultaneously post the individaul earnings, record and payroll journal via a second separate carbon between the earnings record and payroll journal. It's all done in one simple operation . . . through the use of Walker's unique Peg Registration System.

    These Systems will save two thirds of your bookkeeping time and work by simply eliminating 2 steps

2. 3-in-1 Earnings Records provide accurate and comprehensive details of each employees earnings.

3. 3-in-1 Payroll Journals provide accurate posting of all checks issued.

4. Walkers Pegged Panel is the heart of the 3-in-1 Systems. The peg aligment affords accurate transcription and registration.

5. 3-in1 Carbons, designed for the 3-in-1 System faithfully duplicates all entries.

Submit sample check when ordering, give check number you wish to start with, and bank magnetic serial number. Allow four weeks for delivery.

CHAPTER 9

AN EASY METHOD OF DISTRIBUTING THE WORKMEN'S TIME ON THE JOB

In order to obtain accurate labor costs, it is necessary to sub-divide the workmen's time each day, charging the total number of hours worked by all the men on the job to the different kinds of work they did that day. That is not half as difficult as it looks. Suppose we have a job on which there are 2 bricklayers, 2 carpenters and 4 laborers working. (Look at the time sheet in the illustration.) For Thursday (see fourth column) you will see there are 12 hours bricklayers' time; 8 hours carpenters' time and 24 hours time for common laborers on the job, making a total of 44 hours time worked on the job that day. On small jobs where there are not over 15 or 20 men employed, the carpenter or mason foremen should always know what their men are doing (if they don't they should not be foremen). So each day after work, they enter the number of hours time worked by each trade on the different kinds of work. (See the three Labor Distribution Cards.) Note how the time is charged for Thursday, so that the total time charged on the Labor Distribution is exactly the same as that shown in the time book or on the pay-roll sheets. This time should be filled in each day after work and then on the week day the pay-roll period ends, the Labor Distribution forms

																DEDUCTIONS				

WEEKLY PAY-ROLL   SHEET NO. _1_ OF ____

JOB *SMITH STORE BLDG*   WEEK ENDING *JUNE 5, 19 - -*   JOB NO. *103*

OCCU-PATION	EMPLOYEE'S NAME	TAX EX.	M	T	W	T	F	S	S	HOURS	RATE	AMOUNT		F.I.C.A.	FEDERAL INC. TAX	S.I.T.			NET AMOUNT PAID	
LAB	R. PANOZIO	6	–	8	–	8	–	–	–	16	7⁰⁰	112	00	6 55	2 20	– –			103	25
"	JAMES LARSON	5	8	8	8	8	–	–	32	"	224	00	13 10	22 20	3 20			185	50
"	FRANK PARKER	1	8	8	8	8	–	–	32	"	224	00	13 10	39 30	5 13			166	47
"	H. KELLEY	2	8	8	–	8	–	–	24	"	168	00	9 83	19 50	3 25			135	42
CARP	CHAS. KRESSLER	4	8	8	8	–	–	–	24	9¹⁵	219	60	12 85	22 90	3 56			180	29
CARP.	WM. JOHNSON	4	8	8	–	–	–	–	16	"	146	40	8 56	12 10	1 73			124	01
MASON FOR	GEO. WILSON	2	–	–	8	8	–	–	16	10⁰⁰	160	00	9 36	19 50	3 05			128	09
MASON	DAN HUGHES	4	–	–	4	8	–	–	12	9⁵⁰	114	00	6 67	6 50	93			99	90
REG.	O.T.	TOTALS	48	40	44	40	–	–	172		1368	00	80 02	144 20	20 85			1122	93

MFD. IN U.S.A.   FORM C-104   FRANK R. WALKER CO., PUBLISHERS, CHICAGO

Fig. 59. Weekly Time Card and Pay-Roll. Size 4¼ x 6¾ Inches. Illustrating Method of Keeping Workmen's Time on the Job.
C-104.

LABOR DISTRIBUTION

JOB _SMITH STORE BLDG_

CLASS OF WORK _C-6, C-8_

WEEK ENDING _JUNE 5, 19 – –_

SHEET NO. _1_

JOB NO. _103_

	OCCUPATION	M	T	W	T	F	S	S	HOURS	RATE	AMOUNT	
1	C-6 { CARPENTERS	H O L I D A Y	16	16	8	–	–	–	40	9 15	366	00
2	{ LABORERS		8	8	–	–	–	–	16	7 00	112	00
3												
4												
5	C-8 LABORERS		10	16	2	8	–	–	36	7 00	252	00
6												
7												
8												
	TOTAL	C-6								C-8	730	00

	QTY. WORK IN PLACE	PAY ROLL COSTS	LBR. AVERAGE UNIT COST	AVERAGE QUANTITY PER 8 HR. DAY	QTY. WORK IN PLACE	PAY ROLL COSTS	LBR. AVERAGE UNIT COST	AVERAGE QUANTITY PER 8 HR. DAY
PREVIOUS	1816 SF	1362.00	0.75	136 SF	1215 SF	224.70	.185	422 SF
THIS WEEK	605	478.00	0.79	121 "	1216 "	252.00	.207	270 "
TOTAL	2421	1840.00	0.76	132 "	2421 "	476.70	.197	329 "

MFD. IN U.S.A.   FORM C-105   FRANK R. WALKER CO., PUBLISHERS, CHICAGO   (OVER)

Fig. 60. Labor Distribution Size 4¼ x 6¾ Inches. Illustrating Method of Distributing Workmen's Time Each Day. Form C-105.

LABOR DISTRIBUTION

JOB _SMITH STORE BLDG_

CLASS OF WORK

WEEK ENDING _JUNE 5, 19 – –_

SHEET NO. _2_

JOB NO. _103_

	OCCUPATION	M	T	W	T	F	S	S	HOURS	RATE	AMOUNT	
1	LABORERS	H O L I D A Y	–	14	–	14	–	–	–	28	7 00	196	00
2												
3												
4												
5												
6												
7												
8												
	TOTAL											

	QTY. WORK IN PLACE	PAY ROLL COSTS	LBR. AVERAGE UNIT COST	AVERAGE QUANTITY PER 8 HR. DAY	QTY. WORK IN PLACE	PAY ROLL COSTS	LBR. AVERAGE UNIT COST	AVERAGE QUANTITY PER 8 HR. DAY
PREVIOUS	22 CY	182	7.3 CY					
THIS WEEK	22	196	6.3					
TOTAL	44	378	6.8					

MFD. IN U.S.A.   FORM C-105   FRANK R. WALKER CO., PUBLISHERS, CHICAGO   (OVER)

Fig. 61. Labor Distribution. Size 4¼ x 6¾ Inches. Illustrating Method of Distributing Workmen's Time to Placing Concrete for Foundation Walls. Form C-105.

should be turned in with the time book or pay-rolls. The total hours and money on the Labor Distribution forms should balance with the hours and money on the pay-rolls. That's all there is to it and it's as simple as A-B-C, if it is attended to regularly.

What the Labor Distribution Shows You

One Labor Distribution form is made out each week for the different kinds of work being performed, such as Erecting Concrete Forms, Removing Concrete Forms, Mixing and Placing Concrete, Common Brickwork, Face Brickwork, etc., and these change from week to week as the work progresses. You will note that costs on two classes of work may be kept on one sheet.

As mentioned above, the number of hours worked by each trade should be entered on the form for that class of work; then at the end of the pay-roll period, the number of hours are totaled and multiplied by the rate of wages paid the different trades and are entered in the last column headed "Amount." The totals in the "Amount" column must balance with the total on the pay-roll sheets. In the illustrations, you will note the total of the pay-roll for the week is $478.80. Now refer to the three Labor Distribution forms and you will see that they also total $478.80, so from this record you know just where the money was spent. Notice at the bottom of this form the columns headed "Quantity Work in Place," "Pay-Roll Costs," "Labor Average Unit Cost," and "Average Quantity per 8-Hour Day." The amounts in the first column at the side, headed "Previous," are the ones carried forward from last week's Labor Distribution and show just what was spent on each class of work from the beginning of the job to the beginning of this week. The totals of this week's work are entered in the second column headed "This Week," and the lower column headed "Total," gives the total cost of the work from the beginning of the job to the present time, so that this one form gives the total cost of each class of work to date. Now to make out the next week's cards, take the totals as given in the bottom column headed "Total" and enter them in the upper column headed "Previous." This is continued from week to week as long as the work is in progress and when the job is finished, the last form, for each kind of work, gives a complete summary of the cost of that work for the entire job. The first column states the quantity of work in place. In brickwork, this would be the number of thousands of brick laid; in concrete work, the number of cubic feet or cubic yards of concrete placed; the number of square feet of forms erected and removed, etc. The operation is the same regardless of the kind of work from foundation to finish carpentry, plastering, etc.

The third column headed "Labor Average Unit Cost," gives the average labor cost for a unit amount of the work, while the fourth column headed "Average Quantity per 8-Hour Day," gives the average amount of work done by a man per day.

Now turn this card over and note the information given on the back. (See Figure 63.) Note the column headed "Total Labor Hours." Each week the number of hours worked by the different trades, such as Carpenters, Laborers, etc., are entered in these columns. The illustration shows that the carpenters worked 107 hours on erecting forms for concrete foundation walls previous to this week; 40 hours this week, making a total of 147 hours to date; the second column shows that the laborers worked 53 hours previous to this week; 16 hours this week, making a total of 69 hours to date or practically one hour labor time to each two hours carpenter time. This is the information needed when compiling costs that will be of value when making up future estimates on similar work.

Now note the lower column headed "Labor Hours Per Unit." That signifies the number of hours or length of time required by each trade to erect one hundred square feet of forms for concrete foundation walls, lay a thousand common brick; place a cubic yard of concrete; frame and place a thousand feet of lumber, etc., depending upon the kind of work being done.

There are 147 hours time for carpenters, and the front of the card shows 2,421 sq. ft. of wall forms erected. Dividing 2,421 into 147 and multiplying by 100, we find it required 6.07 hours carpenter time to erect 100 sq. ft. of forms for concrete foundation walls.

Now divide 2,421 sq. ft. into 69 hours labor time, multiply by 100 and we find that it took 2.85 hours common labor to each 100 sq. ft. of wall forms erected.

Here Is the Value of This Cost Record

Suppose you are estimating the cost of another job similar to the one described above but in the meantime carpenters' wages have advanced from $3.25 to $3.40 an hour and common laborers' wages from $2.40 to $2.55 an hour. How much should you estimate the work at the new scale of wages?

LABOR DISTRIBUTION

JOB _SMITH STORE BLDG._

CLASS OF WORK _E-22, E-23_   WEEK ENDING

SHEET NO. _3_

JOB NO.

	OCCUPATION	M	T	W	T	F	S	S	HOURS	RATE	AMOUNT	
1	E-22 { MASONS		—	—	4	6	—	—	10	9⁵⁰	95	00
2	LABORERS		—	—	—	10	—	—	10	7⁰⁰	70	00
3												
4												
5	MASON FOREMAN				8	8	—	—	16	10⁰⁰	160	00
6	E-23 { MASONS		—	—	—	2	—	—	2	9⁵⁰	19	00
7	LABORERS		—	—	8	6	—	—	14	7⁰⁰	98	00
8												
	TOTAL	E-22							E-23		442	00

	QTY. WORK IN PLACE	PAY ROLL COSTS	LBR. AVERAGE UNIT COST	AVERAGE QUANTITY PER 8 HR. DAY	QTY. WORK IN PLACE	PAY ROLL COSTS	LBR. AVERAGE UNIT COST	AVERAGE QUANTITY PER 8 HR. DAY
PREVIOUS	—	—				—	—	—
THIS WEEK	1100	165.00	150/M	880	1000	277.00	277/M	444
TOTAL	1100	165.00	150/M	880	1000	277.00	277/M	444

MFD. IN U.S.A.   FORM C-105   FRANK R. WALKER CO., PUBLISHERS, CHICAGO   (OVER)

Fig. 62. Labor Distribution. Size 4¼ x 6¾ Inches. Illustrating Method of Distributing Workmen's Time to Common and Face Brickwork. Form C-105.

COST ANALYSIS RECORD

TOTAL LABOR HOURS   UNIT

	1 CARP	2 LAB	3	4	5 LAB	6	7	8
PREVIOUS	107	53			23			
THIS WEEK	40	16			36			
TOTAL	147	69			59			

LABOR HOURS PER UNIT   UNIT _PER 100 SF_

	1 CARP	2 LAB	3	4	5 LAB	6	7	8
PREVIOUS	5.89	2.92			1.89			
THIS WEEK	6.61	2.64			2.96			
TOTAL	6.07	2.85			2.44			

REMARKS

FOUNDATION WALLS - 12" THICK - 9'-4" HIGH
USED 2⁰ x 8⁰ PANEL FORMS SET VERTICALLY WITH 2⁰ x 1⁶
PANEL FORMS TO MAKE UP ADDITIONAL HEIGHT.

MFD. IN U.S.A.   FORM C-105   FRANK R. WALKER CO., PUBLISHERS, CHICAGO

Fig. 63. Labor Cost Analysis, Back of Labor Distribution. Showing How Workmen's Time Is Carried Forward and Worked Into Hourly Costs for Future Estimates.

OCCU-PATION	EMPLOYEE'S NAME	TAX EX.	M	T	W	T	F	S	S	HOURS	RATE	AMOUNT		F.I.C.A.	FEDERAL INC. TAX	STATE INC. TAX		NET AMOUNT PAID	
LAB	R. PANOZIO	6	1	8	—	8	—	—	—	16	7⁰⁰	112 00		6 55	2 20	— —		103 25	
"	JAMES LARSON	5	2	8	8	8	8	—	—	32	"	224 00		13 10	22 20	3 20		185 50	
"	FRANK PARKER	1	8	8	8	8	8	—	—	32	"	224 00		13 10	39 30	5 13		166 47	
"	H. KELLEY	2	8	8	8	—	8	—	—	24	"	168 00		9 83	19 50	3 25		135 42	
CARP.	CHAS KRESSLER	4	—	8	8	8	—	—	—	24	9¹⁵	219 60		12 85	22 90	3 56		180 29	
"	WM. JOHNSON	4	—	8	8	—	—	—	—	16	"	146 40		8 56	12 10	1 73		124 01	
MASON FOR.	GEO. WILSON	2	0	—	—	8	8	—	—	16	10⁰⁰	160 00		9 36	19 50	3 05		128 09	
MASON	DAN HUGHES	4	—	—	—	4	8	—	—	12	9⁵⁰	114 00		6 67	6 60	93		99 90	
REG. O.T. TOTALS			—	48	40	44	40	—	—	172		1368 00		80 02	144 20	20 85		1122 93	

MFD. IN U.S.A.   FORM C-104   FRANK R. WALKER CO., PUBLISHERS, CHICAGO

Fig. 64. Weekly Time Card and Pay-Roll. Size 4¼ x 6¾ Inches. Illustrating Small Symbols Used by Timekeeper When Checking Workmen's Time on the Job. Form C-104.

With the information given above, it is the easiest thing in the world. You know that it required 6.07 hours carpenter time and 2.85 hours labor time to erect 100 sq. ft. of wall forms. Well, all you do now to get a new accurate estimate is to multiply

Carpenters, 6.07 hours at $3.40 an hour.. $20.64

Laborers, 2.85 hours at $2.55 cents an hour.. 7.27

Total estimated cost per 100 sq. ft. of forms... $27.91

Estimated cost per sq. ft.. 0.28

You will notice the old cost at the lower scale of wages was just $0.266 per sq. ft.

In all our experience compiling costs we have found the only worthwhile method was to keep all costs in units of hours instead of dollars and cents because they can then be used at any time, under any conditions, in any locality and at any scale of wages. Costs compiled in this manner have been of untold value to us and we believe any contractor who tries this system on his own work will find it time well spent.

The Same System For Large Contractors

The system described above is suitable for use on the smaller jobs where the contractor or his foreman distributes the time, but on large jobs where a timekeeper is employed, a slightly different method should be used in obtaining the distribution of the workmen's time.

Here Is What the Timekeeper Does

On large jobs where a timekeeper is employed, it is up to the timekeeper and various crew foremen to distribute the workmen's time to the different classes of work each day.

WEEKLY TIME CHECK REPORT

JOB *SMITH STORE BUILDING - JOB 103*   WEEK ENDING *JUNE 5, 19--*

OCCU-PATION	NAME	CHECK NO.	1 M A.M.	P.M.	2 T A.M.	P.M.	3 W A.M.	P.M.	4 T A.M.	P.M.	5 F A.M.	P.M.	6 S A.M.	P.M.	7 S A.M.	P.M.
LAB	R. PANOZIO	1	✓		C15	C15			C15	C15						
					C15	C15			C15	C15						
"	JAMES LARSON	2	✓		C15	C15	C8	C8	C15	C15	C8	C8				
					C15	C8	C8	C8	C15	C8	C8	C8				
"	FRANK PARKER	3	✓		C8	C8	C8	C8	E23	E23	E23	E23				
					C8	C8	C8	C8	E23	E23	E23	E23				
"	H. KELLEY	4	O		C6	C6	C6	C6			E22	E22				
					C6	C6	C6	C6			E22	E23				
CARP.	CHAS. KRESSLER	5	✓		C6	C6	C6	C6	C6	C6						
					C6	C6	C6	C6	C6	C6						
"	WM. JOHNSON	6	✓		C6	C6	C6	C6								
					C6	C6	C6	C6								
MASON FORE.	GEO. WILSON	7	O						E23	E23	E23	E23				
									E23	E23	E23	E23				
MASON	DAN HUGHES	8	✓							E22	E22	E22				
										E22	E22	E23				
		9														
		0														

MFD. IN U.S.A.   FORM C-118   FRANK R. WALKER CO., PUBLISHERS, CHICAGO

Fig. 65. Weekly Time Check Report. Size 4¼ x 6¾ Inches. Showing Method Used by Timekeeper in Checking and Distributing Workmen's Time on the Job and Charging it to the Various Kinds of Work Being Performed Each Day. Form C-118.

FOREMAN'S REPORT

JOB NO. *103*

JOB *SMITH STORE BUILDING*   DATE *JUNE 3, 19--*

OCCUPATION	NO. OF MEN	DESCRIPTION OF WORK	QUANTITY OF WORK	HOURS	TOTAL HOURS
MASON FOREMAN	1	LAYING FACE BRICK	550	8	8
MASON	1	" " "	—	2	2
"	1	" COMMON BRICK	650	6	6
LABORER	1	HELP MASON - FACE BRICK	—	10	10
"	2	" " - COMMON BRICK	—	6	6
"	1	STRIPPING CONCRETE FOUNDATION WALL FORMS	500 SF	8	8
SIGNED *Geo. Wilson - Foreman*			TOTAL	40	40

FORM P-107   MFD. IN U.S.A. FRANK R. WALKER CO., PUBLISHERS, CHICAGO

Fig. 66. Foreman's Report. Size 4¼ x 6¾ Inches. Turned in by Crew Foreman Each Day, Giving Distribution of Workmen's Time. Form P-107.

The timekeeper may use an ordinary time sheet (Figure 64), using small symbols in the upper part of each square to designate the class of work being done by each man or he may use the Weekly Time Check Report, Figure 65. This is pocket-size (4¼ x 6¾ inches) the same as the other forms and fits in the same ring book.

You will note this form is arranged so that each day's time is divided into four parts, two for the morning and two for the afternoon. As the timekeeper makes his rounds on the jobs, checking the men at work, he places a small symbol in each square provided for the purpose. This represents the kind of work being performed by each man. Each small square represents a two-hour period, the four squares making the 8-hour day. After the men have stopped work for the day, the timekeeper should enter the number of hours worked by each man in the time book or on the pay-roll sheets, and then from the symbols in the Time Check Reports, the number of hours worked by each trade on the different kinds of work should be totaled, as previously described.

In order that the timekeeper's checkings may be verified and all chance of mistake eliminated, each crew foreman turns in a daily report showing the number of men of each trade working in his crew, and what they were doing that day. (See illustration of Foreman's Report, Figure 66.) The timekeeper compares this with his own records and if there is any discrepancy, the matter should be taken up with the foreman at once and straightened out. If this is attended to daily, it will result in the best unit labor costs obtainable.

All other operations are the same as previously described.

Other Labor Distribution Forms

For contractors who prefer a large size Labor Distribution Report, Figure 67 illustrates a satisfactory form that may be used either as a daily, weekly or semi-monthly report.

The first column headed "Class of Work" lists the different kinds of work performed on the job; the second column headed "Occupation" contains the names of the various trades engaged thereon, while the third column headed "Total Hours" gives the total number of hours worked by each trade that is charged to the branches of work listed in the first column.

You will also note there is space for inserting the hourly rate of the different trades, the total amount paid each, together with the total cost of each class of work for the pay-roll period.

The last four columns on this sheet contain space for inserting the amount of each kind of work completed this pay-roll period, the amount completed to date, together with the unit labor costs on each.

By using this form it is possible to keep the distribution limited to a small number of sheets, which will vary according to the size of the job and the different kinds of work performed.

When used as a daily report, the labor hours for the various trades should be inserted each day and totaled. The totals of these daily reports must balance with the pay-roll sheets.

Labor Distribution Report, Figure 68, is a weekly distribution form, containing space for inserting time for seven days of the week, the total number of hours worked by each trade, the total labor cost for the week, together with the total labor cost for each branch of work to date.

Daily Time Sheet and Labor Distribution

Many contractors desire a daily time sheet from each job, together with a distribution showing just what the men were doing and the number of hours on each class of work.

The two Daily Time and Labor Distribution sheets illustrated in Figures 69 and 70 furnish this information with a minimum amount of effort.

The form illustrated in Figure 69 provides space for fourteen different labor classifications each day, together with Employee's Name, Occupation, Number, Hours Worked on Each Labor Classification, Total Hours Worked, Wage Rate, Total Daily Pay for Each Workman and the Total Daily Job Pay-Roll.

The form illustrated in Figure 70 provides space for ten different labor classifications each day and gives costs in money as well as in hours. It gives Employee's Name, Occupation, Number, Hours Worked and Pay on each Labor Classification, Total Hours Worked, Wage Rate, Total Daily Pay for each Workman and the total Daily Job Pay-Roll.

The backs of both sheets contain a Daily Construction and Material Report, Figure 71, for reporting the job activities, together with a record of all materials received.

PRACTICAL

FORM 105-D MFD. IN U.S.A.

NOTE: This report must be made out and sent in to Main Office. Total on Distribution must balance with Payroll Total.

LABOR DISTRIBUTION REPORT

JOB NO. *122*

REPORT NO. *16*

SHEET NO. *1 OF 1*

NAME OF WORK *NEW HIGH SCHOOL* LOCATION *ROCKFORD, ILL.*

DATE *SEPT. 12, 19--*

CLASS OF WORK	OCCUPATION	TOTAL HOURS	HOURLY RATE	AMOUNTS	TOTAL COST	TOTAL COST TO DATE	QUAN. WORK PLACED	UNIT COST	TOTAL QUAN. W'K IN PLACE	AV. UNIT COST TO DATE
JOB SALARIES A-2	SUPT.	8	12 00	96 00						
A-3	TIME KEEPER	8	5 00	40 00						
A-6	CONST. ENGR.	8	9 00	72 00						
A-8	WATCHMAN	16	5 00	80 00						
A-9	LABOR FOREMAN	8	7 50	60 00						
"	CARP. "	8	9 50	76 00						
"	MASON "	8	10 00	80 00	504 00	6578 09				
HAND EXC., PIT & TRENCH B-24	LABORERS	32	7 00	224 00	224 00	931 20	24 CY	9 33	97 CY	9 60
BACK FILL, HAND TM'D B-29	LABORERS	16	7 00	112 00	112 00	662 20	81 CY	1 38		1 40
GRADING, HAND B-35	LABORERS	20	7 00	140 00	140 00	342 00	2100 SF	.06²	5700 SF	.06
PUMPING WATER B-38	LABORERS	4	7 00	28 00	28 00	162 80				
FNDTN WALL FORMS C-6	CARPENTERS	28	9 15	256 20						
	LABORERS	14	7 00	98 00	354 20	3581 90	480 SF	.79	5117 SF	.70
STRIP & CLEAN FORMS C-8	LABORERS	16	7 00	112 00	112 00	508 68	975 SF	.115	4239 SF	.12
SET ANCHOR BOLTS C-9	CARPENTERS	4	9 15	36 60						
	LABORERS	2	7 00	14 00	50 60	313 10	10 EA.	5 06	62 EA.	5 05
FDTN. WALL CONC. C-15	LABORERS	10	7 00	70 00						
	ENGINEER	2	8 50	17 00	87 00	714 35	11 CY	7 90	91 CY	7 85
COLUMN FORMS C-21	CARPENTERS	8	9 15	73 20						
	LABORERS	5	7 00	35 00	108 20	844 80	96 SF	1 12	768 SF	1 10
BEAM FORMS C-25	CARPENTERS	24	9 15	219 60						
	LABORERS	14	7 00	98 00	317 60	807 00	325 SF	98	807 SF	1 00
SOLID SLAB FORMS C-26	CARPENTERS	40	9 15	366 00						
	LABORERS	21	7 00	147 00	513 00	3282 00	665 SF	.77	4376 SF	.75
COLUMN CONC. C-41	LABORERS	5	7 00	35 00						
	ENGINEERS	1	8 50	8 50	43 50	148 68	4 CY	10 88	14 CY	10 62
SLAB BEAM CONC. C-42	LABORERS	41	7 00	287 00						
	ENGINEERS	5	8 50	42 50	329 50	676 20	48 CY	6 86	98 CY	6 90
MONOL. TROWEL FIN. C-59	CEM. MAS. FORE.	8	10 00	80 00						
	CEM. MASONS	32	9 50	304 00						
	LABORERS	8	7 00	56 00	440 00	779 95	2275 SF	.193	4105 SF	.19
SET REINF. STEEL D-23	IRON WORK FORE.	8	9 75	78 00						
	IRON WORKERS	24	9 50	228 00						
	LABORERS	16	7 00	112 00	418 00	962 00	6300 lbs	.066	14,800 Lbs	.065
COMMON BRICK E-22	MASONS	48	9 50	456 00						
	LABORERS	44	7 00	308 00	764 00	126 00	5400	141 00	9,000	140 00
FACE BRICK E-23	MASONS	32	9 50	304 00						
	LABORERS	20	7 00	140 00	444 00	9337 95	1750	253 71	3900	240 50
	TOTALS	616		4989 60	4989 60	23492 90				

FRANK R. WALKER CO., PUBLISHERS, CHICAGO

Fig. 67. Labor Distribution Report. Size 9¼ x 11⅞ Inches. Form 105-D.

PRACTICAL (struck through)
FORM 105-W MFD. IN U.S.A.

NOTE:-This report must be made out and sent in with Pay-roll each Period. Total on Distribution must balance with Pay-roll Total.

LABOR DISTRIBUTION REPORT

REPORT NO. 4

JOB NO. 122

SHEET NO. 1 OF 1

NAME OF WORK NEW HIGH SCHOOL   LOCATION ROCKFORD, ILL.   PAY-ROLL ENDING SEPT. 18, 19--

CLASS OF WORK	OCCUPATION	M	T	W	T	F	S	S	TOTAL HOURS	HOURLY RATE	AMOUNTS	TOTAL COST THIS WEEK	TOTAL COST TO DATE
JOB SALARIES A-2	SUPERINTENDENT	8	8	8	8	8	—	—	40	12 00	480 00		
A-3	TIME KEEPER	8	8	8	8	8	—	—	40	5 00	200 00		
A-6	CONST. ENGR.	8	8	8	8	8	—	—	40	9 00	360 00		
A-8	WATCHMAN	16	16	16	16	16	24	24	128	5 00	640 00		
A-9	LABOR FOREMAN	8	8	8	8	8	—	—	40	7 50	300 00		
"	CARP. "	8	8	8	8	8	—	—	40	9 50	380 00		
"	MASON "	8	8	8	8	8	—	—	40	10 00	400 00	2760 00	8510 00
HAND EXC, PIT & TRENCH B-24	LABORERS	32	24	16	—	—	—	—	72	7 00	504 00	504 00	996 50
BACKFILL, HAND TAMP B-29	LABORERS	16	24	24	24	16	—	—	104	7 00	728 00	728 00	1109 00
GRADING, HAND B-35	LABORERS	20	20	28	48	64	—	—	180	7 00	1260 00	1260 00	1320 00
PUMPING WATER B-38	LABORERS	4	4	4	—	—	—	—	12	7 00	94 00	94 00	192 00
FDTN WALL FORMS C-6	CARPENTERS	28	28	32	28	—	—	—	116	9 15	1061 40		
	LABORERS	14	14	16	14	—	—	—	58	7 00	406 00	1467 40	4253 50
STRIP & CLEAN FORMS C-8	LABORERS	16	56	48	—	8	—	—	128	7 00	896 00	896 00	1095 50
SET ANCHOR BOLTS C-9	CARPENTERS	4	4	—	4	—	—	—	12	9 15	109 80		
	LABORERS	2	2	—	2	—	—	—	6	7 00	42 00	151 80	408 50
FDTN WALL CONC C-15	LABORERS	10	—	—	—	56	—	—	66	7 00	462 00		
	ENGINEER	2	—	—	—	8	—	—	10	8 50	85 00	547 00	1064 00
COLUMN FORMS C-21	CARPENTERS	8	16	16	16	16	—	—	72	9 15	658 00		
	LABORERS	5	8	8	8	8	—	—	37	7 00	259 00	917 80	1498 00
BEAM FORMS C-25	CARPENTERS	24	24	16	32	16	—	—	112	9 15	1024 80		
	LABORERS	14	13	10	18	11	—	—	66	7 00	462 00	1486 80	1732 50
SOLID SLAB FORMS C-26	CARPENTERS	40	32	40	24	40	—	—	176	9 15	1610 40		
	LABORERS	21	19	22	14	21	—	—	97	7 00	679 00	2289 40	4631 00
COLUMN CONC. C-41	LABORERS	5	—	—	14	—	—	—	19	7 00	133 00		
	ENGINEER	1	—	—	2	—	—	—	3	8 50	25 50	158 50	246 00
SLAB & BEAM CONC C-42	LABORERS	41	8	16	42	—	—	—	107	7 00	749 00		
	ENGINEER	5	—	—	6	—	—	—	11	8 50	93 50	842 50	1071 50
MONO TROWEL FIN. C-59	CEM. MAS. FORE.	8	8	8	8	8	—	—	40	10 00	400 00		
	CEM. MASON	32	—	8	32	8	—	—	80.	9 50	760 00		
	LABORERS	8	—	—	8	—	—	—	16	7 00	112 00	1272 00	1353 50
SET REINF STEEL D-23	IRON WORK FORE.	8	8	8	8	8	—	—	40	9 75	390 00		
	IRON WORKERS	24	24	16	16	24	—	—	104	9 50	988 00		
	LABORERS	16	16	16	16	16	—	—	80	7 00	560 00	1938 00	2239 00
COMMON BRICK E-22	MASONS	48	64	64	72	72	—	—	320	9 50	3040 00		
	LABORERS	44	62	60	62	64	—	—	292	7 00	2044 00	5084 00	7960 50
FACE BRICK E-23	MASONS	32	40	40	40	40	—	—	192	9 50	1824 00		
	LABORERS	20	26	28	26	24	—	—	124	7 00	868 00	2692 00	2876 50
	TOTALS	616	608	608	648	592	24	24	3120		25089 20	25089 20	42557 50

FRANK R. WALKER CO., PUBLISHERS, CHICAGO

Fig. 68. Labor Distribution Report. Size 9¼ x 11⅞ Inches. Form 105-W.

DAILY TIME SHEET AND LABOR DISTRIBUTION

JOB. NO. **137** REPORT NO. **25**

NAME **SOUTH SIDE HIGH SCHOOL** SHEET NO. **1**

LOCATION **OMAHA, NEBRASKA** DATE **MAY 14, 19--**

REMARKS:

WEATHER **CLEAR** TEMPERATURE 8 A.M. **52** 1 P.M. **70**

OCCUP-ATION	EMPLOYEE'S NAME	EMPLY. NUMBER	UNLOAD CEMENT	TRENCH EXCAV.	BACK-FILL	FOTN. WALL FORMS	REINF. STEEL	FOTN. WALL CONC.	COL. FORMS	BEAM FORMS	SOL. SLAB FORMS	COM. BRICK	FACE BRICK	CUT STONE	HOURS	RATE	AMOUNT
LAB. FORE.	JAS. BROWN	101	2	2				2		2					8	7^{25}	58 00
LABORER	FRED SMITH	102		4				4							8	7^{00}	56 00
"	JOHN CASTIGLIONE	103	4					4							8	"	56 00
"	FRANK CIMARETTI	105		4	2					2					8	"	56 00
"	HENRY BOZEMAN	107					4	4							8	"	56 00
"	WM. SMITHERS	108				3		5							8	"	56 00
"	DAVE KENT	109	3			2		3							8	"	56 00
"	HARRY CAVANAUGH	110		4				4							8	"	56 00
"	GEO. DOOLITTLE	111		2				4		2					8	"	56 00
"	AXEL SWENSON	114						8							8	"	56 00
"	LARS ANDERSON	115							6	2					8	"	56 00
"	LOUIS SCHMIDT	117							6	2					8	"	56 00
"	WM. BURKE	118									4	2	2		8	"	56 00
"	FRED MARTIN	120									4	2	2		8	"	56 00
CARP. FOREMAN	HENRY BUEHL	150				2			2	2	2				8	9^{40}	75 20
CARPENTER	EINAR OLSON	151				4		4							8	9^{15}	73 20
"	EDWARD SCHLEGAL	152				4		4							8	"	73 20
"	EUGENE HARTLEY	153						8							8	"	73 20
"	TOM JENKINS	155						8							8	"	73 20
"	GUST JOHNSON	156							8						8	"	73 20
"	PETER HOFFMAN	159							8						8	"	73 20
"	ARNOLD PETERSON	160								8					8	"	73 20
"	JACK CALDWELL	161								8					8	"	73 20
IRON WORK FOREMAN	PATRICK MURPHY	180					8								8	9^{75}	78 00
IRON WORKER	JOHN O'BRIEN	181					8								8	9^{50}	76 00
CEMENT MASON	AUGUST NELSON	201						8							8	9^{10}	72 80
MASON FOREMAN	THOR NIELSON	250										4	2	2	8	9^{50}	76 00
MASON	DANIEL FRAZIER	251										4	4		8	9^{50}	76 00
"	GEORGE LARSON	252										8			8	"	76 00
	TOTALS		9	16	2	15	20	38	26	38	22	26	10	10			1901 60

PRACTICAL FORM 505

MFD IN U.S.A.

Fig. 69. Daily Time Sheet and Labor Distribution. Size 8½ x 11 Inches. Form 505.

DAILY CONSTRUCTION REPORT

JOB _SOUTH SIDE HIGH SCHOOL_   LOCATION _OMAHA, NEBRASKA_

WEATHER _CLEAR_   TEMPERATURE _8 A.M. 52_ 1 P.M. _70_ DAY _MONDAY_ DATE _MAY 4, 19--_

WORK PROGRESSED QUITE SATISFACTORILY TODAY. COMPLETED TRENCH EXCAVATION FOR FOUNDATION WALLS AND EXPECT TO COMPLETE FORMWORK FOR SAME TOMORROW. PLACED 38 C.Y. OF FOUNDATION WALL CONCRETE ON NORTH WING. FORMWORK FOR BASEMENT STORY COLUMNS AND FIRST FLOOR SLABS AND BEAMS MOVING SLOWLY, BUT GETTING ORGANIZED. MASONRY WORK JUST GETTING STARTED ON EAST WING; HAVE BEEN HELD UP BY SLOW FACE BRICK DELIVERY.

PLUMBING CONTRACTOR HAD FIVE MEN ON JOB TODAY AND PROMISED TWO MORE FOR TOMORROW. WORKED ON DRAIN LINES INSIDE BUILDING AND EXTERIOR SEWER LINES.

STEAM BOILERS ARRIVED IN TOWN TODAY AND WILL BE UNLOADED AND MOVED TO JOB TOMORROW. HEATING CONTRACTOR WANTS US TO RUSH WORK ON STEAM LINE TRENCHES IN AUDITORIUM AND GYMNASIUM.

ELECTRICAL CONTRACTOR IS KEEPING UP WITH THE REST OF THE JOB. HAS FOUR MAN CREW AND ARE RUNNING CONDUIT IN FORMWORK FOR REINFORCED CONCRETE WORK.

WATERPROOFING CONTRACTOR HAS NOT SHOWED UP YET. SHOULD BE ON JOB SO CHECK UP ON HIM. HE IS HOLDING UP BACK-FILLING OF BASEMENT FOUNDATION WALLS.

MATERIALS RECEIVED

38 C.Y. - READY-MIX CONCRETE - 2500# -	OMAHA MATERIAL SUPPLY CO.
4000 - FACE BRICK	WESTERN CLAY PRODUCTS CO.
9000 - COMMON BRICK	
10 C.Y. - MASON SAND	OMAHA MATERIAL SUPPLY CO.
50 bbls. - MASONRY CEMENT	

PRACTICAL | FORM
505

MFD. IN U.S.A.   FRANK R. WALKER., PUBLISHERS, CHICAGO

Fig. 70. Daily Construction Report. Size 8½ x 11 Inches. Printed on Back of Daily Time Sheet and Labor Distribution. Form 505.

DAILY TIME SHEET AND LABOR DISTRIBUTION

JOB NO. 133 JOB WEST SIDE LIBRARY REPORT NO. 32 SHEET NO. 1 DATE APRIL 15, 19--

REMARKS: LOCATION WEATHER CLOUDY TEMPERATURE 8 A.M. 40 1 P.M. 58

Occupation	Employee's Name	Employee's Number	Unload Partition Tile A-90		Column Forms C-21		Beam Forms C-25		Solid Slab Forms C-26		Column Conc. C-41		Reinf. Steel D-23		Common Brick E-22		Face Brick E-23		Cut Stone Ashlar Facing E-65		Door Bucks G-24		Hours	Rate	Amount
			Hrs.	Amount	Hrs.	Amount	Hrs.	Amount	Hrs.	Amount	Hrs.	Amount	Hrs.	Amount	Hrs.	Amount	Hrs.	Amount	Hrs.	Amount	Hrs.	Amount			
Laborer	James Larson	32													8	56 00							8	7 00	56 00
"	Jim Wilson	33															8	56 00					8	"	56 00
"	Frank Parker	35															4	28 00	4	28 00			8	"	56 00
"	R. Panozio	37													8	56 00							8	"	56 00
"	John Castiglione	39									4	28 00			4	28 00							8	"	56 00
"	Frank Cimaretti	40									4	28 00			4	28 00							8	"	56 00
"	H. Kelley	41					4	28 00	4	28 00													8	"	56 00
"	Sam Ze Bac	43	6	42 00											2	14 00							8	"	56 00
"	Tony Petrella	45									6	42 00			2	14 00							8	"	56 00
"	Andy Burke	46																	8	56 00			8	"	56 00
Cem. Mas.	Dave Rutledge	51									8	72 80											8	9 10	72 80
Iron Worker	J. M. Still	75											8	76 00									8	9 50	76 00
"	Joe Woods	76											8	76 00									8	"	76 00
Carp.	Chas. Kressler	103			2	18 30	2	18 30	4	36 60													8	9 15	73 20
"	Wm. Johnson	104							8	73 20													8	"	73 20
"	Fred Bowers	106					4	36 60	4	36 60													8	"	73 20
"	Sam Olson	108					6	54 90	2	18 30													8	"	73 20
"	B. F. Martin	109							8	73 20													8	"	73 20
"	Harry Steele	110			2	18 30	4	36 60	2	18 30													8	"	73 20
"	Tom Williams	112			4	36 60															4	36 60	8	"	73 20
Mason	Geo. Wilson	201															4	38 00	4	38 00			8	9 50	76 00
"	Dan Hughes	202													5	47 50	3	28 50					8	"	76 00
"	Sam Smith	203													4	38 00	4	38 00					8	"	76 00
"	Robert Gordon	205															4	38 00	4	38 00			8	"	76 00
"	A. C. Wilcox	207													6	57 00	2	19 00					8	"	76 00
"	B. C. Armstrong	208													6	57 00	2	19 00					8	"	76 00
"	James Black	212													4	38 00							4	"	76 00
	TOTALS		6	42 00	18	164 70	16	137 80	26	299 30	22	170 80	16	152 00	53	433 50	31	264 50	20	160 00	4	36 00	212		1791 20

PRACTICAL Form 506 MFD. IN U.S.A FRANK R. WALKER CO., PUBLISHERS, CHICAGO

Fig. 71. Daily Time Sheet and Labor Distribution. Size 8½ x 11 Inches. Form 506.

CHAPTER 10

CONSTRUCTION COST ACCOUNTING

Cost keeping or cost accounting consists of sub-dividing and analyzing the various ledger accounts to show what each class of work actually costs—which yield a profit and which result in a loss.

As an example, assume the estimated labor or pay-roll cost on a certain job is $10,000.00 (this may be either $80 or $80,000 so far as the method is concerned.) After the job has been completed we are surprised to learn that the actual pay-roll costs were $12,000.00 instead of $10,000.00 as estimated, and we have exceeded our estimated cost by $2,000.00, or 20 per cent, resulting in a loss of that amount. Just were the loss occurred is a mystery because there were no detailed costs kept on the job.

Cost keeping consists of distributing the labor and material costs to the different classes of work performed on the job, such as concrete foundations, brick masonry, reinforcing steel, reinforced concrete, carpentry, plastering, etc. By doing this it is possible to tell at any time during construction just where every dollar has been spent, showing just what branches of work produced a profit and those that resulted in loss. In this way, it is possible to discover "leaks" and losses before the work is completed or before it is too late to remedy same.

A contractor may estimate 10,000 brick to complete a certain job but unless the quantities are recorded as the material is delivered, it is possible that he may use 20,000 brick and not know the difference until he starts paying his bills.

Quantity records of both material and labor are much more valuable than costs stated in dollars and cents, because if we have the quantity of material or the number of labor hours necessary to complete a certain amount of work, it is very easy to insert current prices and wages. However, if we have nothing but costs in money, it is almost impossible to check quantity and production costs because prices and wages are continually fluctuating.

Forms Necessary For Keeping Costs

All costs dealing with labor must have their origin on the job because it is there the work is being performed, and only the foremen or timekeeper on the job know just how much time is being spent on each class of work. For that reason it should be their duty to make a correct distribution of the workmen's time each day.

The methods of checking the workmen's time and distributing the labor costs have been fully described on the preceding pages.

As the pay-rolls and labor distribution reports are received from the job each pay-roll period, the various amounts should be entered from the Labor Distribution into the Labor Cost Record, Figure 72, or the Job Cost Record, Figure 74. Care should be used to see that the totals of the distribution report agree with the total pay-roll.

Labor Cost Record

After the labor distributions are received from the job and have been checked to see that they balance with the pay-roll they should be entered in the Labor Cost Record, Figure 72.

This sheet contains a summary of the labor cost of each branch of work, stating the quantity completed, the cost of the work to date, together with the unit costs in money. It also makes possible a comparison of

LABOR COST RECORD

NAME OF WORK *BROAD - OAK GARAGE* LOCATION *N.E. COR. BROADWAY + OAK STS.* SHEET NO. *1*
ARCHITECTS OR ENGINEERS *SMITH + WILSON* OWNER *AUTO SALES CORPORATION* JOB NO. *207*

FORM 108

FRANK R. WALKER CO., PUBLISHERS, CHICAGO

	DATE	DESCRIPTION	JOB SALARIES			TEMP. CONST.			PLANT + EQUIP.			TRENCH EXCAV.			
			Quantity	Unit Cost	AMOUNT	Quantity	Unit Cost	AMOUNT	Quantity	Unit Cost	AMOUNT	Quantity	Unit Cost	AMOUNT	
1	MAR 28	PAYROLL			262 00			256 60			428 0	cy 475	.25	120 00	1
2	APR 6	"			262 00						21 40				2
3	" 13	"			262 00										3
4	" 20	"			404 00						32 60				4
5	" 27	"			404 00										5

Left Hand Page.

Fig. 72. Labor Cost Record. Size 9¼ x 11⅞ Inches. Form 108.

LABOR COST RECORD

NAME OF WORK *BROAD - OAK GARAGE* LOCATION *N.E. COR. BROADWAY + OAK STS.* SHEET NO. *2*
ARCHITECTS OR ENGINEERS *SMITH + WILSON* OWNER *AUTO SALES CORPORATION* JOB NO. *207*

FORM 108

FRANK R. WALKER CO., PUBLISHERS, CHICAGO

	BACKFILLING			PUMPING			CONC. FDTN. FORMS			FDTN. CONCRETE			COMMON BRICK			FACE BRICK			
	Quantity	Unit Cost	AMOUNT	Quantity	Unit Cost	AMOUNT	Quantity	Unit Cost	AMOUNT	Quantity	Unit Cost	AMOUNT	Quantity	Unit Cost	AMOUNT	Quantity	Unit Cost	AMOUNT	
1	CY					12 50	SF 1200	.22	261 30	39	1.55	60 40	M			M			1
2						3 75	4000	.21	852 20	60	1.79	107 20							2
3	326	24	76 40				1200	.21	252 60	20	1.81	36 10	8.6	57.98	498 60	4.3	95.53	410 80	3
4													21.0	55.30	1161 40	2.7	99.33	268 20	4
5													18.6	55.24	1027 50				5

Fig. 72. Labor Cost Record. Size 9¼ x 11⅞ Inches. Form 108.

Right Hand Page.

the labor costs on each branch of work from week to week, and the total of any column gives the total quantity of work in place, the total cost of same, together with the average unit labor cost for the entire job.

Material Cost Record

When material has been delivered to the job and reported O. K., the quantities and amount of the invoice should be entered in the Material Cost Record, Figure 73. The reason for making these entries daily or weekly is to give the contractor an accurate record of his material quantities and costs. This enables him to make comparisons with the estimate at any time during construction. However, should this daily record not be desired the entries may be posted into the Material Cost Record each month when the monthly invoices are recorded.

MATERIAL COST RECORD

NAME OF WORK *BROAD - OAK GARAGE* LOCATION *N.E. CORNER BROADWAY + OAK STS.* SHEET NO. *1*
ARCHITECTS OR ENGINEERS *SMITH & WILSON* OWNER *AUTO SALES CORP.* JOB NO. *207*

FORM 109

FRANK R. WALKER CO., PUBLISHERS, CHICAGO

	DATE	DESCRIPTION	OVERHEAD EXPENSE			TEMP. CONST.			PLANT & EQUIP.			FDTN. FORM MAT'L.			
			Quantity	Unit Price	AMOUNT	Quantity	Unit Price	AMOUNT	Quantity	Unit Price	AMOUNT	Quantity	Unit Price	AMOUNT	
1	APR 8	HETTLER LUMBER CO.				1500	120 00	180 00				1800	120 00	216 00	1
2	" 15	MID-WEST EQUIP. CORP.									192 00				2
3	" 20	AMERICAN SAND & GRAVEL													3
4	MAY 2	WESTERN BRICK CO.													4
5	" 10	CONTRACTORS EQUIP. CO.									64 00				5

Left Hand Page. Fig. 73.

Material Cost Record. Size 9¼ x 11⅞ Inches. Form 109.

The sum of the totals of the Labor Cost Record, Figure 72, and the Material Cost Record, Figure 73, gives the total expenditures for labor and material to date. This does not include any portion of the work that has been sub-let, and the sub-contract amounts would have to be added to obtain the total cost of the job.

Job Cost Record

The Job Cost Record, Figure 74, is for use by contractors who desire a complete cost record of each job but who are not particularly interested in labor and material quantities or unit costs. This is a double page form, having one column for Labor and Material under each classification. The classifications should be filled in according to the kinds of work performed on the job on which they are used.

MATERIAL COST RECORD

NAME OF WORK BROAD-OAK GARAGE   LOCATION N.E. COR. BROADWAY + OAK STS.   SHEET NO. 2
ARCHITECTS OR ENGINEERS SMITH & WILSON   OWNER AUTO SALES CORPORATION   JOB NO. 207

FORM 109   FRANK R. WALKER CO., PUBLISHERS, CHICAGO

	FDTN. CONC. READY-MIX			COMMON BRICK			FACE BRICK			MOTAR CEMENT			LIME			MASON SAND			
	Quantity	Unit Price	AMOUNT	Quantity	Unit Price	AMOUNT	Quantity	Unit Price	AMOUNT	Quantity	Unit Price	AMOUNT	Quantity	Unit Price	AMOUNT	Quantity	Unit Price	AMOUNT	
1	CY			M			M			BBLS			TONS			CY			1
2																			2
3	119	13.00	1547.00							40	4.40	176.00	1	26.00	26.00	15	3.65	54.75	3
4				50	30.00	1500.00	10	62.50	625.00										4
5																			5

Fig. 73. Material Cost Record. Size 9¼ x 11⅞ Inches. Form 109.   Right Hand Page

JOB COST RECORD

NAME OF WORK J.S. WILLIAMS CO. FACTORY   LOCATION 2715 W. 20th ST.   SHEET NO. 1
ARCHITECTS OR ENGINEERS HARPER & HARPER   OWNER J.S. WILLIAMS CO.   JOB NO. 102

FORM 116   FRANK R. WALKER CO. PUBLISHERS, CHICAGO

	DATE	DESCRIPTION	OVERHEAD EXPENSE		TEMPORARY CONST.		PLANT + EQUIPMENT		
			Labor	Material	Labor	Material	Labor	Material	
1	APR 1	AMERICAN BUILDERS SUPPLY							1
2	"	PORTLAND CEMENT STOCK ACCT.							2
3	8	PAYROLL	262.00		76.20		14.60		3
4	10	TRUCKING						10.00	4
5	"	ADANIS LBR + MILLWORK							5

Left Hand Page Fig. 74.   Job Cost Record. Size 9¼ x 11⅞ Inches. Form 116.

JOB COST RECORD

NAME OF WORK J.S. WILLIAMS CO., FACTORY   LOCATION 2715 WEST 20TH ST.   SHEET NO. 2
ARCHITECTS OR ENGINEERS HARPER & HARPER   OWNER J.S. WILLIAMS CO.   JOB NO. 102

FORM 116   FRANK R. WALKER CO., PUBLISHERS, CHICAGO

	EXCAVATING		CONCRETE FDTN. FORMS		FOUNDATION CONC.		COMMON BRICK		FACE BRICK		
	Labor	Material	Labor	Material	Labor	Material	Labor	Material	Labor	Material	
1						2176.00		1230.00			1
2						225.00					2
3	262.80		629.20		98.40		222.00				3
4				352.16							4
5											5

Fig. 74. Job Cost Record. Size 9¼ x 11⅞ Inches. Form 116.   Right Hand Page

Miscellaneous Costs

A plain columnar ruled blank sheet (see Figure 75), is probably the best form to use for sub-dividing and analyzing all classes of miscellaneous accounts carried in the ledger that cannot be conveniently handled in the Labor Cost Record, Material Cost Record or Job Cost Record.

This sheet may be used for all classes of sub-divisions, such as General Expense, Plant and Equipment, etc. A double page form with a wide description column is the most satisfactory sheet to use, as the number of columns can always be increased by inserting short leaves.

Job Recapitulation of Comparison Sheet

The Recapitulation sheet illustrated in Figure 76 is used for making comparisons between estimated and actual costs on each class of work. These comparisons may be made weekly, monthly or at the completion of the job, as preferred.

By referring to the illustration, Figure 76, it will be noted that the first column contains space for inserting the estimated quantities of the various classes of work; the second column is used for stating the estimated unit costs applying to these quantities, while the third column is used for inserting the total estimated cost for each branch of work.

The fourth column contains the actual quantities of work performed, the fifth column the actual unit costs, while the sixth column states the actual total cost of each branch of work.

Total gains over the estimated costs are placed in the seventh column and the unit gains are placed in the eighth column. Total losses over the estimated costs are placed in the ninth column and the unit actual loss is placed in the last column.

This is an excellent form because it furnishes the contractor accurate information regarding the profits and losses on each class of work which may be used to advantage when making up future estimates.

GENERAL EXPENSE

			OFFICE RENT	HEAT & LIGHT	FURN & EQUIP.	OFFICE SUPPLIES	TELEPHONE	TAXES	
1	MAY 1	H. O. STONE & CO.	20000						1
2	" 10	COMMONWEALTH EDISON		1625					2
3	" "	BELL TELEPHONE CO.					2472		3
4	" "	FRANK R. WALKER CO.				3155			4
5	" 11	PAY ROLL							5

Left Hand Page.　　Fig. 75. Columnar Form. Used for General Expense Account. Size 9¼ x 11⅞ Inches. Form 134.

GENERAL EXPENSE

	FIRE INSURANCE	LIABILITY INSURANCE	POSTAGE	TRAVEL EXPENSE	SALARIES ESTIMATOR	SALARIES BOOKKEEP'R	SALARIES STENO	SALARIES CLERK	SALARIES GEN'L. SUPT.	
1										1
2										2
3										3
4										4
5					15000	9000	6500	6000	20000	5

Fig. 75. Columnar Form. Used for General Expense Account. Size 9¼ x 11⅞ Inches. Form 134.　　Right Hand Page.

CHAPTER 1

THE IMPORTANCE OF COSTS AND HOW TO KEEP THEM

Every contractor should realize the importance of keeping accurate costs on the different classes of work performed on each job. It is only by keeping costs that he is able to estimate the cost of new work with any degree of accuracy, and upon the accuracy of the estimates depends to a large degree, the success or failure of the business.

While cost keeping is one of the vital points of a contractor's business, it is usually given less consideration than any other part of the business. The majority of contractors do not seem to realize that the success of their entire business structure depends upon accurate costs, because in most instances it is necessary to quote a price before the work is started, and correct estimates can only be based upon past performances. This applies to the contractor employing only one or two men and conducting the smallest jobbing business as well as to the largest organizations employing hundreds or thousands of men on their different operations.

The entire success of the contractor's business is founded on the one word "Costs." Without an accurate knowledge of costs, a man is totally unprepared to engage in the contracting business and if he does engage in business without this knowledge, he is usually "in" for a series of unprofitable contracts and his career as a contractor will depend upon the size of his bank account.

Costs should be kept on an hourly basis, stating the actual quantity of each class of work performed per hour or per day. For instance, you might say it cost $3.25 to hang a door, but that does not mean anything to the contractor who does not know the wage scale prevailing at the time the work was performed. Costs stated in money only are worthless when wages vary from day to day, but if you have a cost record stating that it requires one hour carpenter time to fit and hang a door, then you always have a basis upon which accurate estimates can be prepared regardless of the wage scale.

Another important item that should be given consideration when figuring costs, is that of taking averages instead of maximum or minimum performances. It is possible to check one man's output for an hour or two when he is working at his best and the results will be altogether different than where averages are taken. There is a certain amount of lost motion in every piece of work and this must be taken into consideration when computing costs. The workmen are usually paid for a full day's time and perhaps 10 or 15 per cent of that time is spent in preparation. For instance, a concrete crew may work an entire day placing runways, building scaffolds, oiling wheelbarrows and concrete carts, preparing the mixer, hoist, etc., in preparation for mixing and placing concrete the following day. This will result in an entire day's time for the crew that must be charged to mixing and placing concrete and not a cubic foot of material placed. The following day with everything in readiness, (due to the previous day's preparation), a large volume of work is placed at very favorable labor costs, but this one day's time is not an accurate cost because it does not include any costs of preparation. The true costs would be obtained by taking the time of the concrete crew for both days and computing the cubic yard cost on that basis.

Another thing that should be taken into consideration is the ability of different workmen. Some men are more competent and able to perform much more work than others, but unless you are absolutely certain of the men who are going to work for you on the next job, the average output of the entire crew should be considered and not the maximum performance of a few individuals.

A great many contractors make no attempt to keep unit labor costs on their work but figure the same price on every job. After the job has been completed and the work has cost them more than they actually received for it, they know from the size of their bank account that they have lost money but are unable to tell just where the loss occurred. The result is that they keep on guessing, figuring one branch of work a little too high and another a little too low until finally they take a job with a large amount of work—figured too low—and they not only lose everything they possess but are placed in debt for years to come. Accurate cost keeping will do more to overcome this condition than anything else can possible do.

WEEKLY PAY-ROLL

...ITH STORE BUILDING WEEK ENDING JUNE 26, 19-- JOB NO. 103

	EMPLOYEE'S NAME	TAX EX.	M	T	W	T	F	S	S	HOURS	RATE	AMOUNT		F.I.C.A.	FEDERAL INC. TAX	S.I.T.		NET AMOUNT PAID	
														DEDUCTIONS					
LAB.	JAMES LARSON	5	E-22 8	E-22 8	E-22 8	E-22 8	E-22 E-67 8	—	—	40	7.00	280	00	16 38	33 90	4 61		225	11
"	FRANK PARKER	1	E-22 8	E-22 8	E-22 8	E-22 8	E-22 8	—	—	40	7.00	280	00	16 38	54 80	6 53		202	29
"	H. KELLEY	2	—	G-26 8	G-7 G-17 8	G-17 G-18 8	G-18 4	—	—	28	7.00	196	00	11 47	24 30	3 95		156	28
CARP.	CHAS. KRESSLER	4	—	G-26 8	G-7 G-17 8	G-17 G-18 8	G-18 4	—	—	28	9.15	256	20	14 99	30 50	4 49		206	22
"	WM. JOHNSON	4	—	G-26 8	G-7 G-3 8	G-3 —	—	—	—	16	9.15	146	40	8 56	12 10	1 73		124	01
MAS. FOR.	GEO. WILSON	2	E-22 8	E-22 8	E-22 8	E-22 8	B E-67 8	—	—	40	10.00	400	00	23 40	75 10	9 02		292	48
MAS.	DAN HUGHES	4	E-22 8	E-22 8	E-22 8	E-22 8	E-22 8	—	—	40	9.50	380	00	22 23	61 50	7 56		288	71
REG.	O.T.	TOTALS	32	56	56	48	40	—	—	232		1938	60	113 41	242 20	37 89		1495	10

MFD. IN U.S.A. FORM C-104 FRANK R. WALKER CO., PUBLISHERS, CHICAGO

Fig. 77. Illustrating Use of Symbols on Weekly Time Card and Pay-Roll. Form C-104.

WEEKLY TIME CHECK REPORT

JOB SMITH STORE BUILDING #103 WEEK ENDING JUNE 26, 19--

OCCU-PATION	NAME	CHECK NO.	1 M A.M.	P.M.	2 T A.M.	P.M.	3 W A.M.	P.M.	4 T A.M.	P.M.	5 F A.M.	P.M.	6 S A.M.	P.M.	7 S A.M.	P.M.
LAB.	JAMES LARSON	1	E-22 E-22	E-22 E-22	E-22 E-22	E-22 E-22	E-22 E-22	E-22 E-22	E-22 E-22	E-22 E-22	E-22 E-22	E-67a E-67c				
"	FRANK PARKER	2	E-22 E-22	E-22 E-22	E-22 E-22	E-22 E-22	E-22 E-22	E-22 E-22	E-22 E-22	E-22 E-22	E-22 E-22	E-22 E-22				
"	H. KELLEY	3			G-26 G-26	G-26 G-26	G-7 G-7	G-17 G-17	G-17 G-17	G-18 G-18	G-18 G-18					
CARP.	CHAS. KRESSLER	4			G-26 G-26	G-26 G-26	G-7 G-7	G-17 G-17	G-17 G-17	G-18 G-18	G-18 G-18					
"	WM. JOHNSON	5			G-26 G-26	G-3 G-3	G-7 G-7	G-3 G-3								
MASON FORE.	GEO. WILSON	6	E-22 E-22	E-22 E-22	E-22 E-22	E-22 E-22	E-22 E-22	E-22 E-22	E-22 E-22	E-22 E-22	E-36 E-22	E-67a E-67c				
MASON	DAN HUGHES	7	E-22 E-22	E-22 E-22	E-22 E-22	E-22 E-22	E-22 E-22	E-22 E-22	E-22 E-22	E-22 E-22	E-22 E-22	E-22 E-22				
		8														
		9														
		0														

MFD. IN U.S.A. FORM C-118 FRANK R. WALKER CO., PUBLISHERS, CHICAGO

Fig. 78. Illustrating Use of Symbols on Weekly Time Check Report.

Any cost system to be valuable to the contractor must be simple, and it should be just as accurate as it is simple, furnishing all the desired information regarding the various classes of work with the lease possible clerical labor.

It should be simple and easy enough that the timekeeper or foreman on the job will readily understand it. This is absolutely necessary in order that the workmen's time may be charged to the different classes of work correctly, otherwise the resulting costs will be absolutely worthless and the contractor using them will be worse off than he would have been had he never attempted to keep costs.

The systems and methods illustrated and described on the following pages have been used on many jobs and under varying conditions, and have been found absolutely reliable. They are very simple and furnish the contractor with more valuable information regarding his business than any other system the writer has ever seen.

A modern cost system is essential to determine the following:

1. Varying costs of labor, material costs and contingencies.
2. Production contract.

Prompt recording of costs are most important.

Why a Cost Schedule is Necessary

In order to keep accurate cost records that will be of value to the contractor using them, it is important that a complete cost schedule giving all of the operations usually encountered in building or other construction work be prepared. This schedule should be uniform for all work, enabling the timekeepers, foremen, superintendents, cost clerks, estimators, etc., to become familiar with it, as this will do much toward simplifying the distribution of the labor hours to the various classes of work. Unless a uniform system is used, there is confusion and the chance of making errors when compiling and tabulating the costs is increased.

The method used in sub-dividing the costs may be as simple or as elaborate as the contractor desires but in order to furnish unit costs that will prove of value when making up future estimates, it is important that each class of work be kept separately, as far as practicable.

Costs may be compiled in dollars and cents if desired, but the most satisfactory method is to compile the costs in hours, and then they may be used for years by merely inserting the current scale of wages. This is the only satisfactory method to use if accurate costs are to be obtained.

However, if unit costs are not desired and the costs are wanted merely for comparison with the total estimated costs, telling which branch of the work is running ahead or behind the estimate, then the costs may be sub-divided into the principal sub-divisions, as "Excavating," "Concrete," "Carpentry," "Masonry," etc., and the totals of these items may be compared with the estimated totals covering the same general classifications.

Cost keeping, like anything else worth while, requires a little time and labor to keep it running smoothly, but the results obtained are worth many times their cost.

The Advantage of Using Symbols to Designate Cost Sub-Divisions

The cost schedule given on the following pages is sub-divided in the same manner as new work should be estimated and each item is given a letter-number symbol as a means of identification. Some contractors use symbols composed entirely of numbers with the various sub-classifications being designated by decimals. The letter-numeral system, however, is more adaptable to the average contractor's needs as it requires less characters to identify an operation and by using letters to designate the general classifications of work they are more distinctive and easier to remember.

The reason for using symbols to designate the work is to enable the timekeeper or foremen who check the workmen's time on the job, to make accurate on-the-spot notations directly in the time book as to what each man is doing. To do this in long hand would be a physical impossibility as most of the operations would require at least several words for an accurate description. For example, a timekeeper or foreman using the cost schedule, may check a workman erecting forms for concrete foundation walls with the symbol C-6, or if he were working in the crew placing concrete for the wall, the symbol would be C-15. Where a carefully prepared cost schedule is used, each symbol designates on particular kind of work.

The cost schedule given on the following pages has been carefully prepared in great detail but may be used to any degree of detail the contractor desires. For example, a man performing hand excavation for footing trenches may be checked as follows: If only a general classification distribution of labor costs is desired, the symbol "B" would indicate that the man was working on a preliminary or earthwork operation. If a more definite classification is required, the symbol "B-20" would indicate the man was working on excavation, fill, grading or pumping. If a detailed sub-classification distribution of costs is desired, the symbol "B-24" identifies the man's occupation as hand excavating for trenches and pits. In the same manner, for a mason laying face brick, the symbol "E" indicates all masonry work, the symbol "E-20" narrows the identification of the work down to brickwork and the symbol "E-23" accurately defines the occupation as laying face or press brick.

In the event the contractor wishes to break down the costs in a particular sub-classification to a further degree this may be accomplished by the addition of lower case letters to the sub-classification symbol. For example, a job having several sizes and kinds of face brick may have the face brick symbol, "E-23," further subdivided into "E-23-a" for regular size brick, "E-23-b" for Roman brick, "E-23-c" for Norman size brick, etc., or the additional sub-division may be used to designate different joint treatments, such as flush cut, concave tooled, raked out, etc.

A Complete Labor Cost Schedule

The cost schedule given on the following pages, is intended to cover nearly all operations, which may be encountered, in the construction of buildings, retaining walls, concrete work in all its branches, roads, paving, etc.

LABOR COST SCHEDULE

"A" classifications include all salaries and labor costs for operations not directly productive in the preliminary work or construction work.

JOB SALARIES

A-   All job salaries, or as follows:
1. Salary of project manager.
2. Salaries of construction superintendents.
3. Salaries of timekeepers and payroll clerks.
4. Salaries of material checkers and clerks.
5. Salaries of cost clerks.
6. Salaries of civil or construction engineers on job.
7. Salaries of stenographers.
8. Salaries of watchmen.
9. Salaries of foremen. (Time spent by foremen working with their tools should be charged to the branch of work involved.)
10. Miscellaneous salaries, such as water boys, errand boys, porter, etc.
11. ....
12. ....

TEMPORARY CONSTRUCTION AND WEATHER CONDITIONS

A- 20. All labor costs for temporary construction and weather conditions, or as follows:
21. Building and maintaining temporary offices, sheds, toilet enclosures, protection over equipment, signs, etc., and removing same at completion.
22. Building and maintaining temporary protection for the public, such as sidewalk bridges, canopies, outrigger platforms, fences, barricades, etc., and removing same at completion. Also providing and maintaining warning signals, lights, lanterns, etc.
23. Building and maintaining temporary partitions and enclosures to isolate the work from new or existing finished space and removing same at completion.
24. Building and maintaining temporary stairs, ladders, ramps, railings, etc., and removing same at completion.
25. Providing and maintaining temporary protection for new or existing construction, such as projecting stone, granite, marble, ornamentation of all types, floors, roofs, window sills, door jambs, etc., and removing same at completion.
26. Providing and maintaining temporary closures in openings for doors, windows, skylights, roof vents, etc., and removing same at completion.
27. Providing and maintaining temporary water lines and removing or deactivating same at completion.
28. Providing and maintaining temporary sewer lines and removing or deactivating same at completion.

29. Providing and maintaining temporary electric light and power and removing same at completion.
30. Providing and maintaining temporary heating of building and removing same at completion.
31. Heating materials and providing protection for construction work during freezing weather.
32. Removing snow from walks, drives, decks, roofs, etc.
33. Providing and maintaining temporary elevator service including protection of cab, doors and jambs. Removing protection and cleaning up at completion.
34. ....
35. ....

REPAIRS, CLEANING AND RUBBISH REMOVAL

A- 40. All labor costs for repairs, cleaning and rubbish removal, or as follows:
41. Cutting and patching for other trades in general, where not chargeable to a specific trade.
42. Patching damaged plaster.
43. Replacing broken glass.
44. Repairing damage caused by construction, to sidewalks, curbs, streets, alleys, public utilities, adjacent buildings, etc.
45. Cleaning exterior and interior glass at completion of job.
46. Cleaning floors at completion of job.
47. Labor to repair and/or replace damaged lawns, trees and shrubs which are noted to remain.
48. Removing and disposing of rubbish, periodically and at completion of job.
49. ....
50. ....

CONSTRUCTION PLANT AND EQUIPMENT

A- 60. All labor costs for unloading, handling, placing or setting up construction plant and equipment and dismantling same for removal at completion of job, or as follows:
61. Unloading, handling and placing power excavating equipment, such as power shovels, hoes, draglines, clamshells, tractors, scrapers, trench-diggers, etc., and removing same at completion.
62. Unloading handling and placing equipment for digging caissons, such as platforms, tripods, winches, buckets, tarpaulins, etc.; dismantling and moving to next well location; dismantling and removing at completion.
63. Unloading, handling and setting up equipment for driving piling and dismantling and removing same at completion.
64. Unloading, handling placing concrete mixers, "Pumpcrete" equipment, hoisting engines, derricks, air compressors, power buggies, pumps, etc., and removing same at completion.
65. Handling materials and erecting hoisting towers, skip hoists, etc., for concrete, brick and other building materials; dismantling and removing same at completion. (Give general description.)
66. Handling materials and erecting all types of scaffolding, except ordinary "horse" scaffolds which are charged against the classification in which they are used; dismantling and removing same at completion.
67. Handling materials and building runway panels and supports for same. This account should include only make-up and repair labor as costs of placing runways into position for use in pouring concrete, etc., should be charged against the specific items involved.
68. Receiving and taking care of small tools, such as hammers, shovels, picks, sledges, bullpoints, etc.; sharpening small tools and maintaining wheelbarrows, buggies, carts, etc.
69. Labor costs for driving trucks and automobiles not chargeable to other classifications. This account includes labor involved in local transportation of personnel and pick-up of supplies, light tools and materials.
70. ....
71. ....

UNLOADING MATERIALS

This classification includes only unloading various classes of materials from cars or trucks and placing in storage piles for future use—in other words, where the materials require double handling.

When materials are unloaded from cars or trucks for immediate use, the unloading and handling is charged directly to the class of work on which the materials are to be used.

A- 80. All labor costs for unloading materials from cars or trucks, or as follows:
81. Unloading crushed stone or gravel.
82. Unloading lightweight aggregates, such as cinders, slag, Vermiculite, Waylite, etc.
83. Unloading sand.
84. Unloading cement, including storing of same in sheds.
85. Unloading common, hollow and paving brick, including placing in piles. (State whether brick are stacked in piles or merely dumped.)
86. Unloading face or press brick, including stacking in piles.
87. Unloading cement blocks, including stacking in piles. (State whether blocks are made of regular or lightweight concrete.)
88. Unloading hollow clay back-up tile, including stacking in piles.

89. Unloading hollow clay tile shapes for beam and girder covering and tile floor arches, including stacking in piles.
90. Unloading hollow clay partition tile, including stacking in piles.
91. Unloading gypsum partition tile, including stacking in piles.
92. Unloading glazed structural facing tile, including stacking in piles.
93. Unloading glass blocks, including stacking in piles.
94. Unloading dimension lumber of all kinds, including stacking in piles.
95. Unloading plywood, wallboard, building board, etc., including stacking in piles.
96. Unloading rubble stone, rustic stone, cobble stone and random or split face ashlar, including placing in stock piles. (State type of material.)
97. Unloading cut stone, granite, terra cotta, imitation stone and granite, etc., including placing in storage areas. (State type of material.)
98. ....
99.

....

"B" Classifications include all labor costs for the preliminary operations of wrecking, clearing, shoring, underpinning, sheet piling, etc. Also included are all earthwork operations and heavy duty foundation work, such as caissons, piling, etc.

WRECKING AND CLEARING

B- All labor costs for preparing the site in advance of the actual construction work, or as follows:
1. Wrecking old buildings and removing all materials, rubbish and debris.
2. Moving existing buildings to new locations.
3. Clearing site of trees, brush, etc., and burning or removing same.
4. Removing old floor slabs, walks, curbs, pavements, etc., and disposing of same.
5. Removing existing masonry or concrete foundations, etc., and disposing of same.
6. Exposing and removing, capping or de-activating existing utilities, such as sewer lines, water lines, gas lines, etc.
7. Salvaging, storing and protecting items specifically noted to remain the property of the Owner, or to be reused.
8. ....
9.

....

UNDERPINNING, SHORING AND SHEET PILING

B- 10. All labor costs for underpinning, shoring and sheet piling work, or as follows:
11. Underpinning of existing foundations, piers, etc., including excavation, formwork, reinforcing steel, concrete grouting, etc.
12. Shoring and needling of adjacent construction, including placing cribbing, drums, jacks, walers, braces, posts, etc. Also cutting holes or sockets in present walls and patching after completion.
13. Handling and driving steel sheet piling. (For equipment set-up and removal, refer to A-60.)
14. Handling and driving wood sheet piling. (For equipment set-up and removal, refer to A-60.)
15. Pulling and removing sheet piling. (State whether steel or wood).
16. Sheeting and bracing banks of excavations.
17. ....
18.

....

EXCAVATION, FILL, GRADING AND DE-WATERING

B- 20. All labor costs for excavation, fill, grading and de-watering operations, or as follows:
The following classifications are intended to cover only the actual operations described. Labor costs for bringing equipment to the job and setting up ready for work together with labor costs for dismantling and removing same from job at completion should be charged under "Construction Plant and Equipment." (See A-60.)
21. Stripping top soil and storing in piles for future use.
22. Site grading and general or mass excavation, including loading into hauling units.
23. Excavating trenches and pits for footings, foundation walls, piers, sewers, water lines, etc., including loading hauling units, using power equipment.
24. Excavating trenches and pits as above, including loading hauling units, using hand labor.
25. Rock excavation, including drilling holes, blasting and loading broken rock into hauling units.
26. Excavating for walks and pavements, including loading hauling units. (State whether done with power equipment or by hand labor.)
27. Excavating for curb and gutter, including loading hauling units. (State whether done with power equipment or by hand labor.)

28. Digging test holes and making soundings.
29. Backfilling, including consolidation by puddling or compaction by tamping. (State whether done with power equipment or by hand labor.)
30. Placing earth fill inside of buildings, including compaction.
31. Placing site grading fill, including compaction.
32. Placing and compacting fill material, such as sand, crushed stone, gravel, slag, cinders, etc., under concrete floors, walks and pavements.
33. Laying tile drains, including placing crushed stone or gravel bed and cover.
34. Spreading top soil. (State whether done with power equipment or by hand labor.)
35. Grading earth surfaces to elevation. (State whether done with power equipment or by hand labor.)
36. Special sub-grade compaction for roads, runways, heavy-duty floors, etc., using tandem rollers or other power equipment.
37. Disposing of excess excavated material. This item should cover only the labor cost of hauling and dumping as loading is included in the various excavating items.
38. Ordinary pumping, using small, individual, centrifugal or diaphragm pumps.
39. Installation, operation and removal of wellpoint systems for de-watering.
40. ....
41. ....

CAISSONS

B- 50 All labor costs for caisson work, or as follows:
       All labor costs for unloading, setting up, moving and removing equipment should be charged to classification A-62.
51. Excavating caissons, including only the time of excavating, hoisting, handling and loading excavated material into hauling units.
52. Unloading, handling and placing wood lagging and iron rings for "Chicago" method caissons. Also removing iron rings when placing concrete.
53. Unloading, handling and placing steel cylinders for "Gow" method caissons. Also withdrawing steel cylinders when placing concrete.
54. Disposing of excavated material. (Hauling and dumping only.)
55. Unloading, handling and placing reinforcing steel in caissons.
56. Mixing and placing concrete in caissons, including placing and removing runways.
57. Pumping water from caissons.
58. Installing and maintaining ventilation systems for caissons. (Labor costs for unloading, setting up, dismantling and removing ventilation system equipment should be charged to classification A-62.)
59. Installing and maintaining pneumatic or compressed air systems for caissons, including air locks, decompression chambers, etc. (Main compressor plant labor costs should be charged to classification A-62.)
60. Excavating caissons using boring or drilling type power equipment.
61. ....
62. ....

WOOD AND CONCRETE PILES

B- 70. All labor costs for driving wood and concrete piles, or as follows: Labor costs for transporting pile driving equipment to job and setting up, ready to operate, together with dismantling and removing equipment at completion should be charged to classification A-63.
71. Laying out or locating pile centers.
72. Operating pile driver and driving wood piles, including time of entire crew working on pile driver and wood piles.
73. Cutting off wood piles, after driving, and disposing of cut-offs.
74. Operating pile driver and driving steel shells for cast-in-place concrete piles, including time of entire crew working on pile driver and steel shells.
75. Mixing and placing concrete for cast-in-place piles.
76. Cutting off steel shells, after concreting, and disposing of cut-offs.
77. Making precast concrete piles (if made on job), including forming, setting reinforcing steel, mixing and placing concrete, etc.
78. Operating pile driver and driving precast concrete piles, including time of entire crew working on pile driver and precast piles, except fabricating time.
79. Cutting off precast concrete piles, after driving, and disposing of cut-offs. ....
80. ....
81. ....

"C" classifications include all labor costs for formwork and the missing and placing of concrete and cement work except concrete included in "B" classifications for caissons and piles. Also included are all labor costs for constructing macadam, bituminous surface and asphalt surface paved areas.

FORMWORK FOR CONCRETE FOUNDATIONS AND RETAINING WALLS

C- All labor costs for handling lumber, wood or metal forms, constructing and placing formwork, stripping and cleaning forms for concrete foundations and retaining walls, or as follows:
1. Unloading and handling lumber or wood and metal forms.
2. Forming footings for columns and walls.
3. Forming pile caps.
4. Forming edges of mat foundations.
5. Forming piers.
6. Forming foundation and retaining walls. (State whether forms are built on the job or panel forms of wood, metal or combination wood and metal.)
7. Forming machinery foundations.
8. Stripping forms, cleaning and oiling for re-use.
9. Handling, locating and setting anchor bolts, slots, ties, sleeves, thimbles, boxes, etc., in forms for concrete foundations.

CONCRETE FOR FOUNDATIONS AND RETAINING WALLS

C- 10. All labor costs for placing and removing runways, handling materials, mixing, placing and consolidating concrete for foundations and retaining walls, or as follows:
11. Placing concrete for column and wall footings.
12. Placing concrete for pile caps.
13. Placing concrete for mat foundations.
14. Placing concrete for piers.
15. Placing concrete for foundation and retaining walls.
16. Placing concrete for machinery foundations.
17. Setting and grouting base plates, grillages, etc.
18. ....
19. ....

FORMWORK FOR REINFORCED CONCRETE CONSTRUCTION

C- 20. All labor costs for handling lumber, wood or metal forms, constructing and erecting formwork and stripping and cleaning forms for reinforced concrete work, or as follows:
21. Forming columns, using wood framing or fibre and pulpboard tubing.
22. Erecting metal column forms.
23. Removing and cleaning metal column forms.
24. Forming column heads and brackets.
25. Forming beams, girders and lintels.
26. Forming solid slabs. (State whether wood or metal.)
27. Forming drop heads in flat slabs at columns.
28. Open deck forming for combination slabs.
29. Forming wood pans or domes for combination slabs.
30. Forming for thin slabs over precast concrete joists.
31. Forming stairs.
32. Stripping forms and removing false work, from all types of reinforced concrete work, except columns with metal forms, cleaning and oiling for re-use.
33. Handling, locating and setting inserts, anchor slots, sleeves, boxes, ties, etc., in forms for reinforced concrete.
34. ....
35. ....

PLACING REINFORCED CONCRETE

C- 40. All labor costs for handling materials, placing and removing runways, mixing, hoisting, placing and consolidating concrete for reinforced concrete construction, or as follows:
41. Placing concrete for columns.
42. Placing concrete for slabs and beams, general.
43. Placing concrete for slabs and beams, isolated.
44. Placing concrete for stairs and platforms.
45. Labor for hoisting slabs installed by the lift slab method.
46. ....
47. ....

CONCRETE FLOORS, WALKS, PAVEMENTS, FILLS AND CEMENT FINISHES

C- 50. All labor costs for concrete floors, walks, pavements, curbs and gutters; floor, stair and roof fills; cement finishes and other cement mason work, including handling materials, constructing and placing wood or metal forms, setting screeds, mixing and placing concrete or separate finish topping, screeding, floating, troweling (state whether floating and troweling is by hand or machine), brooming, etc., on cement surfaces, or as follows:

51. Placing wood or metal edge forms for floor on ground, walks, pavements, etc.
52. Placing wood or metal forms for curb and gutter work.
53. Setting wood or metal screeds.
54. Placing concrete for floors on ground, walks, pavements, etc.
55. Placing concrete for floor fill.
56. Placing concrete for roof fill or saddles.
57. Placing concrete fill for steel pan stairs and platforms.
58. Placing concrete for curb and gutter work.
59. Monolithic trowel finishing of concrete floors, walks, pavements, etc.
60. Applying troweling integral finish to floors, walks, etc., including mixing and placing finish material.
61. Applying troweling separate finish to floors, walks, etc., including cleaning and grouting rough slab, and mixing and placing finish material.
62. Float finishing floors, roofs, walks, pavements, etc. (State method.)
63. Finishing stair treads, risers and platforms. (State type of finish.)
64. Finishing curbs and gutters. (State type of finish.)
65. Belting, brooming and other miscellaneous finishing.
66. Locating and placing expansion joints in floors, walks, paving, etc.
67. Running cement cants, including mixing, hoisting and placing material.
68. Running cement sills, including forming, mixing and placing concrete, finishing, etc.
69. Running cement base, including mixing and placing material. (State whether straight or cove base.)
70. Rubbing exposed concrete surfaces. (State whether by hand or machine and give description of work.)
71. Applying floor hardener. (State type of treatment.)
72. Curing and protecting cement finish. (State method.)
73. Vacuum processing of concrete, including handling, setting and removing mats and hose and operating pump. Labor costs for unloading and setting up equipment at start of job and dismantling and loading at completion should be charged to "Construction Plant and Equipment" classification A-64.
74. ....
75. ....

CEMENT GUN WORK

C- 80. All labor costs for handling materials, forming, placing reinforcing material, mixing and placing cement grout, etc., for cement gun work. Labor costs for setting up and dismantling equipment should be charged to "Construction Plant and Equipment" classification A-64.

MACADAM, BITUMINOUS SURFACE & ASPHALT SURFACE PAVED AREAS

C- 90. All labor costs for constructing waterbound macadam, bituminous surface and asphalt surface paved areas, or as follows:
All labor costs for excavating, backfill, preparing sub-grade and placing concrete base slabs should be charged to the proper classifications under "Excavation, etc." and "Concrete Floors, Walks, etc." (See B-20 and C-50.)

91. Hauling, placing, spreading and rolling materials for waterbound macadam paved areas.
92. Hauling, placing, spreading and rolling materials for bituminous surface paved areas.
93. Hauling, placing, spreading and rolling materials for asphalt surface paved areas. (State whether placing over bituminous or concrete base.)
94. ....
95. ....

"D" classifications include all labor costs for metal pans; labor handling and setting clay tile or lightweight concrete block fillers for combination floor slabs; labor handling and setting reinforcing materials; labor handling, setting and grouting precast concrete joists and slabs; all labor costs for clay tile floor arches and beam and girder covering; labor handling and setting clay book tile roof decking; labor handling and setting precast gypsum roof tile and plank; and all labor costs for the installation of poured gypsum roofs.

METAL PANS

D-   All labor costs for unloading, handling, erecting, stripping, cleaning, oiling for re-use and removing metal pans for reinforced concrete floors, or as follows:
1. Unloading and handling metal pans, domes, or tile.

2.   Placing metal pans, domes or tile for combination slabs.
3.   Removing metal pans, cleaning and oiling for re-use.
4.   ....
5.   ....

CLAY TILE OR LIGHTWEIGHT CONCRETE BLOCK FILLERS FOR COMBINATION SLABS

D- 10.   All labor costs for handling and setting clay tile or lightweight concrete block fillers for combination slabs, or
          as follows:
   11.   Handling and setting clay tile or lightweight concrete block fillers.
   12.   Filling voids in clay tile or lightweight concrete block fillers at ends of rows. ....
   13.   ....
   14.   ....

REINFORCING STEEL AND MESH

D- 20.   All labor costs for handling and setting reinforcing steel and mesh in concrete foundations and retaining
          walls, reinforced concrete work, concrete floors, walks, pavements, etc., or as follows:
   21.   Unloading reinforcing steel from cars or trucks, sorting and stockpiling.
   22.   Bending reinforcing steel to detail. (If done on job.)
   23.   Handling and setting reinforcing steel.
   24.   Unloading mesh reinforcing from cars or trucks.
   25.   Handling and placing mesh reinforcing.
   26.   Prestressing steel reinforcement where called for.
   27.   ....

COMBINATION PERMANENT FORM AND REINFORCING MATERIALS

D- 30.   All labor costs for unloading, handling and setting combination permanent form and reinforcing materials,
          or as follows:
   31.   Handling and placing paper-backed mesh over precast concrete or steel joists.
   32.   Handling and setting corrugated steel permanent forms for reinforced concrete slabs. ....
   33.   ....
   34.   ....

PRECAST CONCRETE JOISTS, PLANK AND SLABS

D- 40.   All labor costs for unloading, handling, setting and grouting precast concrete joists, plank and slabs, or as
          follows:
   41.   Handling, setting and grouting "I" section precast concrete joists.
   42.   Handling, setting and grouting precast concrete plank.
   43.   Handling, setting and grouting cored precast concrete slabs.
   44.   Handling, setting and grouting precast concrete rib, flat or channel slabs.
   45.   ....
   46.   ....

CLAY TILE FLOOR ARCHES AND BEAM AND GIRDER COVERING

D- 50.   All labor costs for handling mixing mortar, supporting and placing clay tile floor arches and beam and girder
          covering, or as follows:
   51.   Handling lumber, hoisting and placing temporary wood centering, including removing at completion.
   52.   Handling, hoisting and placing clay tile for floor arches. (State thickness and type of arch.)
   53.   Handling, hoisting and placing clay tile beam and girder covering. (Describe class of work.)
   54.   ....
   55.   ....

HOLLOW CLAY BOOK TILE

D- 60.   All labor costs for mixing mortar, unloading, handling, hoisting and placing hollow clay book tile, or as fol-
          lows:
   61.   Handling and erecting "Tee" irons.
   62.   Handling, hoisting and placing book tile.
   63.   ....
   64.   ....

PRECAST GYPSUM ROOF TILE AND PLANK

D- 70. All labor costs for unloading, handling, hoisting, placing and grouting precast gypsum roof tile and plank, or as follows:
71. Handling and erecting "Tee" irons.
72. Handling, hoisting, placing and grouting short span gypsum roof tile.
73. Handling, hoisting and placing roof plank.
74. ....
75. ....

POURED-IN-PLACE GYPSUM ROOF DECKS

D- 80. All labor costs for unloading and handling materials, forming, placing mesh and mixing, placing and finishing poured-in-place gypsum roof decks, or as follows:
81. Handling and erecting steel sub-purlins.
82. Handling, hoisting and placing permanent form material.
83. Handling, hoisting and placing mesh reinforcing.
84. Handling, mixing, hoisting and placing gypsum material. (State whether wheeled or pumped into place.)
85. Finishing gypsum surface ready for roofing.
86. ....
87. ....

"E" classifications include all labor costs for masonry work of all types including partitions, furring and column covering. Labor building and removing ordinary scaffolding should be charged to these classifications. Labor for major scaffolding of job should be charged to classification A-66.

CONCRETE MASONRY UNITS

E- All labor costs for mixing mortar, building and removing "horsescaffold" and handling, hoisting and laying cement blocks and brick, or as follows:
1. Handling and laying 8-inch cement block foundation walls.
2. Handling and laying 12-inch cement block foundation walls.
3. Handling and laying 4-inch cement block exterior facing above grade.
4. Handling and laying 8-inch cement block exterior walls. (State whether face or rough work.)
5. Handling and laying 12-inch cement block exterior walls. (State whether face or rough work.)
6. Handling and laying 4-inch cement block back-up of other masonry.
7. Handling and laying 8-inch cement block back-up of other masonry.
8. Handling and laying 12-inch cement block back-up of other masonry.
9. Handling and laying cement block cavity walls.
10. Handling and laying cement brick exterior facing.
11. Handling and laying cement brick back-up of other masonry.
12. Handling and laying cement block manholes, catch basins, etc.
13. Laying 4" thick and under block partitions.
14. Laying 6" thick and under block partitions.
15. Laying 8" thick and under block partitions.
16. Laying 12" thick and under block partitions.
17. Laying block wall furring.
18. Laying block column fireproofing.
19. ....

BRICKWORK

E- 20. All labor costs for mixing mortar, building and removing "horse-scaffold" and handling, hoisting and laying brick, or as follows:
21. Handling and laying brick foundation walls.
22. Handling and laying common brick.
23. Handling and laying face or press brick. (State size of brick, bond, joint and kind of mortar used.)
24. Handling and laying twin brick units.
25. Handling and laying brick floors and steps.
26. Handling and laying brick stacks and chimneys.
27. Handling and bricking in boilers.
28. Handling and laying fire brick linings in stacks, chimneys, fireboxes, breechings, etc.
29. Handling and laying brick fireplaces, mantels and hearths.
30. Handling and laying brick manholes, catch basins, etc.
31. ....
32. ....

GLASS MASONRY UNITS

E- 40. All labor costs for mixing mortar, building and removing scaffolds and handling, hoisting and laying glass blocks and glass block masonry accessories, or as follows:
41. Handling and laying standard glass units and accessories in exterior walls.
42. Handling and laying special glass units and accessories in exterior walls.
43. Handling and laying standard glass units and accessories in interior partitions.
44. Handling and laying special glass units and accessories in interior partitions.

CLAY TILE UNITS

E- 50. All labor costs for mixing mortar, erecting and removing scaffolding, building in reinforcement and accessories and handling, hoisting and laying all clay tile units, or as follows:
51. Handling and laying 4-inch free-standing walls. (State size and type of face.)
52. Handling and laying all 6" to 8" free standing walls (state size and type of face).
53. Handling and laying all 10" to 12" free standing walls (state size and type of face).
54. Handling and laying all free standing walls greater than 12" (state size and type of face).
55. Handling and laying 4" backup of other masonry (state size and type of face).
56. Handling and laying 8" backup of other masonry (state size and type of face).
57. Handling and laying 12" or more backup or other masonry.
58. Handling and laying of patented or special shaped tile units.
59. Handling and laying 4" thick and under partition tile.
60. Handling and laying 5" to 8" thick partition tile.
61. Handling and laying 8" to 12" thick partition tile.
62. Handling and laying tile wall furring.
63. Handling and laying tile column fireproofing.
64. ....

GYPSUM TILE UNITS

E- 65. Handling and laying 3" thick and under gypsum tile partition and furring.
66. Handling and laying 4" to 6" thick gypsum partitions.
67. Handling and laying gypsum tile fireproofing.
68. ....
69. ....

STONE, GRANITE, TERRA COTTA, ETC.

E- 70. All labor costs for mixing mortar, building and removing "horse-scaffold" and setting rubble stone, rustic or cobble stone, random or split face ashlar, cut stone, granite, terra cotta, precast concrete or imitation stone and granite, etc., or as follows:
All labor costs for bringing in, setting up, dismantling and removing major scaffolding, derricks, hoisting engines, air compressors, etc., should be charged to the proper classification under "Construction Plant and Equipment." (See A-60.)
71. Labor unloading and handling stone, granite, terra cotta, etc.
72. Laying rubble stone foundation walls.
73. Laying rustic or cobble stone piers, fireplaces, chimneys, fences, etc.
74. Laying random or split face ashlar wall facing, fireplaces, chimneys, etc.
75. Setting cut stone ashlar facing.
76. Setting cut stone columns, bases, caps and other heavy work.
77. Setting cut stone window and door sills, coping and other light work not requiring handling with derricks.
78. Setting granite base and ashlar facing.
79. Setting granite columns, bases, caps and other heavy work.
80. Setting granite steps and platforms.
81. Cutting or carving cut stone or granite, when done on job.
82. Setting architectural terra cotta facing, base, sills, coping, trim, etc.
83. Setting adhesion type ceramic veneer facing.
84. Setting anchored type ceramic veneer facing.
85. Setting precast concrete or imitation stone ashlar facing.
86. Setting precast concrete or imitation stone sills, coping, and other light work.
87. Setting precast facing slabs.
88. ....
89. ....

CLEANING AND POINTING

E- 90. All labor costs for cleaning and pointing masonry surfaces, including hanging and removing swing stages, mixing pointing mortar, raking and pointing joints, washing masonry surfaces with soap suds or acid, steam, etc.

91. ....

92. ....

SANDBLASTING

E- 100. All labor costs for sandblasting masonry surfaces, including hanging and removing swing stages and operating sandblasting equipment. Labor costs for unloading and setting up heavy equipment at start of job and dismantling and loading at completion should be charged to "Construction Plant and Equipment" classification A-64.

101. ....

102. ....

"F" classifications shall include all labor costs for waterproofing, dampproofing and caulking.

WATERPROOFING AND DAMPPROOFING

F- 1. All labor costs for unloading material and equipment, handling materials, setting up equipment, applying waterproofing or dampproofing materials and dismantling and removing equipment at completion, or as follows:

2. Adding integral admixtures to concrete, grout, mortar, etc.
3. Mixing and placing water and damp resisting plaster coats.
4. Applying membrane waterproofing.
5. Applying iron method waterproofing.
6.
6. Applying dampproof or plaster bond paints.
7. Applying transparent liquid water repellants.
8. Applying parging or back-plastering.
9. Bleeding and repairing leaks under hydrostatic pressure.
10. Building in all expansion joint sealers and waterstops.
11. ....

CAULKING

F- 20. All labor costs for setting up equipment, erecting and removing scaffolds and stages and applying all caulking work, or as follows:

21. Applying primer to adjoining surfaces.
22. Installing oakum or rope yarn to joint.
23. Applying caulking bead.
24. Building in metal cap joints.
25. ....

"G" classifications include all labor costs for rough carpentry; fabrication of wood trusses, (if done on job), and field erection of wood trusses; installation of wallboards, insulation, weatherstrips, and vapor seals; erection of millwork and interior finish, including installation of finish hardware; erection of garage doors, fire doors, metal doors, metal windows, etc.; installation of metal trim and case work.

ROUGH CARPENTRY AND TIMBER FRAMING

G- All labor costs for handling materials, framing and erecting or placing rough carpentry or timber framing work, or as follows:

All labor costs for unloading materials from cars for stock piling should be charged to the proper classification under "Unloading Materials." (See A-80.) All lumber delivered direct to job from trucks for immediate use should be charged to the class of work on which it will be used.

1. Handling, framing and erecting wood columns, posts, beams, girders, lintels, etc. (State size of lumber.)
2. Handling, framing and placing foundation wall plates, box sills, floor and ceiling joists. (State whether necessary to frame for joist hangers, stirrups, etc.)
3. Handling and placing cross bridging.
4. Handling, framing and erecting exterior stud walls and interior stud partitions.
5. Handling, framing and erecting roof rafters and trussed rafters. (State type of roof framing.)
6. Handling and installing exterior cornice framing, lookouts, false rafters, etc.

7. Handling and placing sub-flooring and roof sheathing. (State size of lumber and whether laid straight or diagonally.)
8. Handling and placing rough wall sheathing. (State size of lumber and whether laid straight or diagonally.)
9. Handling and placing building paper or deadening felt over sub-flooring and wall or roof sheathing.
10. Handling, framing and placing wood roof saddles and cants.
11. Handling, framing and bolting wood nailers to steel, concrete and masonry. (State size of lumber.)
12. Handling and installing rough wood blocking for doors, windows, cabinets, cases, etc.
13. Handling and placing wood furring strips or sleepers on floors, walls, ceilings, etc. (State method of fastening and class of workmanship.)
14. Handling and placing wood grounds. (State method of fastening and class of workmanship.)
15. ....
16. ....

WOOD TRUSSES

G- 20. All labor costs for handling materials and framing wood truss members, if fabricated on job; unloading loose truss members or assembled trusses, if fabricated in the shop; assembling trusses; and erecting wood trusses in place, or as follows:
21. Handling and framing wood truss members.
22. Assembling wood trusses.
23. Erecting wood trusses.
24. ....
25. ....

EXTERIOR FINISHED CARPENTRY

G- 30. All labor costs for handling materials and erecting or placing exterior finished carpentry, or as follows:
31. Handling and placing siding or shingles.
32. Handling and installing frames and sash including storm sash and screens.
33. Handling and installing door frames and doors including storm doors and screens, wood and plastic garage doors.
34. Handling and erecting porch construction including posts, columns, railings, ceiling boards, flooring, etc.
35. Handling and erecting exterior wood steps and railings.
36. Handling and erecting wood gutters.
37. Handling and placing other wood trim including water table moldings, cornices, corner boards, gables, dormers, etc.
38. Handling and erecting unattached wood including fences, gates, trellises, etc.
39. ....
40. ....

INSULATION

G- 50. All labor costs for unloading, handling and placing insulation of all kinds, or as follows:
51. Handling and placing batt or blanket type insulation.
52. Handling and placing pellet or granule type insulation.
53. Handling and placing reflective type insulation.
54. Handling and placing board type or rigid insulation.
55. Handling and placing corkboard insulation.
56. ....
57. ....

WEATHERSTRIPS AND VAPOR SEALS

G- 60. All labor costs for handling materials and installing weatherstrips and vapor seals, or as follows:
61. Weatherstripping doors and windows.
62. Placing vapor seal papers or fabrics.
63. ....
64. ....

INTERIOR FINISHED CARPENTRY AND MILLWORK

G- 70. All labor costs for unloading, handling and erecting all interior finished carpentry and millwork, or as follows:
71. Handling and erecting interior door frames and stops.
72. Handling, fitting and installing all interior doors.
73. Handling and erecting interior frames and sash.

74. Handling, fitting and installing interior trim, base and shelving.
75. Handling, fitting and installing interior paneling.
76. Handling and erecting interior wood stairs and railings.
77. Handling and installing casework, cabinets, cupboards, counters, finished shelving, mantels, window seats, built-in closet accessories, etc.
78. Handling and installing wood flooring.
79. Back priming.
80. ....

WALLBOARDS

G- 90. All labor costs for unloading, handling and erecting all wallboard work, or as follows:
91. Handling, erecting, taping and sanding gypsum plasterboard.
92. Handling and erecting fiberboard, paneling and battens.
93. Handling and erecting insulating plank.
94. Handling and erecting prefinished panels and batten strips.
95. ....

FINISH HARDWARE

G-100. All labor costs for unloading, handling, installing and adjusting all finished hardware.

"H" classifications include all labor costs for unloading, handling and erecting structural steel, lightweight steel framing, miscellaneous and ornamental metals, hollow metals and rolled metal windows and doors.

STRUCTURAL STEEL

H- All labor costs for unloading, handling, erecting and reveting, welding or bolting structural steel of all kinds, or as follows:

All labor costs for bringing in, setting up, dismantling and removing derricks, hoisting engines, air compressors, etc. should be charged to the proper classification under "Construction Plant and Equipment." (See A-60.)

1. Unloading structural steel from cars or trucks and distributing in storage yard.
2. Hauling structural steel from storage yard to point of erection.
3. Erecting structural steel. (State type of construction, such as wall bearing, skeleton frame, trusses, arches, etc.)
4. Riveting, welding or bolting structural steel connections. (State type of connection.)
5. Labor placing miscellaneous items of structural steel, such as loose lintels, lally columns, shelf angles, grillage, loose beams and struts, etc.
6. Unloading, handling and erecting steel stacks, tanks, etc.
7. Touch up painting in field.
8. ....
9. ....

LIGHTWEIGHT STEEL FRAMING

H- 10. All labor costs for unloading, handling and erecting lightweight steel framing, or as follows:
11. Unloading lightweight steel framing material at job.
12. Handling and erecting steel joists, including installation of bridging and bottom chord extensions.
13. Handling and erecting junior steel beams.
14. Handling and erecting Stran-Steel construction.
15. Touch up coat of paint in field.
16. ....
17. ....

STEEL DECKING

H- 20. All labor costs for unloading, handling and erecting steel decking of all kinds, or as follows:
21. Handling and erecting ribbed type steel decking.
22. Handling and erecting cellular type steel decking.
23. ....
24. ....

MISCELLANEOUS AND ORNAMENTAL METAL

H- 30. All labor costs for unloading, handling and erecting miscellaneous and ornamental metal of all kinds, or as follows:
31. Unloading miscellaneous and ornamental metal at job.
32. Handling and placing steel or cast iron frames for openings in floors, walls and roofs, including covers or gratings for same.
33. Handling and placing steel angle or cast iron corner guards and bumpers, bar gratings, door and window guards, bearing plates, etc.
34. Assembling and erecting steel or ornamental iron stairs, including balustrades and railings.
35. Assembling and erecting steel fire escapes.
36. Handling and erecting ornamental iron, aluminum or bronze entrance rails, porch columns, plaques, grilles, etc.
37. Handling and erecting steel or ornamental iron ladders and pipe railings.
38. Assembling and erecting steel or aluminum flagpoles. (State whether ground, roof or outrigger type.)
39. Handling and erecting ornamental iron, aluminum, bronze or copper store front metal.
40. Handling and erecting all metal curtain wall construction including grid and spandrel panels.
41. Handling and installing metal specialties and prefabricated metal items including metal shelving, closet fittings, copings, hoods, laundry chutes, lockers, louvers, mail chutes, etc.
42. Touch up field coat of paint.
43. ....
44. ....

HOLLOW METALS

H- 50. All labor costs for unloading, handling and erecting all hollow metal work, or as follows:
51. Handling and installing hollow metal doors, frames and anchors.
52. Handling and installing hollow metal windows, frames and anchors.
53. Handling and erecting hollow metal partitions, doors and borrowed lights.
54. Handling and installing metal base, chair rails, door trim and other metal trim.
55. Touch up coat of paint in field.
56. Handling and installing weatherstripping for above.
57. ....
58. ....

ROLLED AND EXTRUDED METALS

H- 60. All labor costs for handling and erecting all rolled and extruded metal work, or as follows:
61. Handling, erecting and adjusting all rolled and extruded metal windows, frames and hardware.
62. Handling, erecting and adjusting all rolled and extruded metal doors, frames and hardware.
63. Handling and installing weatherstripping for above.
64. Touch up field coat of paint for above.
65. ....

"J" classifications include all labor costs for lathing and plain or ornamental plastering.

LATHING

J-   All labor costs for unloading, handling and placing lath materials of all kinds, or as follows:
1. Unloading lathing materials of all kinds at job.
2. Placing gypsum or insulating lath on wood studs, furring strips and ceiling joists.
3. Placing metal lath on wood studs, furring strips and ceiling joists.
4. Placing gypsum or insulating lath on metal furring channels.
5. Placing metal lath on metal furring channels.
6. Erecting suspended gypsum lath ceilings, including placing hangers, runners and furring channels.
7. Erecting suspended metal lath ceilings, including placing hangers, runners and furring channels.
8. Erecting metal lath and channel furring on structural steel columns and beams for fireproofing.
9. Erecting metal lath and channel framing for curtain walls, hanging screens, etc.
10. Erecting long length gypsum lath for solid gypsum plaster partitions, including placing floor and ceiling runners.
11. Erecting gypsum lath on steel studs for hollow steel stud plastered partitions, including placing steel studs, tracks and shoes.
12. Erecting metal lath partitions.
13. Erecting metal lath and channel framing for ornamental plaster beams, cornices, etc.
14. Placing corner beads, cornerites, door and window trim, base screeds, concealed picture mould, etc. (State whether applied to masonry, wood framing, etc.)
15. ....
16. ....

INTERIOR PLASTERING

J- 20. All labor costs for unloading materials, building and removing scaffold, mixing materials and applying plaster to interior walls and ceilings, or as follows:
21. Unloading plastering materials and equipment at job.
22. Building and removing plasterer's scaffold.
23. Mixing and applying scratch coat to interior walls and ceilings. (State whether sand or lightweight aggregate is used.)
24. Mixing and applying brown coat to interior walls and ceilings. (State whether sand or lightweight aggregate is used.)
25. Mixing and applying white or finish coat to interior walls and ceilings.
26. Mixing and applying sand finish coat to interior walls and ceilings.
27. Mixing and applying finish coat of Keene's cement or other cement plaster used for interior finishing. (State whether walls are plain or blocked off into squares.)
28. Mixing and applying finish coat of Caen cement plaster. (State whether walls are plain or blocked off into squares.)
29. Running cement base, including mixing and placing material. (State whether base is plain or coved.)
30. Running ceiling coves.
31. Mixing and applying coat of sound absorbing plaster.
32. ....
33. ....

EXTERIOR PLASTER AND STUCCO

J- 40. All labor costs for unloading materials, building and removing scaffold, mixing materials and applying cement plaster or stucco to exterior surfaces, or as follows:
41. Unloading plastering materials and equipment at job.
42. Building and removing plasterer's scaffold.
43. Mixing and applying scratch coat to exterior surfaces.
44. Mixing and applying brown coat to exterior surfaces.
45. Mixing and applying troweled finish coat of portland cement plaster to exterior surfaces.
46. Mixing and applying float finish coat of portland cement plaster to exterior surfaces.
47. Mixing and applying rough cast finishing materials to exterior surfaces. (State whether dry or wet cast.)
48. Running exterior cornices, coves and other trim.
49. ....
50. ....

ORNAMENTAL PLASTERING

J- 60. All labor costs for ornamental plastering work, or as follows:
61. Making templates, mixing materials and running plain ornamental plaster cornice under 1'-0" in girth.
62. Making templates, mixing materials and running plain ornamental plaster cornice over 1'-0" in girth.
63. Making models, moulds, etc. for ornamental cast work, such as columns, pilasters, bases, caps, brackets, plaques, cornice and beam enrichments, figures, etc.
64. Mixing materials and casting all classes of ornamentation as mentioned above.
65. Sticking cast plaster ornaments to plain plaster cornices and beams.
66. Handling and setting cast ornaments, such as columns, pilasters, bases, caps, brackets, plaques, figures, etc.
67. ....
68. ....

"K" classifications include all labor costs for sheet metal work, roofing and siding.

GUTTERS, DOWNSPOUTS, FLASHING, ETC.

K- All labor costs for unloading, handling and erecting materials for metal gutters, downspouts, flashings, etc., or as follows:
1. Hauling material to job and unloading same.
2. Handling and erecting metal eaves trough or gutter.
3. Handling and erecting metal conductor pipe or downspout.
4. Handling and erecting metal flashing and counter-flashing.
5. Handling and erecting metal hips, valleys, ridges, etc.
6. ....
7. ....

METAL SKYLIGHTS AND VENTILATORS

K- 10. All labor costs for unloading, assembling and erecting metal skylights and roof ventilators, or as follows:
    11. Unloading skylight and ventilator material at job.
    12. Erecting stationary skylights.
    13. Erecting vented skylights.
    14. Installing operating devices for skylight vents.
    15. Erecting gravity type roof ventilators.
    16. Erecting power operated roof ventilators.
    17. Erecting sheet metal duct work for ventilators.
    18. ....
    19. ....

METAL ROOFS AND SIDING

K- 20. All labor costs for unloading, handling and placing materials for metal roofs, such as flat or standing seam tin and copper decks, corrugated galvanized iron, aluminum or protected metal roofing and siding, etc., or as follows:
    21. Hauling material to job and unloading same.
    22. Placing flat seam metal decks.
    23. Placing standing seam metal decks.
    24. Placing corrugated metal siding on wood or steel framing.
    25. Placing corrugated metal roofing on wood or steel framing.
    26. Placing V-crimped metal roofing on wood or steel framing.
    27. Handling and placing prefinished metal siding and vertical paneling.
    28. Handling, installing and fitting metal soffits, facias, returns, gables and trim.
    29. Handling and installing prefinished metal roofing tiles and shingles.
    30. Handling and erecting prefabricated metal buildings and sheds.
    31. ....
    32. ....

ROOFING AND SIDING

K- 40. All labor costs for unloading, handling and placing asphalt shingle roofing and siding, asbestos shingle roofing and siding, composition roofing, slate roofing, tile roofing, corrugated asbestos roofing and siding, etc., or as follows:
    41. Unloading roofing or siding materials at job.
    42. Placing asphalt shingle roofing.
    43. Placing asphalt shingle siding.
    44. Placing ready-to-lay roll roofing.
    45. Placing insulating siding.
    46. Placing asbestos shingle roofing.
    47. Placing asbestos shingle siding.
    48. Placing large-sheet asbestos siding.
    49. Installing composition or built-up roofs.
    50. Placing slate roofing.
    51. Placing tile roofing.
    52. Placing corrugated asbestos roofing on wood or steel framing.
    53. Placing corrugated asbestos siding on wood or steel framing.
    54. Placing sheet plastic roofing.
    55. Placing fluid plastic roofing.
    56. ....
    57. ....

"L" classifications include all labor costs for hauling, unloading and handling glazing materials and doing glazing work of all kinds.

GLASS AND GLAZING

L- All labor costs for hauling glazing materials to job and unloading same, handling materials and glazing windows, doors, borrowed lights, etc., handling and setting insulating glass, handling and setting leaded or art glass, handling and setting plate glass in store fronts, etc., handling and setting structural glass for walls, wainscots and ceilings, handling and setting mirrors, etc., or as follows:
    1. Hauling glazing materials to job and unloading and distributing same.
    2. Handling and setting plain window glass in putty.
    3. Handling and setting plain window glass using wood stops.
    4. Handling and setting plate glass in putty.

5. Handling and setting plate glass using wood stops.
6. Glazing steel sash.
7. Handling and setting insulating glass.
8. Handling and setting leaded or art glass.
9. Handling and setting plate glass in store fronts.
10. Handling and setting structural glass for exterior base courses, walls, etc.
11. Handling and setting structural glass for interior walls and wainscoting.
12. Handling and setting structural glass for ceilings.
13. Handling and setting tempered glass partitions and doors.
14. Handling and setting mirrors.
15. Handling and setting spandrel glass.
16. Handling and setting Plexiglas.
17. ....
18. ....

"M" classifications include all labor costs for painting and decorating work of all kinds.

EXTERIOR PAINTING

M- All labor costs for hauling, unloading and handling materials and equipment from shop to job, hanging painter's scaffold, applying paint to exterior surfaces of all kinds and removing scaffolding and materials at completion, or as follows:
1. Hauling, unloading and handling materials and equipment from shop to job.
2. Hanging and erecting scaffolds as needed to reach work.
3. Applying prime and finished coats to wood siding.
4. Applying prime and finished coats to wood trim.
5. Applying stain or paint to wood wall shingles.
6. Applying stain or paint to wood roof shingles.
7. Applying prime and finished coats to wood ceilings.
8. Applying prime and finished coats to wood decks.
9. Applying prime and finished coats to miscellaneous and ornamental metals.
10. Applying prime and finished coats to metal doors and sash.
11. Applying prime and finished coats to sheet metal work.
12. Applying prime and finished coats to brick and block work.
13. Applying prime and finished coats to stucco work.
14. Applying prime and finished coats to concrete work.
15. Removing existing coats of paint.
16. Protecting and cleaning adjacent work.
17. ....
18. ....

INTERIOR PAINTING AND DECORATING

M- 20. All labor costs for hauling, unloading and handling materials and equipment from shop to job, scaffolding, painting and decorating interior surfaces of all kinds, and removing scaffolding and equipment at completion, or as follows:
21. Hauling, unloading and handling materials and equipment from shop to job.
22. Priming and back-priming interior wood work. (State whether done at mill or on job.)
23. Applying each additional coat, after the first, to interior wood work.
24. Applying stain or bleach, filler, shellac, varnish or lacquer, etc., to interior wood work, including sanding between coats.
25. Applying seal coat to plastered walls and ceilings. (State whether brushed, rolled or sprayed.)
26. Applying each additional coat, after sealing, to plastered walls and ceilings. (State whether brushed, rolled or sprayed.)
27. Applying wall size to plastered surfaces.
28. Hanging wall paper or other similar material.
29. Applying stain, filler, shellac, varnish or penetrating finish, wax, etc., to finish wood floors, stairs, etc.
30. Removing existing coats of paint.
31. Protecting and cleaning adjacent work.
32. ....
33. ....

"N" classifications include all labor costs for marble and slate work of all kinds and terrazzo, art marble, ceramic, quarry, plastic and metal tile.

INTERIOR MARBLE

N-   All labor costs for hauling, unloading and handling interior marble material from shop to job and setting interior marble of all kinds, or as follows:

1. Hauling, unloading and handling marble material from shop to job.
2. Setting interior marble base.
3. Setting marble wainscot and wall facing.
4. Setting marble partitions and backs.
5. Laying interior marble floor tile, including cement underbed.
6. Rubbing or smoothing marble floors.
7. Setting interior marble stair treads, risers, stringers, platforms, balustrades and railings.
8. Setting miscellaneous interior marble items, such as thresholds, window stools, counter tops, door and window trim, etc. ....
9. ....
10. ....

EXTERIOR MARBLE

N- 20. All labor costs for hauling, unloading and handling exterior marble material from shop to job, making mortar and setting exterior marble of all kinds, or as follows:
All labor costs for bringing in, setting up, dismantling and removing major scaffolding, derricks, hoisting engines, air compressors, etc., should be charged to the proper classification under "Construction Plant and Equipment." (See A-60.)

21. Unloading and distributing exterior marble material on job.
22. Handling and setting exterior marble base and water-table courses.
23. Handling and setting exterior marble ashlar facing.
24. Handling and setting exterior marble columns, bases, caps and other heavy work.
25. Handling and setting exterior marble steps, platforms, balustrades, etc.
26. Carving marble, when done on job. ....
27. ....
28. ....

INTERIOR SLATE

N- 40. All labor costs for hauling, unloading and handling interior slate material from shop to job and setting interior slate of all kinds, or as follows:

41. Hauling, unloading and handling slate material from shop to job.
42. Setting interior slate base.
43. Setting slate wainscot and wall facing.
44. Setting slate partitions and backs.
45. Laying interior slate floors, including cement underbed.
46. Rubbing or smoothing slate floors.
47. Setting interior slate stair treads, risers and platforms.
48. Setting miscellaneous interior slate items, such as thresholds, window stools, counter tops, etc. ....
49. ....

TERRAZZO

N- 50. All labor costs for hauling, unloading and handling terrazzo materials and equipment from shop to job, mixing materials, placing cement underbed, setting metal dividers and laying and grinding terrazzo floors and base, stair treads, risers and platforms, wainscot and partitions, etc., or as follows:

51. Hauling, unloading and handling terrazzo materials and equipment from shop to job.
52. Mixing materials, placing cement underbed, setting metal dividers and laying and grinding terrazzo for floors.
53. Mixing materials and running and grinding terrazzo for base.
54. Mixing materials, placing cement underbed, setting metal dividers and laying and grinding terrazzo for stair treads and platforms.
55. Mixing materials and running and grinding terrazzo for stair risers and stringers.
56. Mixing materials and placing and grinding terrazzo partitions and wainscot. Metal lath and channel framing or furring and scratch coat of plaster should be charged to the proper "J" classification. ....
57. ....
58. ....

ART MARBLE

N- 60. All labor costs for hauling, unloading and handling art marble materials and equipment from shop to job, mixing and placing cement setting beds and setting art marble of all kinds, or as follows:
61. Hauling, unloading and handling art marble materials and equipment from shop to job.
62. Mixing and placing cement setting bed and laying art marble floors.
63. Handling and setting art marble base.
64. Mixing and placing cement setting bed and laying art marble stair treads, platforms risers, stringers, etc.
65. Handling and setting art marble wainscoting and wall facing.
66. Handling and setting miscellaneous art marble items, such as thresholds, window stools, door and window trim, counter tops, etc.
67. ....
68. ....

CERAMIC TILE, QUARRY TILE, PLASTIC TILE AND METAL TILE

N- 70. All labor costs for hauling, unloading and handling ceramic quarry, plastic and metal tile materials and equipment from shop to job, mixing materials, placing cement setting beds or spreading adhesive and installing tile floors, base, wainscoting, wall and ceiling facing, etc., or as follows:
71. Hauling, unloading and handling ceramic quarry, plastic or metal tile materials and equipment from shop to job.
72. Mixing and placing cement underbed and laying ceramic tile floors, using tile mounted on paper.
73. Mixing and placing cement underbed and laying ceramic tile floors using unmounted tile.
74. Mixing and placing cement underbed and laying quarry tile floors.
75. Mixing and placing cement underbed and setting ceramic tile base.
76. Mixing and placing cement underbed and setting quarry tile base.
77. Mixing and placing cement underbed and setting ceramic tile wainscoting, wall facing and ceiling facing.
78. Spreading adhesive and setting ceramic tile wainscoting, wall facing and ceiling facing, including grouting joints.
79. Spreading adhesive and setting plastic tile wainscoting, wall facing and ceiling facing.
80. Spreading adhesive and setting metal tile wainscoting, wall facing and ceiling facing.
81. ....
82. ....

"O" classifications include all labor costs for the installation of acoustical tile work of all kinds.

ACOUSTICAL TILE

O- All labor costs for hauling, unloading, handling and installing all acoustical tile work including suspension systems, adhesives, furring clips, etc., or as follows:
1. Hauling, unloading and handling acoustical tile and accessories from shop to job.
2. Erecting scaffolds.
3. Installing tile with adhesive directly to ceiling or walls.
4. Installing tile on concealed suspension system hung from ceiling.
5. Installing tile on exposed grid system hung from ceiling.
6. Installing tile on furring clips on walls.
7. ....
8. ....

"P" classifications include all labor costs for the installation of resilient floor and wall coverings of all kinds.

RESILIENT TILE FLOORING AND BASE

P- All labor costs for hauling, unloading and handling resilient tile floor and base materials from shop to job, priming concrete floors, laying lining felt over wood floors, laying resilient tile floors, placing resilient material base, cleaning and waxing floors and base at completion, etc., or as follows:
1. Hauling, unloading and handling resilient tile floor and base materials and equipment from shop to job.
2. Priming concrete floors.
3. Laying lining felt over wood floors.
4. Laying asphalt tile floors.
5. Laying vinyl asbestos tile floors.
6. Laying pure vinyl tile floors.
7. Laying rubber tile floors.
8. Laying cork tile floors.
9. Placing rubber or vinyl base.

10. Cleaning, waxing and protecting floors and base.
11. ....
12. ....

RESILIENT SHEET FLOOR AND WALL COVERING

P- 20   All labor costs for hauling, unloading and handling resilient sheet floor and wall covering materials and equipment from shop to job, laying felt lining, laying resilient sheet floor covering, installing resilient sheet wall covering, cleaning and waxing floors and walls, etc., or as follows:
21. Hauling, unloading and handling resilient sheet floor and wall covering materials and equipment from shop to job.
22. Laying lining felt.
23. Laying linoleum floor covering.
24. Laying sheet rubber floor covering.
25. Laying sheet plastic floor covering.
26. Laying sheet cork floor covering.
27. Installing linoleum wall covering.
28. Installing sheet rubber wall covering.
29. Installing sheet plastic wall covering.
30. Installing sheet cork wall covering.
31. Cleaning and waxing floors and walls.
32. ....
33. ....

"Q" classifications include all labor costs for the installation of vertical transportation equipment of all kinds.

ELEVATORS, ESCALATORS, LIFTS, CONVEYORS, ETC.

Q-   All labor costs for unloading, handling, installing and putting into operation elevators, escalators, lifts, conveyors, etc. of all kinds, or as follows:
1. Installation of passenger elevators.
2. Installation of freight elevators.
3. Installation of sidewalk elevators.
4. Installation of escalators.
5. Installation of dumbwaiters.
6. Installation of conveyors.
7. Installation of moving sidewalks.
8. Installation of pneumatic tube systems.
9. ....
10. ....

"R" classifications include all labor costs for sewer work, plumbing and gas fitting.

SEWER WORK

R-   All labor costs for unloading and handling materials and doing sewer work of all kinds, or as follows:
        All labor costs for excavation and backfill should be charged to the proper classification under "Excavation, etc." (See B-20.)
        All labor costs for building masonry manholes, catch-basins, etc. should be charged to the proper classification under "Cement Blocks, etc." or "Brickwork." (See E-12 or E-30.)
1. Hauling, unloading and handling materials for sewer work.
2. Laying sanitary or storm sewer mains.
3. Laying lateral sanitary or storm sewer lines.
4. Connecting new sewer lines to existing mains.
5. Installation of septic tank and tile drainage field.
6. ....
7. ....

PLUMBING

R- 10. All labor costs for hauling, unloading and handling materials and equipment and doing plumbing work of all kinds, or as follows:
        All labor costs for excavation and backfill should be charged to the proper classification under "Excavation, etc." (See B-20.)
11. Hauling, unloading and handling materials and equipment for plumbing work.
12. Roughing in sanitary drain lines for plumbing fixtures, including vents through roofs.

13. Installing storm drain lines.
14. Laying water mains.
15. Laying lateral water lines or bringing in water supply from existing water mains.
16. Roughing in supply lines for plumbing fixtures.
17. Handling and setting plumbing fixtures.
18. Handling and installing hot water heaters, storage tanks, house tanks, etc.
19. Handling and installing pumps of all kinds.
20. Installing fire lines and standpipes.
21. Covering water pipes.
22. Erecting toilet and shower cabinets (if union rules include this work).
23. ....
24. ....

GAS FITTING

R- 30. All labor costs for hauling, unloading and handling materials and equipment and doing gas fitting work of all kinds, or as follows:
   All labor costs for excavation and backfill should be charged to the proper classification under "Excavation, etc." (See B-20.)
31. Hauling, unloading and handling materials and equipment for gas fitting work.
32. Laying gas mains.
33. Laying lateral gas lines or bringing in gas service from existing mains.
34. Roughing in gas lines to appliances.
35. Unloading, handling, setting and connecting appliances.
36. ....
37. ....

"S" classifications include all labor costs for the installation of sprinkler systems.

SPRINKLER WORK

S- All labor costs for hauling, unloading and handling materials and equipment and doing sprinkler work of all kinds, or as follows:
1. Hauling, unloading and handling materials and equipment for sprinkler work.
2. Laying out and placing pipe hangers.
3. Installing sprinkler mains.
4. Installing sprinkler laterals.
5. Installing sprinkler heads.
6. Installing attic or roof tank.
7. Installing fire hydrants.
8. Installing pumps.
9. ....
10. ....

"T" classifications include all labor costs for heating work.

WARM AIR HEATING

T- All labor costs for hauling, unloading and handling materials and equipment and installing and putting into operation warm air heating systems, or as follows:
1. Hauling, unloading and handling materials and equipment for warm air heating systems.
2. Assembling and setting up gravity type warm air furnaces.
3. Assembling and setting up blower type warm air furnaces.
4. Assembling and setting up combination blower type heating and cooling units.
5. Asembling and setting up pipeless type warm air furnaces.
6. Installing furnace pipe or ducts.
7. Installing register faces, grilles, etc.
8. Installing electrical controls.
9. Installing insulation on ductwork and filter system.

STEAM AND HOT WATER HEATING

T- All labor costs for hauling, unloading and handling materials and equipment and installing and putting into operation steam or hot water heating systems, or as follows:
11. Hauling, unloading and handling materials and equipment for installing steam or hot water heating systems.
12. Unloading, handling, assembling and setting boilers.

13. Running mains and risers and roughing in to radiation.
14. Setting and connecting radiators, convectors, etc.
15. Running and connecting base board radiation.
16. Installing radiant heating panels, including fabrication if done on job.
17. Installing booster pumps, vacuum pumps, etc.
18. Assembling and installing stoker equipment.
19. Assembling and installing coal handling equipment.
20. Assembling and installing ash handling equipment.
21. Installing oil burners.
22. Unloading, handling and installing oil storage tanks, including piping to burners. Labor costs for excavating, backfilling and concrete foundations should be charged to their respective classifications. (See B-20, C-, C-10.)
23. Installing gas burners and connecting to gas supply.
24. Installing electrical controls.
25. Installing pipe and boiler covering.
26. ....
27. ....

ELECTRICAL HEATING

T- 30. All labor costs for hauling, unloading and handling materials and equipment; and installing and putting into operation all electrical heating systems, or as follows:
31. Bringing power from main panel to unit.
32. Installing electric warm air furnace.
33. Installing through-the-wall heating, cooling and ventilating units.
34. Installing heat pumps.
35. Installing embedded radiant coils.
36. Installing baseboard units.
37. Installing convector units.
38. Installing radiant units.
39. Installing controls for above.
40. ....
41. ....

"U" classifications include all labor costs for air conditioning, ventilation and refrigeration work.

AIR CONDITIONING

U- All labor costs for hauling, unloading and handling materials and equipment and installing and putting into operation air conditioning systems, or as follows:
1. Hauling, unloading and handling materials and equipment for installing air conditioning systems.
2. Asembling and setting package unit air conditioning machines for small volume installations, including connecting to water supply and waste piping.
3. Assembling and setting air conditioning equipment for large volume installations, including connecting to water supply and waste piping.
4. Installing duct work.
5. Installing register faces, grilles, louvres, etc.
6. Installing fans and blowers.
7. Installing electrical controls.
8. Installing filter systems.
9. Installing duct insulation.
10. Installing cooling towers.
11. ....
12. ....

VENTILATION

U- 20. All labor costs for hauling, unloading and handling materials and equipment and installing and putting into operation ventilating systems, or as follows:
21. Hauling, unloading and handling materials and equipment for installing ventilating systems.
22. Assembling and installing gravity type roof ventilators.
23. Assembling and installing power operated roof ventilators.
24. Assembling and installing fans and blowers for mechanical ventilation systems.
25. Installing duct work.
26. Installing register faces, grilles, louvres, etc.
27. Installing electrical controls.

28. Installing filter systems.
29. ....
30. ....

REFRIGERATION

U- 40. All labor costs for hauling, unloading and handling materials and equipment and installing and putting into operation refrigeration systems, or as follows:
41. Hauling, unloading and handling materials and equipment for installing refrigeration systems.
42. Assembling and setting refrigeration machines for central plant installations in apartment buildings, hotels, etc.
43. Running piping and setting and connecting expansion boxes for central plant installations.
44. Assembling and setting refrigeration machines for commercial and industrial installations.
45. Running piping for commercial and industrial installations.
46. Installing refrigerating coils.
47. Installing electrical work.
48. ....
49. ....

"V" classifications include all labor costs for electrical work.

ELECTRICAL WORK

V- All labor costs for hauling, unloading and handling materials and equipment and doing electrical work of all kinds, or as follows:
1. Hauling, unloading and handling materials and equipment for electrical work.
2. Locating and setting boxes for outlets, switches, etc.
3. Running armored or non-metallic sheathed cable in frame construction.
4. Running thin wall or rigid conduit.
5. Bringing in service and setting and connecting fuse boxes, panel boards, etc.
6. Pulling wires.
7. Installing switches, receptacles, etc.
8. Installing lighting fixtures.
9. Installing power wiring, including handling and setting generators, switch gear, transformers, etc., and cost of appliances and devices furnished by other contractors.
10. ....
11. ....

EXTRA WORK

"X" classifications are intended to cover all labor costs for work, ordered by the architect or owner, in addition to the original contract. Each extra work order received should be given a number such as "X-1," "X-2," etc. and all money spent for labor on an order should be charged to its own account, thus distinguishing it from costs chargeable to the original contract.

KEEPING ACCURATE MATERIAL COSTS

In order to keep accurate costs of the various kinds of material used in the different branches of work, a system of sub-dividing material costs should be used, similar to the one used for labor costs.

In the material cost schedule described in the following pages, the second letter, "M," in each schedule is used to designate the charge as a material cost. The same system of symbols is used throughout in order that the labor and material cost schedules will agree.

MATERIAL COST SCHEDULE

"AM" classifications include all material costs for operations not directly productive in the preliminary work or construction work.

OVERHEAD EXPENSE

(See Chapter XX)

AM- All material costs for job overhead expense, or as follows:
1. General job overhead expenses, such as telephone and telegraph, stationery, postage, carfare, photographs,

         job office supplies, job traveling expenses, etc.
2. Permits, street obstruction bonds, inspection fees, etc.
3. Liability and compensation insurance, comprehensive insurance, etc.
4. Surety bonds.
5. ....
6. ....

TEMPORARY CONSTRUCTION AND WEATHER CONDITONS

AM- 20. All material costs for temporary construction and weather conditions, or as follows:
     21. Material costs for temporary offices, sheds, enclosures, toilet facilities, etc.
     22. Material costs for temporary protection for the public, including sidewalks, bridges, canopies, fences, barricades and lights, etc.
     23. Material costs for temporary partitions, etc.
     24. Material costs for temporary stairs, ladders, ramps, etc.
     25. Material costs for temporary protection for new or existing construction.
     26. Material costs for temporary closures for doors, windows, etc.
     27. Material costs for temporary water and sewer lines or amount of sub-contract, if work is sub-let. Charges for water consumed should also be included in this classification.
     28. Material costs for temporary electric light and power or amount of sub-contract, if work is sub-let. Charges for electrical energy consumed should also be included in this classification.
     29. Material costs for temporary heating of buildings.
     30. Material costs for heating materials and protecting construction work during freezing weather.
     31. Material costs for temporary signs.
     32. ....
     33. ....

REPAIRS, CLEANING AND RUBBISH REMOVAL

AM- 40. All material costs for repairs, cleaning and rubbish removal, or as follows:
     41. Material costs for cutting, patching and repairing for other trades in general, where not chargeable to a specific trade, including patching damaged plaster and replacing broken glass.
     42. Material costs for repairing damage to sidewalks, curbs, streets, etc.
     43. Material costs for cleaning building, including exterior and interior glass. Also included in this classification are amounts of sub-contracts, if work is sub-let, and cartage and dumping charges for rubbish.
     44. Material costs for replacing trees and other planting and landscaping features which are specifically noted to remain.
     45. ....
     46. ....

CONSTRUCTION PLANT AND EQUIPMENT

AM- 60. All job costs for tools, plant and equipment, including rentals, if any equipment is rented, or if contractor's own equipment is used, the amount chargeable to the job for its use, or as follows:
     61. All job costs for excavating equipment, such as power shovels, hoes, draglines, clamshells, tractors, etc., including fuel and lubricating materials for operation.
     62. All job costs for caisson digging plant and equipment, such as platforms, tripods, winches, buckets, tarpaulins, etc.
     63. All job costs for pile driving equipment, including fuel and lubricating materials for operation.
     64. All job costs for general plant and equipment, such as concrete mixers, hoisting engines, derricks, air compressors, power buggies, pumps, etc., including fuel and lubricating materials for operation.
     65. All job costs for hoisting towers, skip hoists, major scaffolding, etc.
     66. All material costs for concrete runways and supports for same.
     67. All job costs for small tools and equipment, such as hammers, shovels, picks, sledges, bullpoints, wheelbarrows, buggies, carts, hose, etc.
     68. All truck and automobile expense.
     69. ....
     70. ....

"BM" classifications include all material costs for the preliminary operations of wrecking, clearing, shoring, underpinning, sheet piling, etc. Also included are all material costs for earth work operations and heavy duty foundation work, such as caissons, piling, etc.

WRECKING AND CLEARING

BM-   All material costs for preparing the site in advance of the actual construction work, or as follows:
1. All job costs for tools, equipment, etc. used in connection with wrecking old buildings, or amount of sub-contract, if work is sub-let.
2. All job costs for tools, equipment, etc. used in connection with moving existing buildings to new locations, or amount of sub-contract, if work is sub-let.
3. All job costs for tools, equipment, etc. used in connection with clearing the site, including removing old floors, walks, pavements, existing masonry or concrete foundations, etc.
4. All job costs for tools, equipment, etc. used in connection with exposing and removing, capping or de-activating existing utilities.
5. All job costs for tools, equipment, etc. used in connection with salvaging and storing items specifically noted to remain the property of the Owner or to be reused.
6. ....
7. ....

UNDERPINNING, SHORING AND SHEET PILING

BM- 10. All material costs for underpinning, shoring and sheet piling work, amount of sub-contract, if work is sub-let, or as follows:
11. Material costs for underpinning work, including forms, reinforcing steel, concrete, etc.
12. All job costs for materials used in connection with shoring work, including cost or rental of drums, jacks, timbers, etc.
13. All job costs for materials used in connection with steel or wood sheet piling work.
14. ....
15. ....

EXCAVATION, FILL, GRADING AND DE-WATERING

BM- 20. All costs for materials used in connection with excavation, fill, grading and de-watering work, that are not directly chargeable to Plant and Equipment, amount of sub-contract, if work is sub-let, or as follows:
21. Cost of dynamite, blasting caps, etc. used in rock excavation.
22. Cost of fill materials, such as earth, sand, gravel or crushed stone, cinders, etc., when brought in from outside sources.
23. Cost of drain tile, tar paper for joints, bed and cover material, etc.
24. All job costs for materials and equipment used in connection with wellpoint systems for de-watering, including rental of equipment.
25. All job costs for tools, equipment, etc., used in connection with all boring and test pits which are specifically part of the contract.
26. ....
27. ....

CAISSONS

BM- 50. All costs for materials used in connection with caisson work, amount of sub-contract, if work is sub-let, or as follows:
51. Cost of wood lagging, iron rings, bolts, steel shells, etc. used in connection with excavating caissons.
52. Cost of cement used in concrete for caissons.
53. Cost of gravel or crushed stone used in concrete for caissons.
54. Cost of sand used in concrete for caissons.
55. Cost of batched materials used in concrete for caissons.
56. Cost of ready-mixed concrete for caissons.
57. Cost of reinforcing steel used in caissons.
58. ....
59. ....

WOOD AND CONCRETE PILES

BM- 70. All costs for materials, used in connection with wood and concrete piling work, that are not directly chargeable to Plant and Equipment, amount of sub-contract, if work is sub-let, or as follows:
71. Cost of wood piles.
72. Cost of metal shells for cast-in-place concrete piles.
73. Cost of precast concrete piles.
74. Cost of form materials for precast concrete piles, if cast on job.
75. Cost of cement for concrete piles.
76. Cost of gravel or crushed stone for concrete piles.

77. Cost of sand for concrete piles.
78. Cost of batched materials for concrete piles.
79. Cost of ready-mixed concrete for concrete piles.
80. Cost of reinforcing steel for concrete piles.
81. ....
82. ....

"CM" classifications include all material costs for formwork, concrete and cement work, except concrete included in caissons and piles, and macadam, bituminous surfacing and asphalt surfacing materials.

FORMWORK FOR CONCRETE FOUNDATIONS AND RETAINING WALLS

CM-   All costs for materials used in connection with formwork for concrete foundations and retaining walls, or as follows:
1. Cost of lumber for wood forms.
2. Cost of impregnated fibre tubing for forms.
3. Cost or rental of wood, metal or combination wood and metal form panels, including erection hardware.
4. Cost of nails, wire, strap iron, ties, etc.
5. Cost of anchor bolts, anchor slots, anchor ties, sleeves, thimbles, etc.
6. Cost of paraffin oil or other form coating.
7. ....
8. ....

CONCRETE FOR FOUNDATIONS AND RETAINING WALLS

CM- 10. All material costs for concrete in foundations and retaining walls, or as follows:
11. Cost of cement used in concrete foundations.
12. Cost of gravel or crushed stone used in concrete foundations.
13. Cost of sand used in concrete foundations.
14. Cost of batched materials used in concrete foundations.
15. Cost of ready-mixed concrete for foundations.
16. ....
17. ....

FORMWORK FOR REINFORCED CONCRETE CONSTRUCTION

CM- 20. All costs for materials used in connection with wood formwork for reinforced concrete construction, or as follows:
21. Cost of lumber for wood forms.
22. Cost or rental of wood, metal or combination wood and metal form panels, including erection hardware.
23. Cost or rental of metal column moulds, or amount of sub-contract, if work is sub-let.
24. Cost of impregnated fibre tubing for forms.
25. Cost or rental of column clamps, adjustable shores, etc., including cartage.
26. Cost of nails, wire, strap iron, ties, etc.
27. Cost of inserts, anchor slots, anchor ties, sleeves, etc.
28. Cost of paraffin oil or other form coating.
29. ....
30. ....

PLACING REINFORCED CONCRETE

CM- 40. All material costs for concrete in reinforced concrete construction, or as follows:
41. Cost of cement used in reinforced concrete.
42. Cost of gravel or crushed stone used in reinforced concrete.
43. Cost of sand used in reinforced concrete.
44. Cost of batched materials used in reinforced concrete.
45. Cost of ready-mixed concrete for reinforced concrete construction.
46. Cost of tools and equipment to hoist concrete floor slabs where lift slab method is specified.
47. ....
48. ....

CONCRETE FLOORS, WALKS, PAVEMENTS, FILLS AND CEMENT FINISHES

CM- 50. All material costs for concrete floors, walks, pavements, curbs and gutters; floor, stair and roof fills; cement finishes and other cement mason work; amount of sub-contract, if work is sub-let, or as follows:

51. Cost of lumber for wood forms.
52. Cost or rental of metal forms.
53. Cost of material for wood or metal screeds.
54. Cost of nails, wire, strap iron, etc.
55. Cost of cement for concrete or cement topping.
56. Cost of gravel or crushed stone for concrete or cement topping.
57. Cost of sand for concrete or cement topping.
58. Cost of light weight aggregate for concrete.
59. Cost of batched materials for concrete.
60. Cost of ready-mixed concrete.
61. Cost of coloring material for cement floors, etc.
62. Cost of floor hardening materials.
63. Cost of expansion joint materials.
64. Cost of material for curing and protecting cement finishes.
65. ....
66. ....

CEMENT GUN WORK

CM- 80. All material costs for cement gun work, including forms, reinforcing, grout materials, etc., or amount of sub-contract if work is sub-let.

MACADAM, BITUMINOUS SURFACE AND ASPHALT SURFACE PAVED AREAS

CM- 90. All costs for materials used in connection with waterbound macadam, bituminous surfaced and asphalt sur-faced paved areas, amount of sub-contract, if work is sub-let, or as follows:
91. Costs of materials for waterbound macadam paved areas.
92. Costs of materials for bituminous surfaced paved areas.
93. Costs of materials for asphalt surfaced paved areas.
94. ....
95. ....

"DM" classifications include all material costs for metal pans; material costs for clay tile or lightweight concrete block fillers for combination floor slabs; material costs for reinforcing steel; material costs for combination permanent form and reinforcing materials; material costs for precast concrete joists and slabs; material costs for clay tile floor arches and beam and girder covering; material costs for clay book tile decking, gypsum roof tile and plank and poured gypsum roofs; amounts of sub-contracts, if work is sub-let.

METAL PANS

DM-
All material costs for metal pans, amount of sub-contract, if work is sub-let, or as follows:
1. Cost or rental of metal pans, domes or tile for combination slabs.
2. Cost of nails, etc.
3. ....
4. ....

CLAY TILE OR LIGHTWEIGHT CONCRETE BLOCK FILLERS FOR COMBINATION SLABS

DM- 10. All material costs for clay tile or lightweight concrete block fillers for combination slabs, or as follows:
11. Cost of clay tile fillers.
12. Cost of lightweight concrete block fillers.
13. Material cost of mortar for filling voids in tile or block at ends of rows.
14. ....
15. ....

REINFORCING STEEL AND MESH

DM- 20. All material costs for reinforcing steel and mesh or amount of sub-contract, if work is sub-let, or as follows:
21. Cost of reinforcing steel, including cartage.
22. Cost of reinforcing mesh, including cartage.
23. Cost of accessories, such as spacer bars, chairs, welded stirrups, etc.
24. Cost of tie wire.
25. Cost of tools and equipment for prestressing steel reinforcement.
26. ....
27. ....

COMBINATION PERMANENT FORM AND REINFORCING MATERIALS

DM- 30. All material costs for combination permanent form and reinforcing materials or amount of sub-contract, if work is sub-let, or as follows:
    31. Cost of paper-backed mesh, including clips, ties, etc.
    32. Cost of corrugated steel permanent forms, including clips, washers, etc.
    33. Cost of welding materials.
    34. ....
    35. ....

PRECAST CONCRETE JOISTS, PLANK AND SLABS

DM- 40. All material costs for precast concrete joists, plank and slabs or amount of sub-contract, if work is sub-let, or as follows:
    41. Cost of precast concrete joists.
    42. Cost of precast concrete plank.
    43. Cost of cored precast concrete slabs.
    44. Cost of precast concrete rib, flat, or channel slabs.
    45. Material costs of grout for leveling and pointing.
    46. ....
    47. ....

CLAY TILE FLOOR ARCHES AND BEAM AND GIRDER COVERING

DM- 50. All material costs for clay tile floor arches and beam and girder covering or amount of sub-contract, if work is sub-let, or as follows:
    51. Cost of temporary centering material, including lumber, hangers, etc.
    52. Cost of clay tile for floor arches.
    53. Cost of clay tile for beam and girder covering
    54. Cost of cement for mortar.
    55. Cost of lime for mortar.
    56. Cost of sand for mortar.
    57. ....
    58. ....

HOLLOW CLAY BOOK TILE

DM- 60. All material costs for hollow clay book tile roof decking or amount of sub-contract, if work is sub-let, or as follows:
    61. Cost of "Tee" irons, including connection materials.
    62. Cost of hollow clay book tile.
    63. Cost of mortar materials.
    64. ....
    65. ....

PRECAST GYPSUM ROOF TILE AND PLANK

DM- 70. All material costs for precast gypsum roof tile and plank or amount of sub-contract, if work is sub-let, or as follows:
    71. Cost of "Tee" irons, including connection materials.
    72. Cost of short span gypsum roof tile
    73. Cost of gypsum roof plank.
    74. Cost of grout materials.
    75. ....
    76. ....

POURED-IN-PLACE GYPSUM ROOF DECKS

DM- 80. All material costs for poured-in-place gypsum roof decks or amount of sub-contract, if work is sub-let, or as follows:
    81. Cost of steel sub-purlins, including connection materials.
    82. Cost of permanent form material.
    83. Cost of mesh reinforcing material.

84. Cost of gypsum material.
85. ....
86. ....

"EM" classifications include all material costs for masonry work of all kinds partitions, furring and column covering.

CONCRETE MASONRY UNITS

EM-   All material costs for cement block and brick work, or as follows:
1. Cost of cement blocks.
2. Cost of cement brick.
3. Cost of cinder block.
4. Cost of glazed block.
5. Cost of cement for mortar.
6. Cost of lime for mortar.
7. Cost of sand for mortar.
8. Cost of color, waterproofing or other additives for mortar.
9. ....
10. ....

BRICKWORK

EM- 20. All Material costs for brickwork of all kinds, or as follows:
21. Cost of common brick.
22. Cost of face, press or glazed brick.
23. Cost of special brick units including twin, oversize, SCR, solar, floor brick, etc.
24. Cost of radial brick for stacks and chimneys, or sub-contract amount if work is sub-let.
25. Cost of fire brick.
26. Cost of fire clay.
27. Cost of cement for mortar.
28. Cost of lime for mortar.
29. Cost of sand for mortar.
30. Cost of color, waterproofing, or other additives for mortar.
31. Cost of wall ties, anchors, etc.
32. ....
33. ....

GLASS MASONRY UNITS

EM- 40. All material costs for glass block masonry, including accessories, or as follows:
41. Cost of standard glass units.
42. Cost of special glass units including color and sculptured units.
43. Cost of cement for mortar.
44. Cost of lime for mortar.
45. Cost of sand for mortar.
46. Cost of waterproofing for mortar.
47. Cost of reinforcing mesh and anchors.
48. Cost of asphalt emulsion and expansion strips.
49. Cost of oakum and caulking.

CLAY TILE UNITS

EM- 50. All material costs for clay tile work, or as follows:
51. Cost of load bearing tile.
52. Cost of partition tile.
53. Cost of furring tile.
54. Cost of glazed tile.
55. Cost of SCR "Acoustile."
56. Cost of backup tile.
57. Cost of solar screen tile.
58. Cost of flue tile units.
59. Cost of vitrified coping tile
60. Cost of raggle blocks.
61. Cost of cement for mortar.
62. Cost of lime for mortar.
63. Cost of sand for mortar.

GYPSUM TILE UNITS

EM- 65. All material costs for gypsum tile units or as follows:
    66. Cost of gypsum tile units.
    67. Cost of partition tile cement.
    68. Cost of sand for mortar.
    69. Cost of asphalt felt at columns.

STONE, GRANITE, TERRA COTTA, ETC.

EM- 70. All material costs for rubble stone, rustic or cobble stone, random or split face ashlar, cut stone, granite, terra cotta, precast concrete or imitation stone and granite, and work of a similar nature or amount of sub-contract, if work is sub-let, or as follows:
    71. Cost of rubble stone, including cartage.
    72. Cost of rustic or cobble stone, including cartage.
    73. Cost of random or split face ashlar, including cartage.
    74. Cost of cut stone, including cartage.
    75. Cost of granite, including cartage.
    76. Cost of architectural terra cotta, including cartage.
    77. Cost of ceramic veneer, including cartage.
    78. Cost of precast concrete or imitation stone, including cartage.
    79. Cost of precast facing slabs, including cartage.
    80. Cost of cement for mortar.
    81. Cost of lime for mortar.
    82. Cost of sand for mortar.
    83. Cost of anchors, ties, etc.
    84. ....
    85. ....

CLEANING AND POINTING

EM- 90. All material costs for cleaning and pointing masonry surfaces or amount of sub-contract, if work is sub-let, or as follows:
    91. Cost of materials for tuck-pointing mortar.
    92. Cost of soap powder, acid or other materials for cleaning.
    93. Cost of equipment and tools necessary for steam cleaning.
    94. ....
    95. ....

SANDBLASTING

EM-100. All material costs for sandblasting masonry surfaces or amount of sub-contract, if work is sub-let.

    "FM" classifications include all material costs for waterproofing, dampproofing, and caulking.

WATERPROOFING AND DAMPPROOFING

FM- 1. All material costs for waterproofing and dampproofing work or amount of sub-contract, if work is sub-let, or as follows:
    2. Cost of integral waterproofing compounds.
    3. Cost of water and damp resisting materials used in plaster coats.
    4. Cost of cement and sand used in water and damp resisting plaster coats.
    5. Cost of felt or fabric used for membrane waterproofing.
    6. Cost of pitch or asphalt used in membrane waterproofing.
    7. Cost of materials for iron method waterproofing.
    8. Cost of dampproof or plaster bond paints.
    9. Cost of materials for parging or back-plastering work.
    10. Cost of transparent liquid water repellents.
    11. Cost of materials for repairing leaks under hydrostatic pressure.
    12. Cost of expansion joint sealers and water stops.
    13. ....
    14. ....

CAULKING

FM- 20. All material costs for caulking, or as follows:
    21. Cost of primer.
    22. Cost of oakum or rope yarn.
    23. Cost of caulking compound.
    24. Cost of metal joint caps.
    25. ....
    26. ....

"GM" classifications include all material costs for rough carpentry, wood trusses, wallboards, insulation, weather-strips, vapor seals, millwork and interior finish, finish hardware, garage doors, fire doors, metal doors, metal windows, metal trim and casework, etc.

ROUGH CARPENTRY AND TIMBER FRAMING

GM- All material costs for rough carpentry and timber framing, or as follows:
    1. Cost of lumber for timber framing.
    2. Cost of dimension lumber for studs, joists, rafters, etc.
    3. Cost of lumber for sub-flooring, wall and roof sheathing, etc.
    4. Cost of building paper and deadening felt.
    5. Cost of wood furring strips, sleepers, grounds, etc.
    6. Cost of treated lumber.
    7. Cost of rough hardware.
    8. ....
    9. ....

WOOD TRUSSES

GM- 20. All material costs for wood trusses or amount of sub-contract, if work is sub-let, or as follows:
    21. Cost of lumber for wood trusses.
    22. Cost of bolts, split rings, washers, etc. for truss connections.
    23. Cost of laminated wood trusses.
    24. Cost of prefabricated wood trusses.
    25. ....
    26. ....

EXTERIOR FINISHED CARPENTRY

GM- 30. All material costs for exterior finished carpentry, or as follows:
    31. Cost of siding or shingles.
    32. Cost of frames and sash for windows, including storm sash and screens.
    33. Cost of door frames and doors, including storm doors and screens, wood and plastic garage doors.
    34. Cost of porch construction including posts, columns, railings, ceiling boards, flooring, etc.
    35. Cost of exterior wood steps and railings.
    36. Cost of wood gutters.
    37. Cost of other wood trim including water table moldings, cornices, corner boards, gables, dormers, etc.
    38. Cost of unattached wood including fences, gates, trellises, duck-boards, etc.
    39. Rough hardware for above.
    40. ....
    41. ....

INSULATION

GM- 50. All material costs for insulation of all kinds or amount of sub-contract, if work is sub-let, or as follows:
    51. Cost of batt or blanket type insulation.
    52. Cost of pellet or granule type insulation.
    53. Cost of reflective type insulation.
    54. Cost of board type or rigid insulation.
    55. Cost of cork insulation materials or amount of sub-contract, if work is sub-let.
    56. Cost of nails, staples, wire and other fastening materials.
    57. ....
    58. ....

WEATHERSTRIPS AND VAPOR SEALS

GM- 60. All material costs for weatherstrips, vapor seals, or as follows:
    61. Cost of weatherstripping materials or amount of sub-contract, if work is sub-let.
    62. Material cost of vapor seal papers and fabrics, including fastening devices. ....
    63. ....
    64. ....

INTERIOR FINISHED CARPENTRY AND MILLWORK

GM- 70. All material costs for all interior carpentry, or as follows:
    71. Cost of interior doors.
    72. Cost of all interior door frames and stops.
    73. Cost of interior sash and frames.
    74. Cost of interior trim and base and shelving.
    75. Cost of interior paneling.
    76. Cost of interior wood stairs and railings.
    77. Cost of casework, cabinets, cupboards, counters, finished shelving, mantels, window seats, built-in closet accessories, etc.
    78. Cost of wood flooring.
    79. Cost of materials for back priming.
    80. Cost of rough hardware. ....
    81. ....
    82. ....

WALLBOARDS

GM- 90. Cost of all wallboards, or as follows:
    91. Cost of gypsum plasterboard.
    92. Cost of tape, joint treatment fasteners, trim, runners, corner beads and laminating adhesive for plaster-board.
    93. Cost of fiberboard.
    94. Cost of insulating plank.
    95. Cost of prefinished panels.
    96. Cost of fastening devices for above. ....
    97. ....
    98. ....

FINISH HARDWARE

GM-100. Material costs of finish hardware of every description or amount of sub-contract if work is sub-let.

"HM" classifications include all material costs for structural steel, lightweight steel framing, miscellaneous and ornamental metals, hollow metals and rolled metal windows and doors.

STRUCTURAL STEEL

HM-   All material costs for structural steel of all kinds or amount of sub-contract, if work is sub-let, or as follows:
    1. Cost of structural steel shapes.
    2. Cost of bolts, rivets and welding rods used in connections.
    3. Cost of material for shop coat of paint. ....
    4. ....
    5. ....

LIGHTWEIGHT STEEL FRAMING

HM- 10. All material costs for lightweight steel framing or amount of sub-contract, if work is sub-let, or as follows:
    11. Cost of steel joists, including bridging, bottom chord extensions, connecting materials, etc.
    12. Cost of junior steel beams, including connecting materials.
    13. Cost of Stran-Steel construction members, including connecting materials.
    14. Cost of materials for shop coat of paint. ....
    15. ....
    16. ....

STEEL DECKING

HM- 20. All material costs for steel decking of all kinds or amount of sub-contract, if work is sub-let, or as follows:
21. Cost of ribbed type steel decking, including connecting materials.
22. Cost of cellular type steel decking, including connecting materials.
23. ....
24. ....

MISCELLANEOUS AND ORNAMENTAL METAL

HM- 30. All material costs for miscellaneous and ornamental metal or amount of sub-contract, if work is sub-let, or as follows:
31. Cost of all kinds of miscellaneous iron work, such as steel or cast iron frames for openings and covers or gratings for same; steel or cast iron corner guards, bumpers, bar gratings, door and window guards, etc,; bearing plates, joist hangers and stirrups, post caps, etc.
32. Cost of steel or ornamental iron stairs, platforms and railing.
33. Cost of steel fire escapes.
34. Cost of all miscellaneous ornamental work of wrought and cast iron, brass, bronze, stainless and chrome steel and aluminum work including railins, bulletin and directory borads, fences and gates, grilles and plaques, porch columns, etc.
35. Cost of steel or ornamental iron ladders and pipe railings.
36. Cost of steel or aluminum flagpoles.
37. Cost of ornamental iron, aluminum, bronze or copper store front metal.
38. Cost of curtain wall material including grid and metal spandrel panels and connections.
39. Cost of all metal specialties and prefabricated metal items including metal shelving, closet fittings, metal copings, metal hoods, laundry chutes, lockers, louvers, mail chutes, etc.
40. Cost of material for shop coats of paint.
41. ....
42. ....

HOLLOW METALS

HM- 50. All material costs of all hollow metal work, or as follows:
51. Cost of hollow metal doors and frames and anchors.
52. Cost of hollow metal windows and frames and anchors.
53. Cost of hollow metal partitions and doors and borrowed lights.
54. Cost of hollow metal trim including base, chair rails, door trim, picture molds, etc.
55. Cost of material for any shop coats of paint for above.
56. Cost of weatherstrips for above.
57. ....
58. ....

ROLLED AND EXTRUDED METALS

HM- 60. All material costs of all rolled metals, or as follows:
61. Cost of all rolled and extruded metal windows and frames including operating hardware and anchors.
62. Cost of all rolled and extruded metal doors and frames and anchors.
63. Cost of all rough and finished hardware and anchors and fastenings for above.
64. Cost of weatherstrips for above.
65. Cost of shop costs of paint for above.
66. ....
67. ....

"JM" classifications include all material costs for lathing and plain or ornamental plastering.

LATHING

JM- All material costs for lathing materials of all kinds or amount of sub-contract, if work is sub-let, or as follows:
1. Cost of gypsum or insulating lath, including nails, etc.
2. Cost of metal lath, including nails, clips, etc.
3. Cost of hangers, pencil rods, runners, channels, etc. for framing suspension systems and partitions.
4. Cost of steel studs, tracks and shoes for framing hollow steel stud partitions.
5. Cost of floor and ceiling runners for solid gypsum plaster partitions.

6.   Cost of corner beads, cornerites door and window trim, base screeds, concealed picture mould, etc.
7.   ....
8.   ....

INTERIOR PLASTERING

20. All material costs for interior plastering work or amount of sub-contract, if work is sub-let, or as follows:
21. Cost of lime and hair or fiber used in lime plaster.
22. Cost of gypsum cement plaster.
23. Cost of sand used in plaster.
24. Cost of lightweight aggregate, such as perlite or vermiculite, used in plaster.
25. Cost of finishing materials, plaster of paris, etc.
26. Cost of Keene's cement and other special finishing materials.
27. Cost of sound absorbing plaster. ....
28. ....
29. ....

EXTERIOR PLASTER AND STUCCO

JM- 40. All material costs for exterior plaster and stucco work or amount of sub-contract, if work is sub-let, or as follows:
41. Cost of portland cement or other exterior stucco materials.
42. Cost of sand used in exterior plaster.
43. Cost of aggregates for rough cast finish. ....
44. ....
45. ....

ORNAMENTAL PLASTERING

JM- 60. All material costs for ornamental plastering work or amount of sub-contract, if work is sub-let, or as follows:
61. Cost of materials for making templates, moulds, models, etc.
62. Cost of materials for running or casting and sticking plaster ornamentation of all kinds. ....
63. ....
64.

"KM" classifications include all material costs for sheet metal work, roofing and siding.

GUTTERS, DOWNSPOUTS, FLASHING, ETC.

KM-   All material costs for metal gutters, downspouts, flashing, etc., or amount of sub-contract, if work is sub-let, or as follows:
1.   Cost of metal eaves trough or gutters, conductor pipes or downspouts, conductor heads, etc.
2.   Cost of metal flashing and counter-flashing.
3.   Cost of metal hips, valleys, ridges, etc.
4.   ....
5.   ....

METAL SKYLIGHTS AND VENTILATORS

KM- 10. All materials costs for metal skylights and roof ventilators or amount of sub-contract, if work is sub-let, or as follows:
11. Cost of metal skylights, including operations for vents.
12. Cost of roof ventilators.
13. Cost of material for sheet metal duct work.
14. Cost of plastic skylights.
15. ....
16. ....

METAL ROOFS AND SIDING

KM- 20. All material costs for metal roofs and siding or amount of sub-contract, if work is sub-let, or as follows:
21. Cost of materials for flat seam or standing seam metal decks.
22. Cost of materials for corrugated metal roofing and siding.
23. Cost of materials for V-crimped metal roofing

24. Cost of prefinished metal siding and vertical paneling.
25. Cost of prefinished metal soffits, facias, returns, gables and trim.
26. Cost of prefinished roofing tiles and shingles.
27. Cost of prefabricated metal buildings and sheds.
28. ....
29. ....

ROOFING AND SIDING

KM- 40. All material costs for asphalt and shingle roofing and siding, asbestos shingle roofing and siding, built-up roofing, slate roofing, tile roofing, corrugated asbestos roofing and siding, etc. or amount of sub-contract, if work is sub-let, or as follows:
41. Cost of all materials for asphalt shingle roofing and siding work, including nails and felt underlayment.
42. Cost of all materials for asbestos shingle roofing and siding work, including nails and felt underlayment.
43. Cost of ready-to-lay roll roofing, including nails and cement.
44. Cost of all materials for insulating siding work, including nails, special corners, wood or metal trims at doors and windows, etc.
45. Cost of all materials for large-sheet asbestos siding, including nails, etc.
46. Cost of roofing felt for built-up roofs.
47. Cost of asphalt or pitch for built-up roofs.
48. Cost of gravel or slag for built-up roofs.
49. Cost of all materials for slate roofing work, including nails, felt, etc.
50. Cost of all materials for tile roofing work, including nails, felt, etc.
51. Cost of all materials for corrugated asbestos roofing and siding work, including materials for connecting to wood or steel framing.
52. Cost of sheet plastic roofing.
53. Cost of fluid plastic roofing.
54. ....
55. ....

"LM" classifications include all material costs for glazing work of all kinds.

GLASS AND GLAZING

LM- All material costs for glass and glazing materials of all kinds or amount of sub-contract, if work is sub-let, or as follows:
1. Cost of plain window glass.
2. Cost of plate glass.
3. Cost of insulating glass.
4. Cost of leaded or art glass.
5. Cost of structural glass.
6. Cost of tempered glass.
7. Cost of spandrel glass.
8. Cost of Plexiglas.
9. Cost of mirrors.
10. Cost of putty, glazing clips, setting blocks, gaskets.
11. ....
12. ....

"MM" classifications include all material costs for painting and decorating work of all kinds.

EXTERIOR PAINTING

MM- All material costs for exterior painting work or amount of sub-contract, if work is sub-let, or as follows:
1. Cost of material for painting wood trim.
2. Cost of material for painting wood siding.
3. Cost of material for painting wood wall shingles.
4. Cost of material for painting roof shingles.
5. Cost of material for painting wood ceilings.
6. Cost of material for painting wood decks.
7. Cost of material for painting miscellaneous and ornamental metals.
8. Cost of material for painting metal doors and sash.
9. Cost of material for painting sheet metal.
10. Cost of material for painting brick.
11. Cost of material for painting block.
12. Cost of material for painting concrete.
13. Cost of material for painting stucco.

14. Cost of material for removing paint.
15. Cost of material for preparing surfaces.
16. ....
17. ....

INTERIOR PAINTING AND DECORATING

MM- 20. All material costs for interior painting and decorating work or amount of sub-contract, if work is sub-let, or as follows:
21. Cost of material to remove paint.
22. Cost of material to prepare surfaces.
23. Cost of material to prime walls and ceilings.
24. Cost of material to prime woodwork.
25. Cost of material to prime metal work.
26. Cost of material to prime flooring.
27. Cost of material to finish walls and ceilings.
28. Cost of material to finish woodwork.
29. Cost of material to finish metal work.
30. Cost of material to finish textured work.
31. Cost of material to finish flooring.
32. Cost of wallpaper, canvas, burlap, vinyl, or other wall covering.
33. Cost of adhesive for wall covering.
34. ....
35. ....

"NM" classifications include all material costs for marble, slate work of all kinds, and terrazzo, art marble, ceramic, quarry, plastic and metal tile.

INTERIOR MARBLE

NM-   All material costs for interior marble work or amount of sub-contract, if work is sub-let, or as follows:
1. Cost of marble material of all kinds.
2. Cost of plaster of paris, anchors, etc.
3. Cost of cement and sand used in setting beds for marble floors.
4. ....
5. ....

EXTERIOR MARBLE

NM- 20. All material costs for exterior marble work or amount of sub-contract, if work is sub-let, or as follows:
21. Cost of marble material.
22. Cost of mortar materials.
23. Cost of anchors, ties, etc.
24. ....
25. ....

INTERIOR SLATE

NM- 40. All material costs for interior slate work or amount of sub-contract, if work is sub-let, or as follows:
41. Cost of slate material.
42. Cost of plaster of paris, anchors, etc.
43. Cost of cement and sand used in setting beds for slate floors.
44. ....
45. ....

TERRAZZO

NM-   All material costs for terrazzo work of all kinds or amount of sub-contract, if work is sub-let, or as follows:
51. Cost of marble chips used in terrazzo.
52. Cost of cement used in terrazzo.
53. Cost of sand used in terrazzo.
54. Cost of metal dividing strips, non-slip inserts, etc.
55. ....
56. ....

ART MARBLE

NM- 60. All material costs for art marble work of all kinds or amount of sub-contract, if work is sub-let, or as follows:
61. Cost of art marble material.
62. Cost of plaster of pairs, anchors, etc.
63. Cost of cement and sand used in setting beds for art marble floors.
64. ....
65. ....

CERAMIC TILE, QUARRY TILE, PLASTIC TILE AND METAL TILE

NM- 70. All material costs for ceramic, quarry, plastic and metal tile work or amount of sub-contract, if work is sub-let, or as follows:
71. Cost of ceramic tile materials of all kinds.
72. Cost of quarry tile materials of all kinds.
73. Cost of plastic tile materials of all kinds.
74. Cost of metal tile materials of all kinds.
75. Cost of cement and sand for setting beds and grout.
76. Cost of adhesive and cleaner.
77. Cost of metal trims, such as corners, dividers, etc.
78. ....
79. ....

"OM" classifications include materials costs for acoustical tile work of all kinds.

ACOUSTICAL TILE

OM- 1. Cost of acoustical tile.
2. Cost of suspension system.
3. Cost of adhesive.
4. Cost of wall furring.
5. ....
6. ....

"PM" classifications include material costs for resilient floor and wall coverings of all kinds.

RESILIENT TILE FLOOR AND BASE

PM- All material costs for resilient tile flooring and base or amount of sub-contract, if work is sub-let, or as follows:
1. Cost of asphalt tile.
2. Cost of linotile.
3. Cost of plastic or vinyl tile.
4. Cost of rubber tile.
5. Cost of cork tile.
6. Cost of vinyl cove base.
7. Cost of rubber cove base.
8. Cost of lining felt.
9. Cost of mastic or cement.
10. Cost of cleaner and wax.
11. ....
12. ....

RESILIENT SHEET FLOOR AND WALL COVERING

PM- 20. All material costs for resilient sheet floor and wall covering or amount of sub-contract, if work is sub-let, or as follows:
21. Cost of linoleum floor and wall covering.
22. Cost of sheet rubber floor and wall covering.
23. Cost of sheet plastic floor and wall covering.
24. Cost of sheet cork floor and wall covering.
25. Cost of lining felt.
26. Cost of mastic or cement.

27.   Cost of cleaner and wax.
28.   ....
29.   ....

"QM" classifications include all material costs for the installation of vertical transportation equipment of all kinds.

ELEVATORS, ESCALATORS, LIFTS, CONVEYORS, ETC.

QM-   All material costs for installation of elevators, escalators, lifts, conveyors, etc. or amount of sub-contract, if
          work is sub-let.

"RM" classifications include all material costs for sewer work, plumbing and gas fitting.

SEWER WORK

RM-   All material costs for sewer work or amount of sub-contract, if work is sub-let, or as follows:
1.   Cost of sewer tile or pipe.
2.   Cost of joint materials.
3.   Cost of septic tank, if required.
4.   ....
5.   ....

PLUMBING

RM- 10.   All material costs for plumbing work of all kinds or amount of sub-contract, if work is sub-let, or as follows:
11.   Cost of pipe and fittings of all kinds.
12.   Cost of joint materials.
13.   Cost of fixtures of all kinds.
14.   Cost of hot water heaters, tanks, etc.
15.   Cost of pumps of all kinds.
16.   Cost of dish washers, laundry equipment and other appliances.
17.   Cost of pipe covering materials.
18.   Cost of toilet and shower enclosures.
19.   Cost of water softener and filters.
20.   ....
21.   ....

GAS FITTING

RM- 30.   All material costs for gas fitting work of all kinds or amount of sub-contract, if work is sub-let, or as follows:
31.   Cost of pipe and fittings.
32.   Cost of joint materials.
33.   Cost of appliances, such as gas ranges, dryers, etc.
34.   ....
35.   ....

"SM" classifications include all material costs for the installation of sprinkler systems.

SPRINKLER WORK

SM-   All material costs for sprinkler work or amount of sub-contract, if work is sub-let, or as follows:
1.   Cost of pipe and fittings.
2.   Cost of joint materials.
3.   Cost of sprinkler heads.
4.   Cost of hangers, etc.
5.   Cost of tanks.
6.   Cost of hydrants.
7.   Cost of pumps.
8.   ....
9.   ....

"TM" classifications include all material costs for heating work.

WARM AIR HEATING

TM-   All material costs for warm air heating installations or amount of sub-contract, if work is sub-let, or as follows:
1. Cost of gravity type warm air furnaces.
2. Cost of blower type warm air furnaces.
3. Cost of combination blower type heating and cooling units.
4. Cost of pipeless type warm air furnaces.
5. Cost of pipe or ducts.
6. Cost of register faces, grilles, dampers, etc.
7. Cost of electrical controls.
8. Cost of duct insulation.
9. Cost of filters.

STEAM AND HOT WATER HEATING

TM- 10.   All material costs for steam or hot water heating installations or amount of sub-contract, if work is sub-let, or as follows:
11. Cost of boilers.
12. Cost of pipe and fittings.
13. Cost of joint materials.
14. Cost of radiators, convectors, etc.
15. Cost of baseboard radiation.
16. Cost of radiant heating panel materials.
17. Cost of pumps of all kinds.
18. Cost of stokers.
19. Cost of coal handling equipment.
20. Cost of ash handling equipment.
21. Cost of oil burners.
22. Cost of oil storage tanks.
23. Cost of gas burners.
24. Cost of electrical controls.
25. Cost of pipe and boiler covering materials.
26. ....
27. ....

ELECTRICAL HEATING

TM- 30.   All material costs for elctrical heating work, or amount of sub-contract, if work is sub-let, or as follows:
31. Cost of electric warm air furnace.
32. Cost of through-the-wall heating ventilating units.
33. Cost of heat pumps.
34. Cost of embedded radiant coils.
35. Cost of baseboard units.
36. Cost of convector units.
37. Cost of radiant units.
38. Cost of conduit, outlet boxes, controls and wiring for above.
39. ....
40. ....

"UM" classifications include all material costs for air conditioning, ventilation and refrigeration work.

AIR CONDITIONING

UM-   All material costs for air conditioning work or amount of sub-contract, if work is sub-let, or as follows:
1. Cost of package unit air conditioning machines.
2. Cost of large volume capacity air conditioning equipment.
3. Cost of pipe and fittings.
4. Cost of joint materials.
5. Cost of material for duct work.
6. Cost of register faces, grilles, louvres, etc.
7. Cost of fans and blowers.
8. Cost of electrical controls.
9. Cost of filter systems.
10. Cost of duct insulation.

11. Cost of cooling tower.
12. ....
13. ....

VENTILATION

UM- 20. All material costs for ventilation work or amount of sub-contract, if work is sub-let, or as follows:
21. Cost of roof ventilators.
22. Cost of fans and blowers for mechanical ventilation systems.
23. Cost of material for duct work.
24. Cost of register faces, grilles, louvres, etc.
25. Cost of electrical controls.
26. Cost of filter system.
27. ....
28. ....

REFRIGERATION

UM- 40. All material costs for refrigeration work or amount of sub-contract, if work is sub-let, or as follows:
41. Cost of refrigeration machines.
42. Cost of pipe and fittings.
43. Cost of joint materials.
44. Cost of expansion boxes.
45. Cost of refrigeration coils.
46. Cost of electrical controls.
47. ....
48. ....

"VM" classifications include all material costs for electrical work.

ELECTRICAL WORK

VM-   All material costs for electrical work or amount of sub-contract, if work is sub-let, or as follows:
1. Cost of outlet boxes of all kinds.
2. Cost of armored or non-metallic sheathed cable.
3. Cost of thin wall or rigid conduit.
4. Cost of entrance material, fuse boxes, panel boards, etc.
5. Cost of all kinds of wire.
6. Cost of switches, receptacles, etc.
7. Cost of all kinds of lighting fixtures.
8. Cost of transformers, generators, switch gear and other power wiring equipment and appliances, and devices furnished by other contractors.
9. ....
10. ....

EXTRA WORK

"XM" classifications are intended to cover all material costs for work, ordered by the architect or owner, in addition to the original contract. Each extra work order received should be given a number, such as "X-1," "X-2," etc. an all money spent for material on an order should be charged to its own account, thus distinguishing it from costs chargeable to the original contract.

KEEPING AN ACCURATE COST RECORD OF THE
OVERHEAD EXPENSE OF CONDUCTING YOUR BUSINESS
(See Chapter XX)

An important account that should be kept by every contractor is an accurate record of the cost of conducting his business—ascertaining just what his fixed expenses are regardless of the amount of business transacted, as there is a certain amount of overhead in every business whether any contracts are obtained or not.

This should include such items as office rent, rental of storage yard or warehouse, telephone, telegraph, printing and stationery, advertising, association dues, legal expenses, office salaries, such as stenographers, bookkeepers, clerks, estimators, etc.

By sub-dividing the total overhead expense according to the schedule given on the following pages, it is possible to tell just how the overhead is divided, what proportion is constant or fixed and what proportion fluctuates with the amount of business transacted.

A satisfactory method of keeping overhead or general expense accounts is by the use of columnar forms similar to Figure 75.

COST SCHEDULE OF CONTRACTOR'S OVERHEAD OR GENERAL EXPENSE ACCOUNTS

"Z" classifications include all salaries for main office overhead, salaries of caretakers and watchmen for the storage yard, labor costs for maintaining and repairing tools and equipment at the storage yard, when not chargeable to any particular job, labor costs for handling and hauling tools and equipment to and from jobs, when not chargeable to the jobs, etc.

OFFICE SALARIES

Z-   All main office salaries, or as follows:
1. Salary of President, if a corporation, or of owner, if an individual.
2. Salary of Vice-President or General Manager.
3. Salary of Secretary.
4. Salary of Treasurer.
5. Salary of General Superintendent or Supervising Engineer.
6. Salaries of estimators, quantity surveyors, checkers, etc.
7. Salaries of designing engineers, draftsmen, etc.
8. Salaries of expediting department personnel.
9. Salaries of change order department personnel.
10. Salaries of accountants, bookkeepers, stenographers, clerks, etc.
11. ....
12. ....

EQUIPMENT STORAGE YARD LABOR COSTS

Z- 20. All salaries and labor costs for running and maintaining the equipment storage yard, including tool and equipment repair labor costs not chargeable to any particular job; labor costs for handling and hauling tools and equipment to and from job when not chargeable to the jobs, or as follows:
21. Salaries of caretaker and watchmen.
22. Salaries of mechanics and helpers engaged in repairing and maintaining tools and equipment.
23. Salaries of truckdrivers and helpers.
24. ....
25. ....

"ZM" classifications include all expenses, except salaries and wages, for keeping and maintaining the main office and equipment storage yard and costs of construction tools and equipment including repairs to same.

OFFICE EXPENSES

ZM-   All expenses for keeping and maintaining the main office, or as follows:
1. Cost or rental of office and expenses for maintaining of same.
2. Expenses for utilities, such as heat, light, water, etc.
3. Cost of janitor service, window washing, etc.
4. Cost of all office supplies, such as stationery, postage, pencils, drinking water, towel service, magazine subscriptions, etc.
5. Telephone and telegraph.
6. Taxes and license fees.
7. Fire, liability, compensation and other insurance not chargeable to any particular job.
8. Club and association dues and assessments.
9. Traveling expenses not chargeable to any particular job.
10. Advertising and entertainment expenses.
11. ....
12. ....

EQUIPMENT STORAGE YARD EXPENSES

ZM- 20. All expenses for keeping and maintaining the equipment storage yard, or as follows:
21. Cost or rental of equipment storage yard and expenses for maintenance of same.
22. Expenses for utilities, such as heat, light, water, etc.
23. Cost of storage yard stationery, such as equipment charts, daily use forms, transfer cards, shipping tickets, etc.
24. Cost of supplies, such as tire patching materials, bolts, nuts, washers, saw blades, twist drills, lubricating materials. etc.
25. Taxes and license fees.
26. Fire, liability, compensation and other insurance not chargeable to any particular job. ....
27. ....
28. ....

OFFICE AND STORAGE YARD FURNITURE AND EQUIPMENT

All expenditures for Office and Storage Yard Furniture and Equipment are capital expenditures and must be depreciated each year in accordance with schedule of the Internal Revenue Bureau.

ZM- 30. All cost for office and storage yard furniture and equipment, or as follows:
31. Desks, chairs, tables, etc.
32. Filing cabinets, safes, etc.
33. Typewriters, adding and calculating machines, etc.
34. Shop equipment such as bench grinders, drill presses, lathes, welding equipment, etc. ....
35. ....
36. ....

CONSTRUCTION TOOLS AND EQUIPMENT

All expenditures for Construction Tools and Equipment are capital expenditures and must be depreciated over a period of years in accordance with schedule of the Internal Revenue Bureau.

ZM- 40. All costs of construction tools and equipment, including costs of parts and materials for repairing same when not chargeable to any particular job, or as follows:
41. Cost of power excavating equipment, such as power shovels, hoes, draglines, clamshells, tractors, scrapers, trench diggers, etc.
42. Cost of equipment for caisson work, such as tripods, platforms, winches, buckets, tarpaulins, etc.
43. Cost of pile driving equipment.
44. Cost of concrete mixers, mortar mixers, "Pumpcrete" equipment, etc.
45. Cost of hoisting towers, hoisting engines, skip hoists, booms, derricks, etc.
46. Cost of air compressors and air tools.
47. Cost of pumps, gasoline engines, motors, saw rigs, power hand tools, etc.
48. Cost of scaffolding, scaffold plank, swing stages, brick trusses, etc.
49. Cost of chains, cable, rope, blocks, sheaves, turnbuckles, etc., that are not directly chargeable to other equipment.
50. Cost of concrete buggies, wheelbarrows, lumber carts, dollies, etc.
51. Cost of small tools, such as shovels, picks, hammers, sledges, chisels, bullpoints, etc.
52. Cost of trucks and automobiles. ....
53. ....
54. ....

CHAPTER 12

HOW THE COSTS SHOULD BE KEPT ON THE JOB

Costs should be kept in the same manner as new work is estimated, if they are to be valuable to the person using them. This permits a comparison between estimated and actual costs during construction and enables the contractor to tell just where his losses or profits are coming from. In the event of loss, they warn him in sufficient time so that he may investigate and change his methods before it is too late.

In order to be of maximum value all labor costs should state the average number of hours required by each trade to perform a certain unit of work, as this enables the contractor and estimator to use these costs at any future time by merely inserting the wage scale prevailing at the time the work is to be performed.

So that the timekeeper or job foreman may become familiar with the correct methods of distributing the workmen's time and measuring the work in units that will be of value to the estimator, complete descriptions and examples are given on the following pages covering the different branches of work, stating just how the work should be measured an illustrating how the Labor Distribution should be filled in for the various labor classifications.

Wage rates and productivity records quoted below are for general example only and, of course, must be checked against current wages and conditions prevailing in the community involved, conditions which may vary widely throughout the country.

This should result in a uniformity of method on the different jobs and furnish costs that will be of maximum value to the contractor and estimator.

Job Salaries

The account for Job Salaries should take care of all cost of supervision, such as superintendent, timekeepers, material clerks, civil or construction engineers, day and night watchmen, etc., as these are expenses that cannot be charged to any one branch of work and constitute the general item of overseeing and managing.

The various foremen on the job, such as labor foreman, mason foreman, carpenter foreman, etc., should also be charged to overhead expense unless they actually work with their tools. While it may not be customary to do this, it is really the proper charge, especially where accurate unit costs are desired. For instance, if the mason foreman is paid a straight salary, with no deductions for lost time, this would ordinarily be charged to Masonry, but perhaps there are several weeks of bad weather where it is practically impossible for bricklayers to work. This results in an abnormal labor cost for brick laying because the foreman's time is charged to Masonry, regardless of the fact that there was no work done, while perhaps the bricklayers are actually performing a good day's work every day they work, and without the burden of excessive overhead charges the labor costs would be very favorable. This same condition applies to every branch of work on the average construction job. For this reason it is advisable to include the time of all non-working foremen under the head of Job Salaries, where accurate unit costs are desired. Figure 79 shows how the Labor Distribution should be filled in when reporting charges against Job Salaries, showing the various labor charges for the week and the total from the beginning of the work up to the present.

Temporary Construction and Weather Conditions

Separate costs should be kept on labor required for the various items of temporary construction, temporary utilities, weather conditions, etc., as these items, while necessary to the job as a whole, cannot be otherwise charged without distorting the true unit costs of the actual construction work.

Fig. 79. Labor Distribution and Costs of Job Salaries. Form C-105.

Fig. 80. Labor Distribution and Costs of Temporary Buildings. Form C-105.

COST ANALYSIS RECORD

	TOTAL LABOR HOURS		UNIT					
	1 CARP	2 LAB.	3	4	5	6	7	8
PREVIOUS	48	32						
THIS WEEK	68	40						
TOTAL	116	72						

	LABOR HOURS PER UNIT		UNIT PER M FEET LUMBER					
	1 CARP	2 LAB.	3	4	5	6	7	8
PREVIOUS	8.00	5.33						
THIS WEEK	8.50	5.00						
TOTAL	8.28	5.14						

REMARKS

CONSTRUCTION - FLOOR 2x6 JOISTS ON 4x12 MUDSILLS, 1x6 D&M ROUGH FLOORING

WALLS, 2x4 STUDS, 25/32" INSUL. SHEATHING OUTSIDE, 1/2" CELOTEX INSIDE

ROOF, SINGLE SLANT, 2x6 RAFTERS, 1x6 ROOF SHEATHING, ROLL ROOFING

4 LT. BARN SASH, 5 X-PAN DOORS   STOVE HEAT

MFD. IN U.S.A.   FORM C-105   FRANK R. WALKER CO., PUBLISHERS, CHICAGO

Fig. 81. Analyzed Labor Costs of Temporary Buildings. Form C-105.

To obtain unit costs on this work for future reference, quantities of some sort must be applied to the total costs. In the case of the temporary job office, sheds for the men and tools, temporary protection for the public, temporary partitions, temporary ladders, stairs, ramps, railings, protection for new and existing construction, etc., the number of feet of lumber, board measure, used in their construction may be employed and the costs computed at a certain price per thousand feet, or for approximate estimating, the costs may be computed on a lineal, square or cubic foot basis, whichever is applicable. For temporary closures of doors, windows, roof openings, etc., the average size of each type of opening should be given and the number of openings used to obtain a unit cost per opening. Labor costs for the installation and removal of temporary utilities are usually kept on a lump sum basis with a separate account for each utility, such as temporary water, temporary sewer, temporary light and power, etc. The labor cost involved in providing temporary heat for the building may be reduced to a unit cost per square foot of area or cubic foot of volume of the structure. Labor cost for heating materials and protecting construction against freezing may be expressed in the same units as the work affected, such as cubic yards of concrete, thousands of brick, square feet of separate floor finish, etc.

Labor Distribution Figure 80 illustrates how labor costs should be kept, covering the construction of temporary buildings or enclosures. The back of the form, Figure 81, gives the number of hours worked by each trade, together with the length of time required to complete any particular unit of work.

Repairs, Cleaning and Rubbish Removal

Another group of costs which should be kept separate from the actual construction costs are those for repairs, cleaning and rubbish removal.

Most of these items are simply kept on a lump sum basis, but for a few it may be desirable to have unit costs, such as cleaning exterior and interior glass, which may be kept on a square foot or per opening basis, cleaning floors on a square foot basis, etc.

For the item of rubbish removal, it is difficult to obtain unit costs, as a great variety of operations are involved, so it is best to leave the cost record on a lump sum basis, as illustrated in Labor Distribution Figure 82, and to give a description of the work in the space for remarks, along with the record of labor hours, on the back of the form, as shown in Figure 83.

Construction Plant and Equipment

The labor cost in connection with all plant and equipment used on the job should also be kept as a separate item, as these items will do much toward furnishing unbalanced unit costs when they are charged direct to the branches of work for which they are constructed. As an example, suppose a hoisting tower is constructed for hoisting concrete. If the tower has to be a certain height, it will cost just as much to build it, whether there are 1,000 or 10,000 cubic yards of concrete in the job. If the cost of constructing the tower was charged direct to concrete, it would be impossible to tell how much the tower cost, or how it affected the cubic yard cost of placing the concrete.

Labor Distribution Figure 84 gives the labor cost of constructing a tower for hoisting building materials. Assuming this hoist is 80 feet high with double platform cages, the cost records give sufficient information to enable the estimator to compute the cost of similar towers with very little trouble. The back of the form, Figure 85, gives the number of hours worked by each trade, so that the costs may be easily obtained even though the hoist were to be constructed at a totally different wage scale.

Unloading Materials

On jobs where the materials are delivered on cars and it is necessary to unload them from the cars to the ground, into material hoppers, or load them into trucks for hauling to the job, distribution at the job, etc., it is advisable to keep separate labor costs of unloading, in order that comparisons of cost may be made where prices are quoted for materials delivered to the job by truck.

The cost schedule given in the previous pages contains a complete schedule of unloading costs, covering all classes of construction materials which are ordinarily shipped in bulk and on which accurate labor costs are obtainable.

Fig. 82. Labor Distribution and Costs of Removing Rubbish. Form C-105.

LABOR DISTRIBUTION

JOB CENTRAL HIGH SCHOOL   SHEET NO. 3
CLASS OF WORK A-47   WEEK ENDING JAN 9, 19--   JOB NO. 110

OCCUPATION	M	T	W	T	F	S	HOURS	RATE	AMOUNT
1 LABORERS	1 8	–	8	8	1	–	24		
2									
3									
4									
5									
6									
7									
8									
TOTAL									

	QTY. WORK IN PLACE	PAY ROLL COSTS	LBR. AVERAGE UNIT COST	AVERAGE QUANTITY PER 8 HR. DAY		QTY. WORK IN PLACE	PAY ROLL COSTS	LBR. AVERAGE UNIT COST	AVERAGE QUANTITY PER 8 HR. DAY
PREVIOUS									
THIS WEEK									
TOTAL									

MFD. IN U.S.A.   FORM C-105   FRANK R. WALKER CO., PUBLISHERS, CHICAGO   (OVER)

COST ANALYSIS RECORD

TOTAL LABOR HOURS	UNIT						
	1 LAB	2	3	4	5	6	7	8
PREVIOUS	56							
THIS WEEK	54							
TOTAL	80							

LABOR HOURS PER UNIT	UNIT						
	1	2	3	4	5	6	7	8
PREVIOUS								
THIS WEEK								
TOTAL								

REMARKS: BURNING SCRAP LUMBER, LOADING MASONRY RUBBISH INTO TRUCK FOR SPREADING ON CONSTRUCTION ROAD (2 LOADS OF 5 CY EACH)

MFD. IN U.S.A.   FORM C-105   FRANK R. WALKER CO., PUBLISHERS, CHICAGO

Fig. 83. Analyzed Labor Costs of Removing Rubbish. Form C-105.

LABOR DISTRIBUTION

JOB CENTRAL HIGH SCHOOL   SHEET NO. 4
CLASS OF WORK A-65   WEEK ENDING JAN 12, 19--   JOB NO. 110

OCCUPATION	M	T	W	T	F	S	S	HOURS	RATE	AMOUNT
1 CARPENTERS	24	24	24	24	24	–	–	120		
2 LABORERS	16	16	16	16	8	–	–	72		
3										
4										
5										
6										
7										
8										
TOTAL										

	QTY. WORK IN PLACE	PAY ROLL COSTS	LBR. AVERAGE UNIT COST	AVERAGE QUANTITY PER 8 HR. DAY		QTY. WORK IN PLACE	PAY ROLL COSTS	LBR. AVERAGE UNIT COST	AVERAGE QUANTITY PER 8 HR. DAY
PREVIOUS	55' OF TOWER								
THIS WEEK	25' " " DBL CAGE								
TOTAL	80' COMPL.								

MFD. IN U.S.A.   FORM C-105   FRANK R. WALKER CO., PUBLISHERS, CHICAGO   (OVER)

Fig. 84. Labor Distribution and Costs of Erecting a Wood Hoisting Tower. Form C-105.

Labor Distribution Figure 86 illustrates the correct method of keeping costs of unloading sand and gravel from cars using a crane equipped for this purpose. The first column gives the number of cubic yards unloaded; the second column gives the total labor cost, the third column gives the average unloading cost per cubic yard, while the fourth column gives the average number of cubic yards unloaded per 8-hour day. It must be remembered that to obtain the full cost of the unloading operation an equipment charge will have to be added to the labor cost.

The back of the form, Figure 87, gives the total number of hours worked by each trade in the first column headed "Total Labor Hours," while the second column headed "Labor Hours Per Unit," gives the length of time required by each trade to unload one cubic yard of sand or gravel. The labor costs of unloading all bulk materials, such as sand, gravel, crushed stone, cinders or slag should be computed by the cubic yard or by the ton, as a workable unit may be obtained from the use of either.

When unloading cement from the cars, the costs should give the number of barrels or bags of cement unloaded. If the cement is shipped in bulk, the contents are easily obtained from the invoices or if shipped in bags, the total number of bags unloaded will give the necessary information.

The cost of unloading brick of all kinds is invariably based on a unit of 1,000 brick. When keeping costs on work of this kind it is advisable to mention the kind of brick unloaded and whether they were dumped or carefully piled for future use.

Labor Distribution Figure 88 illustrates the correct method of keeping labor costs of unloading common and face brick. The first column gives the number of brick unloaded, the second column gives the total labor cost of unloading same, the third column gives the average unit labor cost per thousand brick, while the fourth column gives the average number of brick a man unloaded per 8-hour day.

The back of the form, Figure 89, gives the total number of hours worked by each trade in the first column headed "Total Labor Hours," while the second column headed "Labor Hours per Unit," gives the length of time required to unload a thousand brick.

When unloading hollow tile from the cars, it is advisable to keep the costs according to the number of square feet of each size of tile unloaded or by the ton. Separate ton prices should be kept on the different sizes of tile as it costs more to unload a ton of 4-inch tile than a ton of 8-inch tile, because there are about twice as many pieces of the former to load and unload.

Labor Distribution Figure 90 illustrates the correct method of keeping labor costs on unloading hollow tile. The symbol "A-90-a" is used to designate 4-inch tile and the symbol "A-90-c" to designate 8-inch tile. The first column gives the total number of square feet of tile unloaded, the second column gives the total labor cost unloading same, the third column gives the unloading costs per 1,000 square feet, while the fourth column gives the average number of square feet of tile a man unloaded per 8-hour day. The back of the form, Figure 91, gives the total number of hours worked by each trade in the first column headed "Total Labor Hours," while the second column headed "Labor Hours Per Unit," gives the length of time required to unload 1,000 square feet of tile.

When unloading lumber from cars, the costs should give the number of feet of lumber, board measure, unloaded, as lumber is invariably estimated on this basis.

Wrecking and Clearing

It is very difficult to compile costs on wrecking and clearing operations that will prove of value to the estimator because every job is different and, in the case of wrecking, the men are usually removing several kinds of material during the day, making it very difficult to measure the old work in units that would prove valuable in estimating other jobs. For this reason, most of the costs are kept separate from the other work on a lump sum basis with a differentiation being made only between the major items as outlined in the cost schedule given on previous pages.

There are, however, several items of work in this classification which are more or less consistent in nature, regardless of the job. These include the removal of floor slabs, walks, pavements, curbs, etc., and the demolition of existing foundations. Unit costs may be obtained on this work, as the quantities of work may be determined by field measurements, and the units of measure generally used are per square foot or square yard for slabs, walks, pavements, etc., and per cubic foot or cubic yard for foundations. Removal of curbing may be figured on a lineal foot basis but should always be described as to type and cross-sectional size.

Labor Distribution Figure 92 illustrates the correct method of keeping costs on breaking and removing

COST ANALYSIS RECORD

TOTAL LABOR HOURS — UNIT

	1 CARP	2 LAB.	3	4	5	6	7	8
PREVIOUS	130	78						
THIS WEEK	120	72						
TOTAL	250	150						

UNIT PER LIN. FT. OF HOISTING TOWER

LABOR HOURS PER UNIT

	1 CARP	2 LAB.	3	4	5	6	7	8
PREVIOUS	2.36	1.42						
THIS WEEK	4.80	2.88						
TOTAL	3.13	1.88						

REMARKS: CONSTRUCTION – 4×4 UPRIGHTS, 2×4 GUIDES, 2×6 CROSS BRACING AND TIES TO BUILDING AT EACH FLOOR. DOUBLE PLATFORM CAGE.

MFD. IN U.S.A. FORM C-105   FRANK R. WALKER CO., PUBLISHERS, CHICAGO

Fig. 85. Analyzed Labor Costs of Erecting a Wood Hoisting Tower.

LABOR DISTRIBUTION

SHEET NO. 5   JOB NO. 110
JOB Central High School
CLASS OF WORK A-81, A-83
WEEK ENDING Jan 9, 19—

OCCUPATION	M	T	W	T	F	S	S	HOURS	PAY ROLL COSTS	LBR. AVERAGE UNIT COST	QTY. WORK IN PLACE	AVERAGE QUANTITY PER 8 HR. DAY	RATE	AMOUNT
1 A-81 Crane Operator	1	4	3	1	1			7						
2 Laborer	1	4	3	1	1			7						
3														
4														
5 A-83 Crane Operator	1	2	1	1	1			3						
6 Laborer	1	2	1	1	1			3						
7														
8														
TOTAL									A-81			A-83		

	QTY. WORK IN PLACE	AVERAGE QUANTITY PER 8 HR. DAY		QTY. WORK IN PLACE	AVERAGE QUANTITY PER 8 HR. DAY
PREVIOUS	1400 CY	249 CY		700 CY	255 CY
THIS WEEK	210	240		105	280
TOTAL	1610	248		805	258

(OVER)

MFD. IN U.S.A. FORM C-105   FRANK R. WALKER CO., PUBLISHERS, CHICAGO

Fig. 86. Labor Distribution and Costs of Unloading Sand and Gravel from Cars.

COST ANALYSIS RECORD

TOTAL LABOR HOURS — UNIT

	1 CRANE OPER.	2 LAB.	3	4	5 CRANE OPER	6 LAB.	7	8
PREVIOUS	45	45			22	22		
THIS WEEK	7	7			3	3		
TOTAL	52	52			25	25		

LABOR HOURS PER UNIT — UNIT PER CUBIC YARD

	1 CRANE OPER.	2 LAB.	3	4	5 CRANE OPER.	6 LAB.	7	8
PREVIOUS	.032	.032			.031	.031		
THIS WEEK	.033	.033			.029	.029		
TOTAL	.032	.032			.031	.031		

REMARKS: USED CRANE WITH ½ CY REHANDLER BUCKET.

MFD. IN U.S.A. FORM C-105   FRANK R. WALKER CO., PUBLISHERS, CHICAGO

Fig. 87. Analyzed Labor Costs of Unloading Sand and Gravel from Cars.

Fig. 88 — LABOR DISTRIBUTION

JOB: Central High School CLASS OF WORK: A-85, A-86 WEEK ENDING Jan 9, 19-- SHEET NO. 6 JOB NO. 110

OCCUPATION	M	T	W	T	F	S	S	HOURS	RATE	AMOUNT
1 A-85 LABORERS	-	16	10	8	-	-	-	34		
2										
3										
4										
5 A-86 LABORERS	32	16	13	-	-	-	-	61		
6										
7										
8										

TOTAL A-85 A-86

	QTY. WORK IN PLACE	PAY ROLL COSTS	LBR. AVERAGE UNIT COST	AVERAGE QUANTITY PER 8 HR. DAY	QTY. WORK IN PLACE	PAY ROLL COSTS	LBR. AVERAGE UNIT COST	AVERAGE QUANTITY PER 8 HR. DAY
PREVIOUS	55 M		.6670	2074				2715
THIS WEEK	27 M		.6350	2074				2625
TOTAL	82 M		.6560	40 M				2667

MFD. IN U.S.A. FORM C-105 FRANK R. WALKER CO., PUBLISHERS, CHICAGO (OVER)

Fig. 88. Labor Distribution and Costs of Unloading Brick from Cars.

Fig. 89 — COST ANALYSIS RECORD

UNIT PER 1000 BRICK

TOTAL LABOR HOURS	1 LAB.	2	3	4	5 LAB.	6	7	8
PREVIOUS	66				59			
THIS WEEK	34				61			
TOTAL	100				120			

LABOR HOURS PER UNIT	1 LAB.	2	3	4	5 LAB.	6	7	8
PREVIOUS	1.20				2.95			
THIS WEEK	1.26				3.05			
TOTAL	1.22				3.00			

REMARKS: Common brick unloaded from cars, dumped in piles around job. Face brick unloaded from cars, stacked in piles around job.

MFD. IN U.S.A. FORM C-105 FRANK R. WALKER CO., PUBLISHERS, CHICAGO

Fig. 89. Analyzed Labor Costs of Unloading Brick from Cars.

Fig. 90 — LABOR DISTRIBUTION

JOB: Central High School CLASS OF WORK: A-90-a, A-90-c WEEK ENDING Jan 23, 19-- SHEET NO. 7 JOB NO. 110

OCCUPATION	M	T	W	T	F	S	S	HOURS	RATE	AMOUNT
1 A-90-a LABORERS	32	32	18	-	-	-	-	82		
2										
3										
4										
5 A-90-c LABORERS	-	-	14	24	-	-	-	38		
6										
7										
8										

TOTAL A-90-a 4" TILE A-90-c 8" TILE

	QTY. WORK IN PLACE	PAY ROLL COSTS	LBR. AVERAGE UNIT COST	AVERAGE QUANTITY PER 8 HR. DAY	QTY. WORK IN PLACE	PAY ROLL COSTS	LBR. AVERAGE UNIT COST	AVERAGE QUANTITY PER 8 HR. DAY
PREVIOUS	4800 SF		PER M SF	960 SF	—		PER M SF	
THIS WEEK	10500			1024	3000 SF			632 SF
TOTAL	15300			1003	3000			632

MFD. IN U.S.A. FORM C-105 FRANK R. WALKER CO., PUBLISHERS, CHICAGO (OVER)

Fig. 90. Labor Distribution and Costs of Unloading Hollow Clay Tile from Trucks.

concrete pavements and the demolition of old concrete foundations. The first column gives the quantity of pavement removed, the second column gives the total labor cost to date, the third column the average unit cost for removing one square foot of pavement, while the fourth column gives the average number of square feet of pavement removed by one laborer in an 8-hour day. Columns five to eight furnish the same information regarding the breaking and removing of old concrete foundations.

The back of the form, Figure 93, subdivides the total labor costs, giving the total number of hours worked by each trade in the first column headed "Total Labor Hours," while the second column headed "Labor Hours Per Unit," gives the length of time required by each trade to break and remove 100 square feet of pavement or 100 cubic feet of foundations.

Underpinning, Shoring and Sheet Piling

Keeping labor costs on underpinning work is not very difficult but their value as a reference for estimating future work is questionable, as conditions vary widely in this type of work. Most contractors reduce the labor cost of underpinning work to a cost per cubic foot of concrete used for the underpinning and include in this cost all the labor required for excavation, forming, setting reinforcing steel, placing concrete and grouting.

Shoring and needling labor costs are usually kept on a lump sum basis as it would be extremely difficult to arrive at any unit cost which would have any reference value.

Labor costs of sheet piling work are usually reduced to a cost per square foot of steel or wood sheet piling driven and should be accompanied by a description of the method of driving. Separate square foot costs should be kept on the labor required to pull the piling, if called for at the completion of the work.

Labor Distribution Figure 94 illustrates the correct method of keeping labor costs on placing and removing sheeting and bracing for trench excavations. The first column gives the number of square feet of trench walls braced, the second column gives the total labor cost to date, the third column gives the average cost of placing one square foot of trench bracing and the fourth column indicates the average number of square feet of trench wall braced by a man in an 8-hour day. Columns five to eight give the same information regarding the removal of the trench bracing.

The back of the form, Figure 95, gives the total number of hours worked by each trade in the first column headed "Total Labor Hours," while the second column headed "Labor Hours Per Unit," gives the length of time required by each trade to place and remove 100 square feet of sheeting and bracing for trench excavation.

Excavation, Fill, Grading and De-Watering

When keeping costs on excavation, fill, grading and de-watering, all quantities used to obtain unit costs should be expressed in the same units employed in estimating the job, that is, cubic yards for excavation and fill, square feet for grading work, etc. Costs on ordinary pumping are kept on a lump sum basis, but for the installation, operation and removal of wellpoint systems it is wise to keep separate costs, not only for these three phases of operation, but to break down the installation costs into the various component items, such as installation of wellpoints, header pipe, discharge pipe, pumps, etc., and then to reduce these figures to workable unit costs.

It is safe to say that today most work of this kind is done with the aid of power equipment. The labor costs involved in bringing the equipment to the job, setting up ready for operation, dismantling at completion and removing from the job should be kept separate from the labor costs of the actual work and should be charged to the proper account under Construction Plant and Equipment as outlined in the Cost Schedule previously given. This is necessary to prevent the true production costs from being unbalanced, as the costs for moving each piece of equipment will be the same regardless of the quantity of work to be done.

On excavation work, where the excavated material must be loaded into hauling units and transported to another location for disposal, the labor costs for digging and loading should be kept separate from the labor costs for hauling and disposal. Labor Distribution Figure 96 illustrates the correct method of keeping labor costs on work of this kind. The first column gives the number of cubic yards excavated, the second column gives the total labor cost to date, the third column gives the average cost per cubic yard, while the fourth column states the average number of cubic yards excavated and loaded by the crew in an 8-hour day.

Fig. 91 — COST ANALYSIS RECORD

TOTAL LABOR HOURS	1 LAB.	2	3	4	UNIT 5 LAB.	6	7	8
PREVIOUS	40							
THIS WEEK	82				38			
TOTAL	122				38			

LABOR HOURS PER UNIT	1 LAB.	2	3	4	UNIT 5 LAB.	6	7	8
PREVIOUS	8.33							
THIS WEEK	7.82				12.67			
TOTAL	7.97				12.67			

REMARKS

UNLOADED TILE FROM TRUCKS AND STACKED IN PILES.

MFD. IN U.S.A.   FORM C-105   FRANK R. WALKER CO., PUBLISHERS, CHICAGO

Fig. 91. Analyzed Labor Costs of Unloading Hollow Clay Tile from Trucks.

Fig. 92 — LABOR DISTRIBUTION

SHEET NO. 8

JOB _CENTRAL HIGH SCHOOL_   WEEK ENDING _Nov. 14, 19—_   JOB NO. 110

CLASS OF WORK _B-4   B-5_

	OCCUPATION	M	T	W	T	F	S	S	HOURS	RATE	AMOUNT
1	B-4 LABORERS	20	10	10	—	—			40		
2	COMPRESSOR OPER.	8	4	4	—	—			16		
3											
4											
5	B-5 LABORERS	—	10	10	20	20			60		
6	COMPRESSOR OPER.	—	4	4	8	8			24		
7											
8											

TOTAL

B-4 6" CONCRETE PVMT.

	QTY. WORK IN PLACE	PAY ROLL COSTS	AVERAGE QUANTITY PER 8 HR. DAY	LBR. AVERAGE UNIT COST
PREVIOUS	—			—
THIS WEEK	1150 SF		230 SF	
TOTAL	1150		230	

B-5 12" CONC. FDTN.

	QTY. WORK IN PLACE	PAY ROLL COSTS	AVERAGE QUANTITY PER 8 HR. DAY	LBR. AVERAGE UNIT COST
PREVIOUS	—			—
THIS WEEK	725 CF		97 CF	
TOTAL	725		97	

(OVER)

MFD. IN U.S.A.   FORM C-105   FRANK R. WALKER CO., PUBLISHERS, CHICAGO

Fig. 92. Labor Distribution and Costs of Breaking and Removing Old Concrete Pavement and Foundation Walls.

Fig. 93 — COST ANALYSIS RECORD

TOTAL LABOR HOURS	1 LAB	2 COMPR. OPER.	3	4	UNIT 5 LAB	6 COMPR. OPER.	7	8
PREVIOUS	—	—			—	—		
THIS WEEK	40	16			60	24		
TOTAL	40	16			60	24		

UNIT PER 100 SF – 6" CONC. PVMT
UNIT PER 100 CF – 12" CONC. FDTN. WALL

LABOR HOURS PER UNIT	1 LAB.	2 COMPR. OPER.	3	4	5 LAB.	6 COMPR. OPER.	7	8
PREVIOUS	—	—			—	—		
THIS WEEK	3.48	1.39			8.28	3.31		
TOTAL	3.48	1.39			8.28	3.31		

REMARKS

NO REINFORCING STEEL IN PAVEMENT OR FOUNDATION WALLS.
ALL BROKEN CONCRETE LOADED INTO TRUCKS FOR DISPOSAL.

MFD. IN U.S.A.   FORM C-105   FRANK R. WALKER CO., PUBLISHERS, CHICAGO

Fig. 93. Analyzed Labor Costs of Breaking and Removing Old Concrete Pavement and Foundation Walls.

Fig. 94. Labor Distribution and Costs of Placing and Removing Trench Bracing.

LABOR DISTRIBUTION

JOB CENTRAL HIGH SCHOOL SHEET NO. 9
CLASS OF WORK B-16-a, B-16-b WEEK ENDING DEC 11, 19-- JOB NO. 110

OCCUPATION	M	T	W	T	F	S	S	HOURS	RATE	AMOUNT
1 B-16-a LABORERS	32	16	—	—	—	—	—	48		
2										
3										
4										
5 B-16-b LABORERS	—	—	—	24	—	—	—	24		
6										
7										
8										
TOTAL	B-16-a PLACING TRENCH BRACING			B-16-b, REMOVING SAME						

	QTY. WORK IN PLACE	PAY ROLL COSTS	LBR. AVERAGE UNIT COST	AVERAGE QUANTITY PER 8 HR. DAY	QTY. WORK IN PLACE	PAY ROLL COSTS	LBR. AVERAGE UNIT COST	AVERAGE QUANTITY PER 8 HR. DAY
PREVIOUS	820 SF		152 SF	172 SF	1900 SF			633 SF
THIS WEEK	1080		180	177	1900			633 SF
TOTAL	1900		177		1900			

(OVER)

MFD. IN U.S.A. FORM C-105 FRANK R. WALKER CO., PUBLISHERS, CHICAGO

Fig. 95. Analyzed Labor Costs of Placing and Removing Trench Bracing.

COST ANALYSIS RECORD

TOTAL LABOR HOURS   UNIT 5 LAB.

1 LAB.	2	3	4	5 LAB.	6	7	8
PREVIOUS	38						
THIS WEEK	48			24	24		
TOTAL	86			24	24		

LABOR HOURS PER UNIT   UNIT PER 100 SF

1 LAB.	2	3	4	5 LAB.	6	7	8
PREVIOUS	4.64						
THIS WEEK	4.44			1.26	1.26		
TOTAL	4.53			1.26	1.26		

REMARKS   BRACING SEWER TRENCHES 3'-0" WIDE, 7'-0" DEEP

MFD. IN U.S.A. FORM C-105 FRANK R. WALKER CO., PUBLISHERS, CHICAGO

Fig. 96. Labor Distribution and Costs of General Excavation.

LABOR DISTRIBUTION

JOB CENTRAL HIGH SCHOOL SHEET NO. 10
CLASS OF WORK B-22, B-37 WEEK ENDING Nov. 14, 19-- JOB NO. 110

OCCUPATION	M	T	W	T	F	S	S	HOURS	RATE	AMOUNT
1 B-22 SHOVEL OPER.	8	8	8	8	8	—	—	40		
2 LABORER	8	8	8	8	8	—	—	40		
3										
4										
5 B-37 TRUCK DRIVERS	24	24	24	24	24	—	—	120		
6										
7										
8										
TOTAL	B-22					B-37				

	QTY. WORK IN PLACE	PAY ROLL COSTS	LBR. AVERAGE UNIT COST	AVERAGE QUANTITY PER 8 HR. DAY	QTY. WORK IN PLACE	PAY ROLL COSTS	LBR. AVERAGE UNIT COST	AVERAGE QUANTITY PER 8 HR. DAY
PREVIOUS	1950 CY			650 CY	1950 CY			217 CY
THIS WEEK	3610			722	3610			241
TOTAL	5560			695	5560			232

(OVER)

MFD. IN U.S.A. FORM C-105 FRANK R. WALKER CO., PUBLISHERS, CHICAGO

Columns five to eight furnish the same information regarding hauling and disposal. The back of the form, Figure 97, gives the total number of hours worked by each trade in the first column headed "Total Labor Hours," while the second column headed "Labor Hours Per Unit," gives the length of time required to excavate and load or haul and dump one cubic yard of material. Along with the cost analysis, a brief description of the work should be given in the space for remarks, stating the nature of the job, the number, kind and capacity of the equipment used, the distance to the disposal area, etc.

Caissons

When compiling labor costs on caisson work, the cost of bringing the equipment to the job, setting up ready for operation, dismantling at completion and removing from the job should be kept separate from the actual caisson work and charged to the proper account under Construction Plant and Equipment as outlined in the Cost Schedule. For the actual caisson work, separate costs should be kept on each operation involved, such as excavation, lagging, setting reinforcing steel, placing concrete, disposal of excavated materials, etc.

Labor Distribution Figure 98 illustrates the correct method of keeping labor costs on work of this kind. The time of the men performing the different operations is kept separate, in order that the proportionate cost of each operation may be obtained.

The first column of this form gives the total number of cubic yards excavated, the second column gives the total labor cost to date, the third column gives the average cost per cubic yard, while the fourth column gives the number of cubic yards a man excavated per 8-hour day. Columns 5 to 8 contain the same information as columns 1 to 4 regarding caisson lagging.

The back of the form, Figure 99, gives the total number of hours worked by each trade in the first column headed "Total Labor Hours," while the second column headed "Labor Hours Per Unit, gives the length of time required by each trade to excavate one cubic yard or place 1,000 feet, board measure, of lagging.

Wood and Concrete Piles

When compiling labor costs on driving wood or concrete piles, the cost of bringing the pile driving equipment to the job, setting up ready for operation, dismantling the pile driver and removing same at completion should be kept separate and charged to the proper account under Construction Plant and Equipment. This is important because the cost of the above operations will be the same whether there are 300 or 3,000 piles to drive and if figured as a part of the labor cost of driving the piles, would make considerable difference per pile, especially where there are only a small number of piles to drive.

When keeping costs of pile driving, the length of the piles should be given, together with the total number driven each day. This will give the average cost of driving each pile and by obtaining the total number of lineal feet of piles driven, a lineal foot cost may also be obtained.

Where concrete piles are used, it will be necessary to mix and deposit concrete for same. This work should be kept by the cubic foot or cubic yard of concrete placed, as work of this kind is usually estimated on the above basis.

Where wood piles are used it will be necessary to keep a separate record of the time required cutting off the tops of the piles after they have been driven.

Labor Distribution Figure 100 illustrates the correct method of keeping labor costs of driving piles. The fifth column gives the number of piles driven, the sixth column gives the total labor cost driving same, the seventh column gives the average labor cost per pile, while the eighth column gives the average number of piles driven per 8-hour day. The back of this form, Figure 101, gives the total number of hours worked by each trade in the first column headed "Total Labor Hours," while the second column headed "Labor Hours Per Unit," gives the length of time required to drive one pile.

Formwork For Concrete Foundations and Retaining Walls

When keeping costs on formwork for concrete foundations and retaining walls, separate labor costs should be kept on erecting and removing the forms. Also, if wood panel forms are used and are built on the job, the labor cost of fabrication should be kept separate from the erection cost.

COST ANALYSIS RECORD

TOTAL LABOR HOURS — UNIT

	SHOVEL 1 OPER.	2 LAB.	3	4	TRUCK 5 DRIVER	6	7	8
PREVIOUS	24	24			72			
THIS WEEK	40	40			120			
TOTAL	64	64			192			

LABOR HOURS PER UNIT — UNIT PER 100 CUBIC YARDS

	SHOVEL 1 OPER.	2 LAB.	3	4	TRUCK 5 DRIVER	6	7	8
PREVIOUS	1.23	1.23			3.69			
THIS WEEK	1.11	1.11			3.32			
TOTAL	1.15	1.15			3.46			

REMARKS

EXCAVATION - ORDINARY CLAY, DRY, GOOD GOING - USING 1 CY POWER SHOVEL.

HAULING - 1 MILE HAUL TO DUMP - USING 3 - 5 CY TRUCKS.

MFD. IN U.S.A.   FORM C-105   FRANK R. WALKER CO., PUBLISHERS, CHICAGO

Fig. 97. Analyzed Labor Costs of General Excavation.

LABOR DISTRIBUTION

SHEET NO. 11

JOB CENTRAL HIGH SCHOOL   CLASS OF WORK B-51, B-52   WEEK ENDING DEC 5, 19--   JOB NO. 110

	OCCUPATION	M	T	W	T	F	S	S	HOURS	RATE	AMOUNT
1	DIGGERS	32	32	21					117		
2	WINCHMAN	16	16	11					59		
3	LABORERS	28	28	19					103		
4	ENGINEER	24	24	16					88		
5											
6	LAGGERS	16	16	11					59		
7	WINCHMAN	8	8	5					29		
8	LABORERS	20	20	13					73		

(rows 1–4 bracketed as B-51; rows 6–8 bracketed as B-52)

	QTY. WORK IN PLACE	PAY ROLL COSTS	LBR. AVERAGE UNIT COST	AVERAGE QUANTITY PER 8 HR. DAY	QTY. WORK IN PLACE	PAY ROLL COSTS	LBR. AVERAGE UNIT COST	AVERAGE QUANTITY PER 8 HR. DAY
PREVIOUS	65 CY			DIGGERS 9.8 CY	244D FBM			LAGGERS 723 FBM
THIS WEEK	148			10.0	5550			753
TOTAL	213			10.0	7990			743

(OVER)

MFD. IN U.S.A.   FORM C-105   FRANK R. WALKER CO., PUBLISHERS, CHICAGO

Fig. 98. Labor Distribution and Costs of Caisson Excavating and Placing Wood Lagging.

COST ANALYSIS RECORD

TOTAL LABOR HOURS — UNIT

	1 DIGGERS	2 WINCH MAN	3 LAB.	4 ENGR.	5	6 LAGGERS	7 WINCH MAN	8 LAB.
PREVIOUS	53	26	47	42		27	14	33
THIS WEEK	117	59	103	88		59	29	73
TOTAL	170	85	150	130		86	43	106

LABOR HOURS PER UNIT — UNIT PER CY EXCAVATION / PER M FT BM LAGGING

	1 DIGGERS	2 WINCH MAN	3 LAB.	4 ENGR.	5	6 LAGGERS	7 WINCH MAN	8 LAB.
PREVIOUS	0.82	0.40	0.72	0.65		11.1	5.7	13.5
THIS WEEK	0.79	0.40	0.70	0.59		10.6	5.2	13.2
TOTAL	0.80	0.40	0.70	0.61		10.8	5.4	13.3

REMARKS

EXCAVATION - USING PNEUMATIC CLAY SPADES, ELECTRIC WINCHES.

LAGGING - 5'-0" SECTIONS, 2X6 D&M MAPLE

MFD. IN U.S.A.   FORM C-105   FRANK R. WALKER CO., PUBLISHERS, CHICAGO

Fig. 99. Analyzed Labor Costs of Caisson Excavating and Placing Wood Lagging.

Fig. 100. Labor Distribution and Costs of Pile Driving.

Fig. 101. Analyzed Labor Costs of Pile Driving.

LABOR DISTRIBUTION

JOB CENTRAL HIGH SCHOOL   SHEET NO. 13

CLASS OF WORK C-6, C-8   WEEK ENDING DEC 19, 19--   JOB NO. 110

	OCCUPATION	M	T	W	T	F	S	S	HOURS	RATE	AMOUNT
1	C-6 CARPENTERS	48	48	56	64	48	—	—	264		
2	LABORERS	24	24	32	32	24	—	—	136		
3											
4											
5	C-8 LABORERS	16	16	—	—	24	—	—	56		
6											
7											
8											
TOTAL	C-6								C-8		

	QTY. WORK IN PLACE	PAY ROLL COSTS	LBR. AVERAGE UNIT COST	AVERAGE QUANTITY PER 8 HR. DAY	QTY. WORK IN PLACE	PAY ROLL COSTS	LBR. AVERAGE UNIT COST	AVERAGE QUANTITY PER 8 HR. DAY
PREVIOUS	1920 SF			175 SF	1400 SF			350 SF
THIS WEEK	5870			178	2500			357
TOTAL	7790			177	3900			355

MFD. IN U.S.A.   FORM C-105   FRANK R. WALKER CO., PUBLISHERS, CHICAGO   (OVER)

Fig. 102. Labor Distribution and Costs of Erecting and Removing Forms for Concrete Foundation Walls.

Forms are usually estimated by the square foot, taking the measurement of both sides of the wall for which forms will be required. In addition, it is advisable to give the amount of lumber required for each square foot of forms, as the costs may also be given per thousand feet of lumber, board measure.

When reporting labor costs on wall forms, built in place, it is well to mention the size lumber used for the uprights, whether 2x4-inch, 2x6-inch, 3x6-inch, etc., also the distance they are spaced apart and the kind of lumber used for sheathing, as this information is necessary when figuring the quantity of lumber required to construct one square foot of forms.

Labor Distribution Figure 102 illustrates the correct method of reporting the labor cost of erecting and removing wood panel forms for concrete foundation walls. The first column gives the total number of square feet of forms erected, the second column gives the total labor cost erecting same, the third column gives the average labor cost per square foot of forms, while the fourth column gives the average number of square feet of forms erected per 8-hour day. Columns five to eight furnish the same information regarding the cost of removing the forms.

The back of the form, Figure 103, subdivides the total labor costs, giving the total number of hours worked by each trade in the first column headed "Total Labor Hours," while the second column headed "Labor Hours Per Unit," gives the length of time required to handle and place 100 square feet of forms and 1,000 feet of lumber, board measure.

If metal wall forms are used, the costs should be kept in the same manner as described above, using the square foot as the unit of measure.

Concrete For Foundations and Retaining Walls

When keeping costs on mixing and placing concrete for footings, foundations or retaining walls, the costs should always state the number of cubic feet or cubic yards of concrete placed, as this is the usual manner of estimating concrete work. In addition, the method of mixing and placing should be described, as the costs will vary considerably depending on whether the concrete is job mixed or bought ready mixed and also whether it is wheeled to the place of deposit in wheelbarrows, buggies, power buggies, etc., or placed with a crane and bucket.

Labor Distribution Figure 104 illustrates the correct method of keeping costs on mixing and placing concrete. The first column gives the quantity of work in place, the second column gives the total labor cost to date, the third column the average unit cost for placing one cubic yard of concrete, while the fourth column gives the number of cubic yards of concrete a man averaged per 8-hour day.

The back of this form, Figure 105, gives the total number of hours worked by each trade in the first column headed "Total Labor Hours," while the second column headed "Labor Hours Per Unit," gives the length of time required by each trade to mix and place one cubic yard of concrete.

If concrete is placed during freezing weather, necessitating heating the concrete aggregate, such as gravel or crushed stone, sand, water, etc., and also protecting the concrete with manure, straw, tarpaulins, or by the use of temporary heat and salamanders, separate costs should be kept on this item and charged to the proper classification under "Temporary Construction and Weather Conditions," as outlined in the Cost Schedule, as it is necessary to know just what it costs to protect one cubic yard of concrete from freezing under different conditions. This is important, because in many instances the cost of temporary heat and protection is nearly double the labor cost of placing the concrete.

Formwork For Reinforced Concrete Construction

When keeping costs on form work for reinforced concrete construction, separate costs should be kept on each of the various kinds of formwork, such as columns, solid slabs, open deck forms for combination slabs, beams and girders, lintels, stairs, etc. Separate costs should also be kept on removing or "wrecking" the forms after the concrete has been placed and set.

If the form lumber is shipped to the job on cars, separate labor costs should be kept on unloading and placing it in piles and these costs should be charged to the proper classification under "Unloading Materials" as given in the Cost Schedule.

All costs should state the number of square feet of forms framed, erected or removed and the quantity of lumber required to build them, in order that the costs may be computed on both a square foot basis and

COST ANALYSIS RECORD

TOTAL LABOR HOURS — UNIT

	1 CARP.	2 LAB.	3	4	5 LAB.	6	7	8
PREVIOUS	88				32			
THIS WEEK	264				56			
TOTAL	352				88			

LABOR HOURS PER UNIT — UNIT @ PER 100 SF OF FORMS @ M. FT. LUMBER B.M.

	1 CARP.	2 LAB.	3	4	5	6	7	8
PREVIOUS	@ 4.58 @ 22.90	@ 2.50 @ 12.50			@ 2.28 @ 11.40			
THIS WEEK	@ 4.50 @ 22.50	@ 2.32 @ 11.60			@ 2.24 @ 11.20			
TOTAL	@ 4.52 @ 22.60	@ 2.36 @ 11.80			@ 2.26 @ 11.30			

REMARKS

FOUNDATION WALLS — 13" THICK — 7'6" HIGH USING 4° X 8° WOOD PANELS WITH PLYWOOD FACING — PANELS BUILT IN YARD.

MFD. IN U.S.A.   FORM C-105   FRANK R. WALKER CO., PUBLISHERS, CHICAGO

Fig. 103. Analyzed Labor Costs of Erecting and Removing Forms for Concrete Foundation Walls.

LABOR DISTRIBUTION

SHEET NO. 14   JOB NO. 110

JOB CENTRAL HIGH SCHOOL   CLASS OF WORK C-15   WEEK ENDING DEC 19, 19 —

	OCCUPATION	M	T	W	T	F	S	S	HOURS	RATE	AMOUNT
1	LABORERS			16	96	16			128		
2	ENGINEER				2	8			10		
3											
4											
5											
6											
7											
8											
	TOTAL										

	QTY. WORK IN PLACE	PAY ROLL COSTS	LBR. AVERAGE UNIT COST	AVERAGE QUANTITY PER 8 HR. DAY	QTY. WORK IN PLACE	PAY ROLL COSTS	LBR. AVERAGE UNIT COST	AVERAGE QUANTITY PER 8 HR. DAY
PREVIOUS	—	—	PER CY					
THIS WEEK	99 CY			6.19 CY				
TOTAL	99			6.19				

MFD. IN U.S.A.   FORM C-105   FRANK R. WALKER CO., PUBLISHERS, CHICAGO

Fig. 104. Labor Distribution and Costs of Mixing and Placing Concrete for Foundation Walls.

COST ANALYSIS RECORD

TOTAL LABOR HOURS — UNIT

	1 LAB.	2 ENGR.	3	4	5	6	7	8
PREVIOUS	—	—						
THIS WEEK	128	10						
TOTAL	128	10						

LABOR HOURS PER UNIT — UNIT PER CUBIC YARD

	1 LAB	2 ENGR.	3	4	5	6	7	8
PREVIOUS	—	—						
THIS WEEK	1.29	0.101						
TOTAL	1.29	0.101						

REMARKS

CONCRETE IS JOB MIXED IN A 28-S PAVING MIXER, USING BATCHED MATERIALS AND WHEELED INTO PLACE WITH BUGGIES.

MFD. IN U.S.A.   FORM C-105   FRANK R. WALKER CO., PUBLISHERS, CHICAGO

Fig. 105. Analyzed Labor Costs of Mixing and Placing Concrete for Foundation Walls.

per thousand feet of lumber, board measure. Quantities of formwork are usually measured by contact area, that is the area of form surfaces actually coming in contact with the concrete. There are several exceptions to this, notably open deck forms for combination slabs, which are measured as to panel area.

Column forms are usually framed to detail at the job mill or bench and then assembled and erected into place on the job. It is wise to keep the cost of framing or benchwork separate from the erection cost as the forms may be used several times with little or no re-framing.

Labor Distribution Figure 106 illustrates the proper method of keeping costs on framing and erecting wood forms for concrete columns. The first column gives the quantity of work done, the second column gives the total labor cost to date, the third column gives the average cost per square foot of forms, while the fourth column gives the average square feet of forms framed by a man in an 8-hour day. Columns five to eight furnish the same information regarding erection of column forms.

The back of the form, Figure 107, gives the total number of hours worked by each trade in the first column headed "Total Labor Hours," while the second column headed "Labor Hours Per Unit," gives the time required by each trade to frame or erect 100 square feet of column forms or 1,000 feet of lumber, board measure, used for column forms.

If octagonal concrete columns are used, the labor costs are much greater than for square columns, so that if a job contains both square and octagonal columns, separate labor costs should be kept on each.

Very often, concrete columns are designed with brackets to support future construction, crane rails, intermediate lintels, etc. The cost of forming these brackets is usually much higher per square foot than that of the columns and should therefore be kept separate. Quantities of bracket forms may be expressed in square feet but since the areas involved are usually small and rather difficult to compute, most contractors estimate these forms on a piece basis and the costs should be kept in the same manner, stating the average size and number framed, erected or removed.

On jobs where round concrete columns are used, it is customary to use either metal or laminated fiber tubing column molds. The round concrete columns may have either a plain shaft or a flared cap or head at the ceiling. A notation should be made on the cost record, stating whether the columns are plain or have a cap. The labor costs erecting and removing round column molds should state the diameter of the columns, height of same and the total number erected and removed.

Labor Distribution Figure 108 illustrates the correct method of keeping labor costs on this class of work. The first column gives the total number of columns erected, the second column gives the total labor cost on same, the third column gives the average labor cost erecting each column, while the fourth column gives the average number of columns erected per 8-hour day.

The back of the form, Figure 109, divides the total labor costs according to the different trades engaged on the work. The first column headed "Total Labor Hours" gives the total number of hours worked by each trade, while the second column headed "Labor Hours Per Unit," gives the length of time required by each trade to erect one column form. Columns five to eight may be used for recording the costs of removing the forms after the concrete has been placed.

Forms for concrete beams, girders and lintels are usually framed and erected in the same manner as wood column forms, that is, the forms are built to detail on the bench and then assembled and erected into place. Labor costs on this work should therefore be recorded with the benchwork costs kept separate from the erection costs. Costs should also state whether adjustable shores or lumber shores are used for temporary supports.

Labor Distribution Figure 110 illustrates the correct method of keeping costs on framing and erecting beam and girder forms. The first column gives the quantity of beam and girder forms framed at the bench, the second column gives the total labor costs to date, the third column gives the average unit cost of framing a square foot of forms, while the fourth column gives the average number of square feet of forms framed by a carpenter in an 8-hour day. Columns five to eight furnish the same information regarding assembling and erecting the forms into place.

The back of this form, Figure 111, illustrates the method of sub-dividing the total labor costs for final analysis. The first column headed "Total Labor Hours," gives the total number of hours worked by each trade, while the second column headed "Labor Hours Per Unit," gives the length of time required by each trade to frame or erect 100 square feet of beam and girder forms or 1,000 feet of lumber, board measure, used for the forms.

In keeping costs on formwork for reinforced concrete floor slabs, always state the type of slab being formed, such as solid slab forms, open deck forms for combination slabs, etc. The costs should also state the type of shores being used, whether adjustable or ordinary lumber, and the number of feet of lumber,

Fig. 106. Labor Distribution and Costs of Making and Erecting Forms for Reinforced Concrete Columns.

LABOR DISTRIBUTION

JOB CENTRAL HIGH SCHOOL
CLASS OF WORK C-21-a, C-21-b
WEEK ENDING JAN 23, 19-
SHEET NO. 15
JOB NO. 110

OCCUPATION	M	T	W	T	F	S	S	HOURS	RATE	AMOUNT
1 C-21-a CARPENTERS	16	-	8	-	-	1		24		
2 LABORERS	8	-	5	-	-	1		13		
3										
4										
5 C-21-b CARPENTERS	16	32	24	16	-	1		88		
6 LABORERS	8	16	11	8	-	1		43		
7										
8										

C-21-a MAKE UP FORMS | C-21-b ERECT FORMS

	QTY. WORK IN PLACE	PAY ROLL COSTS	LBR. AVERAGE UNIT COST	AVERAGE QUANTITY PER 8 HR. DAY	QTY. WORK IN PLACE	PAY ROLL COSTS	LBR. AVERAGE UNIT COST	AVERAGE QUANTITY PER 8 HR. DAY
PREVIOUS	1960 SF			280 SF	2240 SF			128 SF
THIS WEEK	820			273	1480			135
TOTAL	2780			278	3720			131

MFD. IN U.S.A.   FORM C-105   FRANK R. WALKER CO., PUBLISHERS, CHICAGO   (OVER)

Fig. 107. Analyzed Labor Costs of Making and Erecting Forms for Reinforced Concrete Columns.

COST ANALYSIS RECORD

TOTAL LABOR HOURS — UNIT

	1 CARP	2 LAB.	3	4	5 CARP	6 LAB.	7	8
PREVIOUS	56	24			140	67		
THIS WEEK	24	13			88	43		
TOTAL	80	39			228	110		

UNIT ② PER 100 SF FORMS
② PER M. FT. LUMBER B.M.

LABOR HOURS PER UNIT

	1 CARP	2 LAB.	3	4	5 CARP	6 LAB.	7	8
PREVIOUS	② 2.86 ② 3.61	② 1.33 ② 3.32			② 6.25 ② 29.76	② 2.99 ② 14.24		
THIS WEEK	② 2.93 ② 3.94	② 1.59 ② 7.55			② 5.94 ② 28.31	② 2.91 ② 3.83		
TOTAL	② 2.88 ② 3.70	② 1.40 ② 6.68			② 6.13 ② 29.19	② 2.96 ② 14.08		

REMARKS
COLUMN FORMS AVERAGE 15" x 15" x 11'-0" USING 1" LUMBER WITH STEEL COLUMN CLAMPS - 2.1 FT LUMBER B.M. PER S.F. OF FORMS.

MFD. IN U.S.A.   FORM C-105   FRANK R. WALKER CO., PUBLISHERS, CHICAGO

Fig. 108. Labor Distribution and Costs of Erecting and Removing Metal Column Molds.

LABOR DISTRIBUTION

JOB CENTRAL HIGH SCHOOL
CLASS OF WORK C-22, C-23
WEEK ENDING JAN 23, 19--
SHEET NO. 16
JOB NO. 110

OCCUPATION	M	T	W	T	F	S	S	HOURS	RATE	AMOUNT
1 C-22 SHEET MTL WKR.	16	16	16	16	-	-	-	64		
2										
3										
4										
5 C-23 SHEET MTL WKR.	-	-	-	-	16	-	-	16		
6										
7										
8										

TOTAL   C-22 | C-23

	QTY. WORK IN PLACE	PAY ROLL COSTS	LBR. AVERAGE UNIT COST	AVERAGE QUANTITY PER 8 HR. DAY	QTY. WORK IN PLACE	PAY ROLL COSTS	LBR. AVERAGE UNIT COST	AVERAGE QUANTITY PER 8 HR. DAY
PREVIOUS	23 COLS			2.09 cas	15 COLS			5.0 cas
THIS WEEK	18			2.25	11			5.5
TOTAL	41			2.16	26			5.2

MFD. IN U.S.A.   FORM C-105   FRANK R. WALKER CO., PUBLISHERS, CHICAGO   (OVER)

Fig. 109. Analyzed Labor Costs of Erecting and Removing Metal Column Molds.

COST ANALYSIS RECORD

TOTAL LABOR HOURS

	1 SHT. MTL. WORKER	2	3	4	5 SHT. MTL. WORKER	6	7	8
PREVIOUS	88				24			
THIS WEEK	64				16			
TOTAL	152				40			

UNIT — PER COLUMN

LABOR HOURS PER UNIT

	1 SHT. MTL. WORKER	2	3	4	5 SHT. MTL. WORKER	6	7	8
PREVIOUS	3.82				1.60			
THIS WEEK	3.56				1.46			
TOTAL	3.71				1.54			

REMARKS: ROUND COLUMNS – 30" DIA., 13'-2" HIGH, PLAIN SHAFT, NO CAP.

MFD. IN U.S.A.   FORM C-105   FRANK R. WALKER CO., PUBLISHERS, CHICAGO

Fig. 110. Labor Distribution and Costs of Making and Erecting Forms for Reinforced Concrete Beams and Girders.

LABOR DISTRIBUTION

JOB Central High School
CLASS OF WORK C-25-a, C-25-b
WEEK ENDING Jan 23, 19—
SHEET NO. 17
JOB NO. 110

	OCCUPATION	M	T	W	T	F	S	S	HOURS	RATE	AMOUNT
1	C-25-a { CARPENTERS	16	16	8	—	—	—	—	40		
2	LABORERS	8	6	3	—	—	—	—	17		
3											
4											
5	C-25-b { CARPENTERS	16	16	24	32	32	—	—	120		
6	LABORERS	8	10	17	16	16	—	—	67		
7											
8											

TOTAL   C-25-a MAKE UP FORMS   C-25-b ERECT FORMS

CLASS OF WORK	QTY. WORK IN PLACE	PAY ROLL COSTS	LBR. AVERAGE UNIT COST	AVERAGE QUANTITY PER 8 HR. DAY	QTY. WORK IN PLACE	PAY ROLL COSTS	LBR. AVERAGE UNIT COST	AVERAGE QUANTITY PER 8 HR. DAY
PREVIOUS	292.0 SF			225 SF	4280 SF			159 SF
THIS WEEK	1150			230	2370			158
TOTAL	4070			226	6650			159

MFD. IN U.S.A.   FORM C-105   FRANK R. WALKER CO., PUBLISHERS, CHICAGO   (OVER)

COST ANALYSIS RECORD

TOTAL LABOR HOURS | UNIT

	1 CARP.	2 LAB.	3	4	5 CARP.	6 LAB.	7	8
PREVIOUS	104	50			216	110		
THIS WEEK	40	17			120	67		
TOTAL	144	67			336	177		

LABOR HOURS PER UNIT | UNIT ① PER 100 SF FORMS ② ^ M. Fl. LUMBER B.M.

	1 CARP.	2 LAB.	3	4	5 CARP.	6 LAB.	7	8
PREVIOUS	① 3.56 ② 17.81	① 1.71 ② 8.56			① 5.04 ② 25.23	① 2.57 ② 12.85		
THIS WEEK	① 3.48 ② 17.39	① 1.48 ② 7.39			① 5.06 ② 25.31	① 2.82 ② 14.14		
TOTAL	① 3.54 ② 17.69	① 1.65 ② 8.23			① 5.05 ② 25.26	① 2.66 ② 13.31		

REMARKS

BEAM FORMS AVERAGE 2 FEET OF LUMBER B.M. PER S.F. OF FORMS,
USING ADJUSTABLE SHORES.

MFD. IN U.S.A.   FORM C-105   FRANK R. WALKER CO., PUBLISHERS, CHICAGO

Fig. 111. Analyzed Labor Costs of Making and Erecting Forms for Reinforced Concrete Beams and Girders.

board measure, required per square foot of forms. If several types of floor construction or different methods are contained in the job, separate costs should be kept on each.

As an example of the correct method of keeping costs on formwork for reinforced concrete floors, refer to Labor Distribution Figure 112. The first column gives the total number of square feet of solid slab forms framed and erected, the seond column gives the total labor costs for this work to date, the third column shows the average unit labor cost per square foot of forms, while the fourth column gives the average number of square feet of forms framed and erected by a carpenter in an 8-hour day. Columns five to eight furnish the same information regarding open deck forms for combination slabs.

The back of the form, Figure 113, gives the total number of hours worked by each trade in the first column headed "Total Labor Hours," while the second column headed "Labor Hours Per Unit," gives the time required by each trade to frame and erect 100 square feet of forms or 1,000 feet of lumber, board measure, used for the forms.

On jobs having what is commonly termed flat slab construction (without beams or girders below the floors), it is customary to have a depression four or five feet square and 4 to 8 inches deep formed below the ceiling level at the column heads for the extra strength required at those points. If possible, it is advisable to keep separate labor costs framing and erecting these depressions, as experience has shown it is much more expensive to frame the depressions than the slab forms themselves, and for this reason, separate costs are advisable.

All kinds of wood forms for reinforced concrete are usually "wrecked" or removed by common laborers after the concrete has been placed. For this reason the costs do not vary as much in removing the forms as in framing and erecting them. However, separate labor costs should be kept on removing all kinds of wood forms, using only one sub-division for slab, beam, girder, lintel and column forms. The cost of removing the forms should be given in square feet and per 1,000 feet of lumber, board measure. It is advisable to keep the costs both on a square foot and board measure basis, particularly on slab forms, as a light concrete floor having low ceilings may require only 2½ feet of lumber per square foot of floor area, while a heavy floor with high ceilings may require 4 feet of lumber per square foot of floor. If the costs were not figured on a board measure basis, there would appear to be too much variation in the square foot costs, while in reality the costs per 1,000 feet of lumber would be very close.

Placing Reinforced Concrete

Inasmuch as concrete may be mixed and placed in many different ways, with widely varying costs, it is important that every contractor should have accurate information regarding the most economical methods of handling and placing same, and this is only obtained by keeping accurate costs on the various operations performed under different job conditions.

Concrete is usually estimated by the cubic foot or cubic yard containing 27 cubic feet, and the costs should be kept on the same basis. For mass concrete work, the cubic yard basis is more satisfactory.

If concrete materials, such as sand, gravel, crushed stone, cement, etc., are delivered to the job in cars, separate labor costs should be kept on unloading them, as described on the previous pages under "Unloading Materials." The units of measure are also fully described under this heading.

The labor cost of handling the cement from the storage shed to the mixer; labor loading wheelbarrows containing sand, gravel or crushed stone and wheeling same to the mixer; the labor required attending the concrete mixer, the time of the engineer on the mixer, if any; the labor cost of hoisting, dumping and placing the concrete, which includes the labor tamping, spading and grading, should all be charged under this classification, as these are the usual operations necessary for mixing and placing concrete. Also included under this heading are all labor costs for handling, placing and removing temporary runways required for wheeling concrete into place.

If the concrete is placed by means of a crane and bucket or if "Pumpcrete" equipment is used, this should be menioned, in order that the costs may not be confused with concrete that is placed where wheelbarrows or concrete carts are used. Always state the class of work performed and the method of mixing and handling the concrete, as this is important if the costs are to be used as the basis of other estimates or for comparison with other jobs.

In addition, separate costs should be kept on placing the different kinds of reinforced concrete, such as columns, ordinary slabs and beams, isolated slabs and beams, stairs, etc., as these costs will vary considerably.

Fig. 112. Labor Distribution and Costs of Erecting Forms for Reinforced Concrete Floors.

Fig. 113. Analyzed Labor Costs of Erecting Forms for Reinforced Concrete Floors.

LABOR DISTRIBUTION

JOB CENTRAL HIGH SCHOOL   SHEET NO. 19

CLASS OF WORK C-41, C-42   WEEK ENDING JAN 23, 19--   JOB NO. 110

OCCUPATION	M	T	W	T	F	S	S	HOURS	RATE	AMOUNT
1 LABORERS	—	—	—	68	—	—	—	68		
2 C-41 MIXER ENGR.	—	—	—	4	—	—	—	4		
3 HOIST "	—	—	—	4	—	—	—	4		
4										
5 LABORERS	—	—	—	24	112	—	—	136		
6 C-42 MIXER ENGR.	—	—	—	1	8	—	—	8		
7 HOIST "	—	—	—	1	8	—	—	8		
8										
TOTAL C-41								C-42		

	QTY. WORK IN PLACE	PAY ROLL COSTS	LBR. AVERAGE UNIT COST	AVERAGE QUANTITY PER 8 HR. DAY	QTY. WORK IN PLACE	PAY ROLL COSTS	LBR. AVERAGE UNIT COST	AVERAGE QUANTITY PER 8 HR. DAY
PREVIOUS	83 CY			8.51 CY	186 CY			9.79 CY
THIS WEEK	75			8.82	170			10.00
TOTAL	158			8.66	356			9.89

MFD. IN U.S.A.   FORM C-105   FRANK R. WALKER CO., PUBLISHERS, CHICAGO   (OVER)

Fig. 114. Labor Distribution and Costs of Mixing and Placing Reinforced Concrete.

Labor Distribution Figure 114 illustrates the correct method of recording the labor costs of mixing and placing reinforced concrete. The first column gives the total number of cubic yards of column concrete placed, the second column gives the total labor cost on same, the third column gives the average labor cost per cubic yard, while the fourth column gives the average number of cubic yards of column concrete mixed and placed by one laborer in an 8-hour day. Columns five to eight furnish the same information regarding placing ordinary slab and beam concrete.

The back of the form, Figure 115, sub-divides the costs. The first column headed "Total Labor Hours" gives the total number of hours worked by each trade, while the second column headed "Labor Hours Per Unit," gives the length of time required by each trade to mix and place one cubic yard of concrete.

If concrete is placed during freezing weather, making it necessary to heat all sand, gravel, crushed stone and water and protect the concrete from freezing by means of tarpaulins, salamanders or other temporary heat, separate costs should be kept on all labor required in the protection of the concrete and charged to the proper classification under "Temporary Construction and Weather Conditions," as outlined in the Cost Schedule, in order that these costs may be reduced to a cubic yard basis. It is important to know just what amount must be added for each cubic yard of concrete placed during the winter months.

Concrete Floors, Walks, Pavements, Fills and Cement Finishes

When keeping costs on the different kinds of concrete and cement work included under this heading, a large number of labor classifications are necessary to obtain unit costs that will prove of value to the contractor or estimator. For instance, on concrete floors, walks, pavements, etc., the first step necessary, after the sub-grade has been prepared, is the placing of wood or metal edge forms or screeds to the proper height so that the concrete may be contained and struck off at the correct elevation. This should be kept as a separate labor item. Following this, the job is ready to receive the concrete base and separate costs should be kept on the mixing and placing of same. After the concrete is in place, some sort of finishing operations are usually required and may be screeding, floating, monolithic troweling or the application of an integral or separate finish. There may be one or a combination of several of these finishes required in the total job and separate costs should be kept on each.

All of the various operations are sub-divided in the Cost Schedule given on previous pages which will serve as a guide for the proper breakdown of costs.

Many contractors will not care to sub-divide the costs to such an extent; perhaps two sub-divisions will be sufficient, one for placing the concrete and the other for setting the screeds and performing the finishing operations including the cost of mixing and applying the finish topping, if required.

Labor Distribution Figure 116 illustrates this method. The labor hours and costs are sub-divided according to the cost schedule, C-53, 54 and 59, but the unit costs are stated only in terms of C-54 and 59. Refer to the cost schedule under "C-50" for full explanation of the symbols mentioned.

The first column gives the number of cubic yards of concrete placed, the second column gives the total cost of same, the third column gives the average labor cost per cubic yard of concrete, while column four gives the average number of cubic yards of concrete a laborer placed per 8-hour day.

The separate labor cost of setting the screeds and finishing the floor is given in columns five to eight. Column five gives the total number of square feet of finish, column six gives the total labor cost, column seven the average labor cost per square foot, while column eight gives the number of square feet of finish a cement mason completed per 8-hour day.

The back of this form, Figure 117, gives the total number of hours worked by each trade, in the first column headed "Total Labor Hours," while the second column headed "Labor Hours Per Unit," gives the length of time required by each trade to place one cubic yard of basement floor concrete or complete 100 square feet of monolithic cement floor finish. This column gives the estimator the necessary information for preparing future estimates on similar work at different wage scales.

When keeping labor costs of mixing and placing rough concrete floor fill and fill between wood sleepers, or when placing slag, cinder or other concrete fill on roofs to give them a pitch toward drains, the cost report should contain a general description of the work, kind of concrete, thickness of fill, etc., together with the number of square feet of fill placed, as work of this kind is ordinarily figured by the square-foot.

When doing concrete curb work, the labor costs should state the type of curb involved, curb dimensions (thickness, height or width), and the number of lineal feet installed.

Fig. 115

COST ANALYSIS RECORD

| | TOTAL LABOR HOURS | | | | UNIT | | | |
	1 LAB.	2 MIXER ENGR.	3 HOIST ENGR.	4	5 LAB.	6 MIXER ENGR.	7 HOIST ENGR.	8
PREVIOUS	78	5	5		152	10	10	
THIS WEEK	68	4	4		136	9	9	
TOTAL	146	9	9		288	19	19	

UNIT — PER CUBIC YARD

| | LABOR HOURS PER UNIT | | | | | | | |
	1 LAB.	2 MIXER ENGR.	3 HOIST ENGR.	4	5 LAB.	6 MIXER ENGR.	7 HOIST ENGR.	8
PREVIOUS	0.94	0.063	0.063		0.82	0.054	0.054	
THIS WEEK	0.91	0.053	0.053		0.80	0.053	0.053	
TOTAL	0.92	0.057	0.057		0.81	0.053	0.053	

REMARKS

COLUMN CONCRETE - JOB MIXED IN 28-S MIXER, BATCHED MATERIALS, HOISTED 1 STORY, WHEELED INTO PLACE WITH BUGGIES. SLAB & BEAM CONCRETE - SAME.

MFD. IN U.S.A.   FORM C-105   FRANK R. WALKER CO., PUBLISHERS, CHICAGO

Fig. 115. Analyzed Labor Costs of Mixing and Placing Reinforced Concrete.

Fig. 116

LABOR DISTRIBUTION

JOB CENTRAL HIGH SCHOOL   SHEET NO. 20
CLASS OF WORK C-54, C-59 INCL. SET SCREENS   WEEK ENDING APRIL 24, 19--   JOB NO. 110

	OCCUPATION	M	T	W	T	F	S	S	QTY. WORK IN PLACE	LBR. AVERAGE UNIT COST	PAY ROLL COSTS	HOURS	RATE	AMOUNT	AVERAGE QUANTITY PER 8 HR. DAY
1	C-54 LABORERS			8	44							52			
2	MIXED ENGR.				4							4			
3															
4	C-53 CEMENT MASONS			16	10							26			
5	LABORERS			2	1							3			
6	C-59 CEMENT MASONS					38						38			
7	LABORERS					16						16			
8															

TOTAL — C-54 — C-59

	QTY. WORK IN PLACE	LBR. AVERAGE UNIT COST	PAY ROLL COSTS	AVERAGE QUANTITY PER 8 HR. DAY
PREVIOUS	74 CY			11.4 CY
THIS WEEK	4800 SF			600 SF
TOTAL	74			11.4
	4800			600

MFD. IN U.S.A.   FORM C-105   FRANK R. WALKER CO., PUBLISHERS, CHICAGO

Fig. 116. Labor Distribution and Costs of Placing Concrete Floors.

Fig. 117

COST ANALYSIS RECORD

| | TOTAL LABOR HOURS | | | | UNIT | | | |
	1 LAB.	2 MIXED ENGR.	3	4	5 CEMENT MASONS	6 LAB.	7	8
PREVIOUS	—				—			
THIS WEEK	52	4			64	19		
TOTAL	52	4			64	19		

UNIT — PER CY OF CONCRETE / PER 100 SF MONO. TROWEL FINISH

| | LABOR HOURS PER UNIT | | | | | | | |
	1 LAB.	2 MIXED ENGR.	3	4	5 CEMENT MASONS	6 LAB.	7	8
PREVIOUS	—				—			
THIS WEEK	0.70	0.054			1.33	0.40		
TOTAL	0.70	0.054			1.33	0.40		

REMARKS

BSMT. FLOOR SLAB - 5" CONCRETE WITH MONOLITHIC TROWEL FINISH CONCRETE - JOB MIXED, 28-S MIXER, BATCHED MATERIALS, ABOUT 1/2 WHEELED IN BUGGIES. FINISH - HAND RODDED, POWER FLOATED, POWER TROWELED, (3 TIMES) HAND BURNISHED ONCE OVER.

MFD. IN U.S.A.   FORM C-105   FRANK R. WALKER CO., PUBLISHERS, CHICAGO

Fig. 117. Analyzed Labor Costs of Placing Concrete Floors.

All labor costs for excavation and grading, required for the installation of curb work, should be kept separate and charged to the proper classification under "Excavation, etc." as given in the Cost Schedule on previous pages.

Concrete curb work, like concrete floors, walks and pavements, also involves several different classifications of work, and here again, most contractors prefer not to sub-divide the costs for each operation and simply compute an aggregate unit cost per lineal foot of curb placed. The workmen's time, however, should be distributed in accordance with the various labor operations performed, so that it is possible to check any or all individual operations, if desired.

Labor Distribution Figure 118 illustrates the proper method of keeping costs on the installation of concrete curb work. The labor hours and total costs are sub-divided according to the Cost Schedule items C-52, 58 and 64, but the unit cost is stated only in terms of C-58. (See Cost Schedule for explanation of symbols.)

The first column gives the total number of lineal feet of concrete curb placed, the second column gives the total cost of same, the third column the average unit cost per lineal foot, while the fourth column states the number of lineal feet of curb completed per 8-hour day of cement mason time.

The back of this form, Figure 119, sub-divides the labor hours into workable units for reference when preparing future estimates.

All labor costs for the balance of the items in this Cost Schedule classification of cement work, (See Cost Schedule C-50,) should be kept in the same way as for concrete floors, walks and pavements and concrete curbs, with separate time classifications being made where more than one operation of work is involved and a single unit cost being computed in terms of square feet, lineal feet or whatever unit is applicable.

Cement Gun Work

When keeping costs on cement gun work, all labor costs for bringing equipment to job, setting up ready for operation, dismantling at completion and removing from job should be kept separate and charged to the proper item under "Construction Plant and Equipment" as given in the Cost Schedule on previous pages.

Cost records of cement gun work should always contain a brief description of the job, such as thickness of application, type of forms used where required, kind of reinforcing if required, method of finishing, etc. Labor costs for each operation should be kept separate and reduced to workable units for future reference in estimating. If desired, an aggregate unit cost may then be computed per square foot of complete cement gun work.

Macadam, Bituminous Surface and Asphalt Surface Paved Areas

When constructing macadam, bituminous surface and asphalt surface paved areas, there is always a certain amount of earthwork which must be done before the actual pavement can be placed. Labor costs for this work should be kept separate and charged to the proper classification under "Excavation, etc.," as outlined in the Cost Schedule given on previous pages.

Inasmuch as pavement specifications vary widely, depending on the location of the job and the use for which it is intended, it is necessary for the contractor who does a large volume of this work, to keep separate labor costs on each operation, such as placing base course, priming, placing seal coat bituminous material, placing seal coat aggregate, placing asphalt binder, placing asphalt surface course, etc. These costs should be reduced to unit costs based on per gallon of bituminous material and per ton or cubic yard of aggregate or asphalt material.

For the contractor, who only does small occasional jobs of this type, keeping the men's time separate for each operation and reducing the total costs to an aggregate unit cost per square yard of pavement should serve the purpose.

In either case, the cost records should include a complete description of the work, to be of any value in estimating future jobs.

Fig. 118

PRACTICAL

LABOR DISTRIBUTION

JOB CENTRAL HIGH SCHOOL
CLASS OF WORK C-58 INCL. FORMS, CONC. & FIN. WEEK ENDING MAY 8, 1977
SHEET NO. 21 JOB NO. 110

	OCCUPATION	M	T	W	T	F	S	S	HOURS	RATE	AMOUNT
1	C-52 { CEMENT MASONS	16	16	8	8	1	1	1	56		
2	{ LABORERS	8	8	4	3	1	1	1	31		
3											
4	C-58 LABORERS	12	24	24	24	1	1	1	84		
5											
6	C-64 CEMENT MASONS	—	3	3	3	2	1	1	11		
7											
8											
	TOTAL										

	QTY. WORK IN PLACE	PAY ROLL COSTS	LBR. AVERAGE UNIT COST	AVERAGE QUANTITY PER 8 HR. DAY
PREVIOUS	200 LF			C&F MASONS 41.0 LF
THIS WEEK	350			41.8
TOTAL	550			41.5

MFD. IN U.S.A. FORM C-105 FRANK R. WALKER CO., PUBLISHERS, CHICAGO

(OVER)

Fig. 118. Labor Distribution and Costs of Placing Concrete Combination Curb and Gutter.

Fig. 119

COST ANALYSIS RECORD

TOTAL LABOR HOURS		UNIT							
	1 CEMENT MASONS	2 LAB.	3	4	5	6	7	8	
PREVIOUS	39	66							
THIS WEEK	67	115							
TOTAL	106	181							

LABOR HOURS PER UNIT		UNIT PER LINEAL FOOT							
	1 CEMENT MASONS	2 LAB.	3	4	5	6	7	8	
PREVIOUS	0.195	0.330							
THIS WEEK	0.191	0.329							
TOTAL	0.193	0.329							

REMARKS
CONCRETE COMBINATION CURB & GUTTER – 24" X 12" – WOOD FORMS – USING 6 S CONCRETE MIXER – MONOLITHIC TROWEL FINISH.

MFD. IN U.S.A. FORM C-105 FRANK R. WALKER CO., PUBLISHERS, CHICAGO

Fig. 119. Analyzed Labor Costs of Placing Concrete Combination Curb and Gutter.

Fig. 120

PRACTICAL

LABOR DISTRIBUTION

JOB CENTRAL HIGH SCHOOL
CLASS OF WORK D-2, D-3 WEEK ENDING JAN 23, 19--
SHEET NO. 22 JOB NO. 110

	OCCUPATION	M	T	W	T	F	S	S	HOURS	RATE	AMOUNT
1	D-2 { CARPENTERS	—	—	5	16	—	—	—	21		
2	{ LABORERS	—	—	16	12	—	—	—	28		
3											
4											
5	D-3 LABORERS	16	9	—	—	—	—	—	25		
6											
7											
8											
	TOTAL	D-2						D-3			

	QTY. WORK IN PLACE	PAY ROLL COSTS	LBR. AVERAGE UNIT COST	AVERAGE QUANTITY PER 8 HR. DAY	QTY. WORK IN PLACE	PAY ROLL COSTS	LBR. AVERAGE UNIT COST	AVERAGE QUANTITY PER 8 HR. DAY
PREVIOUS	4796 SF			CARP. 1066 SF	2291 SF			797 SF
THIS WEEK	2772			1056	2505			802
TOTAL	7568			1062	4796			799

MFD. IN U.S.A. FORM C-105 FRANK R. WALKER CO., PUBLISHERS, CHICAGO (OVER)

Fig. 120. Labor Distribution and Costs of Placing and Removing Metal Pans for Concrete Joist Slabs.

Metal Pans

When keeping costs on placing and removing metal pans used in the construction of concrete joist slabs, the labor cost of bringing the pans to the job, including unloading, should be kept as a separate item. Placing costs should also be kept separate from costs of removing, cleaning and oiling pans when the concrete has attained sufficient strength.

Metal pan work is measured by the total area of the slab in which it is used, including the area of the beams enclosing the slab and the interior beams.

Labor Distribution Figure 120 illustrates the correct method of keeping costs on this class of work. The first column gives the number of square feet of pan slab, the second column gives the total cost to date, the third column gives the average unit cost per square foot of pan slab, while the fourth column gives the average number of square feet of pan slab in which pans were placed by a mechanic in an 8-hour day. Columns five to eight furnish the same information regarding the removal, cleaning and oiling of the pans.

The back of the form, Figure 121, divides the total labor costs according to the different trades engaged on the work. The first column headed "Total Labor Hours" gives the total number of hours worked by each trade, while the second column headed "Labor Hours Per Unit," gives the number of hours required by each trade to place or remove metal pans for 100 square feet of slab.

Clay Tile or Lightweight Concrete Block Fillers For Combination Slabs

In keeping costs of handling and placing clay tile fillers or lightweight concrete "soffitile" for combination concrete joist slabs, the costs should be based on the number of square feet of tile placed. When reporting costs on work of this kind, always state the kind, face size and depth of tile.

For an example of the method used in keeping costs of handling and placing clay tile fillers for combination slabs, refer to Labor Distribution Figure 122. The first column gives the number of square feet of tile placed, the second column gives the total payroll cost, the third column the unit labor cost per square foot of tile, while the fourth column gives the average number of square feet of tile placed per 8-hour day. Columns five to eight furnish the same information regarding filling voids in tile fillers with mortar at the ends of each row.

The back of the form, Figure 123, gives the total number of hours worked by each trade in the first column headed "Total Labor Hours," while the second column headed "Labor Hours Per Unit" gives the length of time required to handle and place 100 square feet of tile and fill the end voids in 100 pieces of tile.

Reinforcing Steel and Mesh

In keeping costs on reinforcing steel and steel mesh reinforcing work, the units of measure should be per pound or ton of reinforcing rods and per square foot of mesh reinforcing.

Separate labor costs should be kept for each operation of the work, for both rods and mesh, as outlined in the Cost Schedule given on previous pages.

The labor cost of unloading reinforcing material, sorting and stockpiling should be recorded as one item.

If the steel is sent to the job in stock lengths, making it necessary to cut and bend it on the job before placing, separate labor costs should be kept on this work. When reporting bending costs, always give the average size of the bars, viz., from ½ to ¾ inch, etc., as the lighter the steel the higher the bending costs average per pound or ton.

If the steel is sent to the job cut to length and bent, then it will be necessary to keep costs only on handling, hoisting, placing and tieing the reinforcing steel ready to receive the concrete. Always give the average size of the bars, because as a general rule, the lighter the steel, the more it costs to place it.

Labor Distribution Figure 124 illustrates the correct method of reporting the labor cost of handling and placing reinforcing steel. The first column gives the total weight of the steel placed, the second column gives the total labor cost placing same, the third column gives the average labor cost per ton, while the fourth column gives the average amount of steel placed and tied per 8-hour day.

The back of the form, Figure 125, sub-divides the total labor costs. The first column headed "Total Labor Hours," gives the total number of hours worked by each trade, while the second column headed

Fig. 121. Analyzed Labor Costs of Placing and Removing Metal Pans for Concrete Joist Slabs.

COST ANALYSIS RECORD

TOTAL LABOR HOURS				UNIT			
1 CARP.	2 LAB.	3	4	5 LAB.	6	7	8
PREVIOUS 36	48			23			
THIS WEEK 21	28			25			
TOTAL 57	76			48			

LABOR HOURS PER UNIT				UNIT PER 100 SF SLAB AREA			
1 CARP.	2 LAB.	3	4	5 LAB.	6	7	8
PREVIOUS 0.13	1.00			1.0			
THIS WEEK 0.76	1.01			1.0			
TOTAL 0.75	1.00			1.0			

REMARKS

PANS, IN GENERAL, ARE 20" X 8" SPACED 25" O.C.

MFD. IN U.S.A.   FORM C-105   FRANK R. WALKER CO., PUBLISHERS, CHICAGO

Fig. 122. Labor Distribution and Costs of Placing Clay Tile Fillers for Combination Concrete Joist Slabs.

LABOR DISTRIBUTION

JOB CENTRAL HIGH SCHOOL
CLASS OF WORK D-11, D-12
WEEK ENDING
SHEET NO. 23
JOB NO. 110

	OCCUPATION	M	T	W	T	F	S	S	HOURS	RATE	AMOUNT
1 D-11	MASONS	1	1	7	1	1	1	1	14		
2	LABORERS	1	1	37	31	1	1	1	68		
3											
4											
5 D-12	MASONS	1	1	1	1	1	1				
6	LABORERS	1	1	1	1	1	1				
7											
8											
TOTAL											

	QTY. WORK IN PLACE	PAY ROLL COSTS	LBR. AVERAGE UNIT COST	AVERAGE QUANTITY PER 8 HR. DAY	QTY. WORK IN PLACE	PAY ROLL COSTS	LBR. AVERAGE UNIT COST	AVERAGE QUANTITY PER 8 HR. DAY
	D-11			MASON		D-12		MASON
PREVIOUS	1444 SF		—	825 SF	104 Pcs		—	832 Pcs
THIS WEEK	1444 SF	—	—	825	104 Pcs	—	—	832
TOTAL	1444			825	104			832

(OVER)

MFD. IN U.S.A.   FORM C-105   FRANK R. WALKER CO., PUBLISHERS, CHICAGO

COST ANALYSIS RECORD

TOTAL LABOR HOURS				UNIT			
1 MASON	2 LAB.	3	4	5 MASON	6 LAB.	7	8
PREVIOUS —	—						
THIS WEEK 14	68			1	1		
TOTAL 14	68			1	1		

LABOR HOURS PER UNIT				UNIT PER 100 SF TILE FILLERS / PER 100 PCS. TILE ENDS			
1 MASON	2 LAB.	3	4	5 MASON	6 LAB.	7	8
PREVIOUS —	—						
THIS WEEK 0.97	4.71			0.96	0.96		
TOTAL 0.97	4.71			0.96	0.96		

REMARKS

CLAY TILE FILLERS - 12"X12" FACE - 8" THICK - 18" O.C.
STRAIGHT RUN JOB - NOT MUCH CUTTING - END VOIDS
FILLED WITH MORTAR.

MFD. IN U.S.A.   FORM C-105   FRANK R. WALKER CO., PUBLISHERS, CHICAGO

Fig. 123. Analyzed Labor Costs of Placing Clay Tile Fillers for Combination Concrete Joist Slabs.

Fig. 124. Labor Distribution and Costs of Unloading and Placing Reinforcing Steel.

LABOR DISTRIBUTION

JOB CENTRAL HIGH SCHOOL — SHEET NO. 24
CLASS OF WORK D-21, D-23 — WEEK ENDING JAN 23, 19-- — JOB NO. 110

	OCCUPATION	M	T	W	T	F	S	S	HOURS	RATE	AMOUNT
1	D-21 LABORERS	-	18	12	12		1		42		
2											
3											
4											
5	D-23 { IRON WORKERS	32	32	32	8		1	1	136		
6	{ LABORERS	-	6	12			1	1	18		
7											
8											
	TOTAL										

	QTY. WORK IN PLACE	PAY ROLL COSTS	LBR. AVERAGE UNIT COST	AVERAGE QUANTITY PER 8 HR. DAY	QTY. WORK IN PLACE	PAY ROLL COSTS	LBR. AVERAGE UNIT COST	AVERAGE QUANTITY PER 8 HR. DAY
	D-21				D-23			
PREVIOUS	65 TON			2.60 TON	52 TON			0.504 TON
THIS WEEK	14			2.67	9			0.529
TOTAL	79			2.61	61			0.507

MFD. IN U.S.A.   FORM C-105   FRANK R. WALKER CO., PUBLISHERS, CHICAGO   (OVER)

Fig. 125. Analyzed Labor Costs of Unloading and Placing Reinforcing Steel.

COST ANALYSIS RECORD

UNIT IRON PER TON, 2000 LBS.

TOTAL LABOR HOURS

	1 LAB.	2	3	4	5 IRON WORKERS	6 LAB.	7	8
PREVIOUS	200				826	110		
THIS WEEK	42				136	18		
TOTAL	242				962	128		

LABOR HOURS PER UNIT

	1 LAB.	2	3	4	5 IRON WORKERS	6 LAB.	7	8
PREVIOUS	3.08				15.9	2.12		
THIS WEEK	3.00				15.1	2.00		
TOTAL	3.06				15.8	2.10		

REMARKS: AVERAGE SIZE STEEL RODS - 3/4" to 1" - PLACED IN SLABS AND BEAMS.

MFD. IN U.S.A.   FORM C-105   FRANK R. WALKER CO., PUBLISHERS, CHICAGO

LABOR DISTRIBUTION

JOB CENTRAL HIGH SCHOOL — SHEET NO. 25
CLASS OF WORK D-32 — WEEK ENDING FEB 27, 19-- — JOB NO. 110

	OCCUPATION	M	T	W	T	F	S	S	HOURS	RATE	AMOUNT
1	D-32 { IRON WORKERS	-	-	12	24	-	-	-	36		
2	{ LABORERS	-	-	12	16	-	-	-	28		
3											
4											
5											
6											
7											
8											
	TOTAL										

	QTY. WORK IN PLACE	PAY ROLL COSTS	LBR. AVERAGE UNIT COST	AVERAGE QUANTITY PER 8 HR. DAY	QTY. WORK IN PLACE	PAY ROLL COSTS	LBR. AVERAGE UNIT COST	AVERAGE QUANTITY PER 8 HR. DAY
PREVIOUS	-	-	-					
THIS WEEK	3440 SF			764 SF				
TOTAL	3440			764				

MFD. IN U.S.A.   FORM C-105   FRANK R. WALKER CO., PUBLISHERS, CHICAGO   (OVER)

Fig. 126. Labor Distribution and Costs of Placing Corrugated Steel Permanent Forms.

"Labor Hours Per Unit," gives the length of time required to unload, sort and stockpile or handle and place one ton of reinforcing steel.

Combination Permanent Form and Reinforcing Materials

When keeping costs on the installation of combination permanent form and reinforcing materials, the unit of measure to use is per square foot of slab area. The costs should always contain a description of the material used and the type of installation.

On large jobs, where the major portion of slab forms is composed of this material, it is desirable to keep separate costs on the various operations involved, such as unloading, hoisting, placing and welding. For smaller installations, however, only an aggregate unit cost is usually required to check the progress of the work and to provide information for future reference.

Labor Distribution Figure 126 illustrates the correct method of keeping costs on the installation of corrugated steel form material over pipe tunnels. The first column gives the total area of slab formed, the second column gives the total payroll cost to date, the third column gives the average labor cost per square foot of slab forms, while the fourth column gives the average amount of slab forms installed by a man in an 8-hour day.

The back of the form, Figure 127, gives an analysis of the costs in man hours. The first column headed "Total Labor Hours" gives the total hours worked by each trade, while the second column headed "Labor Hours Per Unit," gives the number of hours required by each trade to install 100 square feet of corrugated steel permanent form material.

Precast Concrete Joists, Plank and Slabs

When keeping costs on the installation of precast concrete joists, plank and slabs, the units of measure to use are per piece for joists and per square foot for plank and slabs.

On large jobs the labor cost of each operation, such as unloading, hoisting, placing and grouting, should be kept separate but small installation costs are usually kept on an aggregate unit cost basis.

Cost records for this work should always contain a description of the material used, the size of the job and the method of installation.

For the correct method of keeping costs on handling, setting and grouting precast concrete rib slabs for a small roof area, refer to Labor Distribution Figure 128. The first column gives the area of slabs installed, the second column gives the total payroll costs to date, the third column gives the average unit cost per square foot of slabs, while the fourth column gives the average number of square feet of slab installed by a mason in an 8-hour day.

The back of the form, Figure 129, gives the total number of hours worked by each trade in the first column headed "Total Labor Hours," while the second column headed "Labor Hours Per Unit," gives the length of time required by each trade to unload, handle, hoist, place and grout 100 square feet of precast concrete rib slabs.

Clay Tile Floor Arches and Beam and Girder Covering

When erecting clay tile floor arches, formerly a widely used floor system in steel skeleton construction, it is necessary to first construct temporary centering to support the floor arches until the mortar sets supporting the arch tile, after which the temporary wood centering may be removed.

Separate labor costs should be kept of the time required for erecting and removing the temporary wood centering and separate costs on handling and setting the tile floor arches. If possible, separate costs should also be kept on arches of different thicknesses.

Labor Distribution Figure 130 illustrates the correct method of keeping costs on tile floor arches. The labor costs under "D-51" cover the cost of erecting and removing temporary wood centers, while the costs given under "D-52" cover the cost of handling and setting the floor arches.

The first column gives the number of square feet of temporary wood centering erected and removed, the second column gives the total labor cost, the third column gives the average unit labor cost per square foot of centering, while the fourth column gives the average number of square feet of centering erected and re-

Fig. 127 — COST ANALYSIS RECORD

TOTAL LABOR HOURS — UNIT

	1 IRON WORKERS	2 LAB.	3	4	5	6	7	8
PREVIOUS	—	—						
THIS WEEK	36	28						
TOTAL	36	28						

LABOR HOURS PER UNIT — UNIT PER 100 SF

	1 IRON WORKERS	2 LAB.	3	4	5	6	7	8
PREVIOUS	—	—						
THIS WEEK	1.05	0.81						
TOTAL	1.05	0.81						

REMARKS: CORRUGATED STEEL PERMANENT FORMS – INSTALLED OVER PIPE TUNNELS IN AUDITORIUM & GYM.

MFD. IN U.S.A. FORM C-105 FRANK R. WALKER CO., PUBLISHERS, CHICAGO

Fig. 127. Analyzed Labor Costs of Placing Corrugated Steel Permanent Forms.

Fig. 128 — LABOR DISTRIBUTION

SHEET NO. 26 JOB NO. 110
WEEK ENDING APRIL 10, 19--
JOB CENTRAL HIGH SCHOOL
CLASS OF WORK D-44

OCCUPATION	M	T	W	T	F	S	S	HOURS	RATE	AMOUNT
1 MASONS	16	16	4	—	—	—	—	36		
2 CRANE OPR.	8	8	—	—	—	—	—	16		
3 IRON WORKER	8	8	—	—	—	—	—	16		
4 LABORERS	56	48	22	—	—	—	—	126		
5										
6										
7										
8										
TOTAL										

	QTY. WORK IN PLACE	PAY ROLL COSTS	LBR. AVERAGE UNIT COST	AVERAGE QUANTITY PER 8 HR. DAY	QTY. WORK IN PLACE	PAY ROLL COSTS	LBR. AVERAGE UNIT COST	AVERAGE QUANTITY PER 8 HR. DAY
PREVIOUS			—	—				
THIS WEEK	4500 SF		—	1000 SF				
TOTAL	4500		—	1000				

MFD. IN U.S.A. FORM C-105 FRANK R. WALKER CO., PUBLISHERS, CHICAGO

Fig. 128. Labor Distribution and Costs of Handling and Setting Precast Concrete Roof Slabs.

Fig. 129 — COST ANALYSIS RECORD

TOTAL LABOR HOURS — UNIT

	1 MASONS	2 CRANE OPR	3 IRON WORKER	4 LAB.	5	6	7	8
PREVIOUS	—	—	—	—				
THIS WEEK	36	16	16	126				
TOTAL	36	16	16	126				

LABOR HOURS PER UNIT — UNIT PER 100 SF

	1 MASONS	2 CRANE OPR.	3 IRON WORKER	4 LAB.	5	6	7	8
PREVIOUS	—	—	—	—				
THIS WEEK	0.80	0.36	0.36	2.8				
TOTAL	0.80	0.36	0.36	2.8				

REMARKS

PRECAST CONCRETE RIB SLABS FOR ROOF OVER STAGE IN AUDITORIUM. SIMPLE, FLAT ROOF WITH ONE LARGE SKYLIGHT OPENING. HOISTED WITH TRUCK CRANE.

MFD. IN U.S.A. FORM C-105 FRANK R. WALKER CO., PUBLISHERS, CHICAGO

Fig. 129. Analyzed Labor Costs of Handling and Setting Precast Concrete Roof Slabs.

Fig. 130. Labor Distribution and Costs of Setting Tile Floor Arches.

LABOR DISTRIBUTION

JOB CENTRAL HIGH SCHOOL   SHEET NO. 27
CLASS OF WORK D-51, D-52   WEEK ENDING APRIL 10, 19--   JOB NO. 110

OCCUPATION	M	T	W	T	F	S	S	HOURS	RATE	AMOUNT
1 D-51 LABORERS	40	44	-	22	-			106		
2										
3										
4										
5 D-52 { MASONS	24	16	12	-				52		
6 LABORERS	72	48	36	-				156		
7										
8										
TOTAL D-51										D-52

	QTY. WORK IN PLACE	PAY ROLL COSTS	LBR. AVERAGE UNIT COST	AVERAGE QUANTITY PER 8 HR. DAY	QTY. WORK IN PLACE	PAY ROLL COSTS	LBR. AVERAGE UNIT COST	AVERAGE QUANTITY PER 8 HR. DAY
PREVIOUS	4200 SF			162 SF	4000 SF			MASON 334 SF
THIS WEEK	2100			158	2300			354
TOTAL	6300			160	6300			341

MFD. IN U.S.A.   FORM C-105   FRANK R. WALKER CO., PUBLISHERS, CHICAGO   (OVER)

Fig. 131. Analyzed Labor Costs of Setting Tile Floor Arches.

COST ANALYSIS RECORD

UNIT

TOTAL LABOR HOURS

	1 LAB.	2	3	4	5 MASONS	6 LAB.	7	8
PREVIOUS	208				96	280		
THIS WEEK	106				52	156		
TOTAL	314				148	436		

UNIT PER 100 SF

LABOR HOURS PER UNIT

	1 LAB.	2	3	4	5 MASONS	6 LAB.	7	8
PREVIOUS	4.95				2.40	7.00		
THIS WEEK	5.05				2.26	6.78		
TOTAL	4.98				2.35	6.92		

REMARKS

8" CLAY TILE ARCHES IN BOILER HOUSE MEZZANINE.

MFD. IN U.S.A.   FORM C-105   FRANK R. WALKER CO., PUBLISHERS, CHICAGO

LABOR DISTRIBUTION

JOB CENTRAL HIGH SCHOOL   SHEET NO. 28
CLASS OF WORK D-71, D-72   WEEK ENDING APRIL 17, 19--   JOB NO. 110

OCCUPATION	M	T	W	T	F	S	S	HOURS	RATE	AMOUNT
1 D-71 { IRON WORKERS	27	26	24	—	—	—	—	77		
2 { CRANE OPR.	3	2	—	—	—	—	—	5		
3										
4										
5 D-72 { TILE SETTERS	16	16	16	16	16	—	—	80		
6 { IRON WORKER	5	6	8	8	8	—	—	27		
7 { CRANE OPR.	5	6	8	8	8	—	—	27		
8 LABORERS	48	48	48	48	48	—	—	240		
TOTAL D-71								D-72		

	QTY. WORK IN PLACE	PAY ROLL COSTS	LBR. AVERAGE UNIT COST	AVERAGE QUANTITY PER 8 HR. DAY	QTY. WORK IN PLACE	PAY ROLL COSTS	LBR. AVERAGE UNIT COST	AVERAGE QUANTITY PER 8 HR. DAY
PREVIOUS	16.74 TON			6.27 TON	29,500 SF			TILE SETTER 1054 SF
THIS WEEK	4.86			6.31	10,500			1050
TOTAL	21.60			6.28	40,000			1053

MFD. IN U.S.A.   FORM C-105   FRANK R. WALKER CO., PUBLISHERS, CHICAGO   (OVER)

Fig. 132. Labor Distribution and Costs of Handling and Setting Gypsum Roof Tile.

moved in an 8-hour day. Columns five to eight give the same information regarding the cost of handling and setting the floor arches.

The back of the form, Figure 131, gives the number of hours worked by each trade in the first column headed "Total Labor Hours," while the second column headed "Labor Hours Per Unit" gives the length of time required by each trade to erect and remove 100 square feet of temporary wood centering or handle and set 100 square feet of clay tile floor arches.

When reporting labor costs on covering steel beams and girders with clay tile fireproofing, the costs should be given in square feet, where the beams or girders are over one foot in depth, and in lineal feet when they are less than one foot in depth. When reporting these costs, always describe the class of work, as it is important to know the method used and tile necessary to fire-proof special shapes and sections of steel.

Hollow Clay Book Tile and Precast Gypsum Roof Tile and Plank

When keeping costs on the installation of hollow clay book tile and precast gypsum roof tile or plank, separate costs should be kept on the placing and welding of "Tee" irons or sub purlins, required for their support. The unit of measure usually used in reporting costs on this work is per pound or ton of "Tee" irons erected.

Labor costs on the installation of the roof tile or plank are generally computed on a square foot basis.

Cost reports on this type of work should always state the kind of material used, whether the roof is flat or pitched, height required to be hoisted, etc.

Labor Distribution Figure 132 illustrates the correct method of keeping costs on the installation of a precast, short span, gypsum tile roof deck. The first column gives the quantity of "Tee" irons erected and welded, the second column gives the total payroll cost to date for this work, the third column gives the average unit cost per ton of steel "Tee" iron, while the fourth column gives the average number of tons of "Tee" irons erected and welded by an ironworker in an 8-hour day. Columns five to eight furnish the same information regarding the handling, hoisting and placing of the precast gypsum roof tile.

The back of the form, Figure 133, analyzes the costs on a labor hour basis. The first column headed "Total Labor Hours," gives the total hours worked by each trade, while the second column headed "Labor Hours Per Unit," gives the length of time required to erect and weld one ton of "Tee" irons or handle, hoist and place 100 square feet of precast short span gypsum roof tile.

Poured-In-Place Gypsum Roof Decks

The construction of poured-in-place gypsum roof decks involves several different labor operations, which include erecting and welding "Tee" iron sub-purlins, placing permanent form material, placing reinforcing material, placing gypsum material and finishing gypsum surface ready to receive roofing. Separate labor costs should be kept on each of the various operations to insure having adequate records for reference in estimating future jobs, as the costs may vary due to changes in design or materials specified. All cost records on this type of work should contain a brief but comprehensive description of the work, giving the kind of materials used and the nature of the job.

Concrete Masonry Units

When keeping costs on cement block and cement brick masonry, separate costs should be kept on the different kinds of work, such as foundation walls, exterior walls and facing, back-up, etc. Costs should also state the kind of mortar used and the type of joint treatment, such as flush cut, tooled, raked, etc.

Labor Distribution Figure 134 shows the correct method of keeping costs on concrete block masonry. The first column gives the number of block laid, the second column gives the labor cost to date, the third column the average cost per block, while the fourth column gives the average number of block laid by a mason in an 8-hour day.

The back of the form, Figure 135, gives the total labor hours worked by each trade in the first column headed "Total Labor Hours," while the second column headed "Labor Hours Per Unit," gives the length of time required by each trade to lay 100 concrete block.

Fig. 133 — COST ANALYSIS RECORD

	1 IRON WORKERS	2 CRANE OPR.	3	4	5 TILE SETTERS	6 IRON WORKER	7 CRANE OPR.	8 LAB.
TOTAL LABOR HOURS								
PREVIOUS	267	19			224	77	77	672
THIS WEEK	77	5			80	27	27	240
TOTAL	344	24			304	104	104	912
LABOR HOURS PER UNIT — UNIT PER 100 SF OF GYP. TILE								
PREVIOUS	15.9	1.13			0.76	0.26	0.26	2.28
THIS WEEK	15.8	1.03			0.76	0.26	0.26	2.28
TOTAL	15.9	1.11			0.76	0.26	0.26	2.28

REMARKS: SHORT SPAN GYPSUM ROOF TILE, SUPPORTED ON "TEE" IRONS ON LOW-RISE PITCHED GYM ROOF. 82'-0" HIGH, GROUND TO ROOF. HOISTED WITH TRUCK CRANE.

MFD. IN U.S.A.   FORM C-105   FRANK R. WALKER CO., PUBLISHERS, CHICAGO

Fig. 133. Analyzed Labor Costs of Handling and Setting Gypsum Roof Tile.

Fig. 134 — LABOR DISTRIBUTION

SHEET NO. 29

JOB CENTRAL HIGH SCHOOL   CLASS OF WORK E-4   WEEK ENDING FEB 20, 19—   JOB NO. 110

	OCCUPATION	M	T	W	T	F	S	S	HOURS	RATE	AMOUNT
1	MASONS	16	16	16	—	1	—	1	48		
2	LABORERS	16	16	16	—	1	—	1	48		
3											
4											
5											
6											
7											
8											
TOTAL											

	QTY. WORK IN PLACE	LBR. AVERAGE UNIT COST	PAY ROLL COSTS	QTY. WORK IN PLACE	AVERAGE QUANTITY PER 8 HR. DAY	LBR. AVERAGE UNIT COST	PAY ROLL COSTS	AVERAGE QUANTITY PER 8 HR. DAY
PREVIOUS	1500 BLKS				150 BLKS			
THIS WEEK	950				158			
TOTAL	2450				153			

MFD. IN U.S.A.   FORM C-105   FRANK R. WALKER CO., PUBLISHERS, CHICAGO

Fig. 134. Labor Distribution and Costs of Laying Concrete Block.

Fig. 135 — COST ANALYSIS RECORD

	1 MASONS	2 LAB.	3	4	5	6	7	8
TOTAL LABOR HOURS								
PREVIOUS	80	80						
THIS WEEK	48	48						
TOTAL	128	128						
LABOR HOURS PER UNIT — UNIT PER 100 BLOCKS								
PREVIOUS	5.33	5.33						
THIS WEEK	5.05	5.05						
TOTAL	5.22	5.22						

REMARKS: 8" CONCRETE BLOCK EXTERIOR WALLS OF GARAGE & BOILER HOUSE, 8"x8"x16" LIGHT WEIGHT BLOCKS LAID IN LIME-CEMENT MORTAR WITH FLUSH CUT JOINTS — NO HOISTING REQUIRED.

MFD. IN U.S.A.   FORM C-105   FRANK R. WALKER CO., PUBLISHERS, CHICAGO

Fig. 135. Analyzed Labor Costs of Laying Concrete Block.

Brickwork

When keeping costs on all classes of brickwork, a thousand brick is the customary unit of measure.

It is advisable to separate the labor costs on the different kinds of brickwork, as the costs vary greatly on each kind of work, and unless kept separately, they are practically useless as unit costs. This includes all kinds of brick, such as common, face or press brick, fire brick, brick mantels and fire-places, hearths, back-hearths, walks, steps, etc. When reporting labor costs always state the kind of brick laid, size, width and style of mortar joint, whether cut flush, raked out, "V" joint, struck joints, or any other special joint, as this has an important bearing on the cost of the work. Also state the kind of mortar used in laying the brick.

Labor Distribution Figure 136 illustrates the correct method of keeping costs on brick masonry. The first column gives the number of common brick laid, the second column gives the total labor cost, the third column the average cost per thousand brick, while the fourth column gives the number of common brick averaged per 8-hour day. The items under "E-23" include the itemized costs of laying face or press brick. The fifth column states the total number of face brick laid, the sixth column gives the total labor cost, the seventh column the average cost per thousand brick, while the eighth column gives the number of face brick averaged per 8-hour day.

The back of this form, Figure 137, gives the total number of hours worked by each trade in the first column headed "Total Labor Hours," while the second column, headed "Labor Hours Per Unit," gives the length of time required by each trade to lay one thousand common brick or one thousand face brick.

When laying face brick on special work such as fireplaces, brick mantels, etc., it is advisable to report the number of fireplaces completed, stating the approximate number of brick required in each, as it is customary to figure a certain price for labor on each fireplace or mantel.

Glass Masonry Units

When keeping costs on glass block masonry, the unit of measure to use is per block. Separate costs should be kept on the different sizes of blocks and also on the installation of accessories required, if possible. The units of measure for accessories are per lineal foot for expansion strips and wall ties and per piece for wall anchors.

Clay and Gypsum Tile Units

When reporting labor costs on all types of load bearing tile used for structural walls or for backing-up face brick or other exterior masonry facing, it is advisable to report the class of work performed together with the size and description of the tile, as there are a great many sizes and shapes of tile used for this purpose. Costs on work of this kind should be reported by the number of square feet or the number of pieces of tile set, whichever method conforms with that used in estimating the job.

Masonry partitions, furring and column covering work may be done in several different materials, including cement block, hollow clay tile, gypsum tile and structural glazed tile. When keeping costs on this work, the unit of measure for cement block and structural glazed tile partitions, etc., is per piece, while for hollow clay tile or gypsum tile the costs are kept on a square foot basis.

Separate costs should be kept, not only for the different kinds of materials, but for each thickness of block or tile as well. This is important as the thicker the material, the less a man can handle and lay per day. Costs should always state the kind of material, face size and thickness of the block or tile, height of partition, etc. In addition, special shapes for corners, caps, base, etc. are usually required in structural glazed tile work and separate costs should be kept on setting these pieces, if possible.

Labor Distribution Figure 140 illustrates the correct method of keeping costs on 4 and 6-inch hollow clay tile partitions. The first column gives the number of square feet of 4-inch tile laid, the second column gives the total labor cost, the third column gives the average cost per square foot, while the fourth column gives the average number of square feet set per 8-hour day. Columns five to eight give the same costs on 6-inch tile.

The back of the form, Figure 141, gives the total number of hours worked by each trade in the first column headed "Total Labor Hours," while the second column headed "Labor Hours Per Unit," gives the length of time required by each trade to handle and set 100 square feet of 4 or 6-inch hollow clay partition tile.

Fig. 136 — LABOR DISTRIBUTION

JOB CENTRAL HIGH SCHOOL   SHEET NO. 30
CLASS OF WORK E-22, E-23   WEEK ENDING Feb 13, 19--   JOB NO. 110

	OCCUPATION	M	T	W	T	F	S	S	HOURS	RATE	AMOUNT
1	E-22 { MASONS	14	48	40	48	40	1	1	224		
2	LABORERS		44	44	44	44	1	1	220		
3											
4											
5	E-23 { MASONS		32	32	32	32	1	1	160		
6	LABORERS		20	20	20	20	1	1	100		
7											
8											

TOTAL	E-22				E-23			
	QTY. WORK IN PLACE	PAY ROLL COSTS	LBR. AVERAGE UNIT COST	AVERAGE QUANTITY PER 8 HR. DAY	QTY. WORK IN PLACE	PAY ROLL COSTS	LBR. AVERAGE UNIT COST	AVERAGE QUANTITY PER 8 HR. DAY
PREVIOUS	37.2 M		930	14.1 M				427
THIS WEEK	26.5		946	8.5				425
TOTAL	63.7		937	22.6				426

MFD. IN U.S.A.   FORM C-105   FRANK R. WALKER CO., PUBLISHERS, CHICAGO   (OVER)

Fig. 136. Labor Distribution and Costs of Laying Common and Face Brick.

Fig. 137 — COST ANALYSIS RECORD

UNIT — PER 1000 BRICK

TOTAL LABOR HOURS

	1 MASONS	2 LAB	3	4	5 MASONS	6 LAB	7	8
PREVIOUS	320	316			264	164		
THIS WEEK	224	220			160	100		
TOTAL	544	536			424	264		

LABOR HOURS PER UNIT

	1 MASONS	2 LAB	3	4	5 MASONS	6 LAB	7	8
PREVIOUS	8.60	8.50			18.7	11.6		
THIS WEEK	8.45	8.30			18.8	11.8		
TOTAL	8.54	8.41			18.8	11.7		

REMARKS: COMMON BRICK BACK-UP - SOME 12" FREESTANDING WALLS - LIME - CEMENT MORTAR. FACE BRICK - 3/8" CONCAVE TOOLED JOINTS - COMMON BOND - FULL HEADERS EVERY 6TH COURSE - LIME-CEMENT MORTAR - NO HOISTING YET.

MFD. IN U.S.A.   FORM C-105   FRANK R. WALKER CO., PUBLISHERS, CHICAGO

Fig. 137. Analyzed Labor Costs of Laying Common and Face Brick.

Fig. 138 — LABOR DISTRIBUTION

JOB CENTRAL HIGH SCHOOL   SHEET NO. 32
CLASS OF WORK F-11, F-12   WEEK ENDING APRIL 10, 19--   JOB NO. 110

	OCCUPATION	M	T	W	T	F	S	S	HOURS	RATE	AMOUNT
1	F-11 { MASONS	16	16	16	12	16	—	—	76		
2	LABORERS	16	16	16	12	16	—	—	76		
3											
4											
5	F-12 { MASONS	8	8	8	12	8	—	—	44		
6	LABORERS	8	8	8	12	8	—	—	44		
7											
8											

TOTAL	F-11				F-12			
	QTY. WORK IN PLACE	PAY ROLL COSTS	LBR. AVERAGE UNIT COST	AVERAGE QUANTITY PER 8 HR. DAY	QTY. WORK IN PLACE	PAY ROLL COSTS	LBR. AVERAGE UNIT COST	AVERAGE QUANTITY PER 8 HR. DAY
PREVIOUS	2230 SF			194 SF	690 SF			173 SF
THIS WEEK	1820			192	900			164
TOTAL	4050			193	1590			167

MFD. IN U.S.A.   FORM C-105   FRANK R. WALKER CO., PUBLISHERS, CHICAGO   (OVER)

Fig. 138. Labor Distribution and Costs of Setting Partition Tile.

COST ANALYSIS RECORD

TOTAL LABOR HOURS — UNIT

	1 MASONS 2 LAB.	2	3	4	5 MASONS 6 LAB.	7	8
PREVIOUS	92	92			32	32	
THIS WEEK	76	76			44	44	76
TOTAL	168	168			76	76	

LABOR HOURS PER UNIT — UNIT PER 100 S.F.

	1 MASONS 2 LAB	2	3	4	5 MASONS 6 LAB	7	8
PREVIOUS	4.12	4.12			4.64	4.64	
THIS WEEK	4.17	4.17			4.89	4.89	
TOTAL	4.15	4.15			4.78	4.78	

REMARKS

4" & 6" HOLLOW CLAY TILE PARTITIONS — 10'-0" HIGH
LARGE ROOMS — STRAIGHT RUN JOB — MATERIAL HOISTED
ON AUTOMATIC HOIST.

MFD. IN U.S.A.   FORM C-105   FRANK R. WALKER CO., PUBLISHERS, CHICAGO

Fig. 139. Analyzed Labor Costs of Setting Partition Tile.

LABOR DISTRIBUTION

JOB CENTRAL HIGH SCHOOL   WEEK ENDING MAR. 20, 19—   SHEET NO. 31
CLASS OF WORK E-61, E-65   JOB NO. 110

	OCCUPATION	M	T	W	T	F	S	S	HOURS	RATE	AMOUNT
1 E-61	LABORERS	32	32						64		
2											
3											
4											
5	STONE SETTERS	16	16	16	16				80		
6 E-65	DERRICK MEN	32	32	32	32				160		
7	LABORERS	48	48	48	48				240		
8											
TOTAL E-61									E-65		

	QTY. WORK IN PLACE	PAY ROLL COSTS	LBR. AVERAGE UNIT COST	AVERAGE QUANTITY PER 8 HR. DAY	QTY. WORK IN PLACE	PAY ROLL COSTS	LBR. AVERAGE UNIT COST	AVERAGE QUANTITY PER 8 HR. DAY
PREVIOUS	750 CF			150 CF	175 CF			88 CF
THIS WEEK	1220			152	890			89
TOTAL	1970			151	1065			89

MFD. IN U.S.A.   FORM C-105   FRANK R. WALKER CO., PUBLISHERS, CHICAGO   (OVER)

Fig. 140. Labor Distribution and Costs of Handling and Setting Cut Stone.

COST ANALYSIS RECORD

TOTAL LABOR HOURS — UNIT

	1 LAB.	2	3	4	5 STONE SETTERS	6 DERRICK MEN	7 LAB.	8
PREVIOUS	40				16	32	48	
THIS WEEK	64				80	160	240	
TOTAL	104				96	192	288	

LABOR HOURS PER UNIT — UNIT PER 100 CF

	1 LAB.	2	3	4	5 STONE SETTERS	6 DERRICK MEN	7 LAB	8
PREVIOUS	5.33				9.14	18.29	27.43	
THIS WEEK	5.24				8.99	17.98	26.97	
TOTAL	5.28				9.01	18.03	27.04	

REMARKS

COURSED ASHLAR FACING AT MAIN ENTRANCE & AUDITORIUM
ENTRANCE. STONES AVERAGE 30" x 30" x 6" OR ABOUT
470 LBS. PER PIECE.

MFD. IN U.S.A.   FORM C-105   FRANK R. WALKER CO., PUBLISHERS, CHICAGO

Fig. 141. Analyzed Labor Costs of Handling and Setting Cut Stone.

When keeping costs on setting clay tile or cement flue lining, the quantities are measured by the lineal foot of flue lining set. Costs should state the kind of material used and separate costs should be kept on the different sizes.

Cost records on setting vitrified tile wall coping should contain a brief description of the job, such as type of coping (double slant, single slant, etc.), thickness of wall, hoisting height, etc. Separate costs should be kept for the different sizes of coping. The unit of measure to use for computing the costs is per lineal foot of coping set.

Cut Stone, Granite, Terra Cotta, Etc.

Cut stone, granite and terra cotta are usually estimated by the cubic foot, taking the largest dimensions of each piece, so that the labor costs of handling and setting should be figured on the same basis. Granite facing two inches thick and under, ceramic veneer and precast facing slabs are measured on a square foot basis.

Separate costs should be kept on unloading the stone, granite, terra cotta, etc., at the job.

The labor cost of setting should include erecting temporary "horse" scaffold, operating hand or power derricks, setters and helpers handling and setting the stone, granite, terra cotta, etc.

If there is any cutting necessary on the job, such as lewising, dowel holes, carving, fitting, etc., separate labor costs should be kept on this work.

Labor Distribution Figure 138 illustrates the correct method of keeping costs on handling and setting cut stone. The classification "E-61" includes the cost of unloading the stone, sorting, and placing on the job ready for use, while the costs given under "E-65" include all time required handling, hoisting and setting the stone in place.

The first column under "E-61" gives the total number of cubic feet unloaded, the second column gives the total labor cost, the third column the average cost per cubic foot, while the fourth column gives the average number of cubic feet unloaded per 8-hour day.

The total number of cubic feet of stone set is given in the fifth column under the classification "E-65." The sixth column gives the total setting cost, the seventh column the average cost per cubic foot, while the eighth column gives the average number of cubic feet set per 8-hour day.

The back of the form, Figure 139, gives the total number of hours worked by each trade in the first column headed "Total Labor Hours," while the second column headed "Labor Hours Per Unit," gives the length of time required by each trade to unload or handle and set 100 cubic feet of stone.

When computing granite quantities, for thick facing, sills, treads, caps, etc., do not figure any piece of granite less than 12 inches thick, as this is the method used by many quarries and granite cutters when estimating the cost of new work.

The method of keeping labor costs on setting granite, terra cotta, ceramic veneer, precast facing slabs, etc., is the same as that used for stone work, except that for material two inches thick and under the costs are kept on a square foot basis.

Cleaning, Pointing and Sandblasting Masonry

The cost of tuck pointing, sand blasting, washing down and cleaning all kinds of masonry surfaces, such as cut stone, granite, brick, terra cotta, etc., is usually estimated by the square foot, taking the area of the entire surface to be cleaned, and the costs should be stated in the same manner.

The cost record should state clearly the class of work performed as labor costs on the different kinds of cleaning and tuck pointing vary widely.

Water and Damp-Proofing

When keeping costs on water and damp-proofing, the method used will have considerable to do with the manner in which the costs should be kept.

If the water or damp-proofing consists of a plaster coat applied to old surfaces, there is usually some preparation necessary before the work can be started. This usually consists of picking or roughing the old

LABOR DISTRIBUTION

JOB _Central High School_   CLASS OF WORK _F-55-A, F-55-B_   WEEK ENDING _Jan 9, 19--_   SHEET NO. _33_   JOB NO. _110_

	OCCUPATION	M	T	W	T	F	S	S	HOURS	RATE	AMOUNT
1	F-55-A LABORERS	16	14	—	1	1	1	1	30		
2											
3											
4											
5	F-55-B LABORERS	1	2	16	10	—	1	1	28		
6											
7											
8											

TOTAL

	F-55-A, 1st COAT				F-55-B, 2nd COAT			
	QTY. WORK IN PLACE	PAY ROLL COSTS	LBR. AVERAGE UNIT COST	AVERAGE QUANTITY PER 8 HR. DAY	QTY. WORK IN PLACE	PAY ROLL COSTS	LBR. AVERAGE UNIT COST	AVERAGE QUANTITY PER 8 HR. DAY
PREVIOUS	—	—	—		—	—	—	
THIS WEEK	2400 SF			640 SF	2400 SF			686 SF
TOTAL	2400			640	2400			686

MFD. IN U.S.A.   FORM C-105   FRANK R. WALKER CO., PUBLISHERS, CHICAGO

Fig. 142. Labor Distribution and Costs of Exterior Waterproofing.

COST ANALYSIS RECORD

TOTAL LABOR HOURS

	1 LAB.	2	3	4	5 LAB.	6	7	8
PREVIOUS	—				—			
THIS WEEK	30				28			
TOTAL	30				28			

UNIT PER 100 SF

LABOR HOURS PER UNIT

	1 LAB.	2	3	4	5 LAB.	6	7	8
PREVIOUS	—				—			
THIS WEEK	1.25				1.17			
TOTAL	1.25				1.17			

REMARKS

APPLICATION OF 2 COATS OF R.I.W. DAMPPROOFING TO EXTERIOR OF BASEMENT WALLS.

MFD. IN U.S.A.   FORM C-105   FRANK R. WALKER CO., PUBLISHERS, CHICAGO

Fig. 143. Analyzed Labor Costs of Exterior Waterproofing.

LABOR DISTRIBUTION

JOB _Central High School_   SHEET NO. _34_

CLASS OF WORK _G-5_   WEEK ENDING _MAR. 6, 19--_   JOB NO. _110_

	OCCUPATION	M	T	W	T	F	S	S	HOURS	RATE	AMOUNT
1	CARPENTERS	—	24	24	24	8	—	—	80		
2	LABORERS	—	8	8	6	—	—	—	22		
3											
4											
5											
6											
7											
8											

TOTAL

	QTY. WORK IN PLACE	PAY ROLL COSTS	LBR. AVERAGE UNIT COST	AVERAGE QUANTITY PER 8 HR. DAY	QTY. WORK IN PLACE	PAY ROLL COSTS	LBR. AVERAGE UNIT COST	AVERAGE QUANTITY PER 8 HR. DAY
PREVIOUS	—	—	PER M FBM	—				
THIS WEEK	2966 FBM		297 FBM					
TOTAL	2966		297					

MFD. IN U.S.A.   FORM C-105   FRANK R. WALKER CO., PUBLISHERS, CHICAGO   (OVER)

Fig. 144. Labor Distribution and Costs of Framing and Erecting Roof Lumber.

masonry surface to form a bond for the new plaster coat, and then brushing it, using a fibre brush and muriatic acid to remove all loose particles of old concrete. The cost of preparing the walls or surfaces should be kept separate, as some jobs require twice as much preparation as others. These costs should state the number of square feet of surface prepared.

When reporting these costs, give a description of the work stating whether it consisted of one, two or three coats of plaster, the thickness of same, etc. The costs should also state the number of square feet of surface treated.

On jobs where a membrane system of waterproofing is used, consisting of applications of hot or cold composition and waterproofed felt, fabric or burlap, applied in the same manner as a built-up roof, the cost should give a description of the work, whether walls or roofs, together with the number of applications of composition and felt or fabric applied. The costs should also state the number of square feet of surface waterproofed.

On jobs where the damp-proofing consists of one or more applications of heavy paint or similar substance, the costs should always state the kind of surface treated and the number of coats applied. Separate costs should be kept on the first and second coats, if possible, because it is more difficult to apply the first coat on account of the rough surface of the concrete or masonry. After the first coat has been applied the surface is smoother and the additional coats should be applied with considerable less labor. Always state the number of square feet of surface covered.

Labor Distribution Figure 142 illustrates the correct method of keeping costs on work of this kind. The first column gives the number of square feet of surface covered, the second column gives the total labor cost, the third column gives the average labor cost per square foot, while the fourth column gives the average amount of surface a man covered per 8-hour day. On the back of this form, Figure 143, the first column headed "Total Labor Hours," gives the total number of hours worked by each trade, while the second column headed "Labor Hours Per Unit," gives the length of time required to apply waterproof paint to 100 square feet of surface.

Caulking

When keeping costs on caulking around door and window frames with oakum and mastic, a complete description of the work should be given, stating the average sizes of openings, accessibility of the work, kind of material used, method of appliation, etc. Costs on this work are usually given per lineal foot, but may be kept on a per opening basis if the openings are uniform in size.

Rough Carpentry and Timber Framing

Nearly all classes of carpentry, including framing for heavy mill and factory buildings, containing wood posts and girders, heavy wood beams and joists, rough and finish wood flooring, roof sheathing, etc., should be estimated by the thousand feet of lumber, board measure.

On timber framing work, the cost of framing and erecting the wood columns or posts should be kept as a separate item, as this usually includes boring holes through the center of the posts, chamfering the corners, framing for metal bases, caps, etc., as a carpenter will not ordinarily perform a large amount of this kind of work per day and it is important to know just what it costs per thousand feet.

The cost of framing and erecting heavy wood girders, beams and joists should be kept in the same manner, stating whether the corners are chamfered, whether necessary to frame for stirrups, hangers, etc., as these are all important items when estimating the cost of new work.

The labor cost of handling and framing wood floor joists, roof rafters, etc., should be kept separate from heavy construction, as the work is much different and the labor costs also. However, all costs should be stated per thousand feet of lumber, board measure.

Framing for roof saddles, hips, valleys and other light wood construction should be kept separate wherever possible, as there is usually a large amount of cutting and fitting necessary in proportion to the actual quantity of lumber framed.

On dwellings and other types of light frame construction where 2x4 or 2x6-inch lumber is used, the costs should be kept separately, as it requires nearly as much time to frame a 2x4 as a 2x8. Separate labor costs

Fig. 145. Analyzed Labor Costs of Framing and Erecting Roof Lumber.

COST ANALYSIS RECORD

TOTAL LABOR HOURS — UNIT

	1 CARP.	2 LAB.	3	4	5	6	7	8
PREVIOUS	—	—						
THIS WEEK	80	22						
TOTAL	80	22						

LABOR HOURS PER UNIT — UNIT PER 1000 FT. B.M.

	1 CARP.	2 LAB.	3	4	5	6	7	8
PREVIOUS	—	—						
THIS WEEK	27.0	7.4						
TOTAL	27.0	7.4						

REMARKS

GABLE ROOF OVER GARAGE - 2"x8" RAFTERS, 2"x10" RIDGE, 1"x6" COLLAR BEAMS

MFD. IN U.S.A. FORM C-105 FRANK R. WALKER CO., PUBLISHERS, CHICAGO

Fig. 146. Labor Distribution and Costs of Laying Rough Wood Floors.

LABOR DISTRIBUTION   SHEET NO. 35

JOB CENTRAL HIGH SCHOOL   CLASS OF WORK G-7   WEEK ENDING APRIL 10, 19-- JOB NO. 110

	OCCUPATION	M	T	W	T	F	S	S	HOURS	RATE	AMOUNT
1	CARPENTERS	16	16	16	1	1			64		
2	LABORERS	8	8	8	1				32		
3											
4											
5											
6											
7											
8											
TOTAL											

	QTY. WORK IN PLACE	PAY ROLL COSTS	LBR. AVERAGE UNIT COST	AVERAGE QUANTITY PER 8 HR. DAY	QTY. WORK IN PLACE	PAY ROLL COSTS	LBR. AVERAGE UNIT COST	AVERAGE QUANTITY PER 8 HR. DAY
PREVIOUS								
THIS WEEK	5760 FBM		PER M FBM	720 FBM				720 FBM
TOTAL	5760			720				720

MFD. IN U.S.A. FORM C-105 FRANK R. WALKER CO., PUBLISHERS, CHICAGO

(OVER)

COST ANALYSIS RECORD

TOTAL LABOR HOURS					UNIT			
	1 CARP.	2 LAB.	3	4	5	6	7	8
PREVIOUS	—	—						
THIS WEEK	64	32						
TOTAL	64	32						

LABOR HOURS PER UNIT					UNIT PER 1000 FT. B.M.			
	1 CARP.	2 LAB	3	4	5	6	7	8
PREVIOUS	—	—						
THIS WEEK	11.1	5.6						
TOTAL	11.1	5.6						

REMARKS

STAGE SUB-FLOORING - 1"x6" D & M LAID DIAGONALLY OVER WOOD JOISTS

MFD. IN U.S.A.   FORM C-105   FRANK R. WALKER CO., PUBLISHERS, CHICAGO

Fig. 147. Analyzed Labor Costs of Laying Rough Wood Floors.

should be kept on framing exterior stud walls and the costs should always state the quantity of lumber, board measure.

Separate labor costs should also be kept on placing wood sills, floor and ceiling joists, etc., and all costs should state the number of feet of lumber, board measure, framed and erected.

Roof framing is another item that should be kept separately, as work of this kind is considerably more expensive than straight framing, so that care should be used to obtain accurate labor costs on all kinds of roof framing. When reporting the costs be sure to give an accurate description of the roof, whether plain or cut up with gables, dormers, etc., as the more complicated the roof the more difficult it is to frame, and the higher the labor costs.

Labor Distribution Figure 144 illustrates the correct method of keeping costs on roof framing. The first column gives the amount of lumber, board measure, framed and erected, the second column gives the total labor cost, the third column gives the average cost per thousand feet of lumber, while the fourth column give the average amount of lumber, board measure, framed per 8-hour day.

The back of the form, Figure 145, gives the total number of hours worked by each trade in the first column headed "Total Labor Hours," while the second column headed "Labor Hours Per Unit," gives the length of time required to frame and erect a thousand feet of lumber, board measure.

The labor cost of handling and placing all kinds of rough wood flooring should also be kept as a separate item, giving a full description of the kind of flooring used, size of same, viz., 1x4, 1x6, 1x8, 2x6, 2x8, etc., and whether square edge or matched and dressed. It is not advisable to keep the costs of laying more than one size of flooring, roof or wall sheathing together, as the different widths of lumber all require different labor hours, and if they are not kept separate, it will be impossible to tell which are the more expensive kinds to lay.

Separate labor costs should always be kept on sidewall and roof sheathing, and all costs should be kept by the thousand feet of lumber, board measure, mentioning whether sheathing is laid straight or diagonally.

Labor Distribution Figure 146 illustrates the correct method of keeping costs on laying rough wood flooring. The first column gives the total number of feet of flooring laid, the second column gives the total labor cost, the third column gives the average cost per thousand feet, while the fourth column gives the average number of feet placed per 8-hour day.

The back of the form, Figure 147, gives the total number of hours worked by each trade in the first column headed "Total Labor Hours," while the second column headed "Labor Hours Per Unit," gives the length of time required to frame and place 1,000 feet of flooring, board measure.

When laminated flooring, consisting of 2x4, 2x6, 2x8 or 2x10-inch lumber laid on edge and spiked together, is used in heavy mill constructed warehouses, factories, etc., always keep separate costs on this class of work, giving the size of the lumber, method of laying, etc.

In buildings of this type it is also customary to use 2x6 or 3x6-inch tongued and grooved flooring, especially where there are heavy floor loads. Labor costs of flooring of this kind should be kept separate also and the costs should state the quantity of flooring laid, board measure.

The method used in keeping costs on laying flooring of this kind is exactly the same as illustrated in Figures 146 and 147.

Labor costs on placing building paper, deadening felt, etc. should also be kept as separate items and should be reported on a square foot basis. If strips of deadening felt are placed under furring strips or floor sleepers, the costs should be reported by the lineal foot.

When keeping costs on placing wood furring strips on brick or tile walls, the costs will vary according to the class of workmanship required. On ordinary work the strips are nailed direct to the masonry walls and follow the line of the brick or tile, so that the walls are not always plumb and true, while on first class work, it is necessary to wedge the strips out so that they will be perfectly straight. The costs on the two kinds of work vary considerably, and for this reason the class of work should always be recorded.

Wood furring strips of all kinds are measured by the lineal foot or by the number of square feet of wall surface covered, so that the costs should be reported in this manner.

The same method is used when keeping costs on placing wood floor screeds or sleepers, or wood furring strips over floors and on ceilings.

Labor Distribution Figure 148 illustrates the correct method of keeping labor costs on placing wood furring strips on walls. The first column gives the total number of lineal feet placed, the second column gives the total labor cost, the third column gives the average cost per lineal foot, while the fourth column gives the average number of lineal feet placed per 8-hour day.

LABOR DISTRIBUTION

JOB CENTRAL HIGH SCHOOL
CLASS OF WORK G-17
WEEK ENDING APRIL 17, 19--
SHEET NO. 36
JOB NO. 110

	OCCUPATION	M	T	W	T	F	S	S	HOURS	RATE	AMOUNT
1	CARPENTERS	16	16	16	16	16	1	1	80		
2	LABORERS	4	1	4	1	2	1	1	10		
3											
4											
5											
6											
7											
8											
TOTAL											

	QTY. WORK IN PLACE	PAY ROLL COSTS	LBR. AVERAGE UNIT COST	AVERAGE QUANTITY PER 8 HR. DAY	QTY. WORK IN PLACE	PAY ROLL COSTS	LBR. AVERAGE UNIT COST	AVERAGE QUANTITY PER 8 HR. DAY
PREVIOUS	1800 LF			225 LF				
THIS WEEK	2300			230				
TOTAL	4100			228				

MFD. IN U.S.A.   FORM C-105   FRANK R. WALKER CO., PUBLISHERS, CHICAGO   (OVER)

Fig. 148. Labor Distribution and Costs of Placing Wood Furring Strips on Walls.

COST ANALYSIS RECORD

		UNIT	3	4	5	6	7	8

TOTAL LABOR HOURS

	1 CARP.	2 LAB.						
PREVIOUS	64	8						
THIS WEEK	80	10						
TOTAL	144	18						

UNIT PER 100 LF

LABOR HOURS PER UNIT

	1 CARP.	2 LAB.						
PREVIOUS	3.56	0.44						
THIS WEEK	3.48	0.43						
TOTAL	3.52	0.44						

REMARKS

1" X 2" FURRING STRIPS ON INTERIOR OF EXTERIOR MASONRY WALLS — PLACED 12" O.C. — USED CUT NAILS — 1ST CLASS WORKMANSHIP.

MFD. IN U.S.A.   FORM C-105   FRANK R. WALKER CO., PUBLISHERS, CHICAGO

Fig. 149. Analyzed Labor Costs of Placing Wood Furring Strips on Walls.

LABOR DISTRIBUTION

JOB CENTRAL HIGH SCHOOL
CLASS OF WORK G-18
WEEK ENDING APRIL 25, 19--
SHEET NO. 37
JOB NO. 110

	OCCUPATION	M	T	W	T	F	S	S	HOURS	RATE	AMOUNT
1	CARPENTERS	16	16	16	16	16	—	—	80		
2	LABORERS	4	—	4	—	4	—	—	12		
3											
4											
5											
6											
7											
8											
TOTAL											

	QTY. WORK IN PLACE	PAY ROLL COSTS	LBR. AVERAGE UNIT COST	AVERAGE QUANTITY PER 8 HR. DAY	QTY. WORK IN PLACE	PAY ROLL COSTS	LBR. AVERAGE UNIT COST	AVERAGE QUANTITY PER 8 HR. DAY
PREVIOUS	2900 LF			242 LF				
THIS WEEK	2500			250				
TOTAL	5400			246				

MFD. IN U.S.A.   FORM C-105   FRANK R. WALKER CO., PUBLISHERS, CHICAGO   (OVER)

Fig. 150. Labor Distribution and Costs of Placing Wood Grounds.

The back of this form, Figure 149, gives the total number of hours worked by each trade in the first column headed "Total Labor Hours," while the second column headed "Labor Hours Per Unit," gives the length of time required by each trade to place 100 lineal feet of furring strips.

The labor cost of placing wood grounds should also be given by the lineal foot, but the class of work should be fully described because it costs much more to place wood grounds on brick or tile walls where all walls must be plugged at intervals of 12 or 16 inches to provide nailing for the wood grounds, than on wood stud partitions where the grounds can be nailed direct to the studs.

The cost of this work will also vary greatly, depending upon the class of workmanship required, as it costs much more where the grounds must be perfectly straight than where they are allowed to follow the line of the masonry wall or partition.

When placing wood blocking and grounds around window openings in brick or masonry walls the costs may either be given by the number of lineal feet of window opening, i. e., a window 4x7 feet will have 22 lineal feet of grounds and blocking,—or by the number of windows completed,—giving the average size.

Wood grounds for door openings are usually less expensive than for window openings, because the grounds are nailed direct to the wood buck placed in the masonry partition or nailed direct to the stud framing around the door openings. Costs on work of this kind should be given either by the number of door openings completed or by the number of lineal feet of grounds each. A door opening 3x7 feet has 17 lineal feet of grounds on each side of the opening.

Labor Distribution Figure 150 illustrates the correct method of keeping labor costs on placing wood grounds. The first column gives the total number of lineal feet placed, the second column gives the total labor cost, the third column gives the average cost per lineal foot, while the fourth column gives the average number of lineal feet placed per 8-hour day.

The back of this form, Figure 151, gives the total number of hours worked by each trade in the first column headed "Total Labor Hours," while the second column headed "Labor Hours Per Unit," gives the length of time required to place 100 lineal feet of wood grounds.

The labor costs of making and placing wood door bucks in masonry partitions should give the average size of the bucks and the number made and set, as this is the most satisfactory method of keeping costs of this kind.

Labor Distribution Figure 154 illustrates the correct method of keeping costs on the installation of ply-wood roof sheathing. The first column gives the number of square feet of sheathing installed, the second column gives the total labor costs, the third column gives the average cost per square foot, while the fourth column gives the average number of square feet of sheathing placed in an 8-hour day.

The back of the form, Figure 155, gives the total number of hours worked by each trade in the first column headed "Total Labor Hours," while the second column headed "Labor Hours Per Unit," gives the length of time required by each trade to place 100 square feet of plywood roof sheathing.

Wood Trusses

The classification Wood Trusses includes only those designed for clear span structures such as garages, churches, factories, supermarkets, bowling alleys, dance halls, etc. Costs on light trussed rafter construction, used in homes, etc. should be charged to the proper item under Rough Carpentry as outlined in the Cost Schedule given on previous pages.

In wood truss construction, three major labor operations are involved which are as follows: fabrication of members, assembling members and erection of completed trusses. In most cases the fabrication work is done in the shop, but where this work is done on the job, separate costs should be kept. Separate costs should also be kept on assembling labor, when done on the job. If the costs are kept in this manner, the erection costs will be truly representative and will give better information when used as a reference in figuring future jobs.

All labor cost records on wood truss work should contain an accurate description of the trusses, including the amount of lumber, in feet board measure, used for each truss, and the conditions under which they were erected. Fabrication and assembling costs should be reduced to a unit of a thousand feet of lumber, board measure, and also per truss. Erection costs should be the cost per truss.

In addition to the actual truss work, most jobs require bracing between the trusses. Separate cost records

COST ANALYSIS RECORD

TOTAL LABOR HOURS — UNIT

	1 CARP.	2 LAB.	3	4	5	6	7	8
PREVIOUS	96	12						
THIS WEEK	80	12						
TOTAL	176	24						

LABOR HOURS PER UNIT — UNIT PER 100 LF

	1 CARP.	2 LAB.	3	4	5	6	7	8
PREVIOUS	3.31	0.41						
THIS WEEK	3.20	0.48						
TOTAL	3.26	0.44						

REMARKS

5/8" x 2" AND 5/8" x 3" GROUNDS FOR RUNNING TRIM — NAILED TO METAL INSERTS IN TILE PARTITIONS — 1ST CLASS WORKMANSHIP.

MFD. IN U.S.A.   FORM C-105   FRANK R. WALKER CO., PUBLISHERS, CHICAGO

Fig. 151. Analyzed Labor Costs of Placing Wood Grounds.

LABOR DISTRIBUTION

JOB CENTRAL HIGH SCHOOL
CLASS OF WORK G-43
WEEK ENDING MAR. 6, 19—
SHEET NO. 39
JOB NO. 110

	OCCUPATION	M	T	W	T	F	S	S	HOURS	PAY ROLL COSTS	RATE	AMOUNT
1	CARPENTERS		1	1	8	16	1	1	24			
2	LABORERS			1	4	8	1	1	12			
3												
4												
5												
6												
7												
8												
TOTAL												

	QTY. WORK IN PLACE	PAY ROLL COSTS	LBR. AVERAGE UNIT COST	QTY. WORK IN PLACE	AVERAGE QUANTITY PER 8 HR. DAY	PAY ROLL COSTS	LBR. AVERAGE UNIT COST	AVERAGE QUANTITY PER 8 HR. DAY
PREVIOUS								
THIS WEEK	2000 SF			667 SF				
TOTAL	2000			667				

MFD. IN U.S.A.   FORM C-105   FRANK R. WALKER CO., PUBLISHERS, CHICAGO

Fig. 152. Labor Distribution and Costs of Placing Plywood Roof Sheathing.

COST ANALYSIS RECORD

TOTAL LABOR HOURS — UNIT

	1 CARP.	2 LAB.	3	4	5	6	7	8
PREVIOUS	—	—						
THIS WEEK	24	12						
TOTAL	24	12						

LABOR HOURS PER UNIT — UNIT PER 100 SF

	1 CARP.	2 LAB.	3	4	5	6	7	8
PREVIOUS	—	—						
THIS WEEK	1.2	0.6						
TOTAL	1.2	0.6						

REMARKS

5/8" PLYSCORD SHEATHING ON ROOF OF GARAGE 4' x 8' PANELS NAILED TO WOOD RAFTERS.

MFD. IN U.S.A.   FORM C-105   FRANK R. WALKER CO., PUBLISHERS, CHICAGO

Fig. 153. Analyzed Labor Costs of Placing Plywood Roof Sheathing.

Fig. 154. Labor Distribution and Costs of Setting Window Frames.

LABOR DISTRIBUTION

JOB CENTRAL HIGH SCHOOL — SHEET NO. 42
CLASS OF WORK G-73
WEEK ENDING FEB 13, 19-- — JOB NO. 110

OCCUPATION	M	T	W	T	F	S	S	HOURS	RATE	AMOUNT
1 CARPENTERS	16	16						32		
2 LABORERS	8	8						16		
3										
4										
5										
6										
7										
8										
TOTAL										

	QTY. WORK IN PLACE	PAY ROLL COSTS	LBR. AVERAGE UNIT COST	AVERAGE QUANTITY PER 8 HR. DAY	QTY. WORK IN PLACE	PAY ROLL COSTS	LBR. AVERAGE UNIT COST	AVERAGE QUANTITY PER 8 HR. DAY
PREVIOUS								
THIS WEEK	30			7.5 EA.				
TOTAL	30			7.5				

MFD. IN U.S.A. FORM C-105 FRANK R. WALKER CO., PUBLISHERS, CHICAGO (OVER)

Fig. 155. Analyzed Labor Costs of Setting Window Frames.

COST ANALYSIS RECORD

UNIT PER FRAME

TOTAL LABOR HOURS — UNIT 3 4 5 6 7 8

	1 CARP.	2 LAB.
PREVIOUS		
THIS WEEK	32	16
TOTAL	32	16

LABOR HOURS PER UNIT — UNIT 3 4 5 6 7 8

	1 CARP.	2 LAB.
PREVIOUS		
THIS WEEK	1.07	0.53
TOTAL	1.07	0.53

REMARKS
TRIPLE WINDOW FRAMES FOR D.H. WINDOWS.
AVERAGE SIZE 12'-0" X 6'-6"

MFD. IN U.S.A. FORM C-105 FRANK R. WALKER CO., PUBLISHERS, CHICAGO

LABOR DISTRIBUTION

JOB CENTRAL HIGH SCHOOL — SHEET NO. 43
CLASS OF WORK G-74
WEEK ENDING MAY 29, 19-- — JOB NO. 110

OCCUPATION	M	T	W	T	F	S	S	HOURS	RATE	AMOUNT
1 CARPENTERS	16	16	16	16	16	—	—	80		
2 LABORERS	2	—	—	2	—	—	—	4		
3										
4										
5										
6										
7										
8										
TOTAL										

	QTY. WORK IN PLACE	PAY ROLL COSTS	LBR. AVERAGE UNIT COST	AVERAGE QUANTITY PER 8 HR. DAY	QTY. WORK IN PLACE	PAY ROLL COSTS	LBR. AVERAGE UNIT COST	AVERAGE QUANTITY PER 8 HR. DAY
PREVIOUS	20 PRS.			4.45 PRS				
THIS WEEK	50			5.00				
TOTAL	70			4.83				

MFD. IN U.S.A. FORM C-105 FRANK R. WALKER CO., PUBLISHERS, CHICAGO (OVER)

Fig. 156. Labor Distribution and Costs of Fitting and Hanging Wood Sash.

Fig. 157. Analyzed Labor Costs of Fitting and Hanging Wood Sash.

COST ANALYSIS RECORD

TOTAL LABOR HOURS — UNIT

	1 CARP.	2 LAB.	3	4	5	6	7	8
PREVIOUS	36	2						
THIS WEEK	80	4						
TOTAL	116	6						

LABOR HOURS PER UNIT — UNIT PER PAIR OF D.H. SASH

	1 CARP.	2 LAB.	3	4	5	6	7	8
PREVIOUS	1.80	0.100						
THIS WEEK	1.60	0.080						
TOTAL	1.66	0.086						

REMARKS

2¼" D.H. SASH – AVERAGE SIZE 3'-8" X 3'-3" PER SASH. SPRING BALANCED.

MFD. IN U.S.A.   FORM C-105   FRANK R. WALKER CO., PUBLISHERS, CHICAGO

Fig. 158. Labor Distribution and Costs of Placing Rigid Insulation Convector Recesses.

LABOR DISTRIBUTION

JOB CENTRAL HIGH SCHOOL   SHEET NO. 40
CLASS OF WORK G-54   JOB NO. 110
WEEK ENDING JUNE 26, 19--

	OCCUPATION	M	T	W	T	F	S	S	HOURS	RATE	AMOUNT
1	CARPENTERS	8	16	–	8	–	1	1	32		
2	LABORERS	2	2	–	–	1	1	1	5		
3											
4											
5											
6											
7											
8											
TOTAL											

	QTY. WORK IN PLACE	PAY ROLL COSTS	LBR. AVERAGE UNIT COST	AVERAGE QUANTITY PER 8 HR. DAY	QTY. WORK IN PLACE	PAY ROLL COSTS	LBR. AVERAGE UNIT COST	AVERAGE QUANTITY PER 8 HR. DAY
PREVIOUS	550 SF			275 SF				
THIS WEEK	1120			280				
TOTAL	1670			278				

MFD. IN U.S.A.   FORM C-105   FRANK R. WALKER CO., PUBLISHERS, CHICAGO

COST ANALYSIS RECORD

TOTAL LABOR HOURS — UNIT

	1 CARP.	2 LAB.	3	4	5	6	7	8
PREVIOUS	16	3						
THIS WEEK	32	5						
TOTAL	48	8						

LABOR HOURS PER UNIT — UNIT PER 100 SF

	1 CARP.	2 LAB.	3	4	5	6	7	8
PREVIOUS	2.91	0.55						
THIS WEEK	2.86	0.45						
TOTAL	2.88	0.48						

REMARKS

1" RIGID INSULATION LINING IN CONVECTOR RECESSES. AVERAGE OPENINGS 42" X 24" X 6" DEEP. – LINED 4 SIDES & TOP. – STUCK TO MASONRY & METAL SURFACES WITH SPOTTED ADHESIVE.

MFD. IN U.S.A.   FORM C-105   FRANK R. WALKER CO., PUBLISHERS, CHICAGO

Fig. 159. Analyzed Labor Costs of Placing Rigid Insulation in Convector Recesses.

should be kept on this work also and the costs should be given per thousand feet of lumber, board measure, and per set of lateral or cross bracing.

Exterior Finished Carpentry

Labor costs for erecting exterior finished carpentry should be kept separate for each class of work, including the costs of any trucking and handling.

If the window frames or other mill items are sent to the job "knocked down" separate labor costs should be kept of the time required for assembling these items, ready to set.

Separate labor costs should also be kept of the time required handling, hoisting, setting and bracing door and window frames.

Labor Distribution Figure 160 illustrates the correct method of keeping costs on handling, setting and bracing wood window frames. The first column gives the total number of frames set, the second column gives the total labor cost, the third column gives the average labor cost of setting one frame, while the fourth column gives the average number of frames set per 8-hour day.

The back of the form, Figure 161, gives the total number of hours worked by each trade in the first column headed "Total Labor Hours," while the second column headed "Labor Hours Per Unit," gives the length of time required to set one frame.

Separate labor costs should also be kept of the time required fitting and hanging wood sash. The costs should give the number of single sash or pairs of sash fitted and hung. Always state whether sash are stationary, double hung or casement, giving the average size.

Labor Distribution Figure 162 illustrates the correct method of keeping costs on fitting and hanging wood sash. The first column gives the number of wood sash fitted and hung, the second column gives the total labor cost, the third column the average labor cost per pair, while the fourth column gives the number of pairs of sash fitted and hung per 8-hour day.

The back of the form, Figure 163, gives the total number of hours worked by each trade in the first column headed "Total Labor Hours," while the second column headed "Labor Hours Per Unit," gives the length of time required to fit and hang one pair of double hung wood sash.

The labor cost of placing window trim should also be kept as a separate item, mentioning kind of trim used, with or without jamb linings, etc., and the costs should give the total number of window openings trimmed.

In addition, if at all possible, separate costs should also be kept on installing window hardware, such as lifts, sash locks, etc., giving the cost per opening and stating type of hardware, number of pieces per opening, etc.

When setting frames or jambs for doors and borrowed lights, separate cost records should be kept on this work, giving the number of jambs set and the average size of openings. In addition, exterior door frame setting costs should be kept separate from interior openings.

The cost of dipping and laying wood shingles is usually given by the square containing 100 square feet of roof area, or by the thousand shingles. When the square foot method is used, always give the distance the shingles are laid to the weather.

If the shingles are to be dipped in stain before laying and this work is performed by carpenters who are laying the shingles, separate labor costs should be kept on dipping, as there are many jobs on which the shingles are not dipped, and it is advisable to know the real cost of work of this kind.

The cost of handling and laying shingles should also be kept as a separate item, stating the distance the shingles are laid to the weather and whether one or two nails are driven in each shingle.

When keeping labor costs on framing and erecting rough wood stairs, such as are commonly used for rear porches, basements, attics, etc., always give a full description of the stair, length of run, number of treads and risers, etc., as this is of more value than trying to compute the cost of the stairs on the basis of the quantity of lumber used. If it is possible to obtain average costs in hours on framing and erecting a stair containing 10, 12, 14, 16, 18 or 20 risers, they will prove of more value than costs computed by the thousand feet of lumber.

When erecting wood or metal garage doors, if possible, separate costs should be kept on each operation involved, such as setting frames or jamb and head linings, assembling and erecting doors, installing motor operators, etc. Costs should contain a complete description of the work, including size of opening, type of door, door material, method of operation, etc.

Fig. 160 — LABOR DISTRIBUTION

JOB CENTRAL HIGH SCHOOL
CLASS OF WORK G-61
WEEK ENDING JUNE 12, 19--
SHEET NO. 41
JOB NO. 110

OCCUPATION	M	T	W	T	F	S	S	HOURS	RATE	AMOUNT
1 CARPENTERS	8	8	8	6	—	1	—	30		
2										
3										
4										
5										
6										
7										
8										
TOTAL										

	QTY. WORK IN PLACE	PAY ROLL COSTS	LBR. AVERAGE UNIT COST	AVERAGE QUANTITY PER 8 HR. DAY
PREVIOUS				
THIS WEEK	7 OPNGS	99.00	14.14/OPNG	1.87 OPNGS
TOTAL	7	99.00	14.14	1.87

MFD. IN U.S.A. FORM C-105 FRANK R. WALKER CO., PUBLISHERS, CHICAGO

Fig. 160. Labor Distribution and Costs of Placing Metal Weather Strips.

Fig. 161 — COST ANALYSIS RECORD

TOTAL LABOR HOURS
UNIT PER OPENING

	1 CARP.	2	3	4	5	6	7	8
PREVIOUS	—							
THIS WEEK	30							
TOTAL	30							

LABOR HOURS PER UNIT
UNIT PER OPENING

	1 CARP.	2	3	4	5	6	7	8
PREVIOUS	—							
THIS WEEK	4.29							
TOTAL	4.29							

REMARKS: WEATHERSTRIPPING 2¼" DOUBLE ENTRANCE DOORS — SPRING BRONZE JAMBS, HEAD & ASTRAGAL. INTERLOCKING BRONZE THRESHOLD. 27 LF SPRING BRONZE & 6 LF THRESHOLD & CLOSURE STRIP PER OPENING.

MFD. IN U.S.A. FORM C-105 FRANK R. WALKER CO., PUBLISHERS, CHICAGO

Fig. 161. Analyzed Labor Costs of Placing Metal Weather Strips.

Fig. 162 — LABOR DISTRIBUTION

JOB CENTRAL HIGH SCHOOL
CLASS OF WORK G-80, G-82
WEEK ENDING JUNE 26, 19--
SHEET NO. 44
JOB NO. 110

OCCUPATION	M	T	W	T	F	S	S	HOURS	RATE	AMOUNT
1 G-80 CARPENTERS	16	16	16	16	16	—	—	80		
2 LABORERS	4	—	—	4	—	—	—	8		
3										
4										
5 G-82 CARPENTERS	16	16	16	8	8	—	—	64		
6										
7										
8										
TOTAL	G-80							G-82		

	QTY. WORK IN PLACE	PAY ROLL COSTS	LBR. AVERAGE UNIT COST	AVERAGE QUANTITY PER 8 HR. DAY	QTY. WORK IN PLACE	PAY ROLL COSTS	LBR. AVERAGE UNIT COST	AVERAGE QUANTITY PER 8 HR. DAY
PREVIOUS	27 DRS.			6.75 DRS.	172 SIDES			8.60 SIDES
THIS WEEK	70			7.00	70			8.75
TOTAL	97			6.93	242			8.64

MFD. IN U.S.A. FORM C-105 FRANK R. WALKER CO., PUBLISHERS, CHICAGO (OVER)

Fig. 162. Labor Distribution and Costs of Hanging Doors and Trimming Openings.

Insulation

When keeping costs on placing insulation on floors, walls, ceilings, roofs, etc., the type of material should be noted, also the method of application, where material is applied and size of batts, blankets, rolls, sheets, etc.

Separate costs should be kept on each kind of material and, if possible, on each kind of application. Costs should be given by the square foot or by the square containing 100 square feet.

Labor Distribution Figure 156 gives the correct method of keeping labor costs on the installation of rigid insulation lining in convector recesses. The first column give the number of square feet of insulation placed, the second column gives the total labor cost, the third column the average labor cost per square foot, while the fourth column gives the average number of square feet of insulation placed by a carpenter in an 8-hour day.

The back of the form, Figure 157, gives the total number of hours worked by each trade in the first column headed "Total Labor Hours," while the second column, headed "Labor Hours Per Unit," gives the length of time required by each trade to installed 100 square feet of rigid insulation lining in convector recesses.

Weather Strips And Vapor Seals

When placing metal weather strips on doors and windows, separate labor costs should be kept on installing weather strips on double hung windows, French or casement doors and windows, and ordinary doors.

The cost record should give the average size of the doors and windows, the average number of lineal feet of weather strip required per opening and the labor cost should be based on the average length of time required to weatherstrip an opening of a given size.

Labor Distribution Figure 158 illustrates the correct method of keeping costs on installing weather strips. The first column gives the total number of openings weather stripped, the second column gives the total labor cost, the third column the average cost per opening, while the fourth column gives the number of openings of a given size completed per 8-hour day.

The back of the form, Figure 159, gives the total number of hours worked by each trade in the first column headed "Total Labor Hours," while the second column headed "Labor Hours Per Unit," gives the length of time required to weatherstrip one opening.

When placing vapor seal papers or fabrics on walls, floors, ceilings, etc., separate costs should be kept on each kind of material. Costs should be given per square foot or per square containing 100 square feet and should state the kind of material, where applied, method of application, etc.

Interior Finished Carpentry And Millwork

The labor costs of erecting mill work and interior finish may be kept several different ways. Some contractors estimate the cost of erecting the mill work at a certain percentage of the cost of the material, which varies from 30 to 50 per cent. Other contractors prefer to keep the cost of each class of work separately, such as setting door and window frames, fitting and hanging sash, fitting and hanging doors, trimming door and window openings, setting wood base, picture mould, chair rail, wainscot cap, cases, cupboards, etc.

The most satisfactory method is to keep separate labor costs on the different operations mentioned above, as it is then possible to estimate each class of work more accurately than where they are all estimated as a single item.

If the contractor trucks the mill work and interior finish from cars or warehouse to the job, separate labor costs should be kept on this item.

The labor cost of fitting and hanging wood doors should also be kept as a separate item, as this is an important cost account and one on which valuable units may be obtained. Always state the number of doors hung, whether exterior or interior, kind of door, size, thickness, etc.

The cost of trimming door openings, which includes casings, stops, etc., should also be kept as a separate item, giving a description of the trim, number of members, number of sides of trim placed, etc.

Labor Distribution Figure 164 illustrates the correct method of keeping labor costs on fitting and hanging wood doors and trimming door openings. The first column gives the total number of doors hung, the

Fig. 163. Cost Analysis Record

COST ANALYSIS RECORD

TOTAL LABOR HOURS / UNIT

	1 CARP.	2 LAB.	3	4	5 CARP.	6	7	8
PREVIOUS	32	4			160			
THIS WEEK	80	8			64			
TOTAL	112	12			224			

Unit: G-80 PER DOOR, G-82 PER SIDE OF TRIM

LABOR HOURS PER UNIT

	1 CARP.	2 LAB.	3	4	5 CARP.	6	7	8
PREVIOUS	1.19	0.15			0.93			
THIS WEEK	1.14	0.11			0.91			
TOTAL	1.16	0.12			0.93			

REMARKS

INTERIOR, SINGLE, FLUSH DOORS - AVG. 3'0 X 7'0 X 1¾" USED POWER PLANE AND BUTT MORTISER. DOOR TRIM - SINGLE MEMBER - POND. PINE - AVG. 3'0 X 7'0 OPNGS. ALL 1ST CLASS WORKMANSHIP

MFD. IN U.S.A. FORM C-105 FRANK R. WALKER CO., PUBLISHERS, CHICAGO

Fig. 163. Analyzed Labor Costs of Hanging Doors and Trimming Openings.

Fig. 164. Labor Distribution

LABOR DISTRIBUTION

SHEET NO. 45 JOB NO. 110
WEEK ENDING JUNE 26, 19--
JOB CENTRAL HIGH SCHOOL
CLASS OF WORK G-86, G-87

OCCUPATION	M	T	W	T	F	S	S	HOURS	RATE	AMOUNT
1 G-86 {CARPENTERS	11	11	12	10	11			55		
2 {LABORERS	2		1	2				4		
3										
4										
5 G-87 CARPENTERS	5	5	4	6	5			25		
6										
7										
8										

TOTAL

G-86	QTY. WORK IN PLACE	PAY ROLL COSTS	LBR. AVERAGE UNIT COST	AVERAGE QUANTITY PER 8 HR. DAY
PREVIOUS	210 LF			76 LF
THIS WEEK	600			87
TOTAL	810			84

G-87	QTY. WORK IN PLACE	PAY ROLL COSTS	LBR. AVERAGE UNIT COST	AVERAGE QUANTITY PER 8 HR. DAY
PREVIOUS	240 LF			192 LF
THIS WEEK	675			216
TOTAL	915			209

(OVER)

MFD. IN U.S.A. FORM C-105 FRANK R. WALKER CO., PUBLISHERS, CHICAGO

Fig. 164. Labor Distribution and Costs of Placing Wood Base and Picture Mould.

Fig. 165. Cost Analysis Record

COST ANALYSIS RECORD

TOTAL LABOR HOURS / UNIT

	1 CARP.	2 LAB.	3	4	5 CARP.	6	7	8
PREVIOUS	22	2			10			
THIS WEEK	55	4			25			
TOTAL	77	6			35			

LABOR HOURS PER UNIT / UNIT PER 100 LINEAL FEET

	1 CARP.	2 LAB.	3	4	5 CARP.	6	7	8
PREVIOUS	10.5	0.95			4.2			
THIS WEEK	9.2	0.67			3.7			
TOTAL	9.5	0.74			3.8			

REMARKS

3 MEMBER BASE IN LARGE ROOMS - ¾"X 5½" + ⅝"X 1⅝" + ⅝"X ¾" SHOE.
1 MEMBER PICTURE MOULD IN LARGE ROOMS - ⅝"X 2½"
ALL PONDEROSA PINE

MFD. IN U.S.A. FORM C-105 FRANK R. WALKER CO., PUBLISHERS, CHICAGO

Fig. 165. Analyzed Labor Costs of Placing Wood Base and Picture Mould.

second column gives the total labor cost, the third column the average cost per door, while the fourth column gives the average number of doors a carpenter fitted and hung per 8-hour day. Columns five to eight furnish the same information regarding trimming door openings.

The back of the form, Figure 165, gives the total number of hours worked by each trade in the first column headed "Total Labor Hours," while the second column headed "Labor Hours Per Unit," gives the length of time required to fit and hang one door or trim one side of a door opening.

The labor cost of placing wood base, picture mould, chair rail, wood cornices, etc., should all be kept as separate cost items, giving a description of the material erected, size of same, etc., and the costs should be given by the lineal foot.

Labor Distribution Figure 166 illustrates the correct method of keeping costs on placing wood base, picture mould, etc. The first column gives the total number of lineal feet of wood base placed, the second column gives the total labor cost, the third column the average labor cost per lineal foot, while the fourth column gives the average number of lineal feet of base placed per 8-hour day. Columns five to eight give the same information regarding the cost of erecting wood picture mould.

The back of the form, Figure 167, gives the total number of hours worked by each trade in the first column headed "Total Labor Hours," while the second column headed "Labor Hours Per Unit," gives the length of time required to handle and place 100 lineal feet of wood base or picture mould.

The labor costs of handling and setting shop assembled kitchen cases, book cases, display cases, wardrobes, linen cases, etc., should all be kept separately, giving a description of the articles and dimensions, and the costs should be given per square foot of cabinet front face area.

When erecting finish wood stairs, it is difficult to divide the different labor operations, as there are usually only one or two workmen engaged on the work and they lay out the work, set stringers, treads, risers, etc., so that the costs on the above items should be kept as one cost record. A complete description of the stairs should be given, mentioning type of stairs, kind of wood, whether open or box string, number of treads, risers, etc., in order that the information may be used when estimating the cost of future work. All costs should be given per flight of stairs. Where possible, keep a separate record of the labor setting newels, balusters and balustrade, as it is important to know what the costs on erection are where stairs are wanted without newels, hand rail and balusters.

When keeping labor costs on finish wood floors, always mention the kind of flooring, kind of wood, width, size of rooms, etc., as this has considerable bearing on the cost of the work. The costs should state the number of square feet of surface covered, or they may state the number of feet of flooring, board measure. If the floors are to be sanded, separate costs should be kept on this work and the costs should be given by the square foot of floor surface completed.

Labor Distribution Figure 152 illustrates the correct method of keeping labor costs on laying and finishing hardwood floors. The first column gives the total number of square feet of floor laid, the second column gives the total labor cost, the third column gives the average cost per square foot, while the fourth column gives the average amount of floor completed per 8-hour day.

When keeping labor costs on fitting and placing wood shelves in closets, wardrobes, etc., always keep a record of the number of shelves placed, as it costs as much to place a shelf 3 feet long as one 6 feet long, while one contains twice as much lumber as the other.

Wallboards

All labor costs for the erection and installation of plywood, wallboard, etc. should be kept on a square foot basis. For the various materials covered by this classification, refer to the Cost Schedule given on previous pages. All labor costs for installing furring strips or blocking to receive the wallboard, etc. should be charged to the proper item under Rough Carpentry as given in the Cost Schedule. Costs should state the kind of material, size of panels, method of installation, etc.

Structural Iron And Steel Work

When keeping labor costs on structural steel work, the costs should be divided into the following classifications: "H-1," —Unloading steel from cars or trucks, hauling to job, unloading and distributing in storage yard; "H-2," —Cost of hauling steel from storage yard to point of erection; "H-3," —Labor handling, hoisting and erecting structural steel in place and making temporary connections; "H-4," —Labor cost of rivet-

LABOR DISTRIBUTION

JOB CENTRAL HIGH SCHOOL
CLASS OF WORK G-19, G-20
WEEK ENDING JUNE 19, 19--
SHEET NO. 38
JOB NO. 110

OCCUPATION	M	T	W	T	F	S	S	HOURS	RATE	AMOUNT
1 G-19 { CARPENTERS	16	16	-	1	1	1		32		
2 { LABORERS	4	4	-	1	1			8		
3										
4										
5 G-20 CARPENTERS	-	-	16	16	4	1		36		
6										
7										
8										
TOTAL G-19								G-20		

	QTY. WORK IN PLACE	PAY ROLL COSTS	LBR. AVERAGE UNIT COST	AVERAGE QUANTITY PER 8 HR. DAY	QTY. WORK IN PLACE	PAY ROLL COSTS	LBR. AVERAGE UNIT COST	AVERAGE QUANTITY PER 8 HR. DAY
PREVIOUS	3500 SF			292 SF	4800 SF			1067 SF
THIS WEEK	1300			325	4800			1067
TOTAL	4800			300				(OVER)

MFD. IN U.S.A. FORM C-105 FRANK R. WALKER CO., PUBLISHERS, CHICAGO

Fig. 166. Labor Distribution and Costs of Laying Finish Wood Floors.

COST ANALYSIS RECORD

UNIT

TOTAL LABOR HOURS

	1 CARP.	2 LAB.	3	4	5 CARP.	6	7	8
PREVIOUS	96	24						
THIS WEEK	32	8			36			
TOTAL	128	32			36			

UNIT PER 100 SF

LABOR HOURS PER UNIT

	1 CARP.	2 LAB.	3	4	5 CARP.	6	7	8
PREVIOUS	2.74	0.69						
THIS WEEK	2.46	0.62			0.75			
TOTAL	2.67	0.67			0.75			

REMARKS: 7/8" X 2 1/4" FACE MAPLE FLOORING ON STAGE - LAID OVER WOOD SUB-FLOOR.

MFD. IN U.S.A. FORM C-105

Fig. 167. Analyzed Labor Costs of Laying Finish Wood Floors.

LABOR DISTRIBUTION

JOB CENTRAL HIGH SCHOOL
CLASS OF WORK H-3, H-4
WEEK ENDING MAR. 6, 19--
SHEET NO. 46
JOB NO. 110

OCCUPATION	M	T	W	T	F	S	S	HOURS	RATE	AMOUNT
1 { IRON WORK FORE.	8	8	8	8	-	-	-	32		
2 H-3 { IRON WORKERS	40	40	40	40	-	-	-	160		
3 { CRANE OPR.	8	8	8	8	-	-	-	32		
4										
5 H-4 { IRON WORKERS	-	32	32	32	32	-	-	128		
6 { COMPR. OPR.	-	8	8	8	8	-	-	32		
7										
8										
TOTAL H-3								H-4		

	QTY. WORK IN PLACE	PAY ROLL COSTS	LBR. AVERAGE UNIT COST	AVERAGE QUANTITY PER 8 HR. DAY	QTY. WORK IN PLACE	PAY ROLL COSTS	LBR. AVERAGE UNIT COST	AVERAGE QUANTITY PER 8 HR. DAY
PREVIOUS	37 TONS			2467 LBS.	-	-	-	PER GANG
THIS WEEK	31			2583	1100 EA			275 EA
TOTAL	68			2519	1100			275

MFD. IN U.S.A. FORM C-105 FRANK R. WALKER CO., PUBLISHERS, CHICAGO (OVER)

Fig. 168. Labor Distribution and Costs of Erecting and Riveting Structural Steel.

Fig. 169. COST ANALYSIS RECORD

TOTAL LABOR HOURS | **UNIT**

	1 IRON WORK. FORE.	2 IRON WORKERS	3 CRANE OPR.	4	5 IRON WORKERS	6 COMP. OPR.	7	8
PREVIOUS	40	200	40		128	1		
THIS WEEK	32	160	32		128	32		
TOTAL	72	360	72		128	32		

UNIT H-3 PER TON / H-4 PER 100 RIVETS

LABOR HOURS PER UNIT

	1 IRON WORK. FORE.	2 IRON WORKERS	3 CRANE OPR.	4	5 IRON WORKERS	6 COMP. OPR.	7	8
PREVIOUS	1.08	5.41	1.08		11.6	1		
THIS WEEK	1.03	5.16	1.03		11.6	2.91		
TOTAL	1.06	5.29	1.06		11.6	2.91		

REMARKS

LIGHT STEEL FRAMING IN GYM – COLUMNS, ROOF TRUSSES, BALCONY FRAMING.

MFD. IN U.S.A.   FORM C-105   FRANK R. WALKER CO., PUBLISHERS, CHICAGO

Fig. 169. Analyzed Labor Costs of Erecting and Riveting Structural Steel.

Fig. 170. LABOR DISTRIBUTION

JOB CENTRAL HIGH SCHOOL
CLASS OF WORK H-32-A, H-32-B
SHEET NO. 48
JOB NO. 110
WEEK ENDING

OCCUPATION	M	T	W	T	F	S	S	HOURS	RATE	AMOUNT
1 H-32-A IRON WORKERS	32	32	32	32	1	1	1	160		
2 CRANE OPR.	8	8	1	1	1			16		
3										
4										
5 H-32-B IRON WORKERS	8	16	16	16	1	1	1	72		
6										
7										
8										
TOTAL										

H-32-A SET BAR JOISTS   H-32-B WELD BAR JOISTS

	QTY. WORK IN PLACE	PAY ROLL COSTS	LBR. AVERAGE UNIT COST	AVERAGE QUANTITY PER 8 HR. DAY	QTY. WORK IN PLACE	PAY ROLL COSTS	LBR. AVERAGE UNIT COST	AVERAGE QUANTITY PER 8 HR. DAY
PREVIOUS	5 TONS			1250 LBS	—		PER JOIST	JOISTS
THIS WEEK	20			2000	600 JOISTS			67
TOTAL	25			1786	600			67

MFD. IN U.S.A.   FORM C-105   FRANK R. WALKER CO., PUBLISHERS, CHICAGO   [OVER]

Fig. 170. Labor Distribution and Costs of Erecting Steel Bar Joists.

COST ANALYSIS RECORD

TOTAL LABOR HOURS | **UNIT**

	1 IRON WORKERS	2 CRANE OPR.	3	4	5 IRON WORKERS	6	7	8
PREVIOUS	64	8			—			
THIS WEEK	160	16			72			
TOTAL	224	24			72			

LABOR HOURS PER UNIT | UNIT H-32-A PER TON / H-32-B PER JOIST

	1 IRON WORKERS	2 CRANE OPR.	3	4	5 IRON WORKERS	6	7	8
PREVIOUS	12.80	1.60			—			
THIS WEEK	8.00	0.80			0.12			
TOTAL	8.96	0.96			0.12			

REMARKS

STEEL BAR JOISTS, 12" DEEP GENERALLY, FOR 12° SPAN, WEIGHING 80 LBS EACH, SPACED 24" O.C. HOISTED WITH TRUCK CRANE. WELDED TO TOP SHERD OF STEEL TRUSSES

MFD. IN U.S.A.   FORM C-105   FRANK R. WALKER CO., PUBLISHERS, CHICAGO

Fig. 171. Analyzed Labor Costs of Erecting Steel Bar Joists.

ing, welding or bolting permanent connections; "H-5," —Cost of placing miscellaneous items of structural steel, such as loose lintels, lally columns, shelf angles, grillage, loose beams and struts, etc.; "H-6," —Labor cost of unloading, handling and erecting steel stacks, tanks, etc.

Labor costs on structural steel are invariably kept by the ton of 2,000 pounds. Rivets and permanent bolts are usually figured at a certain price each. Welding costs are generally kept per lineal foot of weld. Labor costs for placing loose lintels and lally columns should be kept on a piece basis and should contain a complete description of the item. Costs on erecting shelf angles are usually kept on a lineal foot basis. Always state class of work, whether a bridge, viaduct, steel skeleton, or wall bearing structure, together with the total tonnage in the job.

The correct method of keeping labor costs on erecting steel and driving rivets is illustrated in Labor Distribution Figure 168. The first column gives the total number of tons of steel erected, the second column gives the total labor cost erecting same, the third column the average cost per ton, while the fourth column gives the amount of steel erected per 8-hour day. Columns five to eight furnish similar labor costs on heating and driving rivets.

The back of the form, Figure 169, gives the total number of hours worked by each trade in the first column headed "Total Labor Hours," while the second column headed "Labor Hours Per Unit," gives the length of time required to erect a ton of steel and drive 100 rivets.

Lightweight Steel Framing

The classification of lightweight steel framing includes steel bar joist framing, junior steel beams and metal lumber framing such as Stran-Steel, etc.

When keeping costs on erecting steel bar joists or junior steel beams, the costs should be kept per ton of material erected complete, including bridging, bottom chord extensions, tie rods, anchors, etc. Costs should also contain a description of the work, giving average size of members, length of span, hoisting conditions and method, etc. If possible, separate costs should be kept on welding joists or beams to other steel supports, if required.

Labor Distribution Figure 172 illustrates the correct method of keeping costs on the erection of steel bar joists. The first column gives the weight of steel joists erected, the second column gives the total labor cost to date, the third column gives the average labor cost per ton of joists erected, while the fourth column gives the average amount of joists erected per 8-hour day. Columns five to eight furnish the same information on welding joists to supports.

The back of the form, Figure 173, analyzes the costs on an hourly basis. The first column, headed "Total Labor Hours," gives the number of hours worked by each trade, while the second column, headed "Labor Hours Per Unit," gives the length of time required by each trade to erect one ton of steel bar joists and accessories, and to weld one joist to its supports.

Metal lumber construction, such as Stran-Steel, is frequently used in all parts of the country instead of wood joists and partition studs. It can be used in many types of structures, including residences, school houses, office buildings, apartment buildings, garages, etc., and is similar to wood construction, except that pressed steel members are used instead of wood. Joists are furnished in several sizes from 6 to 9 inches deep and in lengths that meet the requirements of the job.

The labor cost of handling and erecting pressed steel joists should be kept by the number of square feet of floor or roof surface placed. This method is preferable to a weight or tonnage basis, as all sections are light in weight and it does not cost much more to handle and place a 9-inch beam or joist than a 6-inch joist. When reporting the costs, always give the average size of the joists, spacing, etc. The costs should include all field punching and riveting and the placing of all metal bridging.

The erection costs of pressed steel partition framing members should be kept in the same manner as joists, but they should be kept separate from the joists, because there is considerably more punching, riveting, etc., on partition work than on floor joists, unless the material is shop fabricated into panels.

Steel Decking

When reporting costs on steel decking work, separate costs should be kept on the various kinds of material, such as ribbed type, cellular type, etc.

LABOR DISTRIBUTION

JOB CENTRAL HIGH SCHOOL

CLASS OF WORK H-14

WEEK ENDING JUNE 26, 19--

SHEET NO. 47

JOB NO. 110

OCCUPATION	M	T	W	T	F	S	S	HOURS	RATE	AMOUNT
1 ORN. IRON WORKERS	16	16	16	16	16	1	-	80		
2										
3										
4										
5										
6										
7										
8										
TOTAL										

	QTY. WORK IN PLACE	PAY ROLL COSTS	LBR. AVERAGE UNIT COST	AVERAGE QUANTITY PER 8 HR. DAY	QTY. WORK IN PLACE	PAY ROLL COSTS	LBR. AVERAGE UNIT COST	AVERAGE QUANTITY PER 8 HR. DAY
PREVIOUS	6 FLIGHTS		PER FLIGHT	PER FLIGHT 3 1/3 DAYS				
THIS WEEK	3 1/3			3				
TOTAL	9 1/3			3 1/5				

MFD. IN U.S.A.   FORM C-105   FRANK R. WALKER CO., PUBLISHERS, CHICAGO   [OVER]

Fig. 172. Labor Distribution and Costs of Erecting Ornamental Iron Stairs.

COST ANALYSIS RECORD

UNIT PER FLIGHT OF STAIRS

TOTAL LABOR HOURS

	1 ORN. 1 IRON WORKERS	2	3	4	5	6	7	8
PREVIOUS	160							
THIS WEEK	80							
TOTAL	240							

UNIT PER FLIGHT OF STAIRS

LABOR HOURS PER UNIT

	1 ORN. 1 IRON WORKERS	2	3	4	5	6	7	8
PREVIOUS	26.67							
THIS WEEK	24.00							
TOTAL	25.71							

REMARKS

EACH FLIGHT CONTAINS 2 RUNS OF 4' WIDE RISERS & TREADS AND AN 8' X 4' PLATFORM. STAIRS & PLATFORMS ARE STEEL PAN TYPE WITH PIPE RAILS & BALUSTRADES

MFD. IN U.S.A.   FORM C-105   FRANK R. WALKER CO., PUBLISHERS, CHICAGO

Fig. 173. Analyzed Labor Costs of Erecting Ornamental Iron Stairs.

LABOR DISTRIBUTION

JOB CENTRAL HIGH SCHOOL

CLASS OF WORK J-2

WEEK ENDING MAY 8, 19--

SHEET NO. 49

JOB NO. 110

OCCUPATION	M	T	W	T	F	S	S	HOURS	RATE	AMOUNT
1 LATHERS	16	16	16	16	16	-	-	80		
2										
3										
4										
5										
6										
7										
8										
TOTAL										

	QTY. WORK IN PLACE	PAY ROLL COSTS	LBR. AVERAGE UNIT COST	AVERAGE QUANTITY PER 8 HR. DAY	QTY. WORK IN PLACE	PAY ROLL COSTS	LBR. AVERAGE UNIT COST	AVERAGE QUANTITY PER 8 HR. DAY
PREVIOUS	925 SY			92.5 SY				
THIS WEEK	950			95.0				
TOTAL	1875			93.75				

MFD. IN U.S.A.   FORM C-105   FRANK R. WALKER CO., PUBLISHERS, CHICAGO   [OVER]

Fig. 174. Labor Distribution and Costs of Placing Gypsum Lath.

Steel decking labor costs should be reported on a square foot basis and should always contain a complete description of the work, including kind of material, size of panels, method of attachment, hoisting method and conditions, etc.

Miscellaneous And Ornamental Metal

The classification of miscellaneous and ornamental metal includes a wide variety of items and reporting costs on this work is difficult. It is practically impossible to reduce the labor costs of most items to working units and obtain information which will be of any value.

Labor costs for some items, such as curb angles, angle floor frames, metal railings, iron ladders, etc. may be reported on a lineal foot basis. Costs on items, such as cast iron manhole frames and covers, corner guards and bumpers, bar gratings, door and window guards, etc., are usually kept on a piece basis and must contain a complete description of the item to be of value.

It is common practice to keep costs of assembling and erecting steel and iron stairwork on a flight basis, but it is essential that a complete description or sketch of the work, showing stairs, railing, balustrade, platforms, etc., be given along with the costs.

Labor Distribution Figure 170 illustrates the correct method of keeping costs on the erection of iron or steel stairs. The first column gives the number of flights of stairs erected, the second column gives the total labor cost, the third column the average cost per flight of stairs, while the fourth column gives the number of 8-hour man days required to erect one flight of stairs complete.

The back of the form, Figure 171, gives the total number of hours worked by each trade in the first column headed "Total Labor Hours," while the second column headed "Labor Hours Per Unit," gives the length of time required to erect one flight of stairs.

The same method should be used in keeping costs of erecting iron fire escapes.

When keeping labor costs on the erection of metal store fronts, the most practical method is to record the number of hours required to erect a store front complete. A detailed description or illustration of the store front erected should be furnished, showing arrangement of sash, muntins, transom bars, etc., and then this cost may be used when estimating other store fronts of similar construction.

Hollow, Rolled And Extruded Metals

The labor cost of erecting or installing metal doors and windows, metal trim and metal interior finish of all kinds should be kept in exactly the same manner as described for these items in wood. The labor operations are similar, and the same units should be kept on each class of work.

Lathing

On nearly all kinds of lathing the unit of measure is the square yard. When keeping costs on gypsum or insulating board lath work, the costs should state the number of square yards of surface lathed. Give the thickness of the lath in all instances, as this affects the labor costs considerably. Cost should also state the type of lath used, such as plain, perforated, foil-backed, etc., and whether gypsum or insulating board.

Labor Distribution Figure 174 illustrates the correct method of recording the labor costs on placing gypsum lath. The first column gives the total quantity of gypsum lath placed, the second column gives the labor cost applying same, the third column the average labor cost per square yard, while the fourth column gives the number of square yards of lath a man averaged per 8-hour day.

The back of the form, Figure 175, gives the total number of hours worked by each trade in the first column headed "Total Labor Hours," while the second column headed "Labor Hours Per Unit," gives the length of time required to handle and place 100 square yards of gypsum lath.

When keeping costs on suspended gypsum lath ceilings, where the lath is supported on a system of hangers, runners and furring channels, the costs should be kept separate and should state the number of square yards of ceiling lath work installed.

The same method should be used for reporting the costs of lathing work for studless solid gypsum lath and plaster partitions, where long lengths (up to 12'-0') of ½-inch gypsum lath are held vertically by floor and ceiling runners and plastered two sides. Costs on this work should be kept by the square yard of partition lath erected.

Fig. 175 — Cost Analysis Record

COST ANALYSIS RECORD

TOTAL LABOR HOURS — UNIT: PER 100 SQUARE YARDS

	1 LATHERS	2	3	4	5	6	7	8
PREVIOUS	80							
THIS WEEK	80							
TOTAL	160							

LABOR HOURS PER UNIT

	1 LATHERS	2	3	4	5	6	7	8
PREVIOUS	8.65							
THIS WEEK	8.42							
TOTAL	8.53							

REMARKS

3/8" PERFORATED GYPSUM LATH ON WOOD FURRING STRIPS

MFD. IN U.S.A.   FORM C-105   FRANK R. WALKER CO., PUBLISHERS, CHICAGO

Fig. 175. Analyzed Labor Costs of Placing Gypsum Lath.

Fig. 176 — Labor Distribution

LABOR DISTRIBUTION

JOB CENTRAL HIGH SCHOOL   SHEET NO. 50

CLASS OF WORK J-7, J-14-A   JOB NO. 110

WEEK ENDING

	OCCUPATION	M	T	W	T	F	S	S	HOURS	RATE	AMOUNT
1 J-7	LATHERS	32	32	32	32	1	1	1	160		
2											
3											
4											
5 J-14-A	LATHERS	1	8	16	16	1	1	1	40		
6											
7											
8											
TOTAL											

	PAY ROLL COSTS	QTY. WORK IN PLACE	LBR. AVERAGE UNIT COST	AVERAGE QUANTITY PER 8 HR. DAY	PAY ROLL COSTS	QTY. WORK IN PLACE	LBR. AVERAGE UNIT COST	AVERAGE QUANTITY PER 8 HR. DAY
	J-7				J-14-A			
PREVIOUS		185 SY		23.13 SY		1050 LF	0.139/LF	210 LF
THIS WEEK		480		24.00	146.00	1050 LF	0.139/LF	210 LF
TOTAL		665		23.75	146.00			

(OVER)

MFD. IN U.S.A.   FORM C-105   FRANK R. WALKER CO., PUBLISHERS, CHICAGO

Fig. 176. Labor Distribution and Costs of Erecting Metal Lath Suspended Ceilings and Metal Corner Bead.

Fig. 177 — Cost Analysis Record

COST ANALYSIS RECORD

TOTAL LABOR HOURS — UNIT

	1 LATHERS	2	3	4	5 LATHERS	6	7	8
PREVIOUS	64				—			
THIS WEEK	160				40			
TOTAL	224				40			

LABOR HOURS PER UNIT — UNIT: PER 100 SY - SUSP. MET. LATH / PER 100 LF - CORNER BEADS

	1 LATHERS	2	3	4	5 LATHERS	6	7	8
PREVIOUS	34.60				—			
THIS WEEK	33.33				3.81			
TOTAL	33.68				3.81			

REMARKS

SUSPENDED METAL LATH CEILING - HANGERS IN STRUC. SLAB - 1½" CHANNELS, 4° O.C. 3/4" CHANNELS, 12" O.C. - 3.4# METAL LATH. BULLNOSE CORNER BEADS AT WINDOW RETURNS, MITERED AT HEAD.   1ST. CLASS WORKMANSHIP

MFD. IN U.S.A.   FORM C-105   FRANK R. WALKER CO., PUBLISHERS, CHICAGO

Fig. 177. Analyzed Labor Costs of Erecting Metal Lath Suspended Ceilings and Metal Corner Bead.

When metal lath is applied to wood studs or ceiling joists the labor costs should give the number of square yards of surface covered, the same as described for gypsum lath and the costs should be kept in the same manner.

When keeping costs on suspended metal lath ceilings consisting of hangers, metal channels or pencil rods and metal lath, the costs should be kept separately and should state the number of square yards of ceiling erected.

The same method should be used on solid metal lath and plaster partitions, consisting of channel studs covered with metal lath and plastered two sides, or on studless metal lath and plaster partitions with metal lath hanging between ceiling and floor runners. Costs on work of this kind should also be kept by the square yard.

When reporting costs on metal furring for ornamental plaster beams, girders, cornices, etc., the girth of the members should be taken and the costs stated either by the square foot or furring erected or by the lineal foot, where each width of cornice, beam and girder is kept separately.

When keeping costs on erecting corner beads, metal base mould, picture mould, etc., the costs should be given by the lineal foot, stating the number of lineal feet of each class of material erected. It is always well to mention the class of workmanship required when erecting metal corner beads, as the costs vary greatly where it is necessary to plumb the corner beads or where they may be allowed to follow the line of the stud or tile partitions.

Labor Distribution Figure 176 illustrates the correct method of keeping costs on suspended metal ceilings and metal corner beads.

The first column gives the total number of square yards of metal lath ceiling erected, the second column gives the total labor cost, the third column the average labor cost per square yard, while the fourth column gives the average number of square yards of suspended lath ceiling completed per 8-hour day. Columns five to eight give the same information regarding metal corner beads.

The back of the form, Figure 177, gives the total number of hours worked by each trade in the first column headed "Total Labor Hours," while the second column headed "Labor Hours Per Unit," gives the length of time required to erect 100 square yards of suspended metal lath ceiling and 100 lineal feet of metal corner beads.

Interior Plastering

When keeping labor costs on plastering, it is advisable to keep separate costs on building and removing scaffold and each coat of plaster, if possible. The costs are much more valuable if kept in this manner because they give separate labor costs on each operation of the work. By having the labor costs separate in this manner it is very easy to compute the cost of any kind of plaster work accurately.

Plastering costs should always be given by the square yard, the unit of 100 square yards being a satisfactory working unit. Some plasterers make deductions for openings while others do not. Many plasterers make deductions for one-half of all openings containing 15 square feet or over. The method used should always be mentioned on the labor cost records, stating "No openings deducted," "One-half openings deducted," or "Full openings deducted."

A notation should be made stating the kind of base to which the plaster is applied, i.e., gypsum lath, insulating board lath, metal lath, clay or gypsum tile, concrete, etc.

Cost records should also state the kind of plaster and aggregate being used, as it is easier to apply plaster made with lightweight aggregate than ordinary sanded plaster and the labor costs will vary for this reason.

Labor Distribution Figure 178 illustrates the correct method of keeping costs on applying the scratch and brown coats of plaster. The first column gives the total number of square yards of scratch coat applied, the second column gives the total labor cost applying same, the third column the average labor cost per square yard, while the fourth column gives the average number of square yards of scratch coat applied per 8-hour day. Columns five to eight give the same information regarding the cost of the brown coat.

The back of the form, Figure 179, gives the total number of hours worked by each trade in the first column headed "Total Labor Hours," while the second column headed "Labor Hours Per Unit," gives the length of time required to apply 100 square yards of scratch or brown coat plaster.

The same method should be used in keeping costs on the different kinds of finish, such as white or "putty" coat, sand finish, etc., as it is important to know the relative costs of applying the different finish coats.

Fig. 178 — LABOR DISTRIBUTION

JOB CENTRAL HIGH SCHOOL SHEET NO. 51
CLASS OF WORK J-23, J-24 WEEK ENDING MAY 15, 19-- JOB NO. 110

OCCUPATION	M	T	W	T	F	S	S	HOURS	RATE	AMOUNT
1 J-23 { PLASTERERS	16	16	16	—	—	—	—	48		
2 { LABORERS	16	16	16	—	—	—	—	48		
3										
4										
5 J-24 { PLASTERERS	24	24	24	—	—	—	—	120	365	
6 { LABORERS	16	16	16	—	—	—	—	80	265	
7										
8										
TOTAL J-23								J-24		

	QTY. WORK IN PLACE	PAY ROLL COSTS	LBR. AVERAGE UNIT COST	AVERAGE QUANTITY PER 8 HR. DAY	QTY. WORK IN PLACE	PAY ROLL COSTS	LBR. AVERAGE UNIT COST	AVERAGE QUANTITY PER 8 HR. DAY
PREVIOUS	630 SY			158 SY	150 SY			50 SY
THIS WEEK	950			158	800			53.3
TOTAL	1580			158	950			52.8

MFD. IN U.S.A. FORM C-105 FRANK R. WALKER CO., PUBLISHERS, CHICAGO (OVER)

Fig. 178. Labor Distribution and Costs of Applying Scratch and Brown Plaster Coats.

Fig. 179 — COST ANALYSIS RECORD

TOTAL LABOR HOURS			UNIT					
	1 PLAS.	2 LAB.	3	4	5 PLAS.	6 LAB.	7	8
PREVIOUS	32	48			24	16		
THIS WEEK	32	48			120	80		
TOTAL	80	80			144	96		

UNIT PER 100 SQUARE YARDS

LABOR HOURS PER UNIT			UNIT					
	1 PLAS.	2 LAB.	3	4	5 PLAS.	6 LAB.	7	8
PREVIOUS	5.08				16.0	10.7		
THIS WEEK	5.05				15.0	10.0		
TOTAL	5.06				15.2	10.1		

REMARKS

SCRATCH COAT 1:2 GYPSUM & SAND ON METAL LATH CEILING
BROWN COAT 1:3 SAND
1ST CLASS WORKMANSHIP — QUANTITIES BASED ON 1/2
OPENINGS DEDUCTED.

MFD. IN U.S.A. FORM C-105 FRANK R. WALKER CO., PUBLISHERS, CHICAGO

Fig. 179. Analyzed Labor Costs of Applying Scratch and Brown Plaster Coats.

Fig. 180 — LABOR DISTRIBUTION

JOB CENTRAL HIGH SCHOOL SHEET NO. 52
CLASS OF WORK J-25, J-26 WEEK ENDING MAY 22, 19-- JOB NO. 110

OCCUPATION	M	T	W	T	F	S	S	HOURS	RATE	AMOUNT
1 J-25 { PLASTERERS	16	24	32	32	32	—	—	136		
2 { LABORERS	8	12	16	16	16	—	—	68		
3										
4										
5 J-26 { PLASTERERS	16	8	—	—	—	—	—	24		
6 { LABORERS	8	4	—	—	—	—	—	12		
7										
8										
TOTAL J-25								J-26		

	QTY. WORK IN PLACE	PAY ROLL COSTS	LBR. AVERAGE UNIT COST	AVERAGE QUANTITY PER 8 HR. DAY	QTY. WORK IN PLACE	PAY ROLL COSTS	LBR. AVERAGE UNIT COST	AVERAGE QUANTITY PER 8 HR. DAY
PREVIOUS	380 SY			63.3 SY	—	—	—	—
THIS WEEK	1200			70.6	160 SY			53.3 SY
TOTAL	1580			68.7	160			53.3

MFD. IN U.S.A. FORM C-105 FRANK R. WALKER CO., PUBLISHERS, CHICAGO (OVER)

Fig. 180. Labor Distribution and Costs of Applying White and Sand Finish Plaster Coats.

Labor Distribution Figure 180 illustrates the correct method of keeping labor costs on work of this kind. The first column gives the total number of square yards of white or "putty" coat applied, the second column gives the total labor cost, the third column gives the average labor cost per square yard, while the fourth column gives the average number of square yards of white coat applied per 8-hour day. Columns five to eight give the same information regarding the cost of applying sand finish.

The back of this form, Figure 181, gives the total number of hours worked by each trade in the first column headed "Total Labor Hours," while the second column headed "Labor Hours Per Unit," gives the length of time required to apply 100 square yards of white or sand finish plaster.

Separate labor costs should be kept on each kind of special plaster finish, such as Keene's cement, portland cement, Caen-Stone, etc., as it is important to know the labor cost of applying these special finishes.

When running cement base having either a plain or cove bottom, the costs should state the height of the base, the number of lineal feet run, etc. This also applies to ceiling coves, bull nose corners, etc. The radius of the cove or bull nose should always be given and the total number of lineal feet run, as work of this kind is estimated by the lineal foot.

Exterior Plaster And Stucco

Separate labor costs should be kept on applying exterior plaster or stucco and should give separate costs on the different coats of plaster. Quantities should be kept by the square yard, the same as on interior plastering.

Always mention kind of material used, number of coats, kind of finish, and whether applied over metal lath, brick or tile surfaces.

Labor Distribution Figure 182 illustrates the correct method of keeping labor costs on exterior plaster work. The first column gives the number of square yards of scratch coat applied, the second column gives the labor cost applying same, the third column the average labor cost per square yard, while the fourth column gives the average number of square yards of scratch coat applied per 8-hour day. Columns five to eight contain the same information regarding the brown coat.

The back of the form, Figure 183, gives the total number of hours worked by each trade in the first column headed "Total Labor Hours," while the second column headed "Labor Hours Per Unit," gives the length of time required to apply 100 square yards of scratch or brown coat of exterior plaster.

When keeping labor costs on the exterior plaster finish coats, the same method should be used as on the scratch and brown coats. Special finishes, such as float finish, sand finish, rough cast, etc., should be kept separately, in order that accurate labor costs may be obtained on each kind of finish.

Labor Distribution Figure 184 illustrates the correct method of keeping costs on the finishing coat of exterior plaster. The first column gives the number of square yards completed, the second column gives the total labor cost applying same, the third column gives the average labor cost per square yard, while the fourth column gives the average number of square yards of finish coat applied per 8-hr. day.

The back of the form, Figure 185, gives the total number of hours worked by each trade in the first column headed "Total Labor Hours," while the second column headed "Labor Hours Per Unit," gives the length of time required to apply 100 square yards of exterior plaster finish coat.

If cornices or other ornamental work are run in Keene's cement, portland cement or other exterior plaster, separate costs should be kept. If the cornice is less than 12 inches in girth, the cost should be stated in lineal feet, mentioning the girth of the cornice in all instances. If the cornice is more than 12 inches in girth, the costs may be stated either by the lineal or square foot.

Ornamental Plastering

All kinds of ornamental plastering, such as column and pilaster bases and caps, brackets, plaster enrichments for cornice, beams, etc., should be kept separately, as most of this is shop work and sent to the job ready to erect, although on large jobs the plastering contractor often operates a shop right on the premises and makes moulds and casts all the ornamental work on the job. In such instances, separate costs should be kept on the modeling, casting, etc. Costs on this work should be kept by the square foot for all large pieces, or by the piece, giving a description and size of the different pieces modeled and cast.

Plaster cornices are ordinarily run on the job but in some instances they are cast in the shop and merely erected on the job. the method used will affect the cost records.

Fig. 181 — Cost Analysis Record

COST ANALYSIS RECORD							
TOTAL LABOR HOURS				UNIT			
1 PLAS.	2 LAB.	3	4	5 PLAS.	6 LAB.	7	8
PREVIOUS 48	20						
THIS WEEK 136	68			15.0	7.5		
TOTAL 184	88			15.0	7.5		

LABOR HOURS PER UNIT				UNIT PER 100 SQUARE YARDS			
1 PLAS.	2 LAB.	3	4	5 PLAS.	6 LAB.	7	8
PREVIOUS 12.6	5.26						
THIS WEEK 11.3	5.67			15.0	7.5		
TOTAL 11.6	5.54			15.0	7.5		

REMARKS: WHITE FINISH COAT AND SAND FINISH COAT — 1ST CLASS WORKMANSHIP. QUANTITIES BASED ON 1/2 OPENINGS DEDUCTED

MFD. IN U.S.A. FORM C-105 FRANK R. WALKER CO., PUBLISHERS, CHICAGO

Fig. 181. Analyzed Labor Costs of Applying White and Sand Finish Plaster Coats.

Fig. 182 — Labor Distribution

JOB CENTRAL HIGH SCHOOL
CLASS OF WORK J-43 J-44
WEEK ENDING MAY 29 19——
SHEET NO. 53
JOB NO. 110

	OCCUPATION	M	T	W	T	F	S	S	HOURS	RATE	AMOUNT
1 J-43	{ PLASTERERS	16	16						16		
2	{ LABORERS	16	16						16		
3											
4											
5 J-44	{ PLASTERERS	16	16						32		
6	{ LABORERS	8	8						16		
7											
8											
TOTAL											

	QTY. WORK IN PLACE	PAY ROLL COSTS		QTY. WORK IN PLACE	PAY ROLL COSTS	LBR. AVERAGE UNIT COST	AVERAGE QUANTITY PER 8 HR. DAY
J-43	270 SY			270 SY			
J-44	135 SY			135 SY			67.5 SY
PREVIOUS	270			270			67.5
THIS WEEK							
TOTAL							

MFD. IN U.S.A. FORM C-105 FRANK R. WALKER CO., PUBLISHERS, CHICAGO

Fig. 182. Labor Distribution and Costs of Applying Exterior Scratch and Brown Plaster Coats.

Fig. 183 — Cost Analysis Record

COST ANALYSIS RECORD							
TOTAL LABOR HOURS				UNIT			
1 PLAS.	2 LAB.	3	4	5 PLAS.	6 LAB.	7	8
PREVIOUS —	—			—			
THIS WEEK 16	16			32	16		
TOTAL 16	16			32	16		

LABOR HOURS PER UNIT				UNIT PER 100 SQUARE YARDS			
1 PLAS.	2 LAB.	3	4	5 PLAS.	6 LAB.	7	8
PREVIOUS —	—			—			
THIS WEEK 5.93	5.93			11.85	5.93		
TOTAL 5.93	5.93			11.85	5.93		

REMARKS:
EXTERIOR PLASTER SOFFITS — AUDITORIUM & GYM ENTRANCE CANOPIES. SCRATCH COAT — 1:3 — PORTLAND CEM., LIME & SAND ON METAL LATH
BROWN COAT — 1:3 PORTLAND CEM., LIME & SAND ON METAL LATH
NO OPENINGS IN WORK — NET QUANTITIES

MFD. IN U.S.A. FORM C-105 FRANK R. WALKER CO., PUBLISHERS, CHICAGO

Fig. 183. Analyzed Labor Costs of Applying Exterior Scratch and Brown Plaster Coats.

Fig. 184. Labor Distribution and Costs of Applying Exterior Finish Plaster Coat.

Fig. 185. Analyzed Labor Costs of Applying Exterior Finish Plaster Coat.

Fig. 184 — LABOR DISTRIBUTION

JOB: CENTRAL HIGH SCHOOL CLASS OF WORK: J-46 WEEK ENDING MAY 29, 19-- SHEET NO. 54 JOB NO. 110

OCCUPATION	M	T	W	T	F	S	S	HOURS	RATE	AMOUNT
1 PLASTERERS	1	1	1	1	1	1		32		
2 LABORERS	1	1	1	1	1	1		12		
3										
4										
5										
6										
7										
8										
TOTAL										

	QTY. WORK IN PLACE	PAY ROLL COSTS	LBR. AVERAGE UNIT COST	AVERAGE QUANTITY PER 8 HR. DAY
PREVIOUS				
THIS WEEK	270 SY			67.5 SY
TOTAL	270			67.5

FORM C-105 MFD. IN U.S.A. FRANK R. WALKER CO., PUBLISHERS, CHICAGO (OVER)

Fig. 185 — COST ANALYSIS RECORD

UNIT	3	4	5	6	7	8
TOTAL LABOR HOURS	1 PLAS, 2 LAB.					
PREVIOUS						
THIS WEEK	32	12				
TOTAL	32	12				

UNIT PER 100 SQUARE YARDS

LABOR HOURS PER UNIT	3	4	5	6	7	8
	1 PLAS, 2 LAB.					
PREVIOUS						
THIS WEEK	11.85	4.44				
TOTAL	11.85	4.44				

REMARKS: EXTERIOR PLASTER SOFFITS — AUDITORIUM & GYM ENTRANCE CANOPIES — FLOAT FINISH COAT — 1:3 PORTLAND CEMENT & SAND No OPENINGS IN WORK — NET QUANTITIES.

FORM C-105 MFD. IN U.S.A. FRANK R. WALKER CO., PUBLISHERS, CHICAGO

Fig. 186 — LABOR DISTRIBUTION

JOB: CENTRAL HIGH SCHOOL CLASS OF WORK: J-61, J-65 WEEK ENDING JUNE 6, 19-- SHEET NO. 55 JOB NO. 110

OCCUPATION	M	T	W	T	F	S	S	HOURS	RATE	AMOUNT
1 J-61 PLASTERERS	—	18	18	18	18	—	—	72		
2 LABORERS	—	8	8	8	8	—	—	32		
3										
4										
5 J-65 PLASTERERS	—	14	14	14	14	—	—	56		
6										
7										
8										
TOTAL J-61								J-65		

	QTY. WORK IN PLACE	PAY ROLL COSTS	LBR. AVERAGE UNIT COST	AVERAGE QUANTITY PER 8 HR. DAY	QTY. WORK IN PLACE	PAY ROLL COSTS	LBR. AVERAGE UNIT COST	AVERAGE QUANTITY PER 8 HR. DAY
PREVIOUS	140 LF			35 LF	—			—
THIS WEEK	340			38	340 LF			49 LF
TOTAL	480			37	340			49

MFD. IN U.S.A. FORM C-105 FRANK R. WALKER CO., PUBLISHERS, CHICAGO (OVER)

Fig. 186. Labor Distribution and Costs of Running Ornamental Plaster Cornices.

If the ornamental cornices are run on the job, the costs should be kept by the lineal foot if the cornices are less than one foot in girth and by the superficial or square foot if the cornices are more than one foot in girth. If plaster ornaments are to be "stuck" to the cornices, beams or soffits, separate labor costs should state the number of lineal feet of ornament placed.

Labor Distribution Figure 186 illustrates the correct method of keeping costs on work of this kind. The labor under "J-61" includes the time running cornices and the time under "J-65" includes the time sticking ornaments or enrichments to same. The first column gives the number of lineal feet of cornice run, the second column gives the total cost of same, the third column the average labor cost per lineal foot, while the fourth column gives the average number of lineal feet of cornice run per 8-hour day. Column five to eight give the same information regarding the cost of "sticking" plaster ornaments or enrichments.

The back of the form, Figure 187, gives the total number of hours worked by each trade in the first column headed "Total Labor Hours," while the second column headed "Labor Hours Per Unit," gives the length of time required to run 100 lineal feet of cornice or apply ornaments to 100 lineal feet of run cornice.

On all kinds of wall and ceiling panels etc., where the ornaments are "run" or stuck on the walls or ceilings, the costs should be given by the lineal foot.

When setting column bases, caps, etc., the cost should state the number of bases or caps set, together with the size of same, in order that the costs may also be computed on a square foot basis.

Gutters, Downspouts, Flashing, Etc.

Gutters, downspouts, flashings, etc., are made up in the shop and sent to the job where they are assembled and erected, so that the job costs are only erection costs.

When keeping costs on metal eaves trough or gutter work, give the size and style of same, material used, method of hanging, etc., as this will have considerable bearing on the labor costs. Costs on work of this kind should always state the number of lineal feet erected.

This also applies to the labor cost of erecting metal downspouts. Always give the size, style and material of the downspout and the number of lineal feet erected.

Labor Distribution Figure 188 illustrates the correct method of keeping costs on work of this kind. The first column gives the total number of lineal feet of gutter erected, the second column gives the labor cost erecting same, the third column the average labor cost per lineal foot, while the fourth column gives the average number of lineal feet of gutter erected per 8-hour day. Columns five to eight give the same information regarding the erection of metal downspouts.

The back of the form, Figure 189, gives the total number of hours worked by each trade in the first column headed "Total Labor Hours," while the second column headed "Labor Hours Per Unit," gives the length of time required to erect 100 lineal feet of metal gutter or downspouts.

Labor costs for installing or erecting items of sheet metal work, such as metal flashing, counter flashing, hips, valleys, ridges, etc., should be reported separately, in the same manner as for metal eaves trough and downspouts, stating the size, material, etc, in each case.

Labor costs for erecting metal conductor heads are usually kept on a piece basis and should contain a complete description of the work, including size, material, method of attachment, etc.

Metal Skylights And Ventilators

When keeping costs on erecting metal skylights, always give the size, and mention whether single, double pitch or hip skylights, and whether with or without metal curb flashing or side lights. If the skylights have sash, state whether stationary or pivoted. By keeping the costs in this manner it is possible to obtain costs for each skylight and per square foot of roof surface, as these are the units commonly used. When using the square foot method, bear in mind that it costs much less per square foot to set large size skylights than small ones.

Labor Distribution Figure 190 illustrates the correct method of keeping costs on work of this kind. The first column gives the total number of skylights erected, the second column gives the total labor cost, the third column gives the average labor cost per skylight, while the fourth column gives the number of skylights erected per 8-hour day. Columns five to eight give the same costs on a square foot basis.

The back of the form, Figure 191, gives the total number of hours worked by each trade in the first

COST ANALYSIS RECORD

TOTAL LABOR HOURS / UNIT

	1 PLAS.	2 LAB.	3	4	5 PLAS.	6	7	8
PREVIOUS	32	16				1		
THIS WEEK	72	32				56		
TOTAL	104	48				56		

LABOR HOURS PER UNIT — UNIT PER 100 LINEAL FEET

	1 PLAS.	2 LAB.	3	4	5 PLAS.	6	7	8
PREVIOUS	22.9	11.43				1		
THIS WEEK	21.2	9.41				16.5		
TOTAL	21.7	10.00				16.5		

REMARKS

12" CORNICE AND 2"X3" DENTIL ORNAMENTATION — 4" O.C.
IN MAIN LOBBY, MAIN OFFICE AND LIBRARY

MFD. IN U.S.A.   FORM C-105   FRANK R. WALKER CO., PUBLISHERS, CHICAGO

Fig. 187. Analyzed Labor Costs of Running Ornamental Plaster Cornices.

LABOR DISTRIBUTION

SHEET NO. 56

JOB CENTRAL HIGH SCHOOL   WEEK ENDING APRIL 10, 19—   JOB NO. 110

CLASS OF WORK K-2, K-3

	OCCUPATION	M	T	W	T	F	S	S	HOURS	RATE	AMOUNT
1	K-2 (SHEET METAL WKRS	8	2	1	1	1	1	1	10		
2	HELPERS	8	2	1	1	1	1	1	10		
3											
4											
5	K-3 SHEET METAL WKRS	1	6	8	1	1	1	1	14		
6	HELPERS	1	6	8	1	1	1	1	14		
7											
8											

TOTAL K-2   K-3

	QTY. WORK IN PLACE	LBR. AVERAGE UNIT COST	PAY ROLL COSTS	AVERAGE QUANTITY PER 8 HR. DAY	QTY. WORK IN PLACE	LBR. AVERAGE UNIT COST	PAY ROLL COSTS	AVERAGE QUANTITY PER 8 HR. DAY
PREVIOUS	120 LF			120 LF				126 LF
THIS WEEK	160			128	220 LF			126
TOTAL	280			124	220			

(OVER)

MFD. IN U.S.A.   FORM C-105   FRANK R. WALKER CO., PUBLISHERS, CHICAGO

Fig. 188. Labor Distribution and Costs of Erecting Metal Eaves Trough and Down Spouts.

COST ANALYSIS RECORD

TOTAL LABOR HOURS / UNIT

	1 SHEET METAL WORKERS	2 HELPERS	3	4	5 SHEET METAL WORKERS	6 HELPERS	7	8
PREVIOUS	8	8			—	—		
THIS WEEK	10	10			14	14		
TOTAL	18	18			14	14		

LABOR HOURS PER UNIT — UNIT PER 100 LINEAL FEET

	1 SHEET METAL WORKERS	2 HELPERS	3	4	5 SHEET METAL WORKERS	6 HELPERS	7	8
PREVIOUS	6.67	6.67			—	—		
THIS WEEK	6.25	6.25			6.36	6.36		
TOTAL	6.43	6.43			6.36	6.36		

REMARKS

GUTTER — 5" BOX — 12" GIRTH — 16 OZ. COPPER — HUNG TO WOOD
DECKING — DOWNSPOUT — 4" CORRUGATED SQUARE — 16 OZ.
COPPER — 3 STORY RUNS FASTENED TO MASONRY WITH
HOOKS.

MFD. IN U.S.A.   FORM C-105   FRANK R. WALKER CO., PUBLISHERS, CHICAGO

Fig. 189. Analyzed Labor Costs of Erecting Metal Eaves Trough and Down Spouts.

column headed "Total Labor Hours," while the second column headed "Labor Hours Per Unit," gives the length of time required to set one skylight or 100 square feet of skylights.

If sash are used in connection with the skylights, it is well to keep separate costs, if possible, giving the number of mullions, sash, average size of sash, etc.

If sash operating devices are used to open and close the side ventilating sash, the cost of erecting the operators should be given by the number of lineal feet of sash which they control. For instance, if the skylight is 100 feet long with the side sash on both sides operating, there would be 200 lineal feet of operating device to erect, so that the erection costs should be given in this manner.

If metal ventilators are erected on the skylights or other areas, the labor cost of erecting same should be kept separate giving the size of the ventilators, number set, whether gravity type or power operated, etc., in order that accurate unit prices may be obtained.

The cost of erecting metal ventilating ducts should be kept by the square foot of duct placed, obtained by taking the girth of the vent pipes. In many instances these vent pipes are made up complete in the shop, while in others they are made up on the job. If they are made on the job separate costs should be kept of the labor making and erecting, and the costs should state the number of square feet of ducts completed.

Metal Roofs And Siding

All kinds of metal roofing and siding including tin, galvanized iron and copper are estimated by the square foot or by the square containing 100 square feet, so all costs should be kept in the same manner.

When reporting costs on any of the above work, always give a complete description of the job, including kind of material used, type of framing or surface to which applied, pitch of roofs, height of walls, etc., as these are all items that affect the labor costs.

Labor cost records on flat metal roof applications should state the type of joint employed, whether flat seam or standing seam, the average size of sheets used, and should also mention the kind of metal used, such as copper, tin, zinc, galvanized steel or any of the special process materials including Armco, Toncan, etc.

Labor Distribution Figure 192 illustrates the correct method of keeping costs on the application of a standing seam copper roof deck. The first column gives the total number of squares of roof applied, the second column gives the total labor cost, the third column the average cost per square, while the fourth column gives the average number of square feet of roof applied per-8 hour day.

The back of the form, Figure 193, gives the total number of hours worked by each trade in the first column headed "Total Labor Hours," while the second column headed "Labor Hours Per Unit," gives the length of time required to complete 100 square feet of roof.

When placing metal corrugated or V-crimped siding and roofing on warehouses, mill and factory buildings, mining structures, etc., the costs should be kept by the square foot or by the square containing 100 square feet. If the siding and roofing is nailed to wood joists, studs or rafters, it should be mentioned, because on many types of industrial structures the siding and roofing are fastened to a steel frame by means of metal clips. It is important to mention the class of work as the labor costs on the different types of structures vary widely. It is also advisable to mention size of sheets used for both siding and roofing.

All kinds of miscellaneous metal roofs, such as imitation tile, metal shingles, etc., should be kept by the square foot or square containing 100 square feet. Always describe the type of roof, giving size and shape, whether necessary to form hips and valleys, size of the metal shingles, etc.

The labor cost of handling and erecting metal ceilings and sidewalls should be kept by the square foot or by the square containing 100 square feet. On jobs where it is necessary to place wood furring or nailing strips for fastening these units, separate costs should be kept on this work and charged to classification "G-17" under Rough Carpentry.

Labor costs for erecting metal ceilings should be kept separate from costs of wall or wainscot work, to obtain accurate costs on each kind of application. It is more difficult to erect metal ceilings than sidewalls or wainscots and the unit costs will be different for this reason. Costs should contain a general description of the work, i.e., whether areas involved are large or small, whether areas are solid or cut up with openings, height of ceiling, type of units being used, whether application is being made in new or old work, etc., as all these factors will have a bearing on the labor costs.

If metal cornice is installed, where ceiling meets walls, the labor cost of same should be kept as a separate item and should be given per lineal foot, stating the girth of the cornice.

Fig. 190 — LABOR DISTRIBUTION (Sheet No. 57)

JOB CENTRAL HIGH SCHOOL
CLASS OF WORK K-12
WEEK ENDING APRIL 10, 19-- — JOB NO. 110 — SHEET NO. 57

	OCCUPATION	M	T	W	T	F	S	S	HOURS	RATE	AMOUNT
1	SHEET METAL WORKER	1	1	1	8	8	1	1	16		
2	HELPER	1	1	1	8	8	1	1	16		
3											
4											
5											
6											
7											
8											
TOTAL											

	QTY. WORK IN PLACE	PAY ROLL COSTS	LBR. AVERAGE UNIT COST	AVERAGE QUANTITY PER 8 HR. DAY	QTY. WORK IN PLACE	PAY ROLL COSTS	LBR. AVERAGE UNIT COST	AVERAGE QUANTITY PER 8 HR. DAY
PREVIOUS	1 SKYLIGHT 10'x32' 1						PER SF	160 SF
THIS WEEK					320 SF			160
TOTAL					320			(OVER)

MFD. IN U.S.A.   FORM C-105   FRANK R. WALKER CO., PUBLISHERS, CHICAGO

Fig. 190. Labor Distribution and Costs of Erecting Metal Skylights.

Fig. 191 — COST ANALYSIS RECORD

UNIT PER SKYLIGHT — 10' X 32'

TOTAL LABOR HOURS	SHT. MTL. 1 WORKER	2 HELPER	3	4	SHT. MTL. 5 WORKER	6 HELPER	7	8
PREVIOUS	16	16						
THIS WEEK	16	16						
TOTAL	16	16						

UNIT PER 100 SQUARE FEET

LABOR HOURS PER UNIT	SHT. MTL. 1 WORKER	2 HELPER	3	4	SHT. MTL. 5 WORKER	6 HELPER	7	8
PREVIOUS	16	16						
THIS WEEK	16	16						
TOTAL	16	16						

REMARKS: 10' X 32' HIP TYPE, STATIONARY SKYLIGHT OVER STAGE IN AUDITORIUM — SET ON CURB — GLAZING COSTS NOT INCLUDED

MFD. IN U.S.A.   FORM C-105   FRANK R. WALKER CO., PUBLISHERS, CHICAGO

Fig. 191. Analyzed Labor Costs of Erecting Metal Skylights.

Fig. 192 — LABOR DISTRIBUTION (Sheet No. 58)

JOB CENTRAL HIGH SCHOOL
CLASS OF WORK K-23
WEEK ENDING APRIL 17, 19-- — JOB NO. 110 — SHEET NO. 58

	OCCUPATION	M	T	W	T	F	S	S	HOURS	RATE	AMOUNT
1	SHEET MTL. WKR.	8	4	–	–	–	–	–	12		
2	HELPER	8	4	–	–	–	–	–	12		
3											
4											
5											
6											
7											
8											
TOTAL											

	QTY. WORK IN PLACE	PAY ROLL COSTS	LBR. AVERAGE UNIT COST	AVERAGE QUANTITY PER 8 HR. DAY	QTY. WORK IN PLACE	PAY ROLL COSTS	LBR. AVERAGE UNIT COST	AVERAGE QUANTITY PER 8 HR. DAY
PREVIOUS	—	—	—					
THIS WEEK	360 SF			240 SF				
TOTAL	360			240				

MFD. IN U.S.A.   FORM C-105   FRANK R. WALKER CO., PUBLISHERS, CHICAGO   (OVER)

Fig. 192. Labor Distribution and Costs of Placing Standing Seam Metal Roofing.

Roofing and Siding

All kinds of roofing and siding are measured by the square foot or by the square containing 100 square feet, and the costs should be kept in the same manner.

When keeping costs on laying asphalt shingles, always state the kind of shingle used, whether individual or strip shingles, size, distance to weather, weight per square of coverage, together with the size and shape of the roof, or a description of the wall surface, when used for siding.

Labor costs on applying ready roofing, which is sent to the job in rolls, where it is necessary to apply only one thickness of same and either staple or cement the seams, should also contain a complete description of the material and the roof or wall surface to which it is applied.

Costs of applying insulating siding to new or old building walls should also be kept on a square foot or square basis and should contain a complete description of the work. If wood furring strips are required to receive the siding, separate lineal foot costs should be kept on this work. The cost of applying trim moldings around doors, windows, etc., should also be kept separate and given per lineal foot.

Labor costs of applying asbestos shingles to roofs or sidewalls should be kept separate and should contain, in addition to a description of the surface to which applied, the shape of the shingle, size, method of laying, etc., as asbestos shingles are furnished in a variety of sizes and shapes and some methods of laying are more costly than others. Separate costs should also be kept when applying large sheet asbestos for siding, soffits, etc., giving the size of the material, method of fastening, etc. If wood furring strips are required to receive the asbestos shingles or sheets, the labor cost of same should be kept separate and on a lineal foot basis.

When keeping costs on composition or built-up roofs, always give a complete description of the roof, mentioning the number of thicknesses of felt used, the number of moppings of pitch or asphalt required, the amount of gravel or slag used per square, etc., as these are all items that affect the labor costs. If possible, the labor costs applying the pitch or asphalt and laying the felts should be kept separate from the costs of spreading the final pitch or asphalt coat and applying gravel or slag, because by doing this it is possible to estimate the cost of any similar roof, regardless of the number of thicknesses of felt used.

It is also important that the size of the roof be given, together with the distance of the roof above the ground, as the higher the roof, the more it costs to hoist the materials.

Labor Distribution Figure 194 illustrates the correct method of keeping costs on a 4-ply composition roof. The first column gives the total number of squares of 4-ply roofing applied, the second column gives the total labor cost to date, the third column the average labor cost per square, while the fourth column gives the number of squares of roof applied per 8-hour day. Columns five to eight contain the same information regarding the cost of placing and mopping the final asphalt coating and applying the gravel.

The back of this form, Figure 195, gives the total number of hours worked by each trade in the first column headed "Total Labor Hours," while the second column headed "Labor Hours Per Unit," gives the length of time required to apply 100 square feet of 4-ply composition roofing complete.

This same method is used when applying any other kind of built-up roof.

Built-up flashing costs should be kept in the same manner as roofs, except the quantities should be stated in lineal feet of flashing installed, mentioning the width of same.

Slate roof labor costs should also be given by the square, stating size of slate, shape of roof, etc.

Separate labor costs should be kept on the various kinds of clay roofing tile, as the methods of laying vary widely, which affects labor costs likewise.

When laying Spanish or Shingle tile, always state whether tile are laid over wood roof boards or concrete slab, size of tile, shape of roof, method of laying, etc., and the costs should always be given by the square foot or per 100 square feet.

Promenade tile are usually laid in asphalt or cement, and the joints are filled with composition or cement mortar. The size of the tile should always be given, size of roof, method of laying, etc., and the costs should be given by the square foot or by the square containing 100 square feet.

When placing corrugated asbestos siding and roofing, the labor costs are also kept per square foot or square containing 100 square feet and the work should be completely described. In addition to giving the size of the sheets used, height of wall, etc., the cost records should state the type of framing or surface to which this material is applied, i.e., skeleton steel framing, skeleton wood framing, solid wood sheathing, etc., as the costs will vary widely in this respect.

Fig. 193 — COST ANALYSIS RECORD

	TOTAL LABOR HOURS				UNIT			
	1 SHT. MTL. WORKER	2 HELPER	3	4	5	6	7	8
PREVIOUS	1	1						
THIS WEEK	12	12						
TOTAL	12	12						

	LABOR HOURS PER UNIT				UNIT PER 100 SQUARE FEET			
	1 SHT. MTL. WORKER	2 HELPER	3	4	5	6	7	8
PREVIOUS	1	1						
THIS WEEK	3.33	3.33						
TOTAL	3.33	3.33						

REMARKS: 16 OZ. COPPER STANDING SEAM ROOFS OVER BAYS AT LOUNGE, OFFICE & LIBRARY — 120 SF EACH — 45 DEGREE ROOF PITCH — WOOD ROOF DECKS — USED 24" X 96" — 16 OZ. COPPER SHEETS.

MFD. IN U.S.A.   FORM C-105   FRANK R. WALKER CO., PUBLISHERS, CHICAGO

Fig. 193. Analyzed Labor Costs of Placing Standing Seam Metal Roofing.

Fig. 194 — LABOR DISTRIBUTION

SHEET NO. 59
JOB CENTRAL HIGH SCHOOL
CLASS OF WORK K-49-A, K-49-B   WEEK ENDING APRIL 10, 19—   JOB NO. 110

	OCCUPATION	M	T	W	T	F	S	S	HOURS	RATE	AMOUNT
1	K-49-A FOREMAN	5	5	5	5	1	1		25		
2	ROOFERS	48	48	48	48	1	1		240		
3											
4											
5	K-49-B FOREMAN	3	3	3	3	1	1		15		
6	ROOFERS	32	32	32	32	1	1		160		
7											
8											
TOTAL											

K-49-A → K-49-B

	QTY. WORK IN PLACE	PAY ROLL COSTS	LBR. AVERAGE UNIT COST	AVERAGE QUANTITY PER 8 HR. DAY	QTY. WORK IN PLACE	PAY ROLL COSTS	K-49-B TOP COAT & GRAVEL LBR. AVERAGE UNIT COST	AVERAGE QUANTITY PER 8 HR. DAY
PREVIOUS	74 SQS.			62 SF				92 SF
THIS WEEK	190			63				95
TOTAL	264			63				94

(OVER)

MFD. IN U.S.A.   FORM C-105   FRANK R. WALKER CO., PUBLISHERS, CHICAGO

Fig. 194. Labor Distribution and Costs of Applying Composition Roofing.

Fig. 195 — COST ANALYSIS RECORD

	TOTAL LABOR HOURS				UNIT			
	1 FOREMAN	2 ROOFERS	3	4	5 FOREMAN	6 ROOFERS	7	8
PREVIOUS	10	96			6	64		
THIS WEEK	25	240			15	160		
TOTAL	35	336			21	224		

	LABOR HOURS PER UNIT				UNIT PER SQUARE			
	1 FOREMAN	2 ROOFERS	3	4	5 FOREMAN	6 ROOFERS	7	8
PREVIOUS	0.135	1.30			0.081	0.86		
THIS WEEK	0.131	1.26			0.079	0.84		
TOTAL	0.133	1.27			0.080	0.85		

REMARKS: 4-PLY COMPOSITION ROOF ON 3 STORY BUILDING LARGE FLAT AREAS - FEW OPENINGS

MFD. IN U.S.A.   FORM C-105   FRANK R. WALKER CO., PUBLISHERS, CHICAGO

Fig. 195. Analyzed Labor Costs of Applying Composition Roofing.

Glass and Glazing

When keeping labor costs on glass and glazing work, all conditions which will affect the costs, should be mentioned. These include the kind of glass, type of opening, whether set in wood or metal sash, whether set in putty or glazing compound, or with wood or metal stops, etc. The size of the glass should also be given, as the labor costs setting large lights of glass runs considerably more than small lights.

When reporting labor costs on setting plain window glass in putty, keep separate costs on lights up to 12x14 inches in size, lights from 12x14 to 20x28 inches, lights from 20x28 to 30x40 inches, and lights from 30x40 to 40x48. By keeping the labor costs in this manner, it is possible to obtain fairly accurate labor costs on glazing all of the different glass sizes.

Labor Distribution Figure 196 illustrates the correct method of keeping labor costs on setting plain window glass in putty. The first column gives the number of lights of glass set, the second column gives the total labor cost, the third column the average labor cost per light, while the fourth column gives the average number of lights placed per 8-hour day.

The back of the form, Figure 197, gives the total number of hours worked by each trade in the first column headed "Total Labor Hours," while the second column headed "Labor Hours Per Unit," gives the length of time required to glaze 100 lights of glass.

The labor cost of setting plate glass in wood or metal sash, using putty, should be kept in the same manner as plain window glass, as the only difference is the additional thickness and weight of the glass.

When the glass is placed in doors, windows, borrowed lights, etc., and is held in place by wood or metal stops, separate labor costs should be kept on this work, as glazing with stops usually costs more than with putty.

Steel sash is another branch of work on which separate labor costs should be kept as the work is entirely different from the ordinary glazing job. The glass are usually set and held in place by means of metal clips and litharge putty and unless experienced glaziers are used, it will prove exceedingly expensive. The lights may run from 9x12 to 48x16 inches in size. If it is possible to glaze the sash without the use of a scaffold it will have considerable bearing on the cost of the work, as will the weather, as winter work is more expensive than summer work.

Labor Distribution Figure 198 illustrates the correct method of keeping labor costs on glazing steel sash. The first column gives the total number of lights glazed, the second column gives the total labor cost, the third column the average cost per light, while the fourth column gives the number of lights glazed per 8-hour day.

The back of the form, Figure 199, gives the total number of hours worked by glaziers in the first column headed "Total Labor Hours," while the second column headed "Labor Hours Per Unit," gives the length of time required to glaze 100 lights of glass in steel sash.

Labor costs on setting insulating glass, consisting of two lights of glass with a hermetically sealed air space between, should be kept in the same manner as for plain window glass or plate glass, but should be kept separate as the cost will be about twice as much as for single thickness glass.

When glazing leaded or art glass, keep costs separate and give the number of lights glazed, the average size of the lights, the type of sash or opening glazed, and the method of securing glass, whether with putty, wood stops or metal stops, etc.

Separate labor costs should also be kept on setting large plate glass windows, such as store fronts, picture windows, etc., in order that the average number of hours required to handle and set each plate may be obtained. Costs on this work should state size of glass, type of opening glazed, whether metal store front, wood or metal frames, etc.

Labor costs on setting structural glass facing for walls and ceilings should be kept and reported per square foot and should contain a complete description of the job. This includes average size and thickness of glass, whether for exterior or interior application, method of securing, etc. Wall facing costs should be kept separate from ceiling work and the reports should also state whether surfaces are large or small, straight or cut-up, etc.

When setting tempered glass doors and partitions, labor costs should be kept separate for each different size door or partition panel and should contain a complete description of the work, giving size of door or panel, method of hinging, method of locking, etc.

Labor costs for setting mirrors should also be kept separate for each different size and should state type of mirror, size and number of each, method of installation, etc.

LABOR DISTRIBUTION

JOB CENTRAL HIGH SCHOOL
CLASS OF WORK L-2
WEEK ENDING June 12, 19--
SHEET NO. 60
JOB NO. 110

OCCUPATION	M	T	W	T	F	S	S	HOURS	RATE	AMOUNT
1 GLAZIERS	16	16	16	16	16	1	-	80		
2										
3										
4										
5										
6										
7										
8										
TOTAL										

	QTY. WORK IN PLACE	PAY ROLL COSTS	LBR. AVERAGE UNIT COST	AVERAGE QUANTITY PER 8 HR. DAY
PREVIOUS	124 LTS			31 LTS
THIS WEEK	350			35
TOTAL	474			34

MFD. IN U.S.A.   FORM C-105   FRANK R. WALKER CO., PUBLISHERS, CHICAGO   (OVER)

Fig. 196. Labor Distribution and Costs of Glazing Wood Sash.

COST ANALYSIS RECORD

TOTAL LABOR HOURS
UNIT PER 100 LIGHTS

	UNIT							
16 GLAZIERS	2	3	4	5	6	7	8	
PREVIOUS	32							
THIS WEEK	80							
TOTAL	112							

LABOR HOURS PER UNIT
UNIT PER 100 LIGHTS

16 GLAZIERS	2	3	4	5	6	7	8	
PREVIOUS	25.8							
THIS WEEK	22.8							
TOTAL	23.6							

REMARKS

CLASS ROOM WINDOWS - 40"X16" LTS - D.S.A. PLAIN WINDOW GLASS - SET IN PUTTY - WOOD D.H. SASH - OUTSIDE GLAZING - FROM HANGING SCAFFOLD.

MFD. IN U.S.A.   FORM C-105   FRANK R. WALKER CO., PUBLISHERS, CHICAGO

Fig. 197. Analyzed Labor Costs of Glazing Wood Sash.

LABOR DISTRIBUTION

JOB CENTRAL HIGH SCHOOL
CLASS OF WORK L-6
WEEK ENDING JUNE 19, 19--
SHEET NO. 61
JOB NO. 110

OCCUPATION	M	T	W	T	F	S	S	HOURS	RATE	AMOUNT
1 GLAIZERS	16	16	16	16	16	-	-	80		
2										
3										
4										
5										
6										
7										
8										
TOTAL										

	QTY. WORK IN PLACE	PAY ROLL COSTS	LBR. AVERAGE UNIT COST	AVERAGE QUANTITY PER 8 HR. DAY	QTY. WORK IN PLACE	PAY ROLL COSTS	LBR. AVERAGE UNIT COST	AVERAGE QUANTITY PER 8 HR. DAY
PREVIOUS	-	-	-					
THIS WEEK	330 LTS			33 LTS				
TOTAL	330			33				

MFD. IN U.S.A.   FORM C-105   FRANK R. WALKER CO., PUBLISHERS, CHICAGO   (OVER)

Fig. 198. Labor Distribution and Costs of Glazing Metal Sash.

Fig. 199 — COST ANALYSIS RECORD

TOTAL LABOR HOURS | **UNIT**

	1 GLAZIERS	2	3	4	5	6	7	8
PREVIOUS	—							
THIS WEEK	80							
TOTAL	80							

UNIT: PER 100 LIGHTS

LABOR HOURS PER UNIT

	1 GLAZIERS	2	3	4	5	6	7	8
PREVIOUS	—							
THIS WEEK	24.2							
TOTAL	24.2							

REMARKS

GLAZING ARCHITECTURAL PROJECTED STEEL SASH IN GYM. 26" x 15" LTS, D.S.A. — SET IN GLAZING COMPOUND WITH CLIPS. OUTSIDE GLAZED FROM SASH JACKS

MFD. IN U.S.A. FORM C-105 FRANK R. WALKER CO., PUBLISHERS, CHICAGO

Fig. 199. Analyzed Labor Costs of Glazing Metal Sash.

Fig. 200 — LABOR DISTRIBUTION

JOB CENTRAL HIGH SCHOOL SHEET NO. 62
CLASS OF WORK M-2, M-3 JOB NO. 110
WEEK ENDING FEB 20, 19--

	OCCUPATION	M	T	W	T	F	S	S	HOURS	RATE	AMOUNT
1	M-2 PAINTERS	16	16	16	8	16	—	—	72		
2											
3											
4											
5	M-3 PAINTERS	—	—	8	—	—	8	—	8		
6											
7											
8											

TOTAL: M-2 - PRIME COAT   M-3 - 2ND COAT

	PAY ROLL COSTS	QTY. WORK IN PLACE	AVERAGE QUANTITY PER 8 HR. DAY	LBR. AVERAGE UNIT COST	QTY. WORK IN PLACE	AVERAGE QUANTITY PER 8 HR. DAY	LBR. AVERAGE UNIT COST
PREVIOUS		2200 SF	733 SF		1300 SF	867 SF	
THIS WEEK		7000	777		1000	1000	
TOTAL		9200	767		2300	920	

MFD. IN U.S.A. FORM C-105 FRANK R. WALKER CO., PUBLISHERS, CHICAGO

Fig. 200. Labor Distribution and Costs of Applying First and Second Coats of Paint.

Fig. 201 — COST ANALYSIS RECORD

TOTAL LABOR HOURS | **UNIT**

	1 PAINTERS	2	3	4	5 PAINTERS	6	7	8
PREVIOUS	24				12			
THIS WEEK	72				8			
TOTAL	96				20			

UNIT: PER SQUARE

LABOR HOURS PER UNIT

	1 PAINTERS	2	3	4	5 PAINTERS	6	7	8
PREVIOUS	1.09				0.92			
THIS WEEK	1.03				0.80			
TOTAL	1.04				0.87			

REMARKS

FRAMES PRIMED BEFORE ERECTION — 2ND COAT APPLIED AFTER FRAMES WERE SET IN PLACE, FROM INSIDE — NO SCAFFOLDING REQUIRED ALL BRUSH WORK — ORDINARY WORKMANSHIP
WEATHER - CLEAR AND COLD

MFD. IN U.S.A. FORM C-105 FRANK R. WALKER CO., PUBLISHERS, CHICAGO

Fig. 201. Analyzed Labor Costs of Applying First and Second Coats of Paint.

Exterior Painting

Practically all kinds of painting are estimated by the square containing 100 square feet and all labor costs should be kept in the same manner. When measuring the areas painted do not make deductions for openings less than 10'-0"x10'-0".

Labor cost records should state the class of work required, i.e., commercial, residential, government work, etc., also the working conditions, including kind of weather, type of scaffolding, method of application, whether by brush, roller or spray gun, and any other factors which may have a bearing on the costs.

Separate labor costs should be kept on painting the various kinds of materials, such as clapboard, shingles, plywood or sheathing, concrete, brickwork, stucco, etc. Inasmuch as it usually requires more labor to apply the priming coat of paint to wood and rough masonry surfaces, it is advisable to keep this cost separate from the second and all following coats.

Labor Distribution Figure 200 illustrates the correct method of keeping labor costs on priming wood exterior door and window frames. The first column gives the total number of squares primed, the second column gives the total labor cost, the third column the average cost per square, while the fourth column gives the number of squares primed per 8-hour day. Columns five to eight furnish the same information regarding the cost of applying the second and subsequent coats.

The back of the form, Figure 201, gives the total number of hours worked by each trade in the first column headed "Total Labor Hours," while the second column headed "Labor Hours Per Unit," gives the length of time required to apply one square of paint.

The labor costs of painting brick, stone, concrete or stucco surfaces should be kept in the same manner as described above.

When painting structural steel after erection, the labor costs may be kept either by the square of surface painted or by the ton of steel. If kept by the ton, the costs should state the average size and weight per lineal foot of steel sections involved. Costs should also give a complete description of job conditions, including kind of paint used, number of coats, method of application, type of scaffolding, etc.

Cost records for painting towers, tanks, etc, should be kept in the same manner as given for structural steel, except the quantities of work should only be measured per square of surface painted. A complete description of the work must be given along with the costs, in order that the information may be properly classified for future reference.

When reporting costs on painting miscellaneous metal work, such as railings, ladders, grilles, frames, etc., quantities of work should be measured by the lineal foot, where the girth of the item is 1'-0" or under, and by the square foot, where the girth is over 1'-0". The labor costs may then be reduced to a working unit of either per 100 lineal feet or per square containing 100 square feet. Costs should also give the kind of paint used, number of coats, method of application and other essential information describing the work.

Interior Painting and Decorating

When doing interior painting and decorating work, the labor costs should be kept in the same manner as for exterior work, i.e., the cost of the first or priming coat should be kept separate from subsequent coats and the quantities generally should be measured and reported by the square containing 100 square feet. In measuring quantities, no dimension for any trim work, such as base, picture mould, door and window trim, etc., should be taken as less than 1'-0" wide, if taken as an area, and if the work is done as a separate item, the labor cost should be reported on a lineal foot basis.

When painting interior woodwork, the labor cost of priming and back-priming should be kept as a separate item from costs for subsequent coats and should state whether done at the mill or on the job. In addition, costs of each operation before, between and after coats, such as preparing the surface including puttying nail holes, sanding, rubbing, etc., should be kept as separate labor costs, if possible, so that on future jobs, any combination of operations called for by the specifications may be estimated.

Labor costs for natural, bleached or stain finish on interior wood work should be kept the same as for paint finish given above, with each operation being kept separate.

The labor costs on all kinds of applications to plastered surfaces, such as seal coating, painting, stippling, sizing, etc., should be kept by the square containing 100 square feet the same as on other painting. Separate labor costs should be kept on each labor operation, in order to obtain costs on any combination of work.

Labor Distribution Figure 202 illustrates the correct method of keeping labor costs on applying seal coat

Fig. 202

JOB CENTRAL HIGH SCHOOL **LABOR DISTRIBUTION** SHEET NO. 63
CLASS OF WORK M-25, M-26   WEEK ENDING JUNE 26, 19--   JOB NO. 110

OCCUPATION	M	T	W	T	F	S	S	HOURS	RATE	AMOUNT
1 M-25 PAINTERS	16	16	16	16	16	1		80		
2										
3										
4										
5 M-26 PAINTERS	24	24	24	24	24	1		120		
6										
7										
8										
TOTAL										

	M-25				M-26			
	QTY. WORK IN PLACE	PAY ROLL COSTS	LBR. AVERAGE UNIT COST	AVERAGE QUANTITY PER 8 HR. DAY	QTY. WORK IN PLACE	PAY ROLL COSTS	LBR. AVERAGE UNIT COST	AVERAGE QUANTITY PER 8 HR. DAY
PREVIOUS	26000 SF			1733 SF	15000 SF			1250 SF
THIS WEEK	17500			1750	26000			1333
TOTAL	43500			1740	35000			1296

MFD. IN U.S.A. FORM C-105   FRANK R. WALKER CO., PUBLISHERS, CHICAGO   (OVER)

Fig. 202. Labor Distribution and Costs of Sealing and Painting Plastered Surfaces.

Fig. 203

COST ANALYSIS RECORD

UNIT

TOTAL LABOR HOURS

	1 PAINTER	2	3	4	5 PAINTERS	6	7	8
PREVIOUS	120				96			
THIS WEEK	80				120			
TOTAL	200				216			

UNIT PER SQUARE

LABOR HOURS PER UNIT

	1 PAINTER	2	3	4	5 PAINTERS	6	7	8
PREVIOUS	0.46				0.64			
THIS WEEK	0.46				0.60			
TOTAL	0.46				0.62			

REMARKS: SEAL COAT AND FINISH COAT ON PLASTERED WALLS AND CEILINGS. CEILING HEIGHT – 9'-0". – ALL BRUSH WORK – 1ST CLASS WORKMANSHIP. WEATHER – WARM & HUMID.

MFD. IN U.S.A. FORM C-105   FRANK R. WALKER CO., PUBLISHERS, CHICAGO

Fig. 203. Analyzed Labor Costs of Sealing and Painting Plastered Surfaces.

JOB CENTRAL HIGH SCHOOL **LABOR DISTRIBUTION** SHEET NO. 64
CLASS OF WORK M-28   WEEK ENDING JULY 10, 19--   JOB NO. 110

OCCUPATION	M	T	W	T	F	S	S	HOURS	RATE	AMOUNT
1 PAINTERS	—	—	8	8	8	—	—	24		
2										
3										
4										
5										
6										
7										
8										
TOTAL										

	QTY. WORK IN PLACE	PAY ROLL COSTS	LBR. AVERAGE UNIT COST	AVERAGE QUANTITY PER 8 HR. DAY	QTY. WORK IN PLACE	PAY ROLL COSTS	LBR. AVERAGE UNIT COST	AVERAGE QUANTITY PER 8 HR. DAY
PREVIOUS	—	—	—					
THIS WEEK	32 ROLLS			10.67 Rolls				
TOTAL	32			10.67				

MFD. IN U.S.A.   FORM C-105   FRANK R. WALKER CO., PUBLISHERS, CHICAGO   (OVER)

Fig. 204. Labor Distribution and Costs of Hanging Wall Paper.

Fig. 205 — COST ANALYSIS RECORD

TOTAL LABOR HOURS | **UNIT**

	1 PAINTERS	2	3	4	5	6	7	8
PREVIOUS	—							
THIS WEEK	24							
TOTAL	24							

LABOR HOURS PER UNIT | **UNIT PER SINGLE ROLL**

	1 PAINTERS	2	3	4	5	6	7	8
PREVIOUS	—							
THIS WEEK	0.75							
TOTAL	0.75							

REMARKS

PAPERING WALLS IN TEACHER'S LOUNGES – 1ST CLASS WORKMANSHIP – HEAVY WEIGHT, GOOD GRADE PAPER.

MFD. IN U.S.A.   FORM C-105   FRANK R. WALKER CO., PUBLISHERS, CHICAGO

Fig. 205. Analyzed Labor Costs of Hanging Wall Paper.

Fig. 206 — LABOR DISTRIBUTION

JOB CENTRAL HIGH SCHOOL
CLASS OF WORK M-29-A, M-29-B
WEEK ENDING JUNE 19, 19—
SHEET NO. 65   JOB NO. 110

OCCUPATION	M	T	W	T	F	S	S	HOURS	RATE	AMOUNT
1 M-29-A PAINTERS	—	32	1	—	1	—	1	32		
2										
3										
4										
5 M-29-B PAINTERS	—	—	24	—	1	—	1	24		
6										
7										
8										
TOTAL								M-29-A M-29-B		

	QTY. WORK IN PLACE	PAY ROLL COSTS	LBR. AVERAGE UNIT COST	AVERAGE QUANTITY PER 8 HR. DAY	QTY. WORK IN PLACE	PAY ROLL COSTS	LBR. AVERAGE UNIT COST	AVERAGE QUANTITY PER 8 HR. DAY
PREVIOUS	—	—	—					
THIS WEEK	1200 SF			1600 SF	4800 SF			1600 SF
TOTAL	1200			1600	4800			1600

(OVER)

MFD. IN U.S.A.   FORM C-105   FRANK R. WALKER CO., PUBLISHERS, CHICAGO

Fig. 206. Labor Distribution and Costs of Applying Penetration Finish to Wood Floors.

Fig. 207 — COST ANALYSIS RECORD

TOTAL LABOR HOURS | **UNIT**

	1 PAINTERS	2	3	4	5 PAINTERS	6	7	8
PREVIOUS	—				—			
THIS WEEK	32				24			
TOTAL	32				24			

LABOR HOURS PER UNIT | **UNIT PER SQUARE**

	1 PAINTERS	2	3	4	5 PAINTERS	6	7	8
PREVIOUS	—				—			
THIS WEEK	0.67				0.50			
TOTAL	0.67				0.50			

REMARKS

2 COATS PENETRATING FINISH ON HARD MAPLE STAGE FLOOR IN AUDITORIUM

MFD. IN U.S.A.   FORM C-105   FRANK R. WALKER CO., PUBLISHERS, CHICAGO

Fig. 207. Analyzed Labor Costs of Applying Penetration Finish to Wood Floors.

and finish paint coat to plastered surfaces. The first column gives the total number of squares applied, the second column gives the total labor cost, the third column the average labor cost per square, while the fourth column gives the average number of seal coat applied per 8-hour day. Columns five to eight furnish the same information regarding the cost of applying finish coat of lead and oil.

The back of the form, Figure 203, gives the total number of hours worked by each trade in the first column headed "Total Labor Hours," while the second column headed "Labor Hours Per Unit," gives the length of time required to apply one square of seal coat and finish coat to plastered surfaces.

If the walls are to be painted with cold water paint, white-washed or given any other finish, the costs should be kept in the same manner described above.

When keeping labor costs on paper hanging, the costs should state the number of rolls hung. A single roll of paper contains 36 square feet or 4 square yards and a double roll contains just twice as much as a single roll. All prices are usually quoted on a single roll of paper. It is not difficult to keep costs on paper hanging, as it is easy to keep an accurate record of the amount of paper delivered and by subtracting the quantity left, we obtain the net amount of paper used.

Borders, panel strips, etc., should be kept by the yard of 3 lineal feet.

Labor Distribution Figure 204 illustrates the correct method of keeping labor costs on paper hanging. The first column gives the total number of rolls hung, the second column gives the total labor cost to date, the third column gives the labor cost per single roll, while the fourth column gives the number of single rolls of paper hung per 8-hr. day.

The back of the form, Figure 205, gives the total number of hours worked by each trade in the first column headed "Total Labor Hours," while the second column headed "Labor Hours Per Unit," gives the length of time required to hang one single roll of wall paper.

When applying filler, shellac, varnish, penetrating finish, wax, etc., to interior finish wood floors or stairs, separate labor costs should be kept on applying the different coats, reporting all costs by the square of 100 square feet.

Labor Distribution Figure 206 illustrates the correct method of keeping labor costs on applying penetrating finish to hardwood floors. The first column gives the total number of squares receiving first coat of finish, the second column gives the total labor cost, the third column the average cost per square, while the fourth column gives the average number of squares coated per 8-hour day. Columns five to eight furnish the same information regarding applying the second coat of finish.

The back of the form, Figure 207, gives the total number of hours worked by each trade in the first column headed "Total Labor Hours," while the second column headed "Labor Hours Per Unit," gives the length of time required to finish 100 square feet of floor.

The labor costs of applying filler, shellac, varnish, wax, etc., are kept in the same manner.

Interior Marble

The labor costs on erecting and placing all kinds of marble work are usually kept by the lineal or superficial foot, depending upon the class of work installed.

All kinds of narrow marble, such as base, door trim, window trim, wainscot cap, partition stiles, and other work of this kind, should be kept by the lineal foot of marble placed. Separate labor costs should be kept on each class of work but the unit in all cases should be the lineal foot.

When keeping costs on other kinds of marble work, such as wainscoting, partitions, toilet backs, and other work where fairly large size pieces of marble are used, the square or superficial foot method is invariably used. As mentioned above, separate labor costs should be kept on setting the different kinds of marble as given in the Labor Cost Schedule appearing on the previous pages.

Labor Distribution Figure 208 illustrates the correct method of keeping costs on setting interior marble. The first column gives the total number of lineal feet of marble base set, the second column gives the total labor cost, the third column the average unit cost per lineal foot, while the fourth column gives the average number of lineal feet of base set per 8-hour day. Columns five to eight furnish the same information regarding the labor costs of setting marble wainscoting.

The back of the form, Figure 209, gives the total number of hours worked by each trade in the first column headed "Total Labor Hours," while the second column headed "Labor Hours Per Unit," gives the length of time required to place 100 lineal feet of marble base and 100 square feet of marble wainscoting.

When setting marble stall partitions, the costs should state the number of superficial feet of marble set,

Fig. 208 (rotated — Labor Distribution and Costs of Setting Marble Base and Wainscot)

LABOR DISTRIBUTION

JOB CENTRAL HIGH SCHOOL
CLASS OF WORK N-2, N-3
WEEK ENDING JUNE 12, 19--
SHEET NO. 66
JOB NO. 110

	OCCUPATION	M	T	W	T	F	S	S	HOURS	RATE	AMOUNT
1	N-2 { MARBLE SETTERS	8	8	4	1	1	1	1	12		
2	HELPERS	8	8	4	1	1	1	1	12		
3	LABORERS	8	8	1					8		
4											
5	N-3 { MARBLE SETTERS	8	8	12	16	16	16	1	68		
6	HELPERS	8	8	12	16	16	16	1	68		
7	LABORERS	8	8	16	16	16	16	1	72		
8											
	TOTAL										

	QTY. WORK IN PLACE	PAY ROLL COSTS	LBR. AVERAGE UNIT COST	AVERAGE QUANTITY PER 8 HR. DAY	QTY. WORK IN PLACE	PAY ROLL COSTS	LBR. AVERAGE UNIT COST	AVERAGE QUANTITY PER 8 HR. DAY
	N-2				N-3			
PREVIOUS	65 LF			65 LF	247 SF			99 SF
THIS WEEK	110			73	890			105
TOTAL	175			70	1137			103

FORM C-105   MFD. IN U.S.A.   FRANK R. WALKER CO., PUBLISHERS, CHICAGO   (OVER)

Fig. 208. Labor Distribution and Costs of Setting Marble Base and Wainscot.

Fig. 209 (rotated — Analyzed Labor Costs)

COST ANALYSIS RECORD

TOTAL LABOR HOURS
UNIT PER 100 LF BASE

	MARBLE SETTERS 1	HELPERS 2	3 LAB.	4	MARBLE SETTERS 5	6 HELPERS 7 LAB.		8
PREVIOUS	8	8	8	4	20	20	24	8
THIS WEEK	12	12	8		68	68	72	
TOTAL	20	20	16		88	88	96	

LABOR HOURS PER UNIT
UNIT PER 100 SF WAINSCOT

	MARBLE SETTERS 1	2 HELPERS	3 LAB.	4	MARBLE SETTERS 5	6 HELPERS 7 LAB.		8
PREVIOUS	12.3	12.3	12.3		8.1	8.1	8.1	
THIS WEEK	10.9	10.9	7.3		7.6	7.6	8.1	
TOTAL	11.4	11.4	9.1		7.7	7.7	8.4	

REMARKS 4" BASE AND 6'6" HIGH WAINSCOT IN WASHROOMS. 3/4" MARBLE SET ON TILE PARTITIONS.

FORM C-105   MFD. IN U.S.A.   FRANK R. WALKER CO., PUBLISHERS, CHICAGO

Fig. 209. Analyzed Labor Costs of Setting Marble Base and Wainscot.

LABOR DISTRIBUTION

JOB CENTRAL HIGH SCHOOL
CLASS OF WORK O-2, O-3
WEEK ENDING JUNE 26, 19--
SHEET NO. 67
JOB NO. 110

	OCCUPATION	M	T	W	T	F	S	S	HOURS	RATE	AMOUNT
1	TERRAZZO MECH.	16	16	—	—	—	—	—	32		
2	O-2 { HELPERS	24	24	—	—	—	—	—	48		
3	" -GRINDING	24	24	24	24	24	—	—	120		
4											
5	TERRAZZO MECH.	—	—	16	16	16			48		
6	O-3 { HELPERS	—	—	16	16	16			48		
7	" -GRINDING	8	8	—	—	—			16		
8											
	TOTAL	O-2							O-3		

	QTY. WORK IN PLACE	PAY ROLL COSTS	LBR. AVERAGE UNIT COST	AVERAGE QUANTITY PER 8 HR. DAY	QTY. WORK IN PLACE	PAY ROLL COSTS	LBR. AVERAGE UNIT COST	AVERAGE QUANTITY PER 8 HR. DAY
PREVIOUS	1400 SF			125 SF	110 LF			55 LF
THIS WEEK	760			190	290			48
TOTAL	2160			180	400			50

MFD. IN U.S.A.   FORM C-105   FRANK R. WALKER CO., PUBLISHERS, CHICAGO   (OVER)

Fig. 210. Labor Distribution and Cost of Placing Terrazzo Floors and Base.

as described for wainscoting. However, the labor costs setting marble stall fronts and rails should be given by the lineal foot, as marble less than 12 inches wide is usually estimated by the lineal foot.

The labor cost of handling and setting marble floors is also kept by the square foot. If possible, keep separate labor costs on placing the cement fill, laying the tile, and smoothing or rubbing same at completion.

When setting marble stair treads and risers, always give the length, width and thickness of treads and height of risers and the number in each set, as this is important to obtain accurate labor costs.

When setting marble thresholds, plinths, and other similar work, the costs should state the number of pieces set and the size of each. Labor costs for installing counter tops should be kept by the square foot, and costs of door and window trim by the lineal foot.

Exterior Marble

When setting exterior marble work, the labor costs should be kept in the same manner as costs for setting cut stone, granite, ceramic veneer, etc., which have been described on previous pages, as the labor operations involved are the same. Quantities of exterior marble work should be measured by the square foot for facing up to two inches thick and by the cubic foot, if over two inches thick, using the largest dimensions of each piece in computing the "cube."

Interior Slate

The labor costs of handling and setting interior slate work should be kept in the same manner as marble work.

Terrazzo

When keeping costs on terrazzo work, separate costs should be kept on the different kinds of work, as outlined in the Cost Schedule given on previous pages and which includes floors, base, stair treads and platforms, stair risers and stringers, partitions, wainscot, etc.

Terrazzo labor costs may also be further sub-divided, if desired, for the various labor operations involved, such as placing cement underbed, installing metal dividing strips, mixing and placing terrazzo material, and grinding terrazzo to a finished surface.

Quantities for terrazzo work should be measured by the superficial foot for floors, platforms and partitions, and by the lineal foot for base, stair treads, risers and stringers.

Cost records should always give a complete description of the work, stating the type of work, approximate size of job, spacing of divider strips, etc.

Labor Distribution Figure 210 illustrates the correct method of keeping labor costs on terrazzo floors and base. The first column gives the number of square feet of floor placed, the second column gives the total labor cost placing same, the third column the average labor cost per square foot, while the fourth column gives the average number of square feet placed per 8-hour day. Columns five to eight furnish the same information regarding terrazzo base.

The back of this form, Figure 211, gives the total number of hours worked by each trade in the first column headed "Total Labor Hours," while the second column headed "Labor Hours Per Unit," gives the length of time required to complete 100 square feet of floor or 100 lineal feet of base.

Art Marble

When setting art marble work, which is precast terrazzo, shop fabricated into tiles, strips, panels or other shapes, the labor operations are identical with those encountered in setting regular marble work and the labor costs should be kept in the same manner.

Fig. 211. Analyzed Labor Costs of Placing Terrazzo Floors and Base.

COST ANALYSIS RECORD

	TOTAL LABOR HOURS				UNIT			
	1 TERRAZZO MECH	2 HELPER	3 HELPER GRINDING	4	5 TERRAZZO MECH	6 HELPER	7 HELPER GRINDING	8
PREVIOUS	64	96	48	6000 SF	16	16	16	110 LF
THIS WEEK	32	48	120	1560 SF	48	48	16	110 LF
TOTAL	96	142	168	2160 SF	64	64	16	110 LF

	LABOR HOURS PER UNIT				UNIT PER 100 SF FLOOR / PER 100 LF BASE			
	1 TERRAZZO MECH	2 HELPER	3 HELPER GRINDING	4	5 TERRAZZO MECH	6 HELPER	7 HELPER GRINDING	8
PREVIOUS	4.57	6.86	8.00		14.54	14.54	14.54	
THIS WEEK	4.21	6.32	7.69		16.55	16.55	14.54	
TOTAL	4.44	6.58	7.78		16.00	16.00	14.54	

REMARKS

TERRAZZO FLOOR AND BASE IN WASHROOMS. APPROX 20'X18' EACH ROOM. FLOOR HAS METAL DIVIDERS— 3º O.C. BOTH WAYS. BASE IS 6" HIGH WITH COVE.

MFD. IN U.S.A.   FORM C-105   FRANK R. WALKER CO., PUBLISHERS, CHICAGO

Fig. 212. Labor Distribution and Costs of Placing Cement Floor Fill and Laying Ceramic Floor Tile.

LABOR DISTRIBUTION

JOB CENTRAL HIGH SCHOOL   CLASS OF WORK O-42-A, O-42-B   WEEK ENDING JUNE 19, 19—   SHEET NO. 68   JOB NO. 110

OCCUPATION	M	T	W	T	F	S	S	HOURS	PAY ROLL COSTS	RATE	AMOUNT
1 O-42-A TILE SETTER	4	2	2	1	1	1		8			
2 HELPER	4	2	2	1	1	1		8			
3											
4											
5 O-42-B TILE SETTER	4	6	8	8	1	1		32			
6 HELPER	4	6	8	8	1	1		32			
7											
8											
TOTAL											

O-42-A

	QTY. WORK IN PLACE	PAY ROLL COSTS	LBR. AVERAGE UNIT COST	AVERAGE QUANTITY PER 8 HR. DAY
PREVIOUS				
THIS WEEK	500 SF			
TOTAL	500			

O-42-B

	QTY. WORK IN PLACE	PAY ROLL COSTS	HOURS	RATE	AMOUNT	LBR. AVERAGE UNIT COST	AVERAGE QUANTITY PER 8 HR. DAY
PREVIOUS							
THIS WEEK	500 SF						125 SF
TOTAL	500						125

(OVER)

MFD. IN U.S.A.   FORM C-105   FRANK R. WALKER CO., PUBLISHERS, CHICAGO

COST ANALYSIS RECORD

	TOTAL LABOR HOURS				UNIT			
	1 TILE SETTER	2 HELPER	3	4	5 TILE SETTER	6 HELPER	7	8
PREVIOUS	—	—						
THIS WEEK	8	8			32	32		
TOTAL	8	8			32	32		

	LABOR HOURS PER UNIT				UNIT PER 100 SF			
	1 TILE SETTER	2 HELPER	3	4	5 TILE SETTER	6 HELPER	7	8
PREVIOUS	—	—			—	—		
THIS WEEK	1.60	1.60			6.40	6.40		
TOTAL	1.60	1.60			6.40	6.40		

REMARKS

3/4" X 19/16" OBLONG CERAMIC TILE IN BASKETWEAVE PATTERN ON FLOOR OF BIOLOGY LAB. — 2" CEMENT UNDERBED — ROOM 25º X 20º.

MFD. IN U.S.A.   FORM C-105   FRANK R. WALKER CO., PUBLISHERS, CHICAGO

Fig. 213. Analyzed Labor Costs of Placing Cement Floor Fill and Laying Ceramic Floor Tile.

Ceramic Tile, Quarry Tile, Plastic Tile and Metal Tile

The labor costs of placing ceramic tile and quarry tile floors should be kept by the square foot, giving a description of the tile, size, size of rooms or spaces in which tile is laid, etc., as these are all items of importance when preparing estimates on similar work.

It is necessary to place concrete fill 2 to 3 inches thick under the tile and separate labor costs should be kept on this work, as this item does not vary as much as the cost of placing the tile.

Ceramic tile from 3/4-inches in diameter to 3/4x19/16 inches oblong are usually mounted on sheets of paper 12x24 inches in size, which is moistened and removed after the tile have been laid. The labor costs laying all kinds of tile mounted on paper should be kept separately, as they are more easily and rapidly laid than individual tile, which must be laid separately.

Labor Distribution Figure 212 illustrates the correct method of keeping costs on placing cement floor fill and laying ceramic floor tile. The first column gives the total number of square feet of fill placed, the second column gives the total labor cost, the third column the average labor cost per square foot, while the fourth column gives the number of square feet averaged per 8-hour day.

Columns five to eight furnish the same information regarding the cost of laying 3/4x19/16 inch oblong tile, mounted on paper.

The back of the form, Figure 213, gives the total number of hours worked by each trade in the first column headed "Total Labor Hours," while the second column headed "Labor Hours Per Unit," gives the length of time required to place 100 square feet of cement floor fill or 3/4x1 9/16 inch oblong floor tile.

The cost of placing all kinds of unmounted floor tile, 2 or 3 inches in size should be kept separately, as the labor costs run considerably higher than for tile mounted on paper. Always give the size of the rooms, size and kind of tile and the quantities in square feet.

When laying quarry or other tile from 4x4 to 12x12 inches in size, the labor costs should be kept separately, mentioning kind and size of tile, and size of the rooms or spaces in which they are laid. As with other kinds of tile floors, the costs should be stated by the square foot.

When keeping costs on placing ceramic or quarry tile base, such as used in bath rooms, kitchens, etc., the labor costs of setting the base should be kept separate, and the costs should be kept by the lineal foot. Always give the size of the base, whether 4 or 6 inches high. It is important to keep the cost of setting the base separate from the balance of the work as the extra labor required laying out the work, squaring corners, etc., makes this portion of the work relatively more costly than setting wall tile.

The labor cost of setting tile wainscoting should be kept by the superficial foot, giving the size of the tile, 4¼ x4¼, 6x3 or 6x6-inch, which are the sizes most commonly used. Also state whether tile are laid with straight or broken joints and method of setting, whether on a cement underbed or by the use of adhesive.

Labor Distribution Figure 214 illustrates the correct method of keeping labor costs on setting tile base and wainscoting. The first column gives the total number of lineal feet of 4-inch cove base set, the second column gives the total labor cost, the third column the average labor cost per lineal foot, while the fourth column gives the average number of lineal feet of tile base set per 8-hour day. Columns five to eight furnish the same information regarding the labor costs of setting 4¼x4¼ inch tile wainscoting.

The back of this form, Figure 215, gives the total number of hours worked by each trade in the first column headed "Total Labor Units," while the second column headed "Labor Hours Per Unit," gives the length of time required by each trade to set 100 lineal feet of base and 100 square feet of tile wainscoting.

When placing ceramic tile on ceilings and soffits, the labor costs should be kept separate from wall and wainscot work but in the same manner by the superficial foot and stating size of tile, kind of joints, method of application, etc.

Labor costs for plastic tile or metal tile base, wainscot, walls or ceilings should be kept in the same manner as for ceramic tile.

Resilient Tile Flooring And Base

When keeping labor costs on laying resilient tile flooring, separate costs should be kept for the various materials, such as asphalt tile, linotile, plastic tile, rubber tile, cork tile, etc. Costs should state kind of material, size and thickness of tile, kind of surface receiving tile, size of floor, etc., and should be kept by the square foot of floor.

Labor Distribution Figure 216 illustrates the correct method of keeping costs on laying 9 x 9-inch asphalt

Fig. 214. Labor Distribution and Costs of Setting Ceramic Tile Base and Wainscot.

LABOR DISTRIBUTION

JOB CENTRAL HIGH SCHOOL
SHEET NO. 69
CLASS OF WORK O-45, O-47
WEEK ENDING JUNE 12, 19--
JOB NO. 110

	OCCUPATION	M	T	W	T	F	S	S	HOURS	RATE	AMOUNT
1	O-45 { TILE SETTER	2	1	1	1	1			4		
2	HELPER	2	1	1	1	1			4		
3											
4											
5	O-47 { TILE SETTER	6	6	6	6	6		1	36		
6	HELPER	6	6	6	6	6		-	36		
7											
8											
	TOTAL O-45								O-47		

	QTY. WORK IN PLACE	PAY ROLL COSTS	LBR. AVERAGE UNIT COST	AVERAGE QUANTITY PER 8 HR. DAY
PREVIOUS	40 LF			80 LF 196 SF
THIS WEEK	44			88 267
TOTAL	84			84 463

	PAY ROLL COSTS	LBR. AVERAGE UNIT COST	AVERAGE QUANTITY PER 8 HR. DAY
			56 SF
			59
			58

MFD. IN U.S.A. FORM C-105 FRANK R. WALKER CO., PUBLISHERS, CHICAGO (OVER)

Fig. 215. Analyzed Labor Costs of Setting Ceramic Tile Base and Wainscot.

COST ANALYSIS RECORD

TOTAL LABOR HOURS

UNIT	TILE SETTER 1	2 HELPER 3	4	TILE SETTER 5	6 HELPER 7	8
PREVIOUS	4	4		28	28	
THIS WEEK	4	7		36	36	
TOTAL	8	8		64	64	

LABOR HOURS PER UNIT

UNIT PER 100 LF BASE / PER 100 SF WAINSCOT	TILE SETTER 1	2 HELPER 3	4	TILE SETTER 5	6 HELPER 7	8
PREVIOUS	10.0	10.0		14.3	14.3	
THIS WEEK	9.1	9.1		13.5	13.5	
TOTAL	9.5	9.5		13.8	13.8	

REMARKS

CERAMIC TILE BASE & WAINSCOT IN BIOLOGY LAB. - 4" COVE BASE - 4¼" x 4¼" WALL TILE SET IN BLOCK PATTERN WITH STRAIGHT JOINTS. SET IN CEMENT UNDERBED. WAINSCOT 72" HIGH. ROOM SIZE 25ᴰ x 20ᴰ

MFD. IN U.S.A. FORM C-105 FRANK R. WALKER CO., PUBLISHERS, CHICAGO

LABOR DISTRIBUTION

JOB CENTRAL HIGH SCHOOL
SHEET NO. 70
CLASS OF WORK P-4
WEEK ENDING JUNE 26, 19--
JOB NO. 110

	OCCUPATION	M	T	W	T	F	S	S	HOURS	RATE	AMOUNT
1	FLOORING MECHANICS	16	16	16	16	16	-	-	80		
2											
3											
4											
5											
6											
7											
8											
	TOTAL										

	QTY. WORK IN PLACE	PAY ROLL COSTS	LBR. AVERAGE UNIT COST	AVERAGE QUANTITY PER 8 HR. DAY	QTY. WORK IN PLACE	PAY ROLL COSTS	LBR. AVERAGE UNIT COST	AVERAGE QUANTITY PER 8 HR. DAY
PREVIOUS	3050 SF			305 SF				
THIS WEEK	3200			320				
TOTAL	6250			313				

MFD. IN U.S.A. FORM C-105 FRANK R. WALKER CO., PUBLISHERS, CHICAGO (OVER)

Fig. 216. Labor Distribution and Costs of Laying Asphalt Tile Flooring.

tile ⅛-inch thick. The first column gives the total number of square feet laid, the second column gives the total labor cost, the third column the average labor cost per square foot,while the fourth column gives the average number of square feet of asphalt tile placed per 8-hour day.

The back of the form, Figure 217, gives the total number of hours worked by each trade in the first column headed "Total Labor Hours," while the second column headed "Labor Hours Per Unit," gives the length of time required to lay 100 square feet of asphalt tile flooring.

Labor costs for installing asphalt tile or rubber base should be kept in the same manner as for floor tile except the costs should be given on a lineal foot basis.

Labor costs for cleaning and waxing floors and base at completion, should be kept the same as for laying floor tile or installing base.

Resilient Sheet Floor And Wall Covering

When laying resilient sheet floor covering, such as linoleum and sheet rubber, plastic, cork, etc., the labor costs are kept in the same manner as for resilient tile, as described above, i.e., costs are kept on a square foot or square yard basis and should state the kind and thickness of material, kind of surface to which applied, size of rooms, etc.

Labor Distribution Figure 218 illustrates the correct method of keeping costs of laying ¼-inch battleship linoleum. The first column gives the total number of square yards laid, the second column gives the total labor costs, the third column the average labor cost per square yard, while the fourth column gives the average number of square yards laid per 8-hour day.

The back of the form, Figure 219, gives the total number of hours worked by each trade in the first column headed "Total Labor Hours," while the second column headed "Labor Hours Per Unit," gives the length of time required to lay 100 square yards of battleship linoleum floor covering.

Labor costs for applying resilient sheet covering to walls should be kept in the same manner and on the same basis as given above for floor covering.

Labor costs for cleaning and waxing floors and walls, at completion, should be kept the same as for application of the floor or wall covering.

Elevators, Escalators, Lifts, Conveyors, Etc.

When erecting or installing vertical transportation equipment, it is extremely difficult to separate the labor costs for each operation of the work, therefore it is best to record only the total labor cost of the installation, along with a complete description of the equipment and its purpose.

The description should state whether for passenger or freight traffic, type of drive, power requirements, height of travel, rise and run for escalators and conveyors, size of cab, number of stops, type of signals, automatic devices, etc. A description of the type of construction in which the equipment is to be installed should also be given in the cost report.

Sewer Work

When tabulating costs on sewer work, the labor cost of excavating and bracing or shoring banks, and the construction of manholes, etc., should be kept as separate items and charged to their respective classifications as outlined in the Cost Schedule given on previous pages.

The cost of handling and placing sewer pipe for mains should be kept separate from the costs of placing lateral lines and if possible, a separate cost account should be kept for each size pipe, stating size of pipe, number of lineal feet laid, etc.

Labor Distribution Figure 220 illustrates the correct method to use when keeping costs on laying 4 and 6-inch sewer pipe. Column one gives the number of lineal feet of 4-inch sewer pipe laid, column two gives the total labor cost, column three the average unit cost per lineal foot, while column four gives the number of lineal feet of 4-inch pipe laid per 8-hour day. Columns five to eight furnish the same information regarding 6-inch sewer pipe.

The back of this form, Figure 221, gives the total number of hours worked by each trade in the first

Fig. 217. Analyzed Labor Costs of Laying Asphalt Tile Flooring.

COST ANALYSIS RECORD

TOTAL LABOR HOURS — UNIT

	1 FLOORING MECH.	2	3	4	5	6	7	8
PREVIOUS	80							
THIS WEEK	80							
TOTAL	160							

LABOR HOURS PER UNIT — UNIT PER 100 SF

	1 FLOORING MECH.	2	3	4	5	6	7	8
PREVIOUS	2.62							
THIS WEEK	2.50							
TOTAL	2.56							

REMARKS

9" x 9" ASPHALT TILE - 1/8" THICK - IN CLASSROOMS - LAID ON CONCRETE FLOORS. ROOMS APPROX. 25' x 20'.

MFD. IN U.S.A.   FORM C-105   FRANK R. WALKER CO., PUBLISHERS, CHICAGO

Fig. 218. Labor Distribution and Costs of Laying Linoleum Floor Covering.

LABOR DISTRIBUTION

SHEET NO. 71   JOB NO. 110

JOB CENTRAL HIGH SCHOOL
CLASS OF WORK P-23
WEEK ENDING July 10, 19—

OCCUPATION	M	T	W	T	F	S	S	HOURS	RATE	AMOUNT
1 FLOORING MECHANICS	16	16	16	16	16			80		
2										
3										
4										
5										
6										
7										
8										
TOTAL										

	QTY. WORK IN PLACE	PAY ROLL COSTS	LBR. AVERAGE UNIT COST	AVERAGE QUANTITY PER 8 HR. DAY	QTY. WORK IN PLACE	PAY ROLL COSTS	LBR. AVERAGE UNIT COST	AVERAGE QUANTITY PER 8 HR. DAY
PREVIOUS	310 SY			38.8 SY				
THIS WEEK	392			39.2				
TOTAL	702			39.0				

MFD. IN U.S.A.   FORM C-105   FRANK R. WALKER CO., PUBLISHERS, CHICAGO   (OVER)

Fig. 219. Analyzed Labor Costs of Laying Linoleum Floor Covering.

COST ANALYSIS RECORD

TOTAL LABOR HOURS — UNIT

	1 FLOORING MECH	2	3	4	5	6	7	8
PREVIOUS	64							
THIS WEEK	80							
TOTAL	144							

LABOR HOURS PER UNIT — UNIT PER 100 SY

	1 FLOORING MECH.	2	3	4	5	6	7	8
PREVIOUS	20.6							
THIS WEEK	20.4							
TOTAL	20.5							

REMARKS

1/4" BATTLESHIP LINOLEUM LAID IN CORRIDORS, AUDITORIUM AISLES AND SHOP AREA. LAID ON CONCRETE SLAB.

MFD. IN U.S.A.   FORM C-105   FRANK R. WALKER CO., PUBLISHERS, CHICAGO

column headed "Total Labor Hours," while the second column headed "Labor Hours Per Unit," gives the length of time required by each trade to lay 100 lineal feet of 4-inch or 6-inch sewer pipe.

A separate cost record should also be kept on labor for connecting new sewer lines to present mains.

Plumbing

The general classification of Plumbing usually includes, in addition to regular plumbing work, the classifications of Sewer Work and Gas Fitting, and also includes such items as trench excavation, backfill, construction of manholes and basins, etc. The labor costs of these additional classifications and items of work should always be kept separate under their respective headings as outlined in the Cost Schedule and as described on previous and subsequent pages.

When keeping costs on regular plumbing work, separate costs should be kept for the various operations involved, as outlined in the Cost Schedule, and should give a complete description of the work, including size, kind and purpose of piping, number and kind of fixtures, and any other information essential to proper classification of cost data.

Labor costs for all piping work should be kept by the lineal foot of pipe installed with separate costs being kept for each type, such as sanitary drain lines including vent stacks, storm drain lines, water mains, lateral water lines, supply lines and fire lines. If possible, separate costs should be kept for each size of pipe.

Labor Distribution Figure 222 illustrates the correct method for keeping costs on roughing in sanitary drain lines including vent stacks and roughing in supply lines to fixtures. The first column gives the lineal feet of sanitary drain line roughed in, the second column gives the total labor cost, the third column the average cost per lineal foot, while the fourth column gives the average number of lineal feet of sanitary drain line roughed in per 8-hour day. Columns five to eight furnish the same information regarding roughing in water supply lines.

The back of the form, Figure 223, gives the total number of hours worked by each trade in the first column headed "Total Labor Hours," while the second column headed "Labor Hours Per Unit," gives the length of time required to rough in 100 lineal feet of sanitary drain lines or water supply lines.

The labor cost of handling and setting the different fixtures should be kept as a separate item in order to obtain an average cost for placing one fixture. Cost report should state kind and number of each.

Separate cost records should also be kept for handling and setting hot water heaters, storage tanks, house tanks, pumps, etc., giving size and capacity for each piece of equipment.

Labor costs for covering pipes should be kept by the lineal foot with separate costs being kept for each kind of covering material and for each size of pipe.

Gas Fitting

Labor costs on gas fitting work should be recorded in the same manner described above for regular plumbing work, with separate costs being kept for the different operations as outlined in the Cost Schedule. All costs for installing gas piping should be kept by the lineal foot of each size pipe and costs for handling, setting and connecting the different appliances should be reduced to an average cost for one appliance of each kind.

Cost records should contain a complete description of the work, in order that the information may be properly classified for use in estimating future work.

Labor Distribution Figure 224 illustrates the correct method of keeping labor costs on gas-fitting and setting and connecting appliances. The first column gives the number of lineal feet of gas piping completed, the second column gives the total labor cost running same, the third column the average labor cost per lineal foot, while the fourth column gives the average number of lineal feet of piping installed per 8-hour day. Columns five to eight furnish the same information regarding the cost of setting appliances in place and making connections.

The back of the form, Figure 225, gives the total number of hours worked by each trade in the first column headed "Total Labor Hours," while the second column headed "Labor Hours Per Unit," gives the length of time required to rough in 100 lineal feet of pipe or set and connect one appliance complete.

LABOR DISTRIBUTION

JOB _CENTRAL HIGH SCHOOL_
CLASS OF WORK _R-3-A, R-3-B_
WEEK ENDING _APRIL 10, 19--_
SHEET NO. _72_
JOB NO. _110_

OCCUPATION	M	T	W	T	F	S	S	HOURS	RATE	AMOUNT
1 R-3-A PIPE LAYER	4	4	-	6	4	1	1	18		
2										
3										
4										
5 R-3-B PIPE LAYER	2	8	6	2	4	1	1	22		
6										
7										
8										
TOTAL										

R-3-A "4 PIPE R-3-B "6 PIPE

	QTY. WORK IN PLACE	PAY ROLL COSTS	LBR. AVERAGE UNIT COST	AVERAGE QUANTITY PER 8 HR. DAY	QTY. WORK IN PLACE	PAY ROLL COSTS	LBR. AVERAGE UNIT COST	AVERAGE QUANTITY PER 8 HR. DAY
PREVIOUS	166 LF			111 LF	186 LF			93 LF
THIS WEEK	264			117	252			92
TOTAL	430			115	438			92

MFD. IN U.S.A. FORM C-105 FRANK R. WALKER CO., PUBLISHERS, CHICAGO (OVER)

Fig. 220. Labor Distribution and Costs of Placing Sewer Pipe.

COST ANALYSIS RECORD

TOTAL LABOR HOURS
UNIT

	1 PIPE LAYER	2	3	4	5 PIPE LAYER	6	7	8
PREVIOUS	12				16			
THIS WEEK	18				22			
TOTAL	30				38			

LABOR HOURS PER UNIT
UNIT PER 100 LF

	1 PIPE LAYER	2	3	4	5 PIPE LAYER	6	7	8
PREVIOUS	7.23				6.60			
THIS WEEK	6.81				8.73			
TOTAL	6.98				8.68			

REMARKS: 4" AND 6" VITRIFIED SEWER TILE SANITARY LINES. REGULAR MORTAR JOINTS.

MFD. IN U.S.A. FORM C-105 FRANK R. WALKER CO., PUBLISHERS, CHICAGO

Fig. 221. Analyzed Labor Costs of Placing Sewer Pipe.

LABOR DISTRIBUTION

JOB _CENTRAL HIGH SCHOOL_
CLASS OF WORK _R-12, R-16_
WEEK ENDING _APRIL 24, 19--_
SHEET NO. _73_
JOB NO. _110_

OCCUPATION	M	T	W	T	F	S	S	HOURS	RATE	AMOUNT
1 R-12 (PLUMBERS	16	16	16	16	16	-	-	80		
2 (HELPERS	8	8	8	8	8	-	-	40		
3										
4										
5 R-16 PLUMBERS	16	16	16	16	16	-	-	80		
6										
7										
8										
TOTAL R-12								R-16		

	QTY. WORK IN PLACE	PAY ROLL COSTS	LBR. AVERAGE UNIT COST	AVERAGE QUANTITY PER 8 HR. DAY	QTY. WORK IN PLACE	PAY ROLL COSTS	LBR. AVERAGE UNIT COST	AVERAGE QUANTITY PER 8 HR. DAY
PREVIOUS	82 LF			16.4/LF	290 LF			145 LF
THIS WEEK	258		17.2		1550			155
TOTAL	340		17.0		1840			153

MFD. IN U.S.A. FORM C-105 FRANK R. WALKER CO., PUBLISHERS, CHICAGO (OVER)

Fig. 222. Labor Distribution and Costs of Roughing In Sanitary Drain Lines and Supply Lines.

COST ANALYSIS RECORD

Total Labor Hours / Unit

	1 PLUMBERS	2 HELPERS	3	4	5 PLUMBERS	6	7	8
PREVIOUS	32	16			16			
THIS WEEK	80	40			80			
TOTAL	112	56			96			

Labor Hours Per Unit — UNIT PER 100 LF

	1 PLUMBERS	2 HELPERS	3	4	5 PLUMBERS	6	7	8
PREVIOUS	39	19.5			5.5			
THIS WEEK	31	15.5			5.2			
TOTAL	33	16.5			5.2			

REMARKS

SANITARY DRAIN LINES — 4" AND 6" EXTRA HEAVY C.I. SOIL PIPE.
WATER SUPPLY LINES — 1/2", 3/4" AND 1" GALV. STEEL PIPE.

MFD. IN U.S.A.   FORM C-105   FRANK R. WALKER CO., PUBLISHERS, CHICAGO

Fig. 223. Analyzed Labor Costs of Roughing In Sanitary Drain Lines and Supply Lines.

LABOR DISTRIBUTION

JOB CENTRAL HIGH SCHOOL   SHEET NO. 74
CLASS OF WORK R-34, R-35   WEEK ENDING JULY 17, 19—   JOB NO. 110

	OCCUPATION	M	T	W	T	F	S	S	HOURS	RATE	AMOUNT
1 R-34	PLUMBERS	1	16	16	8	1	1	1	40		
2											
3											
4											
5 R-35	PLUMBERS	1	1	8	16	1	1	1	24		
6											
7											
8											
TOTAL	R-34 ... R-35										

	QTY. WORK IN PLACE	PAY ROLL COSTS	LBR. AVERAGE UNIT COST	AVERAGE QUANTITY PER 8 HR. DAY	LBR. AVERAGE UNIT COST (PER UNIT)	AVERAGE QUANTITY PER 8 HR. DAY
PREVIOUS	282 LF			141 LF	RANGE UNITS	4
THIS WEEK	715			143	12	4
TOTAL	997			142	12	

(OVER)

MFD. IN U.S.A.   FORM C-105   FRANK R. WALKER CO., PUBLISHERS, CHICAGO

Fig. 224. Labor Distribution and Costs of Running Gas Pipe and Connecting Appliances.

COST ANALYSIS RECORD

Total Labor Hours / Unit

	1 PLUMBERS	2	3	4	5 PLUMBERS	6	7	8
PREVIOUS	16				—			
THIS WEEK	40				24			
TOTAL	56				24			

Labor Hours Per Unit — UNIT PER 100 LF PIPE, PER RANGE UNIT

	1 PLUMBERS	2	3	4	5 PLUMBERS	6	7	8
PREVIOUS	5.7				—			
THIS WEEK	5.6				2			
TOTAL	5.6				2			

REMARKS

GAS PIPING — 1" & 3/4" BLACK STEEL PIPE.
APPLIANCES — 2 BURNER, COUNTER TOP RANGE UNITS IN DOMESTIC SCIENCE ROOM

MFD. IN U.S.A.   FORM C-105   FRANK R. WALKER CO., PUBLISHERS, CHICAGO

Fig. 225. Analyzed Labor Costs of Running Gas Pipe and Connecting Appliances.

Sprinkler Work

The labor cost of installing sprinkler systems in warehouses, factories, etc., depends largely on whether the installation is being made in new or existing buildings, with the greatest cost differential occuring when installing pipe hangers in concrete ceilings. Cost records should state specifically the type of installation being made so that the cost data may be properly classified. Costs should also state whether system is wet type or dry type where subject to freezing temperatures.

Separate costs should be kept for the different operations of the work, such as laying out and installing pipe hangers, installing mains, installing lateral lines, installing sprinkler heads, installing tanks, etc.

Labor costs for installing hangers should be reduced to an average cost per hanger and should state type of anchorage and kind of construction to which fastened.

All piping costs should be kept on a lineal foot basis with separate costs being kept for each size of pipe, if possible.

Installation costs for sprinkler heads should be kept on a piece basis and should state type of head used, whether standard pendant type, flush type, wall type, etc.

Separate costs should also be kept on installing attic or roof tanks and should contain a complete description of the work, including size and capacity of tank, tank material, type of support, etc.

Warm Air Heating

When keeping job labor costs on warm air heating installations, separate costs should be kept for the various operations involved, such as assembling and setting up heating units, installing duct work, placing diffusers and register faces, installing controls, etc. (See Cost Schedule for breakdown.)

Cost records for setting up furnace should state the type of heating unit used, such as gravity type furnace, blower type furnace, combination blower type heating and cooling unit, pipeless furnace, etc., and should also give the heating capacity in B.t.u. per hour and the kind of fuel to be used, whether coal, gas or oil. For coal burning units, state whether manual or stoker firing is to be used.

Cost records for installing duct work should be kept by the pound of duct material installed and should give the number of outlets served, counting both supply and return outlets, so that an average cost per outlet, for installation of duct work, may be obtained. The costs should also state whether ducts are aluminum or galvanized sheet metal, thickness of metal, and the average size of ducts.

Labor costs for installing diffusers, register faces, grilles, etc., should be kept on a piece basis and should give number installed together with size of same.

Installation costs of heating controls should also be kept on a piece basis and should contain a listing of the control equipment installed.

Steam And Hot Water Heating

The job labor costs on steam and hot water heating installations should be divided as outlined in the Cost Schedule given on previous pages. The different items listed are all separate and distinct labor operations and should be kept separately in order that the costs may be of value when preparing future estimates.

Labor Distribution Figure 226 illustrates the correct method of keeping costs on handling and setting boilers. The first column gives the number and size of boiler set, the second column gives the total labor cost setting same, the third column gives the labor cost per boiler.

Cost records for setting boilers should always contain the name and rating of same in order that costs may be placed in the proper category.

Labor costs for bricking in boilers should be kept separate and charged to the proper classification under "Brickwood" as outlined in the Cost Schedule.

The back of the form, Figure 227, gives the total number of hours worked by each trade in the first column headed "Total Labor Hours," while the second column headed "Labor Hours Per Unit," gives the length of time required to set the boilers.

The labor cost of cutting, fitting and placing all pipe, such as mains, risers, supply and return lines, etc.,

Fig. 226 — Labor Distribution and Costs of Setting Boilers

LABOR DISTRIBUTION

JOB CENTRAL HIGH SCHOOL
CLASS OF WORK T-12 WEEK ENDING MAR 20, 19--
SHEET NO. 75 JOB NO. 110

OCCUPATION	M	T	W	T	F	S	S	HOURS	RATE	AMOUNT
1 PIPE FITTERS	16	16	16	16	1	1	1	64		
2 HELPERS	16	16	16	16	1	1	1	64		
3										
4										
5										
6										
7										
8										

TOTAL	QTY. WORK IN PLACE	PAY ROLL COSTS	LBR. AVERAGE UNIT COST	AVERAGE QUANTITY PER 8 HR. DAY	QTY. WORK IN PLACE	PAY ROLL COSTS	LBR. AVERAGE UNIT COST	AVERAGE QUANTITY PER 8 HR. DAY
PREVIOUS	1 BOILER			1				
THIS WEEK	1			1				
TOTAL	2							

FRANK R. WALKER CO., PUBLISHERS, CHICAGO
MFD. IN U.S.A. FORM C-105 (OVER)

Fig. 226. Labor Distribution and Costs of Setting Boilers.

Fig. 227 — Analyzed Labor Costs of Setting Boilers

COST ANALYSIS RECORD

TOTAL LABOR HOURS — UNIT

	PIPE 1 FITTERS	2 HELPERS	3	4	5	6	7	8
PREVIOUS	80	80						
THIS WEEK	64	64						
TOTAL	144	144						

LABOR HOURS PER UNIT — UNIT PER BOILER

	PIPE 1 FITTERS	2 HELPERS	3	4	5	6	7	8
PREVIOUS	80	80						
THIS WEEK	64	64						
TOTAL	144	144						

REMARKS: CLEAVER-BROOKS, 50 H.P., 6950 SF RADIATION (GROSS STEAM RATING)

FRANK R. WALKER CO., PUBLISHERS, CHICAGO
MFD. IN U.S.A. FORM C-105

Fig. 227. Analyzed Labor Costs of Setting Boilers.

Fig. 228 — Labor Distribution and Costs of Roughing in Supply and Return Lines and Setting Radiation Units

LABOR DISTRIBUTION

JOB CENTRAL HIGH SCHOOL
CLASS OF WORK T-13 WEEK ENDING MAY 1, 19--
SHEET NO. 76 JOB NO. 110

OCCUPATION	M	T	W	T	F	S	S	HOURS	RATE	AMOUNT
1 PIPE FITTERS	16	16	16	16	16	—	—	80		
2										
3										
4										
5										
6										
7										
8										

TOTAL	PER LF PIPE				PER RADIATION UNIT			
	QTY. WORK IN PLACE	PAY ROLL COSTS	LBR. AVERAGE UNIT COST	AVERAGE QUANTITY PER 8 HR. DAY	QTY. WORK IN PLACE	PAY ROLL COSTS	LBR. AVERAGE UNIT COST	AVERAGE QUANTITY PER 8 HR. DAY
PREVIOUS	202 LF			25 LF	FOR 20 UNITS			2.5 UNITS
THIS WEEK	274			27	27			2.7
TOTAL	476			26	47			2.6

MFD. IN U.S.A. FORM C-105 FRANK R. WALKER CO., PUBLISHERS, CHICAGO (OVER)

Fig. 228. Labor Distribution and Costs of Roughing in Supply and Return Lines and Setting Radiation Units.

should all be kept separately, showing just what it costs to install one lineal foot of pipe or to rough in for one radiation unit for both steam and hot water heating systems.

Labor Distribution Figure 228 illustrates the correct method of keeping costs on work of this kind. The first column gives the number of lineal feet of pipe installed, the second column gives the total labor cost, the third column the average cost per lineal foot, while the fourth column gives the average number of lineal feet of pipe installed per 8-hour day. Columns five to eight furnish the same information except that costs are reduced to per radiation until roughed in.

The back of the form, Figure 229, gives the total number of hours worked by each trade in the first column headed "Total Labor Hours," while the second column headed "Labor Hours Per Unit," gives the length of time required to install 100 lineal feet of pipe or rough in to one radiation unit.

Labor costs for handling and installing the different types of radiation units, such as cast iron radiators, convectors, etc., should be kept on a piece basis and cost records should state type and average size of units installed. Labor costs for handling and installing baseboard type radiation units should be kept by the lineal foot, stating type and size of units.

When installing radiant heating panels in floors, ceilings or walls, the labor costs should be kept per lineal foot of coil pipe or tubing and should state kind and size of pipe or tubing used.

Separate costs should be kept on the installation of each piece of equipment, such as booster pumps, vacuum pumps, expansion tanks, stoker equipment, coal handling equipment, ash handling equipment, oil burners, oil storage tanks, gas burners, etc. Costs should contain an adequate description of each item to permit identification when used as reference on future estimates.

When keeping costs on covering boilers with asbestos cement, the costs should be kept on a square foot basis and should contain a description of the work, including thickness of covering, material used, method of application, jacket material, etc.

Pipe covering should be kept by the lineal foot, stating the number of lineal feet of each size of pipe covering placed, together with kind of material used.

Air Conditioning

When recording job labor costs on air conditioning installations, separate costs should be kept for each operation of the work, such as assembling and setting air conditioning unit or equipment, installing duct work, placing diffusers and register faces, grilles and louvres, installing fans and blowers, installing controls, etc.

Labor costs for assembling and setting equipment should state type of equipment installed together with size, capacity, etc., and should include all labor costs for connecting to water supply and waste piping.

Labor costs for duct work required should be kept by the pound of duct material installed and should state kind and gauge of material used.

Separate costs should be kept for handling and placing diffusers and register faces, grilles, louvres, etc., and should state number, type, size, material, etc., for each.

Labor costs for assembling and installing fans and blowers should be kept as separate items, giving size and capacity of unit in each case.

Installation costs for control devices, such as thermostats, humidistats, etc., should be recorded separately for each kind of control, stating number and purpose of same.

Ventilation

Labor costs for installing ventilating systems should be kept in the same manner as previously described for air conditioning installations with separate cost records for each operation of the work. All cost records should contain a complete description of the work.

Labor Distribution Figure 230 illustrates the proper method of keeping costs on erecting gravity type roof ventilators and installing metal duct work for mechanical ventilating systems. The first column gives the number of ventilators erected, the second column gives the total labor cost, the third column the average labor cost per ventilator, while the fourth column gives the average number of ventilators erected per 8-hour day. Columns five to eight furnish the same information regarding the installation of metal duct work for mechanical ventilating systems.

COST ANALYSIS RECORD

Fig. 229

COST ANALYSIS RECORD

TOTAL LABOR HOURS				UNIT			
1 PIPE FITTERS	2	3	4	5 PIPE FITTERS	6	7	8
PREVIOUS				64			
THIS WEEK				80			
TOTAL				144			

UNIT: PER 100 LF PIPE / PER RADIATION UNIT

LABOR HOURS PER UNIT				UNIT			
1 PIPE FITTERS	2	3	4	5 PIPE FITTERS	6	7	8
PREVIOUS 31.7				3.20			
THIS WEEK 29.2				2.96			
TOTAL 30.3				3.06			

REMARKS

STEAM SUPPLY LINES FROM RISER TO RADIATION - 3/4" 1" & 1 1/4" GALV. STEEL PIPE. RETURN LINES - 3/4" & 1" GALV. STEEL PIPE. ALL RADIATION UNITS ARE WALL RECESSED CONVECTORS.

MFD. IN U.S.A.   FORM C-105   FRANK R. WALKER CO., PUBLISHERS, CHICAGO

Fig. 229. Analyzed Labor Costs of Roughing In Supply and Return Lines and Setting Radiation Units.

Fig. 230

LABOR DISTRIBUTION

SHEET NO. 77   JOB NO. 110

JOB CENTRAL HIGH SCHOOL

CLASS OF WORK 4-22, 4-25   WEEK ENDING JULY 3, 19 --

OCCUPATION	M	T	W	T	F	S	S	HOURS	QTY. WORK IN PLACE	LBR. AVERAGE UNIT COST	PAY ROLL COSTS	AVERAGE QUANTITY PER 8 HR. DAY	LBR. AVERAGE UNIT COST	RATE	AMOUNT
1 4-22 SHEET METL. WRK.	1	1	1	1	1			8		—					
2 HELPERS	1	1	1	1	1			8		—					
3															
4															
5 4-25 SHEET METL. WRK.	16	16	16	16	16			72	1420 LBS.	—					
6 HELPERS	8	8	8	8	8			32	1280	—					
7															
8															
TOTAL															

4-22   4-25

	QTY. WORK IN PLACE	PAY ROLL COSTS	LBR. AVERAGE UNIT COST	AVERAGE QUANTITY PER 8 HR. DAY
PREVIOUS	ROOF VENTS 6	—		142 LBS
THIS WEEK	6 VENTS 6	1280		142
TOTAL	6	2700		142

MFD. IN U.S.A.   FORM C-105   FRANK R. WALKER CO., PUBLISHERS, CHICAGO

(OVER)

Fig. 230. Labor Distribution and Costs of Erecting Roof Ventilators and Installing Duct Work for Ventilating Systems.

Fig. 231

COST ANALYSIS RECORD

TOTAL LABOR HOURS				UNIT			
1 SHT. MTL. WORKERS	2 HELPERS	3	4	5 SHT. MTL. WORKERS	6 HELPERS	7	8
PREVIOUS	—	—			80	40		
THIS WEEK	8	8			72	32		
TOTAL	8	8			152	72		

UNIT: PER ROOF VENTILATOR / PER 100 LBS METAL DUCT WORK

LABOR HOURS PER UNIT				UNIT			
1 SHT. MTL. WORKERS	2 HELPERS	3	4	5 SHT. MTL. WORKERS	6 HELPERS	7	8
PREVIOUS	—	—			5.63	2.82		
THIS WEEK	1.33	1.33			5.62	2.50		
TOTAL	1.33	1.33			5.63	2.67		

REMARKS

GRAVITY TYPE ROOF VENTILATORS - 24" DIA - OVER SHOP AREA.
DUCT WORK FOR VENTILATING SYSTEM - 28 GA. GALV. SHEET METAL
MAIN DUCTS - 72" X 18" - BRANCHES REDUCE TO 30" X 6".

MFD. IN U.S.A.   FORM C-105   FRANK R. WALKER CO., PUBLISHERS, CHICAGO

Fig. 231. Analyzed Labor Costs of Erecting Roofing Ventilators and Installing Duct Work for Ventilating Systems.

The back of the form, Figure 231, gives the total number of hours worked by each trade in the first column headed "Total Labor Hours," while the second column, headed "Labor Hours Per Unit," gives the length of time required by each trade to erect one roof ventilator complete or to install 100 pounds of metal duct work for mechanical ventilating systems.

Refrigeration

Inasmuch as the labor operations for installing refrigeration systems are closely similar to those encountered in steam and hot water heating work, the labor costs should be kept and reported in the same manner as described on previous pages under "Steam and Hot Water Heating," with separate costs being kept as outlined in the Cost Schedule.

It is essential that the cost records contain an adequate description of each phase of the work in order to be of value when estimating future jobs.

Electrical Work

When keeping labor costs on electrical work, the cost of locating and setting necessary outlet boxes should be kept as a separate item. In addition, the labor cost of running armored or non-metallic sheathed cable should be kept as a separate item. The cost of running thin wall or rigid conduit up to 1-inch in diameter should be kept as one item, and the cost of running conduit from 1½ to 3 inches in diameter should be kept as another. The larger sizes are more expensive to run on account of the extra labor involved in cutting and bending the pipe, and for that reason the different sizes should be kept separate. All costs should state the number of lineal feet of cable or conduit run and the number of outlets completed.

Many electricians prefer to figure their work at a certain price per outlet, based on outlet boxes, switches, floor and wall receptacles, etc., and when this method is used, it is advisable to obtain average labor cost per outlet including setting outlet boxes and running cable or conduit to same.

Labor Distribution Figure 232 illustrates the correct method of keeping labor costs on setting outlet boxes and running conduit, giving the number of lineal feet of conduit run, and the number of outlets completed. The first column gives the number of lineal feet of conduit run, the second column gives the total labor cost, the third column the average labor cost per lineal foot of conduit, while the fourth column gives the average number of lineal feet of conduit run per 8-hour day. Columns five to eight furnish the same information except the costs are stated in units per outlet. Column five gives the number of outlets installed, column six gives the total labor cost, column seven the average cost per outlet, while the column eight gives the number of outlets installed per 8-hour day.

The back of the form, Figure 233, gives the total number of hours worked by each trade in the first column headed "Total Labor Hours," while the second column headed "Labor Hours Per Unit," gives the length of time required to install 100 lineal feet of conduit or one outlet complete.

Separate costs should also be kept on bringing in service from utility lines and should include all labor necessary for setting meter boxes, fuse boxes or circuit breaker, distribution panels and running service conductors. Costs should state the capacity of the service, type of entrance equipment, kind of conductors and whether run underground or overhead.

The labor cost of pulling wire should also be kept by the lineal foot and by the number of outlets wired, using the same method as described for conduit.

Labor Distribution Figure 234 illustrates the correct method of keeping labor costs of pulling wire, giving costs both by the lineal foot and by the number of outlets wired. The first column gives the total number of lineal feet of wire pulled, the second column gives the total labor cost, the third column the average labor cost per foot, while the fourth column gives the average number of lineal feet of wire pulled per 8-hour day. Columns five to eight furnish the same information, stating the number of outlets wired and the cost per outlet.

The back of the form, Figure 235, gives the total number of hours worked by each trade in the first column headed "Total Labor Hours," while the second column headed "Labor Hours Per Unit," gives the length of time required to pull 100 lineal feet of wire and wire one outlet complete.

Fig. 232. Labor Distribution

PRACTICAL

LABOR DISTRIBUTION

JOB _CENTRAL HIGH SCHOOL_   SHEET NO. _78_

CLASS OF WORK _V-4_   WEEK ENDING _JAN. 16, 19--_   JOB NO. _110_

OCCUPATION	M	T	W	T	F	S	S	HOURS	RATE	AMOUNT
1 ELECTRICIANS	24	24	24	24	24	–	–	120		
2										
3										
4										
5										
6										
7										
8										
TOTAL	PER L.F. CONDUIT					PER OUTLET				

	QTY. WORK IN PLACE	PAY ROLL COSTS	LBR. AVERAGE UNIT COST	AVERAGE QUANTITY PER 8 HR. DAY	QTY. WORK IN PLACE	PAY ROLL COSTS	LBR. AVERAGE UNIT COST	AVERAGE QUANTITY PER 8 HR. DAY
PREVIOUS	1580 FF			61 LF	113 OUTLETS		PER OUTLET	OUTLETS 5.02
THIS WEEK	1070			63	77			5.13
TOTAL	2650			62	190			5.07

MFD. IN U.S.A.   FORM C-105   FRANK R. WALKER CO., PUBLISHERS, CHICAGO   (OVER)

Fig. 232. Labor Distribution and Costs of Setting Outlet Boxes and Running Electric Conduit.

Fig. 233. Cost Analysis Record

COST ANALYSIS RECORD

TOTAL LABOR HOURS				UNIT				
	1 ELEC.	2	3	4	5 ELEC.	6	7	8
PREVIOUS	180							
THIS WEEK	120							
TOTAL	300							

PER 100 LF CONDUIT   PER OUTLET

LABOR HOURS PER UNIT								
	1 ELEC.	2	3	4	5 ELEC.	6	7	8
PREVIOUS	11.4				1.59			
THIS WEEK	11.2				1.56			
TOTAL	11.3				1.58			

REMARKS: THIN WALL CONDUIT AND OUTLET BOXES INSTALLED IN CONCRETE COLUMS AND SLABS.

MFD. IN U.S.A.   FORM C-105   FRANK R. WALKER CO., PUBLISHERS, CHICAGO

Fig. 233. Analyzed Labor Costs of Setting Outlet Boxes and Running Electric Conduit.

Fig. 234. Labor Distribution

PRACTICAL

LABOR DISTRIBUTION

JOB _CENTRAL HIGH SCHOOL_   SHEET NO. _79_

CLASS OF WORK _V-6_   WEEK ENDING _APRIL 24, 19--_   JOB NO. _110_

OCCUPATION	M	T	W	T	F	S	S	HOURS	RATE	AMOUNT
1 ELECTRICIANS	16	16	16	16	16	–	–	80		
2										
3										
4										
5										
6										
7										
8										
TOTAL	PER LF WIRE					PER OUTLET				

	QTY. WORK IN PLACE	PAY ROLL COSTS	LBR. AVERAGE UNIT COST	AVERAGE QUANTITY PER 8 HR. DAY	QTY. WORK IN PLACE	PAY ROLL COSTS	LBR. AVERAGE UNIT COST	AVERAGE QUANTITY PER 8 HR. DAY
PREVIOUS	4200 LF			210 LF	128 OUTLETS		PER OUTLET	OUTLETS 6.4
THIS WEEK	2200			220	71			7.1
TOTAL	6400			213	199			6.6

MFD. IN U.S.A.   FORM C-105   FRANK R. WALKER CO., PUBLISHERS, CHICAGO   (OVER)

Fig. 234. Labor Distribution and Costs of Pulling Electric Wire.

When wiring and installing switches, receptacles, telephones, door bells, annunciators, etc., the costs should give the number of outlets or instruments installed, in order that a unit cost per outlet or instrument may be obtained.

If the lighting fixtures are installed by the wiring contractor, the labor costs should state the number of wall and ceiling fixtures installed, giving a general description of the work.

The labor cost of installing switchboards, generators, motors, and other electrical equipment should be kept as separate items, and the costs should state the number of pieces of equipment installed, with a general description that will be of value when preparing future estimates.

Extra Work

On every job there are usually a number of items not included in the original contract on which it is necessary to keep accurate labor costs. These include all orders for extra work received from the architect, engineer or owner, and for changes or additions made after the original contract was let.

The same Labor Distribution form as used on all other classes of work should be used for reporting extra work. Extra work should be designated by using the symbol "X" as described in the cost schedule. As an example, the symbol "X-21" designates the work as an extra for which a charge should be made, the "X" signifying extra work and the "21" showing that it was the twenty-first extra order on that job. This charge can then be located by referring to "Contract Change Order" No. 21, to see just what that extra order includes. The "Contract Change Order" sheet is illustrated and described in Section 6.

Labor Distribution Figure 236 illustrates the correct method of making out a cost report covered by an extra order. The "X-21" designates the account to which the work is charged.

When the bookkeeper in the office receives a Labor Distribution carrying the symbol "X", he knows at once that it is an extra order and is to be charged as an addition to the regular contract amount.

Work Performed For Sub-Contractors

Occasionally the contractor will be required to perform some work which is included in a sub-contract, either authorized by virtue of an order from the sub-contractor or due to the failure of the sub-contractor to properly complete his work. Typical examples of such work are unloading materials and equipment for sub-contractors, cleaning and removing sub-contractor's rubbish, cutting and patching for which sub-contractor is responsible, removing and replacing imperfect work, etc.

Inasmuch as most of this kind of work is done on a time and material basis, it is advisable to keep adequate cost records to substantiate the labor portion of the charges to be made against the sub-contractor's account.

Labor Distribution Figure 237 illustrates the correct method of keeping costs on work done for a sub-contractor. Note how work is described and identified and also how a statement of material or equipment used is given.

The above information may also be used by the bookkeeper as a basis for computing the charge to be made against the sub-contractor and for billing same.

Equipment

Cost of operating the equipment on a specific job is chargeable to the specific job on an hourly basis.

If a contractor owns equipment, a record of the cost of operating each piece of equipment should be kept.

Depreciation	$_____
Repair and maintenance	$_____
Taxes and insurance	$_____
Total	$_____

COST ANALYSIS RECORD

TOTAL LABOR HOURS

	UNIT	2	3	4	6	7	8
PREVIOUS	1 ELEC.	160			5 ELEC. 160		
THIS WEEK		80			80		
TOTAL		240			240		

UNIT — PER 100 LF WIRE

LABOR HOURS PER UNIT

	UNIT	2	3	4	6	7	8
PREVIOUS	1 ELEC.	3.81			5 ELEC. 1.25		
THIS WEEK		3.64			1.13		
TOTAL		3.76			1.21		

UNIT — PER OUTLET

REMARKS

PULLING #12 WIRE IN THIN WALL TO SWITCHES, RECEPTACLES AND FIXTURE OUTLETS.

MFD. IN U.S.A.   FORM C-105   FRANK R. WALKER CO., PUBLISHERS, CHICAGO

Fig. 235. Analyzed Labor Costs of Pulling Electric Wire.

LABOR DISTRIBUTION

JOB CENTRAL HIGH SCHOOL   SHEET NO. 80
CLASS OF WORK X-21   WEEK ENDING APRIL 17, 19 —   JOB NO. 110

OCCUPATION	M	T	W	T	F	S	S	HOURS	RATE	AMOUNT
1 MASONS		8	8	4	1	1		20		
2 LABORERS		8	8	4	1	1		20		
3										
4										
5 ADDITIONAL 4" HOLLOW TILE PARTITIONS, 3RD FLOOR,										
6 SOUTH WING – ARCHITECT'S CHANGE ORDER NO. 21										
7										
8										

TOTAL

	QTY. WORK IN PLACE	PAY ROLL COSTS	LBR. AVERAGE UNIT COST	AVERAGE QUANTITY PER 8 HR. DAY	QTY. WORK IN PLACE	PAY ROLL COSTS	LBR. AVERAGE UNIT COST	AVERAGE QUANTITY PER 8 HR. DAY
PREVIOUS	1	1	1					
THIS WEEK	1	1	1		1	1	1	COMPLETE
TOTAL								

MFD. IN U.S.A.   FORM C-105   FRANK R. WALKER CO., PUBLISHERS, CHICAGO

Fig. 236. Labor Distribution, Illustrating Method of Keeping Costs on Extra Work.

LABOR DISTRIBUTION

JOB CENTRAL HIGH SCHOOL   SHEET NO. 81
CLASS OF WORK REMOVE RUBBISH FOR PLASTERING CONTRACTOR   WEEK ENDING   JOB NO. 110

OCCUPATION	M	T	W	T	F	S	S	HOURS	RATE	AMOUNT
1 LABOR FOREMAN	—	2	2	2	—	—	—	6		
2 LABORERS	—	32	32	32	16	—	—	112		
3										
4 CLEANING UP AND REMOVING PLASTER RUBBISH AS										
5 ORDERED BY SCARLATTI BROS. PLASTERING CONTRACTORS.										
6 HIRED 5 CY TRUCK AND DRIVER FROM T.F. MARTIN CO.,										
7 EXCAVATORS, – 3½ DAYS.										
8										

TOTAL

	QTY. WORK IN PLACE	PAY ROLL COSTS	LBR. AVERAGE UNIT COST	AVERAGE QUANTITY PER 8 HR. DAY	QTY. WORK IN PLACE	PAY ROLL COSTS	LBR. AVERAGE UNIT COST	AVERAGE QUANTITY PER 8 HR. DAY
PREVIOUS	—	—	—					
THIS WEEK	—	—						
TOTAL	—		—	NOT COMPLETE				

MFD. IN U.S.A.   FORM C-105   FRANK R. WALKER CO., PUBLISHERS, CHICAGO

Fig. 237. Labor Distribution, Illustrating Method of Keeping Costs on Work Done For Sub-Contractors.

The above costs are chargeable to the construction job plus the costs of the operator and the operating expense which should be reduced to an hourly basis.

In some cases the needed equipment for a job may be sub-contracted for or rented. Weekly and monthly rental forms for recording equipment costs are shown in Chapter 20.

CHAPTER 13

COMPLETION OF JOB

Many contractors have one failing in common—being unable to bring their jobs to completion without dragging along for weeks (with a skeleton crew) cleaning up odds and ends of work. In most cases, the blame for this condition can usually be shared by the contractor, architect and owner, but inasmuch as it is the contractor who generally stands to lose the most, he is the one who should make the effort to correct this situation.

In addition to finishing the actual construction work, there are usually a number of other labor items which must be completed before final acceptance of the job, such as final job clean-up, adjusting doors, windows, etc., replacing broken glass, patching damaged plaster, touching up painter's finish where required, starting mechanical equipment into operation, etc. The number and size of these labor operations will vary from small to large depending on the scope of the job.

Then there is always the "paperwork" which must be completed, before the contractor can obtain final payment. In order to be fully prepared for starting negotiations for final payment, the contractor's accounts for the job must be in perfect order; he must know just what he owes and to whom; he must know exactly what is owed to him; all claims for extras and credits must be settled with the owner as well as with sub-contractors, vendors, suppliers, etc.; all backcharges must be computed, approved and applied to the proper account, etc. In addition, the contractor is usually required to obtain final waivers of lien, sworn statements or affidavits for submission to the owner. Also the contractor may be required to furnish written guarantees, bonds, etc. as to the quality of the work.

The following paragraphs are comprised of suggestions, as to methods and forms to use to aid the contractor in overcoming the usual obstacles and delays in completing a construction job.

Completion of Construction Work

In most cases as the job nears the proposed completion date, the contractor is besieged with an array of numerous, comparatively small items of work, which must be completed before the owner and architect will accept the job and make final payment. Also, the owner is usually more interested in furnishings and equipment for his new building than the construction work; the architect or engineer have new projects which occupy most of their attention; the contractor and all of the sub-contractors are more or less concentrating on getting and starting new work; with the result that the job nearing completion receives less and less top-level attention, decisions are difficult to obtain, and the job organization, (what is left of it), is charged with the responsibility of finishing the work to the owner's satisfaction. The final weeks of the job are no time for the contractor to relax his personal supervision, if anything he should increase it and bring the job to a swift conclusion and thus "clinch" the profits he has worked so hard to gain.

As an aid to maintaining the high degree of organization required for a rapid completion of the job, the contractor and his superintendent or foreman should make a thorough inspection of the job some time before the proposed completion date. This should be from two weeks to several months or more, depending on the size of the job. During this inspection, a "punch list" should be prepared containing all items of unfinished work. The contractor may even persuade the owner to make a "punch list" of his own, so that a comparison may be made between the two, thus giving a check on the work yet to be done.

From the "punch list", the contractor can readily determine where to concentrate his efforts. A job meeting should be called and everyone involved should be acquainted with the situation and a schedule of operation worked out so that the job will be finished on time. On larger jobs, this may be required two, three or more times, in order to maintain a tight control over the progress towards job completion. The little time required preparing a "punch list" is reimbursed many times over by a better knowledge of job conditions which should result in better organization, faster progress, happier relations with owner and architect, less waste of labor—and last but not least—more job profit.

Job Clean-Up

Final job clean-up is a tedious, irritating, but very necessary part of the contractor's work in completing a job. If periodic cleaning has been done throughout the life of the job, the final task will be much easier and arguments about backcharges to sub-contractors or others, will be reduced to a minimum. In addition, the job will be much safer for the men and more accessible for equipment moves and material deliveries—a clean job is one of the indications of good organization.

So far as cost to the contractor is concerned the two most important details of the final clean-up operation, is to be sure that each contractor and sub-contractor pays for or does his share of the work, and that the work is done at a time when the space will not be used for further construction work. If possible, arrangements should be made for the owner to take over the space immediately following the cleaning.

Adjustments

Another operation, usually specified and required, is for the contractor to make final adjustments to all working parts of the structure, such as doors, windows, transoms, operators, etc., and to leave everything in perfect working order. In addition, various other items may be included, such as reglazing broken lights, patching damaged plaster, touching up painter's finish, etc. It is also usually required that all mechanical equipment be started, adjusted and put into satisfactory operation.

The work of adjusting doors, windows, etc., should be organized by detailing a crew of men to cover the entire job, doing whatever is necessary to insure smooth and efficient operation of this part of the construction. The foreman of this crew should make a list of all these items, personally inspect them, order his men to make the adjustments required and check each item off the list when the work has been completed. If this work is approached systematically, it will be surprising how much more quickly and less costly, it can be completed than when done in a haphazard manner.

For reglazing, patching plaster, paint touch-up work, etc., the contractor should assume the responsibility of locating and listing where such work is required, determining who is to blame for it and notifying all parties involved. Moreover, he should keep in close touch with the progress of such work, using whatever persuasive means he has, to bring this work to a finish so as not to penalize the rest of the job.

In a similar manner, the contractor should also inspect all sub-contract items which may require adjustment, including plumbing fixtures, fans and blowers, electric switches, receptacles, fixtures, etc., motor operated doors and windows, etc., and determine what items, if any, do not operate properly. This information should be brought promptly to the attention of the sub-contractors involved in order that corrections may be made without delay.

Starting and Operating Mechanical Equipment

Usually included in each division of the mechanical specifications is the requirement of starting and operating for a break-in period all of the mechanical equipment under each respective heading. This includes heating plants, ventilating systems, elevators and escalators, electric power generating equipment, air conditioning systems, etc.

The contractor should check the specifications and contracts of all sub-contractors who might be involved in this requirement and remind them of their obligations in sufficient time to permit the completion of this work during the normal life of the job.

In most cases, satisfactory operation of equipment can be attained before or coincident with the completion of the rest of the work, but in some instances, especially where large scale process piping or unusual mechanical design equipment is involved, the break-in period may extend considerably beyond the job completion date and special negotiations will be required between owner and contractor in order that final payment may be secured.

Request For Final Payment
and Accompanying Documents

Assuming the construction work is complete and acceptable to the owner and architect or engineer, the only remaining obstacle before making application for final payment, is getting the "paperwork" in order for billing. There are no standard requirements which the contractor must follow, and the necessary documents he must submit, with his billing will vary, depending on who the contractor is dealing with and how the work is being financed. On larger work this is usually stated in the job specifications, but on residential building, frequently the mortgage bank or other lending institution, will specify what documents the contractor will be required to furnish.

However, the first requirement, for preparing final job papers, is to bring the bookkeeping accounts for the job up to date, especially the account between contractor and owner and accounts between contractor and each sub-contractor and vendor. This will be comparatively easy, if the contractor employs an adequate bookkeeping and record system.

To bring the accounts up to date, it is essential that the contractor obtain all outstanding bills, including statements of amounts due sub-contractors and vendors for their final month's work plus retained percentages. In addition, these statements should reflect all revisions in contract price, both extras and credits, due to job changes and backcharges. It is at this time that the value of settling revisions in contract price and backcharges, as they occur on the job, will be appreciated most. If left until the end of the job, arguments may take place, and there is danger that some factors may even be completely forgotten resulting in losses to the contractor. When all accounts are brought up to date, the contractor can then prepare his request for final payment, in the form specified or requested by the owner or financing body.

Usually, the contractor is required to submit a sworn statement, along with his requests for both partial and final payments, showing a complete breakdown of the work, with names and addresses of companies participating in the job and showing individual contract amounts, amounts paid to date, amounts requested and balance to complete. Illustrated in Figure 238 is a sworn statement form specified by many architects and owners.

In some cases, only a contractor's affidavit is required, stating that all bills are paid in full or listing exceptions. A form for this purpose is illustrated in Figure 239, and contains sufficient outline phrasing to enable execution of the document with minimum effort.

As a general rule, requests for payments must be accompanied by documents, waiving lien rights on the property, executed by the contractor and all his sub-contractors and vendors. A convenient form for this purpose is illustrated in Figure 240.

Some jobs will require the contractor's personal written guarantee, assuring the owner he is getting good quality materials and workmanship. The contractor should write this on his business letterhead, containing all provisions specified, and submit it with his request for final payment.

On jobs where bonded roofs are specified, the roofing sub-contractor must apply to the roofing materials manufacturer for same, and after roof construction is inspected and approved, bond will be issued for the specified term. In addition to the bond, the roofing contractor is often required to give his written personal guarantee on his work. These documents should accompany the roofing contractor's final billing, so that the contractor may include them with his application for final payment.

If the contractor puts forth the effort to prepare or obtain all specified documents as mentioned above or others that may be required, he has then fulfilled the terms of his contract and is eligible to receive final payment. If not already made, final payments to sub-contractors or vendors, may then take place and the job will be complete.

SWORN STATEMENT FOR CONTRACTOR AND SUBCONTRACTOR TO OWNER

State of ILLINOIS
County of COOK } ss.

The affiant ---- PHILLIP H. ANDREWS ------------------ being first duly sworn, on oath deposes and says that he is (1) Sole Owner of the Andrews Construction Company, of Arlington, Illinois, who has entered into a --

contract with (2) ------John H. Smith of Arlington, Illinois ------------------ owner, for

(3) the General Contract Work on a one-story and basement store building--------------

on the following described premises in said County, to-wit: property known as 656 North Main Street, Arlington, Illinois--------------

That, for the purpose of said contract, the following persons have been contracted with, and have furnished, or are furnishing and preparing materials for, and have done or are doing labor on said improvement. That there is due and to become due them, respectively, the amounts set opposite their names for materials or labor as stated. That this statement is made to said owner____ for the purpose of procuring from said owner____ (4) Partial—Final Payment on said contract, and is a full, true and complete statement of all such persons, and of the amounts paid, due and to become due them.

(1) A member of the firm of, or officer of the corporation of, naming same. If a subcontractor so state and name the contractor. (2) Name of the owner or owners. (3) What the contract or subcontract is for. (4) Partial or Final Payment.

NAME AND ADDRESS	CONTRACT FOR	AMOUNT OF CONTRACT	TOTAL PREVIOUS REQUESTS	AMOUNT OF THIS REQUEST	BALANCE TO COMPLETE
Andrews Construction Co.	General Cond.	$ 3584 00	$ 1500 00	$ 1200 00	$ 884 00
Andrews Construction Co.	Permits, Insurance & Taxes	3657 00	1832 00	350 00	1475 00
Andrews Construction Co.	Const. Plant & Equipment	1075 00	650 00	350 00	75 00
Andrews Construction Co.	Excavation	1851 00	1250 00	325 00	276 00
Andrews Construction Co.	Foundations	8309 00	8309 00	---- --	---- --
Andrews Construction Co.	Cem. Fls. & Walks	2726 00	---- --	1250 00	1476 00
Andrews Construction Co.	Masonry	8498 00	---- --	4500 00	3998 00
McCarthy Stone Co.	Cut Stone Mat'l.	1300 00	---- --	500 00	800 00
Andrews Construction Co.	Rough Carpentry	5778 00	---- --	2600 00	3178 00
Andrews Construction Co.	Fin. Carpentry & Lab.	869 00	---- --	---- --	869 00
Arlington Millwork Co.	Millwork	1275 00	---- --	---- --	1275 00
Weatherseal Co.	Weatherstrips & Caulking	175 00	---- --	---- --	175 00
Clark & Son Plastering Co.	Lath & Plaster	3000 00	---- --	800 00	2200 00
Modern Window Co.	Aluminum Doors & Windows	1250 00	---- --	950 00	300 00
Simpson Sheet Metal Co.	Sheet Metal Work	300 00	---- --	---- --	300 00
Anderson Roofing Co.	Roofing	1675 00	---- --	---- --	1675 00
Arlington Glass Co.	Glass & Glazing	1250 00	---- --	---- --	1250 00
Cook Painting & Decorating Co.	Painting	1375 00	---- --	---- --	1375 00
Adams Iron Works	Misc. Iron & Stl.	1575 00	---- --	975 00	600 00
Link Bros. Hardware Co.	Finish Hardware	325 00	---- --	---- --	325 00
Arlington Plumbing Co.	Plumbing	2200 00	---- --	800 00	1400 00
Hughes Heating Co.	Heating	4200 00	---- --	600 00	3600 00
Kester Electric Co.	Electrical	3510 00	---- --	900 00	2610 00
		59757 00	13541 00	16100 00	30116 00

AMOUNT OF ORIGINAL CONTRACT	$ 59,227.00	TOTAL AMOUNT REQUESTED	$ 29,641.00
EXTRAS TO CONTRACT	$ 580.00	LESS 5 % RETAINED	$ 1,482.05
TOTAL CONTRACT AND EXTRAS	$ 59,807.00	NET AMOUNT EARNED	28,158.95
CREDITS TO CONTRACT	$ 50.00	AMOUNT OF PREVIOUS PAYMENTS	$ 13,541.00
NET AMOUNT OF CONTRACT	$ 59,757.00	AMOUNT DUE THIS PAYMENT	$ 14,617.95
		BALANCE TO COMPLETE	$ 31,598.05

It is understood that the total amount paid to date plus the amount requested in this application shall not exceed _____% of the cost of work completed to date.

I agree to furnish Waivers of Lien for all materials under my contract when demanded.

Signed ANDREWS CONSTRUCTION COMPANY

Sole Owner

Subscribed and sworn to before me this_____day of_____19___

The above sworn statement should be obtained by the owner before each and every payment.   Notary Public

Fig. 238. Contractor's Sworn Statement. Size 8½ x 15 or 8½ x 22 Inches. Form 591.

CONTRACTOR'S AFFIDAVIT

𝔖tate of ___Illinois___ ⎫
⎬ ss.
County of _____Cook_____ ⎭

Office of ___Andrews Construction Company___

___209 E. Elm St., Arlington, Ill.___

___-------- Phillip H. Andrews----------___

being duly sworn on his oath deposes and says that he is ___Sole Owner of the Andrews Construction Co.___

the contractor for the ___------- General Contract ------------------------------------___

for the building erected for_____John H. Smith_____, owner,

on the premises described as foilows, to-wit: ___property known as 656 N. Main Street, Arlington,___

___Cook County, Illinois --___

_____

_____

All the bills for labor and materia! are fully paid and discharged_____------No Execptions -----------------___

_____

_____

_____

𝔗hat___ __he___ makes this affidavit for the purpose of procuring from ___-- John H. Smith, Owner----------___

___--------------------------------___ a ___------------Partial-------------___ payment

of ___Seven Thousand Four Hundred Forty Nine ($7449.00)___ Dollars and ___--------No-------___ Cents

upon ___---------------___ contract for said labor or material or both.

SUBSCRIBED AND SWORN to before me

this_____ day of_____A. D., 19_____

ANDREWS CONSTRUCTION COMPANY

By _____ Sole Owner

_____
NOTARY PUBLIC

~~PRACTICAL~~ FORM 592

FRANK R. WALKER CO., PUBLISHERS, CHICAGO

MFD. IN U. S. A.

Fig. 239. Contractor's Affidavit. Size 8½ x 7 Inches. 592.

WAIVER OF LIEN
MATERIAL OR LABOR

𝔖tate of ___ILLINOIS___ }   ———July 6,———————— 19 --

County of ___COOK___ } ss.

TO ALL WHOM IT MAY CONCERN:

 Whereas __we__ the undersigned ___------ANDREWS CONSTRUCTION COMPANY ------------------------___
ha __ve__ been employed by __--John H. Smith, of Arlington, Illinois, under General Contract---------__
to furnish __all labor, material, equipment and supervision required to complete the construction__
__work --__

for the Building known as __the Smith Store Building located at 656 N. Main Street in the ---------__
City of __Arlington, Illinois ---__

Lot No. ___41___ Section ___12___ Township ___Euclid___ Range ___16___
County of ___Cook___ State of ___Illinois___
NOW, THEREFORE, KNOW YE, That __the Andrews Construction Company -------------------__ the undersigned
for and in consideration of the sum of __Seven Thousand Four Hundred Forty Nine (7449.00)----------__ Dollars
and other good and valuable considerations, the receipt whereof is hereby acknowledged, do hereby waive and release any and all lien, or
claim or right to lien on said above described building and premises under the Statutes of the State of ___Illinois___
relating to Mechanics' Liens, on account of labor or materials, or both, furnished or which may be furnished, by the undersigned to or
on account of the said __---------------General Contract--__
__--__ for said building or premises.

Given under __my__ hand ___ and seal ___ this ___6th___ Day of ___July___ A. D., 19 --

ANDREWS CONSTRUCTION COMPANY

_____ By _____ Sole Owner(SEAL)

_____ (SEAL)

~~PRACTICAL~~ FORM 593

FRANK R. WALKER CO., PUBLISHERS, CHICAGO   MFD. IN U. S. A.

Fig. 240. Waiver of Lien. Size 8½ x 7 Inches. 593.

CHAPTER 14

INTRODUCTION TO BOOKKEEPING

In general, bookkeeping is a systematic recording of business transactions and the object of bookkeeping is to show the proprietor at any time whether his business is being conducted at a profit or at a loss. It also indicates the sources from which the profits and losses arise, and affords a record of all property belonging to the business and the debts owed by the business.

Accounting is concerned with the use of the bookkeeping records from which various summaries or statements are prepared.

Accounting deals with property and rights to property. The sum of the properties owned are called assets, the rights to the properties owned are called equities. The relationship between assets and equities are stated in the following equation:

$$ASSETS = EQUITIES$$

Equities are divided into the rights of owners and the rights of creditors. The equity of the owner or owners is called capital, proprietorship, owner's capital, or net worth.

The accounting equation is shown as follows:

$$ASSETS = LIABILITIES + CAPITAL$$

The residual claim can be indicated as follows:

$$ASSETS - LIABILITIES = CAPTIAL$$

All business transactions are stated in these basic elements of the accounting equation.

ASSETS. All things possessed by a business are measured in a specific number of dollars. The assets are comprised of cash, land, buildings, machinery, equipment, material and so forth. They also include claims for sums of money against individuals or other enterprises. Assets are put into the business either by the owners or by others. The portion of the assets put into the business by the owners or by others and stated in the terms of money and are referred to as their investment or capital.

LIABILITIES: Liabilities are incurred when creditors furnish materials, loans or the performance of services with payment to be made at some future time according to terms of the obligation. The amounts of money owed to the creditors are known as liabilities until paid. Assets also come into a business by performance of services or sale of merchandise, such increases in assets through earnings are known as income to the business.

Net earnings are incurred for a period of time when the income of the business operations are in excess of the business expense and the result is an increase in assets or decrease of liabilities. In cases where expenses exceed the income for the accounting period, the result will be a loss and net decrease in the value of the assets, or increase in the liabilities would be the outcome.

The bookkeeper has the responsibility of keeping a record of the essential dollar and cents information affecting a business. Debits and credits in bookkeeping are as inseparable as plus and minus in arithmetic. Each transaction has two elements expressed in dollars that are equal. The practice is that assets are placed on the left side and the liabilities and equities on the right side.

In a going business changes are constantly taking place. The various business transactions bring about nine changes in the accounting equation: ASSETS = LIABILITIES + CAPITAL.

Increases in assets occur with corresponding:

1. Increase in net worth
2. Increase in liabilities
3. Decrease in assets

Decreases in liabilities occur with corresponding:

1. Increase in net worth
2. Increase in liabilities

3. Decrease in assets

Decreases in net worth occurs with corresponding:

1. Increase in net worth
2. Increase in liabilities
3. Decrease in assets

Double entry bookkeeping is the term applied to current day methods of keeping books. Total debits are always equal to the total credits. Every transaction has a debit and a credit side, this maintains a constant balance.

During the course of the business its transactions will result in the following changes in debits and credits.

Debit for	*Credit for*
Increases in assets	Increases in liabilities
Increases in expenses	Increases in net worth
Decreases in liabilities	Increases in income
Decreases in net worth	Decreases in assets
Decreases in income	Decreases in expenses

Income and expense items are temporary in character and reflect changes during a definite period, and at the end of the period the net result is a profit or loss for the business.

Accounts are divided into five well defined groups common to all enterprises: (1) Asset, (2) Liability, (3) Expense, (4) Income, (5) Net worth. Expense and income accounts are temporary proprietorship accounts. Assets and liabilities are further divided into current assets, fixed assets, current liabilities, long term liabilities, proprietorship or net worth. Current assets are cash or items that will be converted into cash in the regular operation of the business within a year. Current liabilities are obligations, already incurred, which should be paid within a year. Fixed assets are relatively fixed or permanent in nature, such as equipment, buildings and land.

A chart of accounts for a construction contractor is included in this chapter.

Records

The books of original entry are comprised of (1) Contract Register, (2) Cash Receipts and Disbursement Journal, (3) Purchase Journal, (4) General Journal. The purpose of a journal is to record the transactions as they occur in the course of business.

Register of Contracts Journal

An accurate register of contracts should be maintained. Each contract is given a number and the history of each contract is shown in the register. See accompanying schedule.

Cash Receipts and Disbursement Journal

The "Practical" Self-Balancing Journal for cash receipts and disbursements is illustrated in Chapter 15.

Purchase Journal

All unpaid bills at closing date, whether to be paid immediately or later, for materials, expenses and services, are entered in the purchase journal and the construction jobs in progress or completed are to be charged. Also expense and general accounts are to be charged. If a subsidiary ledger of individual accounts is kept, a separate account with each creditor is maintained. See accompanying schedule.

REGISTER OF CONTRACTS JOURNAL

Contract #	Date	Name	Contract Amount	Changes		Total Contract	Date Completed	Date Billed
				Debit	Credit			

General Journal

In addition to the specialized journals described a general journal is necessary to record less common transactions which do not properly belong to one of the specialized journals. It will be needed to record such entries as:

Notes receivable from customers

Notes payable to creditors

Adjustments to correct errors in original entries

Corrections in errors in postings

Transfers in accounts

Closing entries to be made at the end of an accounting period whereby operating accounts are written off to a profit and loss account and the net results transferred to the proprietorship account or to earned surplus account in case of a corporation

Ledger sheets especially designed for a contractors' bookkeeping system are shown in the following pages.

CHART OF ACCOUNTS

ASSETS

1	Cash in bank—general disbursement
2	Cash in bank—Payroll account
3–5	Special bank accounts
6	Petty cash—office
7	Petty cash—field office
8	Securities
10	Accounts receivable—completed contracts
11	Accounts receivable—uncompleted contracts
12	Accounts receivable—other

Chart of Accounts Continued

13	Notes receivable
14	Deposits on bids, plans
16	Inventory—materials and supplies not assigned to jobs in progress
17	Inventory—yard stock
18	Land for development
20	Prepaid insurance
21	Prepaid taxes, licenses, fees
22	Expenses advances
23	Deferred expenses
30	Construction machinery and equipment
30–1	Reserve for depreciation—construction machinery and equipment
31	Trucks and trailers
31–1	Reserve for depreciation—trucks and trailers
32	Automobiles
32–1	Reserve for depreciation—automobiles
33	Tools (other than small tools)
34	Buildings
34–1	Reserve for depreciation—buildings
35	Office equipment
35–1	Reserve for depreciation—office equipment
35	Land

LIABILITIES

50	Notes payable—General borrowing
51	Notes payable—current portion long term loans and mortgages
52	Accounts payable—general trade
53	Due to subcontractors on uncompleted contracts
54	Due to subcontractors on completed contracts
60	Payroll taxes
60–1	Federal income taxes—withheld
60–2	State income taxes—withheld
60–3	Accrued—F.I.C.A. taxes
60–4	Accrued—Federal unemployment taxes
60–5	Accrued—State unemployment taxes
63	Accrued property taxes
64	Other taxes
67	Accrued—Federal income taxes
68	Accrued—State income taxes
70	Accrued payroll
71	Due to joint ventures
73	Billings on uncompleted contracts—less cost
80	Mortgage payable
81	Loans over one year
90	Partners' investment (if partnership)
91	Owners' investment (if sole proprietorship)
92	Personal accounts (if partnership or sole proprietorship)
95	Capital Stock (if corporation)
96	Donated surplus
97	Retained earnings

Operating Accounts

INCOME ACCOUNTS

100	Billings—completed jobs
101	Uncompleted jobs

Chart of Accounts Continued

105	Income from joint ventures
106	Discounts earned
107	Supplies sold
108	Equipment Rentals
109	Equipment sold
110	Profit from sale of securities
111	Other income

COSTS

120	Costs of completed jobs
121	Cost of uncompleted jobs

OVERHEAD—Direct

130	Supervision
131	Indirect labor
132	Payroll taxes
133	Equipment operating expenses
134	Depreciation—machinery and equipment
135	Depreciation—trucks and trailers
136	Depreciation—automobiles
137	Insurance
138	Tool replacements
139	Other expense

GENERAL AND ADMINISTRATION EXPENSE

150	Office salaries
151	Executive salaries
152	Engineering department salaries
153	Engineering department expense
154	Payroll taxes
155	Other taxes and licenses
156	Insurance
157	Maintenance office equipment
158	Depreciation—buildings
159	Depreciation—office equipment
160	Stationery and supplies
161	Postage
162	Telephone
163	Rent
164	Utilities
165	Automobile expense
166	Depreciation—automobiles
167	Advertising
168	General Expense
169	Dues and Subscriptions
170	Contributions
171	Bad debts
172	Professional fees
173	Federal income taxes
174	State income taxes
175	Interest expense
176	Loss on sale of securities

LEFT SIDE   PURCHASE JOURNAL

252

		CREDITOR	AMOUNT		JOB #	JOB #	JOB #	JOB #
1								
2								
3								
4								
5								
6								
7								
8								
9								
10								
11								
12								
13								
14								
15								
16								
17								
18								
19								
20								
21								
22								
23								
24								

Short Form Inserts Form 134-S

PURCHASE JOURNAL   *RIGHT SIDE*

FORM 134   FRANK R. WALKER CO., PUBLISHERS, CHICAGO.

	AUTO EXPENSE	UTILITIES	TAXES LICENSES	TELEPHONE	PROFESSIONAL FEE'S	GENERAL EXPENSE	STATIONERY SUPPLIES	ADVERTISING	OTHER	
1										1
2										2
3										3
4										4
5										5
6										6
7										7
8										8
9										9
10										10
11										11
12										12
13										13
14										14
15										15
16										16
17										17
18										18
19										19
20										20
21										21
22										22
23										23
24										24

PRACTICAL MFD. IN U.S.A.

LEDGER SHEETS

Labor Cost Record #108
Material Cost Record #109
Job Cost Record #116, #1423, #1424, #143, #1657, #167, #142
Recapitulation #117
Sub-Contract #119, #1192
General Ledger, #121, #221, #1212
Monthly Trial Balance, #122-L, #122-S
Cash Journal, #123, #200, #201, #201B, #223, #224, #224-SC
Voucher, #124, #125, #126
Columnar, #134, #134-S, #136
Equipment and Depreciation Record #137
Contract Account, #142
Cash-Bank Record, #150
Architects, #151, #1513, #153
General Expense, #154
Perpetual Stock Record, #156
Profit & Loss Account, #210
Yearly Statement & Recapitulation, #211

**THE ABOVE LISTED FORMS
ARE ILLUSTRATED ON THE
FOLLOWING PAGES**

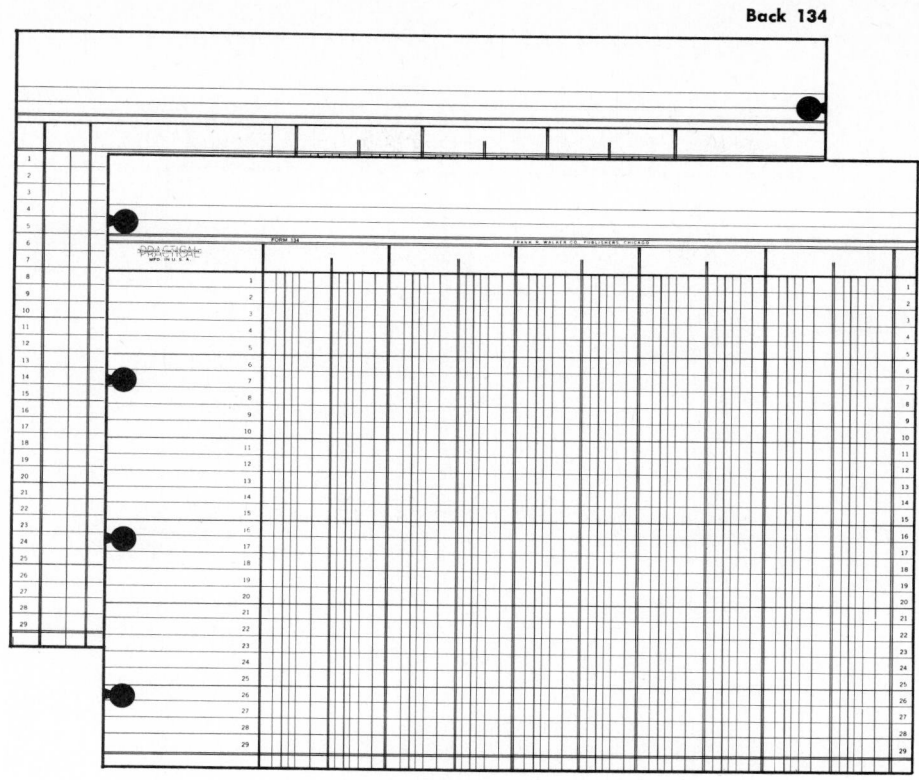

BLANK JOURNAL SHEETS. Form 134.

Left and right hand pages. Used as a purchase journal or for sub-dividing and analyzing all classes of miscellaneous accounts, such as general expense, plant and equipment, taxes, etc. Has description space and columns for debit and credit entries on eight individual accounts.

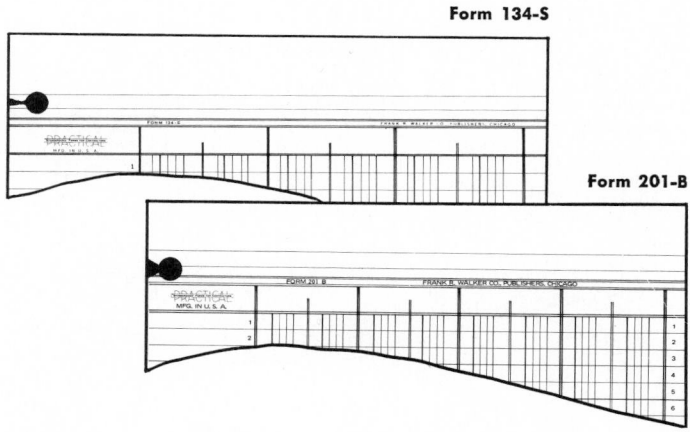

BLANK JOURNAL SHORT SHEETS.

Printed the same on two sides. Inserted in cash journal where additional control accounts or cost Subdivisions are desired. 134-S has 3 debit/credit columns per side. 201-B has 4 debit/credit columns per side.

Back 223

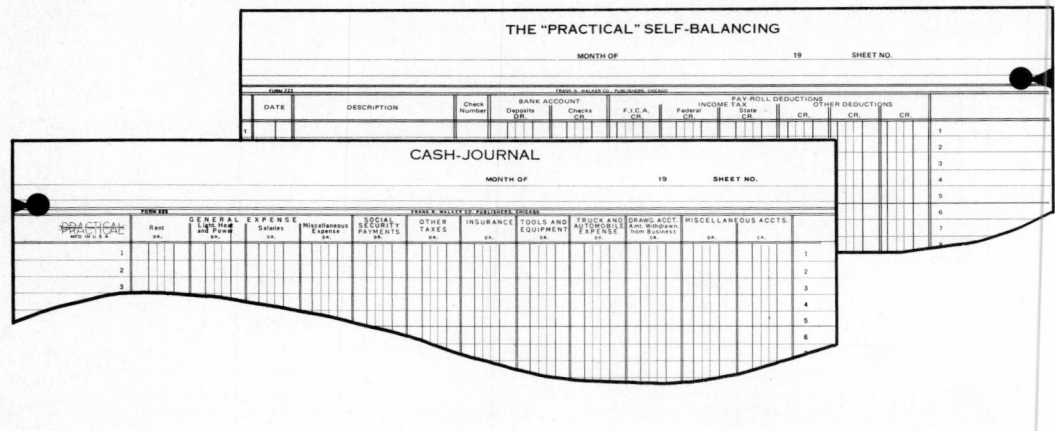

CASH JOURNAL.   Form 223.

Left and right hand pages. When used with the cash journal "short sheets", described on page 256 this form furnishes complete records of every expense entering into a business plus a complete record of all checks written.

Back 123

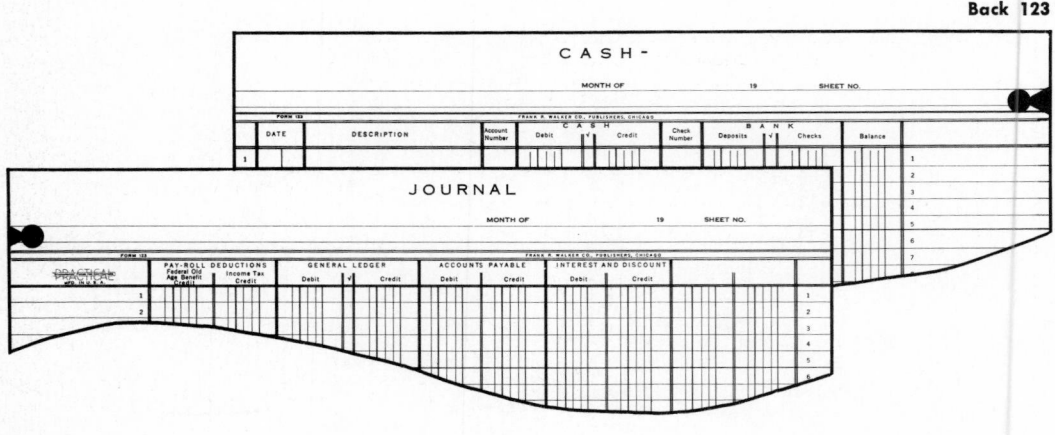

CASH JOURNAL.   Form 123.

Left and right hand pages. This sheet is used as a book of original entry and combines the Journal and Cash Book in one sheet. It furnishes a complete record of all cash receipts and disbursements, deposits and checks, together with any number of general ledger accounts.

Back 200

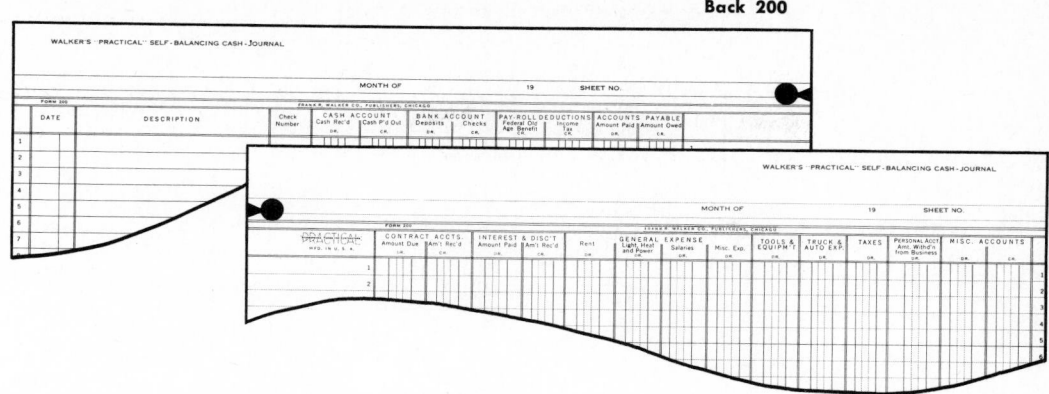

CASH JOURNAL.   Form 200.

Left and right hand pages. This form is similar to cash journal form 223, but it provides additional columns for cash account, accounts payable, contract accounts and interest and discount.

Back 124

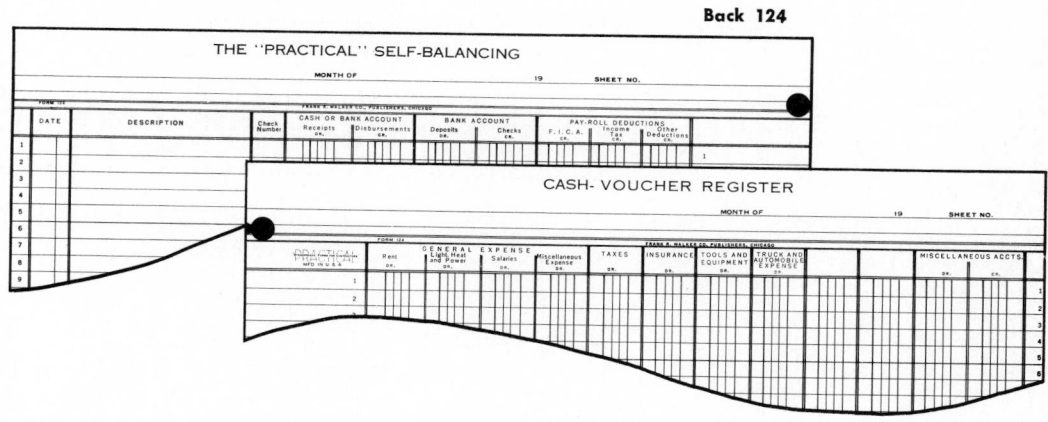

CASH VOUCHER.   REGISTER.   Form 124.

Left and right hand pages. Used primarily with voucher type bookkeeping systems. Furnishes complete records of expenses with records of all checks written.

Back 224

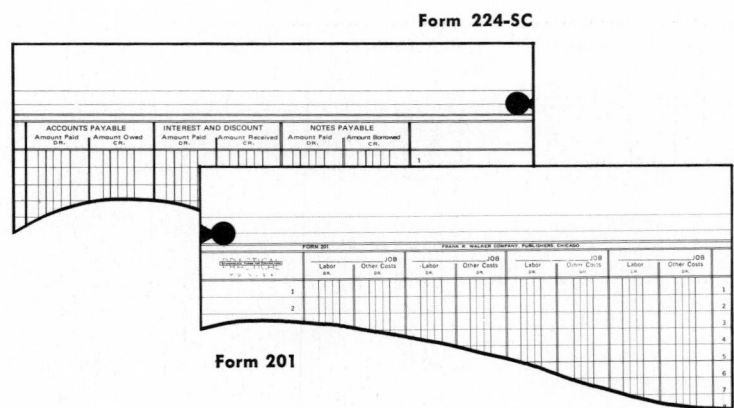

CASH JOURNAL SHORT SHEET.   Form 224.

Left and right hand pages. Used with cash journals when additional control accounts or cost subdivisions are desired.

Form 224-SC

Form 201

CASH JOURNAL SHORT SHEETS.

Printed same on two sides. Used with Cash Journals when additional Control Accounts or Cost Subdivisions are desired.

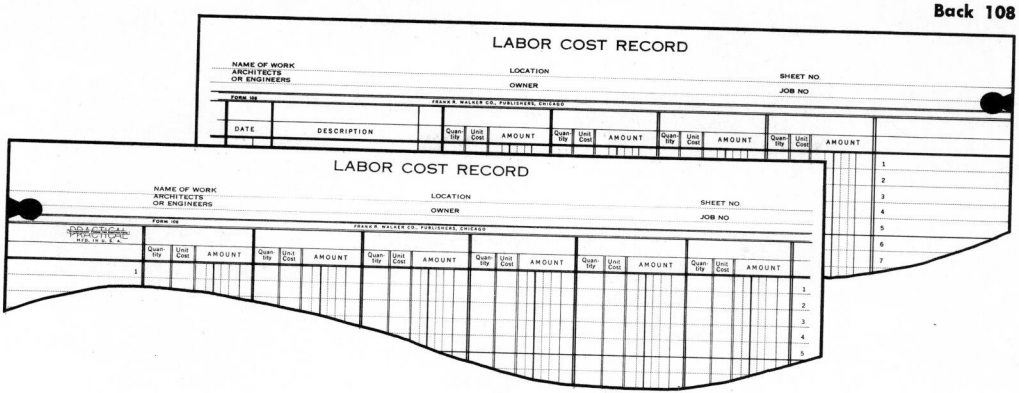

LABOR COST RECORD.   Form 108.

Left and right hand pages. A double page form containing a summary of the labor cost of each branch of work, stating the quantity completed, total cost of the work to date, together with the unit labor costs. Furnishes an accurate record of labor costs from week to week on each class of work. Just the sheet for sub-dividing your payrolls for workmen's compensation or liability insurance.

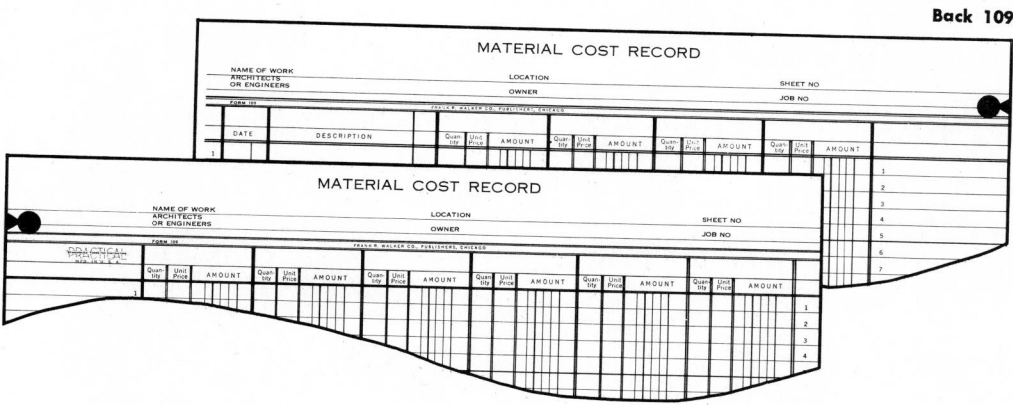

MATERIAL COST RECORD.   Form 109.

Left and right hand pages. A double page form for keeping a record of quantities, unit prices and total costs of each kind of material used on the job, plus miscellaneous expenses such as overhead and equipment rentals. An excellent record for making comparisons between estimated and actual quantities and costs.

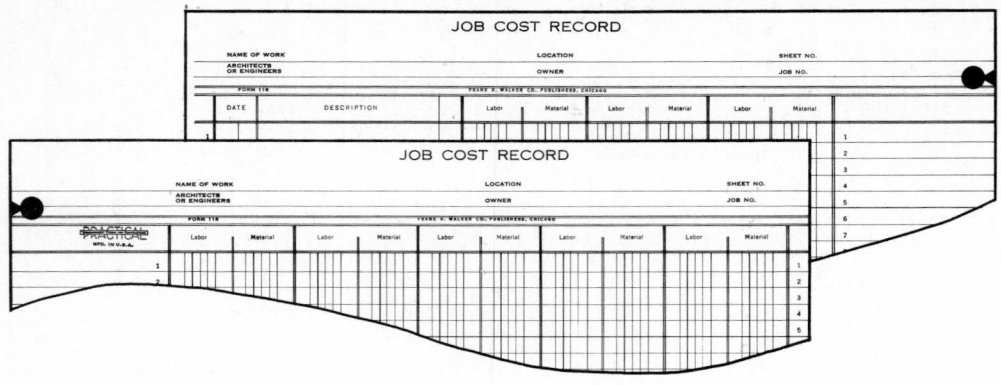

JOB COST RECORD.   Form 116.

Left and right hand pages. For contractors who desire a complete cost record of each class of work but who are not particularly interested in labor and material quantities or unit cost.

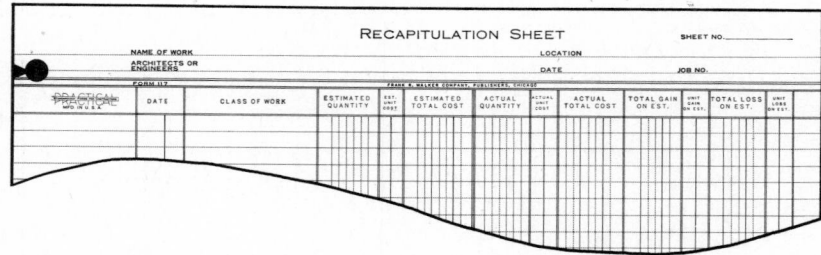

RECAPITULATION SHEET.   Form 117.

Printed the same on two sides. Has columns for entering both estimated and actual quantities and costs for each class of work. Provides accurate information regarding profits and losses on each class of work.

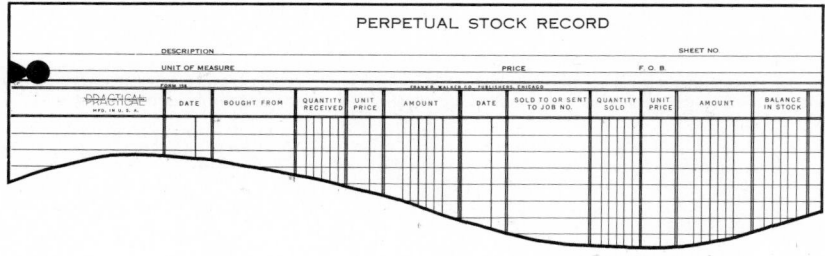

EQUIPMENT AND DEPRECIATION RECORD.   Form 137.

Printed the same on two sides. Contains space for a complete description of each piece of equipment, serial number, from whom purchased, date acquired, how required, estimated life years, yearly depreciation rate, appraised value, date appraised. Provides for recording original cost, capital repairs, depreciation amount per year, total depreciation to date, present book value, operating repairs or expense, and rentals charged or received when the equipment is rented out or when charged to any particular operation.

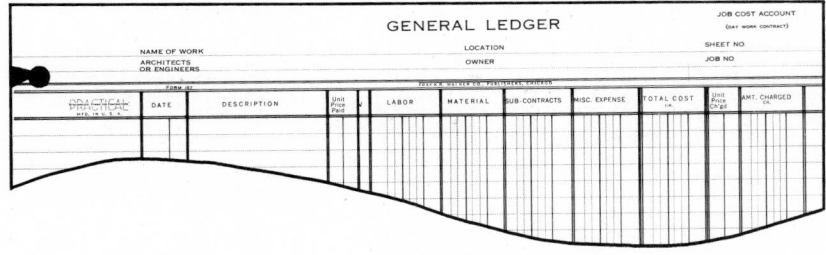

PERPETUAL STOCK RECORD.   Form 156.

Printed the same on two sides. Furnishes a complete record of all material on inventory including quantities, prices, amounts, purchased from, sold to, job charged, plus balances on hand.

GENERAL LEDGER.   Form 167.

Printed the same on two sides. A job cost account for day-work or time and material contracts. Furnishes columns for entering all expenditures and their total costs for the job in addition to the amount charged the customer.

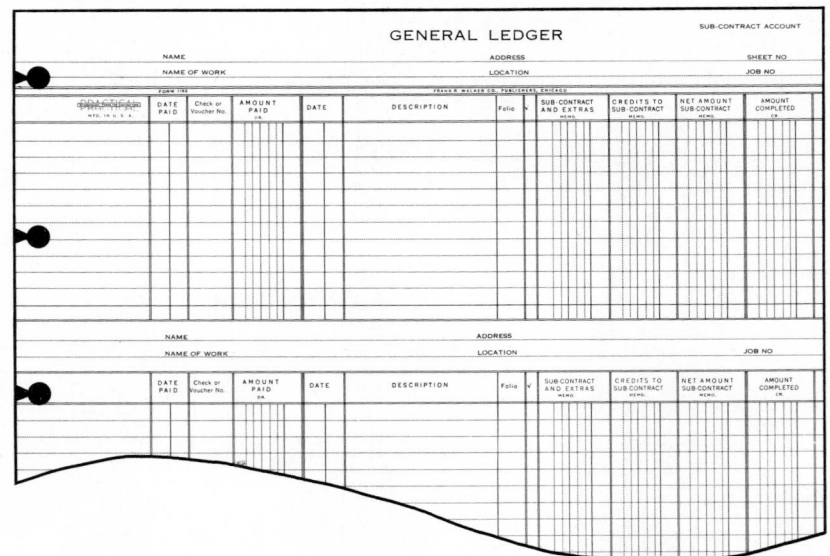

GENERAL LEDGER. Form 1212.

Printed the same on two sides. Used for accounts and notes payable, accounts and notes receivable, and other general ledger accounts. Has space for 2 accounts on each side with column for description debits and credits and a balance.

GENERAL LEDGER. Form 1192.

Printed the same on two sides. Used for keeping the accurate records of your accounts with sub-contracts. Has space for 2 accounts on each side.

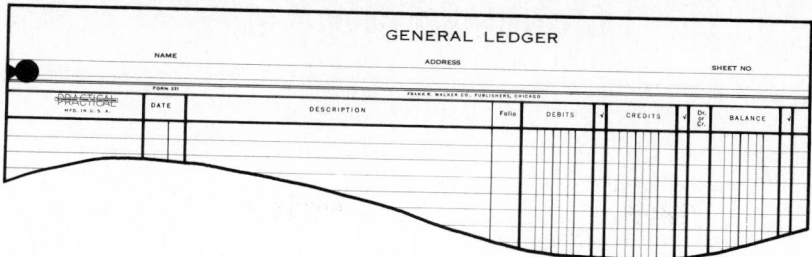

GENERAL LEDGER.   Form 221.

Printed the same on two sides. Used for accounts or notes payable, or accounts and notes receivable, with columns for description, debits, credits, and balances.

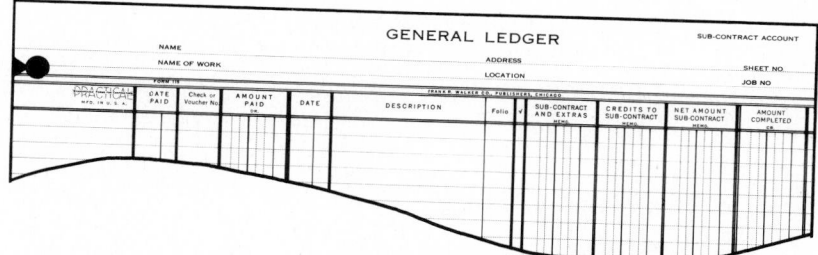

GENERAL LEDGER.   Form 119.

Printed the same on two sides. Used for keeping accurate records of your accounts with Sub-Contractors.

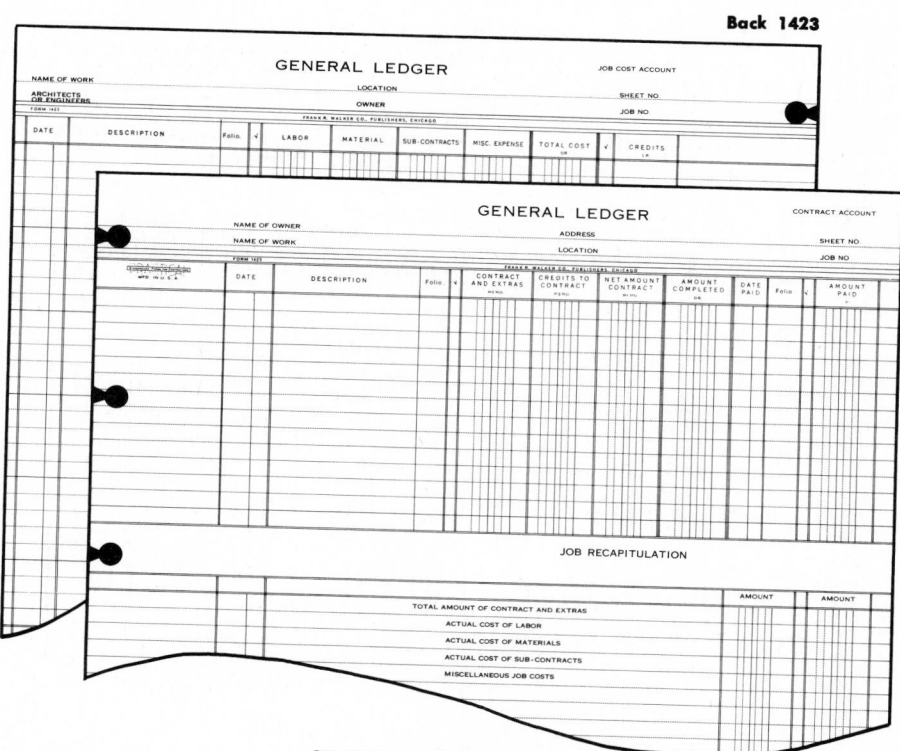

GENERAL LEDGER.   Form 1423.

Left and right hand pages as shown. This form is a combination of the contract account form 142, which is on one side of the sheet and the job cost account, Form 143, is on the other. The right hand sheet, the contract account side, also contains a job recapitulation.

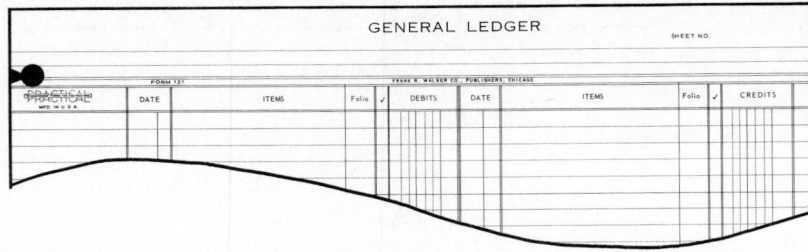

GENERAL LEDGER.   Form 121.

Printed the Same on 2 sides. Used for accounts or notes payable or accounts or notes receivable. Has description, debits, credits, and balances columns.

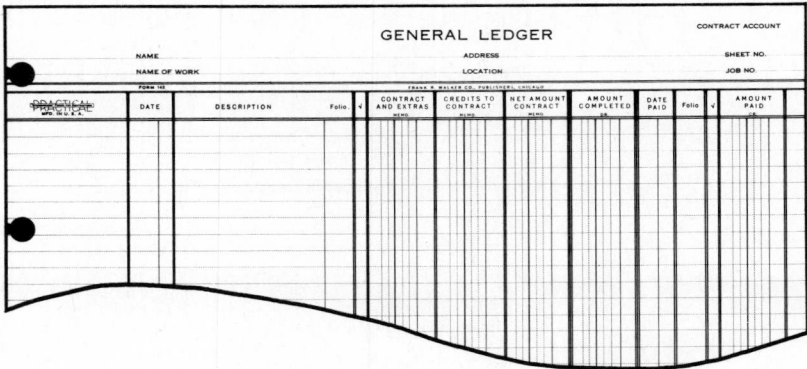

GENERAL LEDGER.   Form 142.

Printed the same on two sides. This sheet contains a complete record of your contracts showing the amount of the original contract together with any extras to same; the amount of any credits or deductions from the contract price; the new amount of the contract; the amount of work completed, together with a record of all payments received.

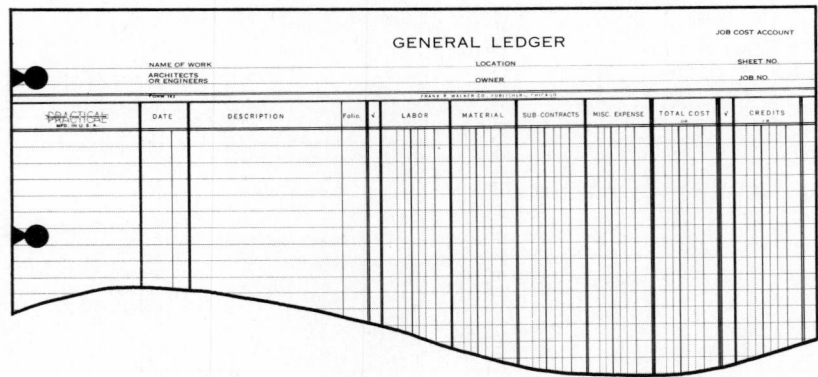

GENERAL LEDGER.   Form 143.

Printed same on two sides. Used for keeping detailed cost for labor, material, sub-contracts and other miscellaneous job expenses.

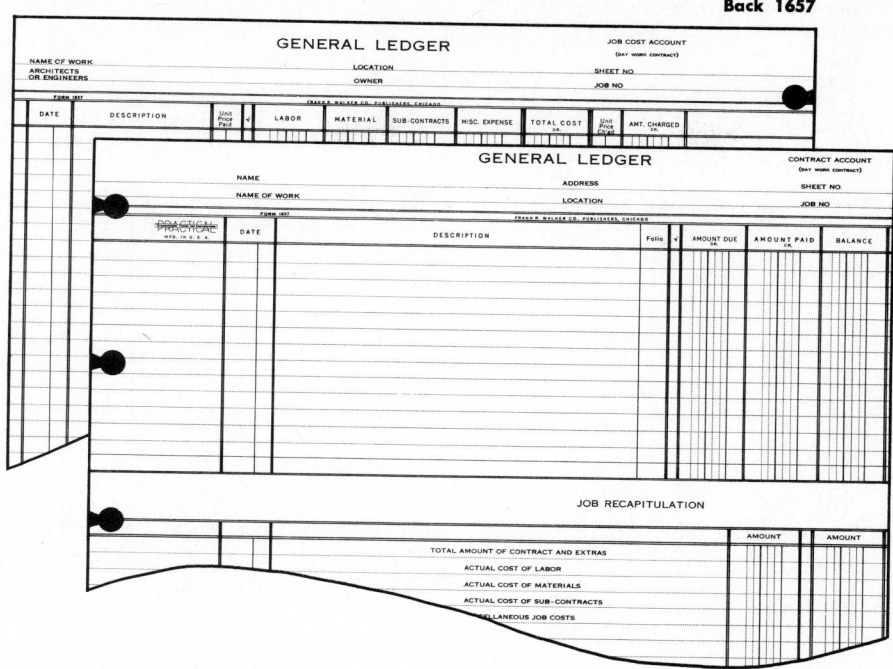

GENERAL LEDGER. Form 1657.

Right and left hand pages. The right hand sheet contains a complete record of each job or contract performed on a day-work or time and material basis plus a job recapitulation. The left hand sheet contains the job cost account, form 143, shown above.

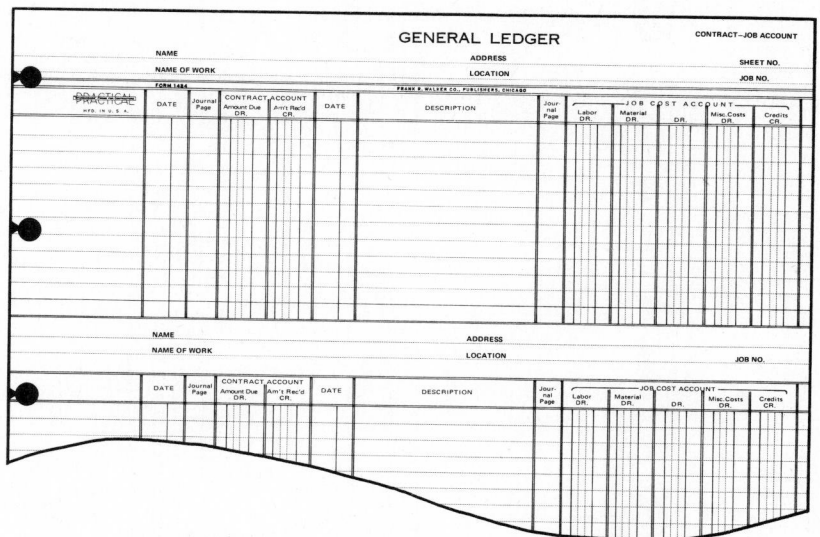

GENERAL LEDGER. Form 1424.

Printed the same on two sides. Used for small jobs or contracts, where the amount is small and only a few entries are necessary. Space is provided for complete records of two jobs on each side of the sheet.

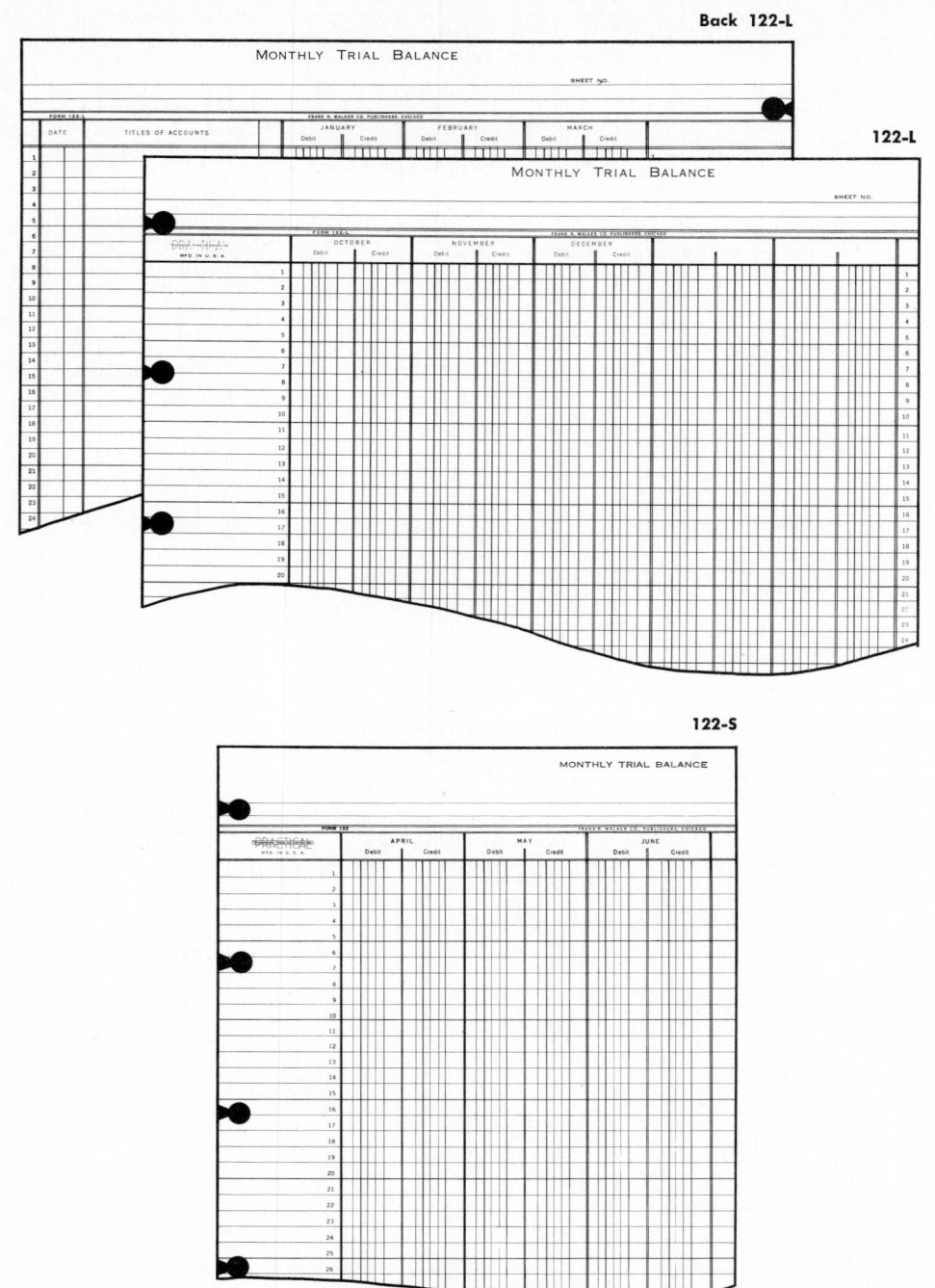

MONTHLY TRIAL BALANCE.

Form 122-L and 122-S used together to provide debit and credit columns for each month of the year for taking off and recording the monthly trial balance.

JOB PROFIT AND LOSS ACCOUNT

FORM 210

FRANK R. WALKER CO., PUBLISHERS, CHICAGO

DATE	NAME OF WORK	LOCATION	JOB NO.	TOTAL AMOUNT OF CONTRACT	ACTUAL COST OF CONTRACT	LOSS ON CONTRACT	PROFIT ON CONTRACT
				TOTAL			

JOB PROFIT AND LOSS ACCOUNT. Form 210.

Printed same on two sides. Used for keeping a record of all job profits or losses. Provides space for date, name of work, location and job number, along with columns for amount of contract, cost of contract with profit or loss on each job.

YEARLY STATEMENT AND RECAPITULATION

FORM 211

FRANK R. WALKER CO., PUBLISHERS, CHICAGO

YEARLY STATEMENT OF ACCOUNTS

ASSETS (WHAT WE OWN)		LIABILITIES (WHAT WE OWE)		YEARLY INCOME RECAPITULATION		
ACCOUNT	AMOUNT	ACCOUNT	AMOUNT		AMOUNT	AMOUNT
Cash on Hand		Proprietor's Account		TOTAL AMOUNT OF COMPLETED CONTRACTS FOR YEAR		
Cash in Bank						
				DEDUCT COST OF COMPLETED CONTRACTS:		
Accounts Receivable		Accounts Payable		MATERIAL COST		
				LABOR COST		
Amount Due on Completed Contracts		Notes Payable		MISC. COSTS		
				TOTAL COST OF CONTRACTS		
Plant and Equipment		Other Loans		GROSS PROFIT ON CONTRACTS		
				DEDUCT:		
Furniture and Fixtures		Mortgages, Etc.		RENT		
				LIGHT, HEAT AND POWER		
Automobiles and Trucks		Other Liabilities:		OFFICE SALARIES		
				MISCELLANEOUS EXPENSES		
Real Estate				TRUCK AND AUTOMOBILE EXPENSES		
				TOOLS AND EQUIPMENT DEPRECIATION		
Merchandise Inventory				TRUCK AND AUTOMOBILE DEPRECIATION		
				FURNITURE AND FIXTURES DEPRECIATION		
Other Assets:				LOSSES FROM BAD DEBTS		
				INTEREST PAID ON BORROWED MONEY		
				TAXES, INSURANCE, ETC.		
				TOTAL		
				ADD OTHER INCOME: { TOTAL BUSINESS INCOME		
				FROM REAL ESTATE		
				INTEREST AND DISCOUNT EARNED		
				BONDS AND MORTGAGES		
TOTAL		TOTAL		TOTAL YEARLY INCOME		

YEARLY STATEMENT AND RECAPITULATION. Form 211.

Printed the same on two sides. Used for making a yearly statement of accounts, and a yearly income recapitulation from which your income tax statement can be compiled.

CHAPTER 15

THE "PRACTICAL" SELF-BALANCING BOOKKEEPING SYSTEM FOR CONTRACTORS

This system of bookkeeping is the easiest any contractor can possibly use, regardless of the size of the business. It is so simple that the contractor who keeps his own books in spare time and doing a business of only a few thousand dollars a year, can handle it with ease.

The Self-Balancing Cash-Journal is the key to the entire system, and the use of this one sheet will furnish all the information any contractor requires to keep complete business records, including a monthly trial balance.

Contractors will find this system not only very simple and easy to keep but also complete and accurate as the most elaborate bookkeeping systems. It furnishes at a glance all the information any contractor requires regarding any part of his business, including costs and expenses.

The various ledger sheets are used for keeping detailed accounts with persons or concerns for whom you are doing work; accounts with those from whom you purchase materials and supplies; detailed costs on your various jobs; accounts with all sub-contractors doing work for you; also miscellaneous accounts, such as Capital Account, Profit and Loss, etc. If a smaller contractor you may or may not use all of them, depending upon the amount of time at your disposal and the information you desire regarding the various classes of accounts. However, all of the accounts may be kept in detail by giving only a few hours to this book one or two evenings a month. The additional information furnished regarding your different jobs and the various expenses in connection with your business will more than repay you for the few hours spent.

Contractors performing larger work and employing a bookkeeper will want complete ledger accounts and we believe that after you have given this system a fair trial, you will be surprised at the ease with which the accounts are kept and the wealth of information furnished.

The Self-Balancing Cash-Journal

As previously mentioned, this sheet is the key to the entire system and furnishes complete records regarding every expense entering into your business.

It is divided into columns covering every class of expenditure entering into a contractor's business. As an example of the ease with which these records are kept, assume you spend $4.20 for gasoline for your truck. Refer to line 4 of this sheet. It shows you paid Nelson's garage $4.20, which is entered in the second column headed "Cash Account-Cash Paid Out-Cr." then on the same line in the ninth column of the right hand page headed "Truck and Auto Expense-Dr." the same amount is entered. This one simple entry gives the amount paid out and what it was spent for. Every other entry is made in exactly the same manner.

At the end of each month this sheet is totaled, and the total amount of all items entered in the columns headed "DR," signifying Debits, should balance with the total of all columns headed "CR," denoting Credits.

This sheet also eliminates the necessity of filling out check book stubs, as it furnishes a complete record of all checks written.

To obtain the bank balance at any time, subtract the total of the fourth column headed "Bank Account-Checks" from the total of the third column headed "Bank Account-Deposits." The difference is your bank balance.

The correct method of handling all classes of accounts on this sheet is given on the following pages, showing actual entries, which are fully illustrated and described.

266

Control Accounts in the Cash-Journal

Each of the columns in the Cash-Journal headed "Cash Account," "Bank Account," "Accounts Payable," "Contract Accounts," "Sub-Contract Accounts," "Job Cost Accounts," etc., are called Control Accounts because they control the receipts and expenditures of each class of accounts in the business. Sufficient control accounts for practically any contractor's business are carried in the Cash-Journal. However, additional control accounts or cost subdivisions may be carried in the Cash-Journal by merely inserting another "short" sheet between the left and right hand pages of the Cash-Journal. This "short" sheet uses the same descriptive column as the left hand Cash-Journal sheet and furnishes six additional "Debit-Credit" control accounts or twelve additional cost subdivisions. Any number of "short" sheets may be used.

The Self-Balancing Cash-Journal, together with the "short" sheets for additional control accounts, furnish records that are complete and flexible enough for any business.

How All Classes of Accounts Should Be Handled in the "Practical" Self-Balancing Bookkeeping System for Contractors

In order that all entries may be perfectly clear to users of this improved system of keeping contractors' accounts, examples are given covering all classes of actual transactions, showing just what entries are necessary for complete records.

1   How to Handle Capital or Money Invested in the Business

Assume the proprietor invests $10,000.00 cash in the business.

How the Entries Should Be Made

Refer to line 1. Make entry as illustrated, entering $10,000.00 in the third column headed "Bank Account-Deposits-Dr."

Now refer to the twelfth column of the right hand page headed "Miscellaneous Accounts-Cr." and enter $10,000.00 on line 1.

If the business is a partnership, separate Capital accounts should be kept for each partner or member of the firm, showing the amount of money invested by each.

If the business is a corporation, this amount should be carried in the ledger under the heading of "Capital Stock Account."

2   Tools, Plant and Equipment, for Use in the Business, Invested Instead of Cash

If the proprietor or members of the firm have tools or equipment they are putting into the business instead of cash, the fair cash value of same should be computed and handled as follows:

How the Entries Should Be Made

Refer to line 2. Make entry as illustrated, entering $2,500.00 in the eighth column of the right hand page headed "Tools and Equipment-Dr." then enter the same amount in the twelfth column of the right hand page headed "Miscellaneous Accounts-Cr."

3   How to Handle Petty Cash

There are certain items of expense that will be paid in cash, such as postage, express, gasoline at filling stations, and other small expenses of this kind.

In order to have cash on hand to provide for these expenditures, assume $25.00 is withdrawn from the bank to take care of these items.

4   **How to Handle Small Expenditures Paid by Cash**

The usual procedure in handling petty cash is to appoint someone to take charge of the fund. Whenever a small disbursement is necessary, the money is paid out and a receipt obtained. When the fund becomes low a check for the total of the disbursements is made to replenish the fund to the original amount and the various disbursement accounts are charged such as, postage, gas, supplies, repairs, etc.

5   **Drawing Account of Proprietor or Partners**

If the business is conducted by an individual or partners, an account should be carried for the proprietor or each partner, headed "Personal Account" or "Drawing Account."

If the business is a corporation, and each active officer or stock holder does not draw a regular salary, then a separate account should be carried for each active member of the corporation.

Assume the proprietor or one of the members of the firm withdraws $100.00 from the business for personal use.

How the Entries Should Be Made

Refer to line 5. The amount withdrawn, $100.00 should be entered in the fourth column headed "Bank Account-Checks-Cr." Now refer to Line 5 in the tenth column of the right hand page headed "Drawing Account-Amount Withdrawn from Business-Dr." and enter $100.00 in this column.

6   **Expenditures for Rent, Light, Heat and Power, Stationery, Advertising and Other Items of "Overhead" or General Expense of Conducting the Business**

In practically every business there will be expenditures for stationery and supplies, rent, light, heat and power, advertising, and other miscellaneous expenses necessary for the successful conduct of the business. This should be charged to Overhead or the General Expense of conducting the business.

Assume you purchase stationery and supplies from Edward's Stationery store amounting to $12.40.

How the Entries Should Be Made

Refer to line 6. The amount of the check, $12.40, should be entered in the fourth column headed "Bank Account-Checks-Cr." Now refer to line 6 in the fourth column of the right hand page headed "General Expense-Misc. Expense-Dr." and enter $12.40.

The item of rent is handled in exactly the same manner. Refer to line 7 of the fourth column headed "Bank Account-Checks-Cr." and to the same line in the first column of the right hand page headed "General Expense-Rent Dr." Note the amount of $60.00 entered in both places.

Electric light and power comes under the same heading. Refer to line 8 of the fourth column headed "Bank Account-Checks-Cr." and to the same line in the second column of the right hand page headed "General Expense-Light, Heat and Power-Dr." Note the amount of $8.80 entered in both places.

7   **Furniture, Typewriters and Other Office Equipment**

Money expended for furniture, typewriters, adding machines and other items of permanent equipment should be charged to the Furniture and Fixture Account, as this is an asset of the business.

Assume you buy furniture amounting to $250.00 from the H. & H. Furniture Company.

How the Entries Should Be Made

Refer to line 9. The amount of $250.00 should be entered in the fourth column headed "Bank Account-Checks-Cr." Now refer to line 9 in the eleventh column of the right hand page headed "Miscellaneous Accounts-Dr." and enter $250.00, as there is no special column for this account.

8   **When Invoices Are Received Covering Materials Purchased**

When materials are purchased for use in the office, on any of your different jobs, or when tools and equipment are purchased, a written order should be given, stating the quantity required, kind of material, price, terms, etc., as this will eliminate controversies regarding terms, payments, etc.

As an example assume you purchase from the City Lumber Company during the month for delivery to the Fred H. Hilles residence, the following materials:

<pre>
        2500 ft. b. m. Y. P. framing lumber
            @ $140.00 per M. $350.00
        40 bbls. portland cement @ $4.50 180.00
        20 cu. yds. gravel @ $3.50.............   70.00 $600.00
</pre>

For the Wm. Smith, Alteration Job, 137 E. Harper Avenue, the following materials were purchased:

<pre>
        400 ft. b. m. clear oak flooring @
            $300.00 ....$120.00
        600 sq. ft. wall board @ $60.00......   36.00
        1 front door lock set...................   20.00 $176.00
                Total...................................... $776.00
</pre>

How the Entries Should Be Made

Refer to line 10. The amount of the invoice, $776.00, should be entered in the second column of the short left hand page headed "Accounts Payable-Amount Owed-Cr." showing this amount of money owed to the City Lumber Company.

Now refer to column five of the short sheet headed "Job Cost Accounts-Total Cost-Dr." and enter the same amount, showing the material is chargeable to various jobs.

9   **When You Pay Invoices Covering Materials Purchased**

Assume the above invoices totaling $776.00 are paid, and you take a cash discount of 2% for paying the bill promptly.

How the Entries Should Be Made

Refer to line 11. A cash discount of 2% of $776.00 amounts to $15.52, so the amount of the check should be $760.48. This should be entered in the fourth column headed "Bank Account-Checks-Cr." Inasmuch as you have saved $15.52 by taking advantage of a cash discount, this amount should be entered in the fourth column of the left hand sheet headed "Interest and Discount-Amount Received-Cr." These two entries total $776.00, the amount of the bill.

You will recollect $776.00 was entered in the second column of the left hand short sheet headed "Accounts Payable-Amount Owed-Cr." before the invoice was paid. Now that the bill is paid, the amount should be entered in the first column headed "Accounts Payable-Amount Paid-Dr." These two columns now balance, showing the bill is paid in full.

10   **Invoices That Are Paid at the Time They are Entered in the Books**

Some contractors do not carry any Accounts Payable in their ledger and enter the amounts of the invoices only at the time they are paid. This saves bookkeeping labor as only one entry is required but it does not give a true picture of the business, as the books never show the amount of money owed by the business but only the amounts paid.

In instances of this kind the only entry is made at the time the bill is paid and then it is charged direct to the proper account.

Assume the account of the City Lumber Company is entered in the books only at the time the invoice is paid.

How the Entries Should Be Made

The net amount of the invoice $760.48 is entered in the fourth column of the left hand Cash-Journal sheet headed "Bank Account-Checks-Cr." and the amount of the discount earned, $15.52 is entered in the fourth column of the left hand short sheet headed "Interest and Discount-Amount Received-Cr." These two entries equal the total amount of the invoice, $776.00.

Now refer to the fifth column of the right hand short sheet headed "Job Cost Accounts-Total Cost-Dr." and enter $776.00

All other invoices paid in this manner are charged direct to the proper account without entering them in an Accounts Payable account.

Many contractors will prefer this method of handling their accounts but as stated above it's disadvantage is that it does not show the amount of money owed by the business, otherwise it is satisfactory and saves bookkeeping labor.

11   When Materials are Purchased for Stock or Resale

When materials are purchased for stock or resale, it will be necessary to keep a stock account for the different kinds of materials handled. This account should be debited when materials are purchased and credited when materials are sold or delivered to your various jobs.

As an example, assume you purchase from the Universal Portland Cement Co., the following:
220 bbls. portland cement @ $3.50...$700.00

How the Entries Should Be Made

Refer to line 12. When the invoice covering the above material is received, the $700.00 should be entered in the second column of the left hand short sheet headed "Accounts Payable-Amount Owed-Cr." showing the amount due the Universal Portland Cement Co. Then the same amount should be entered in the first column of the right hand short sheet headed "Cement-Purchases-Dr." This is later transferred to the stock account in the ledger.

12   When Materials are Taken from Stock and Sold for Cash

When materials purchased for stock are sold for cash, the following entries are necessary:
Assume you sell 50 bbls. of portland cement from stock at $4.50 per bbl., making a total of $225.00.

How the Entries Should Be Made

Refer to line 13. Note the cash sale of cement with $225.00 entered in the first column headed "Cash Account-Cash Received-Dr." Now refer to the second column of the right hand short sheet headed "Cement-Sales-Cr." and enter the same amount. This is later transferred to the Cement Stock account in the ledger.

13   When Materials are Taken from Stock and Sent to the Job

As an example of the method used when materials are taken from stock and sent to a job for use, assume 50 bbls. of portland cement are taken from stock and sent to the Hilles residence and billed at the current market price of $4.50 per bbl.

How the Entries Should Be Made

Refer to line 14. Enter the cost of the cement, $225.00 in the fifth column of the right hand short sheet headed "Job Cost Accounts-Total Cost-Dr." as illustrated. Now enter the same amount in the second column of the right hand short sheet headed "Cement-Sales-Cr." This amount is later transferred to the Cement Stock account in the ledger.

14   ## When You Give a Note for Materials Purchased

When it is not convenient to pay a material concern promptly as their bills come due, a promissory note for the amount of the bill is sometimes given, running for 30 to 60 days, depending upon circumstances.

Assume the $700.00 due the Universal Portland Cement Co., illustrated on line 12, is paid by giving them a note for $700.00 for 30 days, at 6% interest.

How the Entries Should Be Made

Refer to line 15. Universal Portland Cement Co., is entered in the descriptive column. Inasmuch as you are paying their invoice by note instead of by check, the transaction is really one of transferring the amount from Accounts Payable to Notes Payable. The total of their account amounting to $700.00 is entered in the first column of the left hand short sheet headed "Accounts Payable-Amount Paid-Dr." Now enter the same amount in the sixth column headed "Notes Payable-Amount Borrowed-Cr."

15   ## When a Note is Paid at Maturity

At the expiration of 30 days it will be necessary to pay the note of the Universal Portland Cement Co., amounting to $700.00, plus $3.50, interest for 30 days at 6%.

How the Entries Should Be Made

Refer to line 16. Enter $703.50, the amount of the note including $3.50 interest, in the fourth column headed "Bank Account-Checks-Cr." Now refer to the left hand short sheet and enter $3.50 in the third column headed "Interest and Discount-Amount Paid-Dr." Then enter $700.00, the amount of the note, in the fifth column of the left hand short sheet headed "Notes Payable-Amount Paid-Dr."

16   ## How to Handle Pay-Rolls

It is most important that payroll checks be made promptly and correctly for maintaining job morale. Time keeping data is brought in from the field and checked, extended and incorporated into the daily cost reports. As soon as daily time has been approved it is entered on a final weekly payroll record; several such records are shown on pages 44–50.

Deductions from individual payroll checks are made for F.I.C.A. taxes, Federal and State withheld income taxes, insurance, U.S. bonds and other deductions. Individual employees' earnings records are necessary showing the gross earnings, deductions and net pay.

Annual reports of employees' earnings and withheld taxes are required for preparing W-2 forms to be furnished each employee at the end of the year.

The following is a typical entry recording a payroll:

Payroll charged to construction jobs	$	
Payroll, office and general	$	
F.I.C.A. expense (Employer's share	$	
State Unemployed Compensation expense	$	
Federal Unemployment Tax Act	$	
F.I.C.A. tax payable		$
Federal withheld income tax payable		$
State withheld income tax payable		$
U. S. Savings bonds		$
Insurance		$
Net salaries paid		$

Federal withheld taxes are to be deposited with an authorized commercial bank depositary or a Federal Reserve bank. Employers with less than $200 liability at the end of a quarter are not required to make a deposit. Form #941 is a required to be filed quarterly.

Employers with over $200, but under $2,000 liability per month are required to make deposits (Form 501) for the first two calendar months in the quarter before 15th of the suceeding month. For the last month in a quarter employers will not have to make the deposit payment until the last day of the month following the close of the quarter when Form #941 is filed.

Employers with $2000 or more liability per month. If on the 7th, 15th, 22nd or last day of the month the employer's cumulated liability is $2000 or more, a deposit is required within three banking days following the close of such quarter-monthly period.

Form #941 is due on or before the last day of the month following the quarter to be accompanied by the depository receipts showing timely deposits in ffull payment of taxes due for the period.

At the end of the fourth quarter a Copy A of all W-2 forms must be filed by February 28 with the reconciliation Form W-3. In a state where state; and local taxes are withheld the W-2 forms should show this information, i.e. gross earnings and withheld taxes. Reconciliation of State and Local withheld taxes are required.

The Federal Unemployment Tax Act imposes a tax on employees and is based on the first $4,200 wages paid during a calendar year paid an employee. The tax rate for 1974 is 3.2%. Form #940 is required to be filed which is reconciled with State Unemployment taxes paid.

Separate Bank Account For Pay-Rolls

Some contractors carry a special bank account exclusively for pay-rolls, so that pay roll checks are not mixed with checks issued to material dealers, sub-contractors and others covering general business expense.

THE "PRACTICAL" SELF-BALANCING

MONTH OF _____ 19 ___ SHEET NO. ___

1   2   3   4   5   6

FORM 223   FRANK R. WALKER CO., PUBLISHERS, CHICAGO

	DATE	DESCRIPTION	Check Number	BANK ACCOUNT Deposits DR.	BANK ACCOUNT Checks CR.	F.I.C.A. CR.	Federal CR.	State CR.	OTHER DEDUCTIONS CR.			
1	MAR 1	CASH CAPITOL BY OWNER		10000 00								1
2	1	TOOLS & EQUIP. " "										2
3	2	PETTY CASH EXPENSE	1	25 00	25 00							3
4	3	NELSON'S GARAGE			4 20							4
5	4	JOHN SMITH DRAWING ACCT.	2		100 00							5
6	4	EDWARD'S STATIONERY	3		12 40							6
7	6	S.B. JONES - RENT	4		60 00							7
8	7	CITY POWER & LIGHT	5		8 80							8
9	7	H & H FURN. CO.	6		250 00							9
10	8	CITY LUMBER CO.										10
11	9	CITY LUMBER CO.	7		760 48							11
12	9	UNIVERSAL PORT. CEMENT	STOCK ACCT.	225 00								12
13	10	CASH SALE- CEMENT STOCK										13
14	12	CEMENT STOCK ACCT.										14
15	12	UNIVERSAL P.C. Co. 30 DAY NOTE										15
16	12	" " NOTE	8		703 50							16
17	12	PAY ROLLS	9		1869 70	45 30	300 00	50 00				17
18	14	CENTRAL PLASTERING										18
19	15	" "	10		531 25							19
20	15	WESTERN PLBG.Co 30 DAY NOTE										20
21	15	" " NOTE	11		427 13							21
22	20	FRED H. HILLES A/C CONTRACT										22
23	21	" " " "		3400 00								23
24	22	WM. SMITH " "										24
25	22	" " 60 DAY NOTE										25
26	23	" " NOTE		252 50								26
27	26	1ST NAT'L. BANK 60 DAY NOTE		990 00								27
28	30	" " " NOTE	12		1000 00							28
29												29
				14892 50	5752 46	45 30	300 00	50 00				

WALKER'S "PRACTICAL" SELF-BALANCING CASH-JOURNAL

Left Hand Page   Fig. 268. The "Practical" Self-Balancing Cash-Journal, Form 223.

	1	2	3	4	5	6

FORM 224   FRANK R. WALKER CO., PUBLISHERS, CHICAGO

PRACTICAL
MFD. IN U.S.A.

	CONTRACT ACCOUNTS		SUB-CONTRACT ACCOUNTS		JOB COST ACCOUNTS	
	Amount Due DR.	Amount Received CR.	Amount Paid DR.	Amount Due CR.	Total Cost DR.	Amount Complete CR.
1						
2						
3						
4						
5						
6						
7						
8						
9						
10					776 00	
11						
12						
13						
14					225 00	
15						
16						
17					2015 00	
18				625 00	625 00	
19			531 25			
20				500 00	500 00	
21			425 00			
22						
23	4000 00					4000 00
24		3400 00				
25	300 00					300 00
26		250 00				
27						
28						
29	4300 00	3650 00	956 25	1125 00	4141 00	4300 00

(left margin, reading vertically: SHORT SHEET   THE "PRACTICAL" SELF-BALANCING CASH-JOURNAL)

Fig. 269. The "Practical" Self-Balancing Cash-Journal, Form 224.   Right Hand Short Sheet

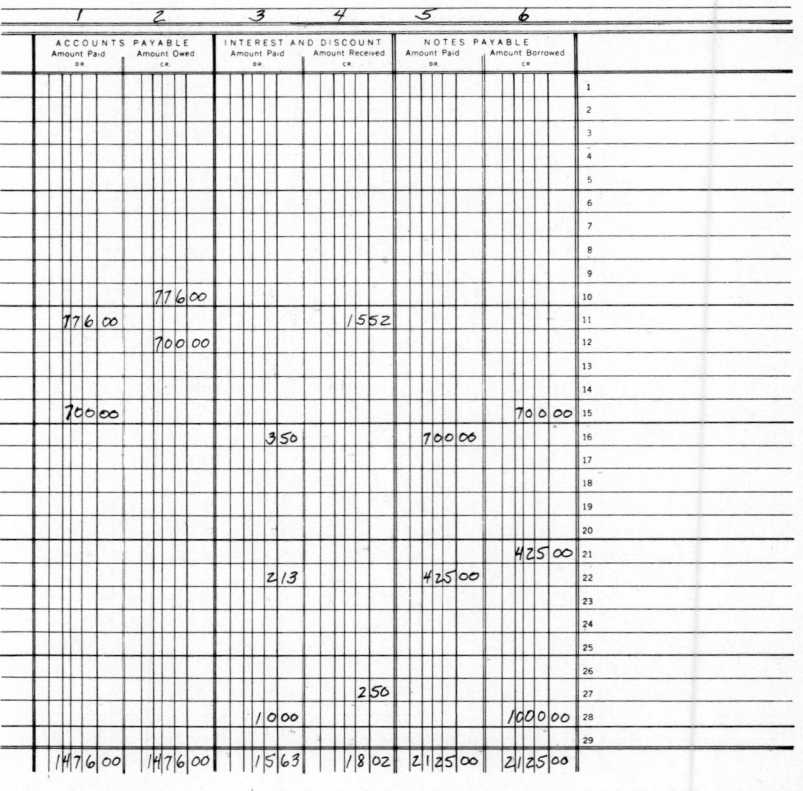

	1		2		3		4		5		6			
	ACCOUNTS PAYABLE				INTEREST AND DISCOUNT				NOTES PAYABLE					
	Amount Paid DR.		Amount Owed CR.		Amount Paid DR.		Amount Received CR.		Amount Paid DR.		Amount Borrowed CR.			
1														
2														
3														
4														
5														
6														
7														
8														
9														
10					776 00									
11	776 00						15 52							
12			700 00											
13														
14														
15	700 00										700 00			
16					3 50				700 00					
17														
18														
19														
20														
21												425 00		
22					2 13				425 00					
23														
24														
25														
26														
27							2 50							
28					10 00							1000 00		
29														
	1476 00		1476 00		15 63		18 02		2125 00		2125 00			

Left Hand Short Sheet   Fig. 269. The "Practical" Self-Balancing Cash-Journal, Form 224.

	PORTLAND PURCHASES DR.	CEMENT SALES CR.	MISC. PURCHASES DR.	SUPPLIES SALES CR.		
1						
2						
3						
4						
5						
6						
7						
8						
9						
10						
11						
12	700 00					
13		225 00				
14		225 00				
15						
16						
17						
18						
19						
20						
21						
22						
23						
24						
25						
26						
27						
28						
29	700 00	450 00				

Fig. 270. Short Columnar Sheet, Form 134-S. Used for Additional Accounts in the Cash-Journal.

Right Hand Short Sheet

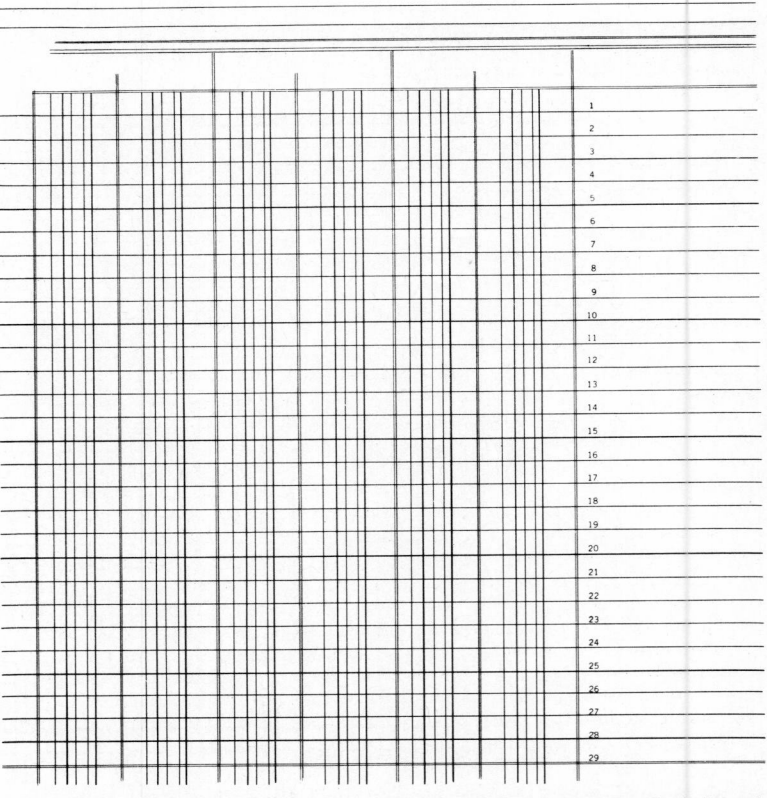

Left Hand Short Sheet   Fig. 270. Short Columnar Sheet, Form 134-S. Used for Additional Accounts in the Cash-Journal.

Instead of listing all individual pay-roll checks in the Cash-Journal, the check numbers may be listed on the regular pay-roll sheet opposite each man's name and amount, and the total of the pay-roll checks entered as one entry, i.e., checks PR-1001 to PR-1026 or $1,869.70, and then as the checks are cashed and returned by the bank, they are checked off the Pay-Roll sheets.

However, if the contractor insists on entering each man's pay-roll check in the Cash-Journal, they may be entered the same as other checks.

If a separate Pay-Roll Account is kept with the Bank, it can either be handled in the first two columns of the Cash-Journal sheet, or a separate Cash-Journal sheet may be used. In this case the amounts withdrawn each week for pay-rolls should be reimbursed from the contractor's general bank account each week.

17   **Invoices or Requests for Payment Received from Sub-Contractors**

When a sub-contractor sends you an invoice or asks for a payment on account of his sub-contract with you the entries are handled as follows: Assume the Central Plastering Co., ask for a payment of $625.000 on account of their contract for plastering the Hilles residence job.

How the Entries Should Be Made

Refer to line 18. The amount of the sub-contractor's invoice or application, amounting to $625.00 should be entered in the fourth column of the right hand short sheet headed "Sub-Contract Accounts-Amount Due Cr." Then the same amount should be entered in the fifth column of the same page headed "Job Cost Accounts-Total Cost-Dr."

CASH-JOURNAL

	Rent DR.	General Expense Light, Heat and Power DR.	Salaries DR.	Miscellaneous Expense DR.	Social Security Payments DR.	Other Taxes DR.	Insurance DR.	Tools and Equipment DR.	Truck and Automobile Expense DR.	Drawg. Acct. Amt. Withdrawn from Business DR.	Miscellaneous Accts. DR.	Miscellaneous Accts. CR.	
1												1000.00	1
2								250.00				250.00	2
3													3
4									4.20				4
5										100.00			5
6				12.40									6
7	60.00												7
8		8.80											8
9													9
10											250.00		10
11													11
12													12
13													13
14													14
15													15
16													16
17			250.00										17
18													18
19													19
20													20
21													21
22													22
23													23
24													24
25													25
26											250.00		26
27												250.00	27
28													28
29	60.00	8.80	250.00	12.40				250.00	4.20	100.00	500.00	1275.00	29

Fig. 268. The "Practical" Self-Balancing Cash-Journal, Form 223.

Right Hand Page

FRANK R. WALKER CO. PUBLISHERS, CHICAGO

FORM 223

PRACTICAL MFD IN U.S.A

PRACTICAL		CERTIFICATE FOR PAYMENT TO CONTRACTOR	Certificate
Job No. 120			No. 22

Date March 15, 19--

TO
THIRTY-FIRST HOME LOAN BANK $ 531.25

STATEMENT	
Contract	$2,390.00
Extras	200.00
TOTAL	$2,590.00
Deductions	142.00
TOTAL	$2,448.00
Total Comp. Wk.	None
Less 0 Retention	-----
Prev. Payments	-----
AMOUNT DUE	$531.25

THIS IS TO CERTIFY, that

------- CENTRAL PLASTERING COMPANY -----------

Contractor for Lathing & Plastering on Fred H. Hilles
Residence at 176 Wayne Avenue, City

is entitled to a -----partial ---------- payment of
------- FIVE HUNDRED THIRTY ONE and 25/100 ------------
-- Dollars
under terms of this contract.

JOHN SMITH & COMPANY, CONTRACTORS

By

Received Amount of above Certificate. CENTRAL PLASTERING COMPANY

By
                                                    Contractor

FORM 596   FRANK R. WALKER CO., PUBLISHERS, CHICAGO   MFD. IN U.S.A.

Fig. 271. Certificate for Payment to Contractor, Form 596. Illustrating Method Used When Paying Sub-Contractors or Material Suppliers by Order on Loan Company instead of by Check.

18   **When Payments are Made to Sub-Contractors**

The contract with the Central Plastering Co., calls for a 15% retained percentage until the completion of the contract, so the amount of the payment should be only $531.25 instead of the $625.00 requested.

How the Entries Should Be Made

Refer to line 19. Enter the amount of the payment, $531.25, in the fourth column headed "Bank Account-Checks-Cr." Now refer to the right hand short sheet and enter $531.25 in the third column headed "Sub-Contract Accounts-Amount Paid-Dr."

19   **When Sub-Contractor is Paid by Note Instead of Cash**

Assume the Western Plumbing Company asks for a payment of $500.00 on account of their contract for the plumbing of the Hilles residence job.

The entries are made in line 20 of columns four and five of the right hand short sheet, exactly as described under Item No. 17.

Instead of paying this account, you give the Western Plumbing Company your 30-day note for $425.00 ($500.00 less 15% retained percentage) for 30 days at 6% interest.

How the Entries Should Be Made

Refer to line 21. The amount of the note ($425.00) given to the sub-contractor as payment is entered in the third column of the right hand short sheet headed "Sub-Contract Accounts-Amount Paid-Dr." and the same amount is entered in the sixth column of the left hand short sheet headed "Notes Payable-Amount Borrowed-Cr." This is merely transferring the account from Amount Due Sub-Contractors to Notes Payable.

20   **When You Pay Sub-Contractors' Note at Maturity**

At the expiration of 30 days it will be necessary to pay the note of the Western Plumbing Company, amounting to $425.00, plus $2.13 interest for 30 days at 6%, total $427.13.

How the Entries Should Be Made

Refer to line 22. Enter $427.13, the total amount of the note and interest in the fourth column headed "Bank Accounts-Checks-Cr." Now refer to the left hand short sheet and enter $2.13, the amount of the interest, in the third column headed "Interest and Discount-Amount Paid-Dr." and $425.00, the amount of the note, in the fifth column of the same sheet headed "Notes Payable-Amount-Dr."

21   When Builders Pay Invoices By Order Instead of By Check

In many instances where operative or merchant builders construct houses and apartments for sale, the buildings are financed largely by loans made by Mortgage Houses, Banks and Building and Loan Associations.

Frequently, instead of paying the builder the actual cash and the builder in turn paying the sub-contractors and material dealers, the builder issues Orders on the Bank or Building and Loan Association, and they pay the sub-contractors and material dealers direct, charging such payments to the account of the builder issuing them and to the job on which the loan was made.

Instead of issuing a check to the sub-contractor or material dealer, the contractor or builder issues an Order, similar to the "Certificate for Payment to Contractor," as illustrated, for a stipulated amount.

The sub-contractor or material dealer presents this Order to the Bank or Building and Loan Association, who pays the sub-contractor or dealer direct, charging the amount paid to the builder who issued same.

In instances of this kind (when using the Self-Balancing Cash-Journal), enter the amounts of the Orders issued to sub-contractors and material dealers in the second column headed "Cash or Bank Account-Disbursements-Cr." This provides separate columns for Orders issued and checks issued on the Contractor's bank account.

All other entries are exactly the same as though the amounts were paid by check.

22   When you Send Architect or Owner Invoice or Request for Payment on Account of Work Performed on Contract

During the progress of work, invoices or requests for payment will be sent by the contractor to the architect or owner covering work performed on contract.

Assume you request a payment of $4,000.00 on the Hilles residence job.

How the Entries Should Be Made

Refer to line 23. The owner should be charged or debited with the $4,000.00 due in the first column of the right hand short sheet headed "Contract Accounts-Amount Due-Dr." and the job on which the work was performed should be credited with $4,000.00 in the sixth column of the same page headed "Job Cost Accounts-Amount Completed-Cr."

23   When You Receive Payment From Owner on Account of Contract

Assume you receive a check on account of the Hilles residence job for $3,400.00, being the amount of your request, less 15% retained percentage, which is in accordance with the terms of the contract.

How the Entries Should Be Made

Refer to line 24. Enter $3,400.00 the amount received, in the third column headed "Bank Account-Deposits-Dr." and enter the same amount in the second column of the right hand short sheet headed "Contract Accounts-Amount Received-Cr."

24   When You Take a Promissory Note from Owner on Account of Contract

On the Wm. Smith Alteration Job you request payment of $300.00 on account of contract. These entries are illustrated on line 25 and are made in exactly the same manner as described under Item 21.

Instead of paying this invoice, Mr. Smith gives you his promissory note for $250.00 on account, running for 60 days at 6% interest.

How the Entries Should Be Made

Refer to line 26. The owner is given credit for the $250.00 in the second column of the right hand short sheet headed "Contract Accounts-Amount Received-Cr." and the same amount is entered in the eleventh column of the right hand page headed "Miscellaneous Accounts-Dr."

25   **When Owner's Note is Paid at Maturity**

At the expiration of the 60-day period, Mr. Smith pays his note amounting to $250.00, plus $2.50 interest, making a total of $252.50.

How the Entries Should Be Made

Refer to line 27. The amount of the note and interest, $252.50, is entered in the third column headed "Bank Account-Deposits-Dr." Now refer to the left hand short sheet, and enter the $2.50 interest in the fourth column headed "Interest and Discount-Amount Received-Cr." The principal amount of the note, $250.00, is entered in the twelfth column of the right hand page headed "Miscellaneous Accounts-Cr."

26   **When You Borrow Money at the Bank**

Suppose you borrow from your bank $1,000.00 for 60 days on your note. The bank deducts the interest, amounting to $10.00, in advance, and credits your account with 990.00, for which you give your promissory note for $1,000.00.

How the Entries Should Be Made

Refer to line 28. Enter the details of the transaction in the Descriptive column, and the amount of money credited to your account in the third column headed "Bank Account-Deposits-Dr." Now refer to line 28 of the left hand short sheet and enter $10.00, the amount of interest paid in the third column headed "Interest and Discount-Amount Paid-Dr." The principal amount of the note, $1,000.00, should be entered in the sixth column of the same page headed "Notes Payable-Amount Borrowed-Cr."

27   **When You Pay the Note at Maturity**

At the expiration of the 60-day period it will be necessary to pay the bank the $1,000.00 borrowed, as described above.

How the Entries Should Be Made

Refer to line 29. Enter $1,000.00, the amount of the note, in the fourth column headed "Bank Account-Checks-Cr." Now refer to the left hand short sheet and enter $1,000.00 in the fifth column headed "Notes Payable-Amount Paid-Dr."

How to Tell at the End of Each Month Whether All Entries Have Been Correctly Made

At the top of each column of both the left and right hand pages, also the left and right short pages, there appears in small letters "DR" and "CR." The "DR" denotes Debits and the "CR" Credits. If you will refer back to the various examples given, you will note that for every entry in a "DR" column, there were also entries in the "CR" columns totaling the same amount. These entries when correctly made, keep the books in balance at all times.

At the end of each month all the columns on both pages should be added up and the total of each column written at the bottom of the page as shown in the illustrations.

After the columns have been totaled, the amounts of all columns having "DR" at the top should be listed and added together. When this is done the totals of all columns having "CR" at the top should be listed and added in the same manner.

If all the entries have been correctly made and your additions are correct, *the total of the "DR" Columns Should Equal the Total of the "CR" Columns. You Then Know Your Books are in Balance,* otherwise there has been a mistake in some of your entries.

The above statement furnishes a complete picture of your business each month, showing the amount of work completed; the amounts you have received on contracts; the amounts due and paid sub-contractors; the cost of your various jobs; the amount of interest paid and the discount and interest earned during the month. It also shows the amount of money borrowed on notes, the amount paid on notes, etc., enabling you to tell the condition of your business at a glance.

This sheet also furnishes a complete trial balance of each month's business.

At the end of each month when the Cash-Journal sheet is totaled and balanced as illustrated and described in the preceding paragraph, the totals of the various accounts should be transferred or "posted" to their proper accounts in the ledger. This enables you to start each month with a "clean" Cash-Journal sheet, while the various ledger accounts contain a complete summary of the year's business up to the current month.

Here is the Manner in Which Your Totals Should Appear in the Cash-Journal

	—Totals for Month—	
	Total of "Dr." Cols.	Total of "Cr." Cols.
Cash or Bank Account	$ 250.00	$ 4.20
Bank Account	14,642.50	5,748.26
Pay-Roll Deductions, Fed. Old Age	....	45.30
Income Tax	....	350.00
Contract Accounts	4,300.00	3.650.00
Sub-Contract Accounts	956.25	1,125.00
Job Cost Accounts	4,141.00	4,300.00
Accounts Payable	1,476.00	1,476.00
Interest and Discount	15.63	18.02
Notes Payable	2,125.00	2,125.00
General Expense, Rent	60.00	....
Light, Heat and Power	8.80	....
Salaries	250.00	....
Miscellaneous Expense	12.40	....
Social Security Payments	....	....
Other Taxes	....	....
Insurance	....	....
Tools and Equipment	2,500.00	....
Truck and Automobile Expense	4.20	....
Drawing Account	100.00	....
Miscellaneous Accounts	500.00	12,750.00
Cement Stock Account	700.00	450.00
	$32,041.78	$32,041.78

The Ledger in the "Practical" Self-Balancing Bookkeeping System

The General Ledger in this improved system is merely a summary of the accounts listed in the different columns of the Cash-Journal sheet, and may be kept in just as much or as little detail as the individual contractor desires.

You will notice there are indexes separating the different classes of accounts listed on the Cash-Journal sheet, such as Cash Account, Bank Account, Accounts Payable, Contract Accounts, Sub-Contract Accounts, Job Cost Accounts, etc. Each class of accounts should be kept under this index heading, so when posting items from the Cash-Journal to the Ledger accounts, all items entered under any particular column heading in the Cash-Journal should be entered under the same index heading in the ledger. For instance, under the heading "Accounts Payable" in the Cash-Journal, the totals of both columns are $1,476.00. Under the index heading "Accounts Payable" in the ledger you have accounts with the City Lumber Company and the Universal Portland Cement Co. The amounts of invoices and payments should be transferred from the Cash-Journal to the individual accounts of these firms, showing the dates and amounts of all

GENERAL LEDGER

CITY LUMBER CO.
212 W. MAIN ST.

SHEET NO. 1

FORM 121   FRANK R. WALKER CO., PUBLISHERS, CHICAGO

DATE	ITEMS	Folio	✓	DEBITS	DATE	ITEMS	Folio	✓	CREDITS	
MAR 9	BY CASH	1		776 00	MAR 8	MERCHANDISE			776 00	

Fig. 272. Debit-Credit Ledger Sheet, Form 121. Used for Keeping Accounts Payable.

GENERAL LEDGER

UNIVERSAL PORTLAND CEMENT CO.
208 So. LASALLE ST.

SHEET NO. 1

FORM 121   FRANK R. WALKER CO., PUBLISHERS, CHICAGO

DATE	ITEMS	Folio	✓	DEBITS	DATE	ITEMS	Folio	✓	CREDITS	
MAR 12	BY NOTE	1		700 00	MAR 9	CEMENT	1		700 00	

Fig. 273. Debit-Credit Ledger Sheet, Form 121. Used for Keeping Accounts Payable.

GENERAL LEDGER

CASH ACCOUNT

SHEET NO. 1

FORM 121   FRANK R. WALKER CO., PUBLISHERS, CHICAGO

DATE	ITEMS	Folio	✓	DEBITS	DATE	ITEMS	Folio	✓	CREDITS	
MAR 30	CASH RECEIPTS	1		250 00	MAR 30	CASH EXPENSES			4 20	

Fig. 274. Debit-Credit Ledger Sheet, Form 121. Used for Keeping Cash Account.

GENERAL LEDGER

FIRST NATIONAL BANK
BANK ACCOUNT

SHEET NO. 1

FORM 121   FRANK R. WALKER CO., PUBLISHERS, CHICAGO

DATE	ITEMS	Folio	✓	DEBITS	DATE	ITEMS	Folio	✓	CREDITS	
MAR 30	DEPOSITS	1		1642 50	MAR 30	CHECKS	1		5748 26	

Fig. 275. Debit-Credit Ledger Sheet, Form 121. Used for Keeping Bank Account.

transactions. These entries should then balance with the total of the "Accounts Payable" columns in the Cash-Journal. The method is simple and it requires very little time to keep your books in first-class condition at all times.

What Accounts Are Necessary in the General Ledger

The ledger should contain just as few accounts as possible to furnish the desired information regarding your business and they should not be itemized in too much detail because every entry requires additional clerical work.

The following accounts will serve the purpose of practically every contractor's business, but different individuals and concerns may desire different information, and in such instances additional ledger accounts may be necessary.

ACCOUNTS PAYABLE. — This account should contain accounts with all firms or individuals from whom you buy materials or supplies regularly on an open account basis. Each account should show the amounts owed and the amounts paid and where possible only one entry should be made for an entire month's business. For example, all of the invoices for any one concern should be totaled and only one entry made each month covering all of them. This also applies to payments made. This will greatly simplify your work and will be found much more satisfactory than attempting to enter each invoice.

Some contractors do not carry any Accounts Payable in their ledger but make the entries only as invoices are paid. This saves bookkeeping labor but does not show what the business owes, only what has been paid.

CASH ACCOUNT. — This account contains a summary of the month's cash transactions. Only one entry is made each month, entering the totals of the Cash Received and Cash Disbursed columns in the Cash-Journal.

BANK ACCOUNT. — An account should be kept under this heading with each bank with whom money is deposited.

At the end of each month the total of the Bank Account column in the Cash-Journal is posted to this account, showing the amount of Deposits and Checks. The difference is the bank balance at the first of each month.

Where accounts are carried with more than one bank or where separate accounts for Pay-rolls are carried, use a separate sheet for each blank account.

CONTRACT ACCOUNTS. — Accounts with all persons or firms for whom you are doing work on a contract basis comes under this heading.

When a contract is received, the amount of the original contract, together with any extras to same, are entered in the first column headed "Contract and Extras."

When deductions or credits affecting the original contract are made, due to work being omitted or changed, the amount of each credit or omission is entered in the second column headed "Credits to Contract."

The net amount of the contract is obtained by subtracting the total amount of the "Credits to Contract" from the total amount of the "Contract and Extras" column. The difference is the net amount of the contract.

Fig. 276. Contract Account, Form 142. Used for Keeping Accounts with Owners or Others for Whom You are Doing Work on a Lump-Sum Basis.

GENERAL LEDGER

CONTRACT ACCOUNT

NAME OF OWNER WILLIAM SMITH   ADDRESS 231 MAIN ST.   SHEET NO 1

NAME OF WORK WM. SMITH ALTERATION JOB   LOCATION 137 E. HARPER AVE.   JOB NO 121

FORM 1423   FRANK R. WALKER CO., PUBLISHERS, CHICAGO

DATE	DESCRIPTION	Folio	√	CONTRACT AND EXTRAS MEMO	CREDITS TO CONTRACT MEMO	NET AMOUNT CONTRACT MEMO	AMOUNT COMPLETED DR	DATE PAID	Folio	√	AMOUNT PAID
MAR 5	CONTRACT AMOUNT			757 00				MAR 22	1		250 00
10	EXTRA SCREENS			28 50				APR 15	2		250 00
17	EXTRA SASH			32 50				JUNE 15	4		258 00
"	OMIT SASH DRIPS				15 00	803 00					758 00
"	" WEATHER STRIPS				45 00	758 00					
22	AMOUNT COMPLETED	1					300 00				
APR 30	" "	2					300 00				
JUNE 15	" "	4					158 00				
				818 00	60 00	758 00	758 00				

JOB RECAPITULATION

	AMOUNT	AMOUNT
TOTAL AMOUNT OF CONTRACT AND EXTRAS		758 00
ACTUAL COST OF LABOR	365 00	
ACTUAL COST OF MATERIALS	176 00	
ACTUAL COST OF SUB-CONTRACTS	82 00	
MISCELLANEOUS JOB COSTS	7 50	
TOTAL COST OF JOB	630 50	630 50
PROFIT ON CONTRACT / LOSS		127 50

NOTE: WRITE PROFITS IN BLACK INK AND LOSSES IN RED INK

Right Hand Page

Fig. 277. Combination Contract-Job Cost Account, Form 1423. Used for Keeping Accounts With Owners or Others for Whom you are Doing Work on a Lump-Sum Basis. Job Cost Account is on Other Side of the Sheet.

The first three columns on this sheet headed "Contract and Extras," "Credits to Contract," and "Net Amount of Contract" are memorandum accounts and are used as a temporary record during the life of the contract. For this reason entries in these three columns are never made through the Cash-Journal and they are not used when taking off the Trial Balance.

The Contract Account is intended to act only as a memorandum account until a payment on the contract has been requested, at which time the Contract Account becomes the Accounts Receivable to the extent of the amount requested.

Each month or at stated intervals when invoices or applications for payment are made to the architect or owner, the amount of each invoice or application should be entered in the fourth column headed "Amount Completed." This column shows what portion of the work was performed each month and the total amount completed to date. It also gives the amount of money to which you are entitled each month during the progress of the work.

As soon as the contractor is entitled to payment on his contract, the owner is debited in the fourth column headed "Amount Completed" and the Job Cost Account should be credited with same amount. These amounts are first entered in the Cash-Journal and then posted to their respective ledger accounts at the end of the month as illustrated and described in the instructions.

As payments are received from the owner, the dates and amounts of all payments are entered in the right hand columns of this sheet headed "Date Paid" and "Amount Paid." These items are also posted from the Cash-Journal.

The difference between the total of the fourth column headed "Amount Completed" and the last column headed "Amount Paid" gives the amount of the retained percentage at any time.

GENERAL LEDGER

SUB-CONTRACT ACCOUNT

NAME CENTRAL PLASTERING CO.   ADDRESS 25 E. JACKSON BLVD.   SHEET NO 1

NAME OF WORK FRED H. HILLES RESIDENCE   LOCATION 176 WAYNE AVE.   JOB NO 120

DATE PAID	Check or Voucher No.	AMOUNT PAID	DATE		DESCRIPTION	Folio	√	SUB-CONTRACT AND EXTRAS	CREDITS TO SUB-CONTRACT	NET AMOUNT SUB-CONTRACT	AMOUNT COMPLETED CR.
MAR 15	14	531 25	MAR	5	PLASTERING CONTRACT			2390 00			
				10	EXTRA PLASTER IN ATTIC			200 00			
				15	OMIT METAL LATH			2590 00	142 00	2448 00	
				14	AMOUNT COMPLETED	1			142 00		625 00

NAME WESTERN PLUMBING CO.   ADDRESS 442 SOUTH BLVD.

NAME OF WORK FRED H. HILLES RESIDENCE   LOCATION 176 WAYNE AVE.   JOB NO 120

DATE PAID	Check or Voucher No.	AMOUNT PAID	DATE		DESCRIPTION	Folio	√	SUB-CONTRACT AND EXTRAS	CREDITS TO SUB-CONTRACT	NET AMOUNT SUB-CONTRACT	AMOUNT COMPLETED CR.
MAR 15	30 DAY NOTE	425 00	MAR	6	PLUMBING CONTRACT			2440 00		2440 00	
				15	AMOUNT COMPLETED	1					500 00

Fig. 278. Sub-Contract Account, Form 1192. Used for Keeping Accounts with Sub-Contractors Doing Work for You. Sub-Contract Account, Form 119, Contains Only One Account on Each Side of Sheet.

When the contract has been completed and the owner has paid the contractor in full, including retained percentage, the totals of the three columns headed "Net Amount of Contract," "Amount Completed" and "Amount Paid" should balance.

When taking off a trial balance, the total of the fourth column headed "Amount Completed" forms the debit account and the last column headed "Amount Paid" forms the credit account.

SUB-CONTRACT ACCOUNTS. — This sheet is used for keeping accounts with your various sub-contractors, such as Plumbing, Heating, Electric Wiring, Painting, Plastering, etc.

When the contractor lets a sub-contract for any branch of work, an account is opened with each sub-contractor.

The amount of the original sub-contract together with any extras to same are entered in the first column headed "Sub-Contract and Extras."

Omissions or changes from the original contract, which involve deductions or credits, are entered in the second column headed "Credits to Sub-Contract."

The net amount of the sub-contract is obtained by subtracting the amount of the "Credits to Sub-Contract" from the total amount of the "Sub-Contract and Extras" column.

The first three columns on the right hand side of this sheet headed "Sub-Contract and Extras," "Credits to Sub-Contract," and "Net Amount of Sub-Contract" are memorandum accounts and are used as a temporary record during the life of the contract. For this reason the entries are not made through the Cash-Journal and they are not used when taking off a trial balance.

As soon as the sub-contractor is entitled to payment under the terms of his contract, the amount of the request or invoice should be entered in the fourth column headed "Amount Completed," and the Job Cost

Account should be charged with same amount in the third column headed "Sub-Contracts." These entries are both made through the Cash-Journal and later posted to the proper Job Cost Account and Sub-Contract account in the ledger.

When the sub-contractor has completed his work, the amount in the fourth column headed "Amount Completed" should be the same as the amount in the third column headed "Net Amount Sub-Contract."

As payments are made by the contractor to the sub-contractor, the dates and amounts of all payments are entered in the left hand columns headed "Date Paid" and "Amount Paid."

The difference between the total of the last column headed "Amount Completed" and the first column headed "Amount Paid" is the amount of the retained percentage held by the contractor at any time during construction.

When the sub-contractor has been paid in full, the totals of the three columns headed "Net Amount Sub-Contract," "Amount Completed," and "Amount Paid" should balance.

When taking off a trial balance, the first column headed "Amount Paid" forms the debit account and the last column headed "Amount Completed" forms the credit account.

JOB COST ACCOUNTS. — This sheet is used for keeping an accurate record of the cost of each job or contract.

As expenditures are made covering labor, material, sub-contracts, and other miscellaneous job expenses, they are entered on this sheet under the proper heading.

The totals of the four columns headed "Labor," "Material," "Sub-Contracts," and "Miscellaneous Expense" gives the total cost of the job and enables the contractor to tell at a glance the total of each class of expenditures.

Each month or at stated intervals when invoices or applications for payment are made to the architect or owner, the date and amount of each invoice or application should be entered on the right hand side of this sheet headed "Credits." This shows the amount of work completed at any date. When the job is completed the total of the "Credits" column should equal the contract price.

The profit or loss on the job is obtained by subtracting the total cost of the job as contained in the four columns headed "Labor," "Material," "Sub-Contracts" and "Miscellaneous Expense" from the total contract price, as given in the right hand column headed "Credits."

When taking off a trial balance, the total of the four columns headed "Labor," "Material," "Sub-Contracts" and "Miscellaneous Expense" form the debit account and the right hand column headed "Credits" is the credit account.

INTEREST AND DISCOUNT. — This account contains the total of all money paid in interest and all money received as interest and all money saved by taking advantage of cash discounts. The total of the Interest and Discount column in the Cash-Journal is transferred to this account at the end of each month.

NOTES PAYABLE. — This account contains a record of all notes given to banks or to individuals for money borrowed or in settlement of accounts.

These totals are merely transferred from the Notes Payable column in the Cash-Journal at the end of each month.

NOTES AND ACCOUNTS RECEIVABLE. — This account in the ledger contains a record of all money due you for which you hold notes, for materials or supplies sold, or any other accounts not covered by Contract.

GENERAL LEDGER

| NAME OF WORK | FRED H. HILLES RESIDENCE | LOCATION | 176 WAYNE AVE. | SHEET NO. | 1 |
| ARCHITECTS OR ENGINEERS | SMITH AND BROWN | OWNER | FRED H. HILLES | JOB NO. | 120 |

JOB COST ACCOUNT

DATE	DESCRIPTION	Folio.	√	LABOR	MATERIAL	SUB-CONTRACTS	MISC. EXPENSE	TOTAL COST	√	CREDITS	
MAR 8	CITY LUMBER CO.	1			600 00						
12	CEMENT FROM STOCK	1			225 00						
12	PAYROLLS	1		1650 00							
14	CENTRAL PLASTERING	1				625 00					
15	WESTERN PLUMBING	1				500 00	360 00				
20	WORK COMPLETED	1								4000 00	

Fig. 279. Job Cost Account, Form 143. Used for Keeping Detailed Costs on Jobs Performed on a Lump-Sum Basis.

GENERAL LEDGER

NAME OF WORK WM. SMITH ALTERATION JOB   LOCATION 137 E. HARPER AVE.   JOB COST ACCOUNT   SHEET NO. 1

ARCHITECTS OR ENGINEERS   OWNER WILLIAM SMITH   JOB NO 121

FORM 1423   FRANK R. WALKER CO., PUBLISHERS, CHICAGO

DATE		DESCRIPTION	Folio	√	LABOR	MATERIAL	SUB-CONTRACTS	MISC. EXPENSE	TOTAL COST OR	√	CREDITS	
MAR	8	CITY LUMBER CO.	1			176 00						
	12	PAY ROLLS	1		365 00							
	22	WORK COMPLETED	1						541 00		300.00	

Fig. 280. Combination Contract-Job Cost Account, Form 1423. Used for Keeping Detailed Costs on Jobs Performed on a Lump-Sum Basis. Contract Account is on Other Side of Sheet.

GENERAL LEDGER
INTEREST AND DISCOUNT

SHEET NO.

FORM 121   FRANK R. WALKER CO., PUBLISHERS, CHICAGO

DATE		ITEMS	Folio	√	DEBITS	DATE		ITEMS	Folio	√	CREDITS	
MAR	30	INTEREST PAID	1		15 63	MAR	30	INT. AND DISC. EARNED	1		18 02	

Fig. 281. Debit-Credit Ledger Sheet, Form 121. Used for Keeping Interest and Discount.

GENERAL LEDGER
NOTES PAYABLE

SHEET NO.

FORM 121   FRANK R. WALKER CO., PUBLISHERS, CHICAGO

DATE		ITEMS	Folio	√	DEBITS	DATE		ITEMS	Folio	√	CREDITS	
MAR	30	NOTES PAID	1		2125 00	MAR	30	NOTES PAYABLE	1		2125 00	

Fig. 282. Debit-Credit Ledger Sheet, Form 121. Used for Keeping Notes Payable.

GENERAL LEDGER
NOTES RECEIVABLE

SHEET NO. 1

FORM 121   FRANK R. WALKER CO., PUBLISHERS, CHICAGO

DATE		ITEMS	Folio	√	DEBITS	DATE		ITEMS	Folio	√	CREDITS	
MAR	22	WM. SMITH – 60 DAY NOTE	1		250 00	MAR	23	WM. SMITH – 60 DAY NOTE	1		250 00	

Fig. 283. Debit-Credit Ledger Sheet, Form 121. Used for Keeping Notes and Accounts Receivable.

GENERAL EXPENSE. — This account contains an accurate record of the overhead or general expense of conducting the business. It should include such items as office rent, heat, lights, stationery, postage, office supplies, telephone, telegraph, advertising, traveling expense in connection with new work being figured, salaries of office employees, such as bookkeepers, stenographers, estimators, etc.

This account enables the contractor to tell at a glance what it costs him to conduct his business and how the overhead expenses are apportioned.

Just one entry is made on this sheet each month, when the totals are brought forward from the four General Expense columns in the Cash-Journal.

Where it is desirable to "break down" the costs in more detail than given in the above illustration, a double page columnar form, similar to illustrations on pages 204 and 205 may be used for this purpose.

There are two methods of handling the "General Expense" account in the ledger. Using the first method, the total cost of the General or Overhead expense of conducting the business is carried as a separate account and at the end of the year is charged off in full, reducing the gross profits of the business by just that amount.

The other method is to charge the various jobs with a certain percentage of the General or Overhead expense. This is extremely difficult to do with any degree of accuracy because a contractor never knows at the beginning of a year the volume of business he will perform during that year and it will be necessary to wait until the end of the year before the total of the General or Overhead expense can be apportioned among the various jobs.

Most contractors will have a certain Overhead expense regardless of the amount of work performed, so it is advisable to carry a separate "General Expense" account and not attempt to pro-rate it among the various jobs.

TOOLS AND EQUIPMENT. — This account should contain a complete record of all expenditures for machinery, tools and equipment necessary to conduct the business. This includes such items as power shovels, hoisting engines, concrete mixers, pile drivers, motor trucks, tractors, air compressors, power saws, pumps, derricks, scaffolding, hoisting towers, conveying machinery, wheelbarrows, small tools, etc.

The sheet illustrated contains all essential information regarding each piece of equipment, such as Complete Description of Same, Serial Number, From Whom Purchased, Date Acquired, How Acquired, Estimated Life Years, Yearly Depreciation Rate, Date Appraised, etc.

This form also provides columns for recording "Original Cost and Capital Repairs," "Depreciation Amount per Year," "Total Depreciation to Date," and "Present Book Value."

It also has a column for recording "Operating Repairs" or Expense, and another column for "Rentals Charged or Received" to be used when the equipment is rented out or when charged to any particular operation.

Repairs, including broken parts and the labor cost of replacing same, that do not prolong the life of the equipment should be charged as a direct expense in the column headed "Operating Repairs," and written off in full at the end of each year. This also applies to labor cleaning, lubricating and maintaining the equipment for ordinary use.

There are two methods of handling the "Tool and Equipment" account in the ledger. One is to charge the original cost of each piece of equipment to the proper account and at the end of the year, depreciate each piece of equipment in accordance with the schedule prepared by the Department of Internal Revenue. Using this method, the various jobs on which the tools and equipment are used are not charged with the

GENERAL LEDGER

GENERAL EXPENSE ACCOUNT

NAME JOHN SMITH & Co.   ADDRESS 412 BELL BLDG.   SHEET NO. 1

GENERAL EXPENSE

	DATE	DESCRIPTION	Folio	√	RENT	LIGHT, HEAT AND POWER	OFFICE SALARIES	MISC. EXPENSE	TOTAL COST DR	√	CREDITS CR
	MAR 6	EDWARD'S STAT. STORE	1					12 40			
	7	S. B. JONES	1		60 00						
	7	CITY POWER & LIGHT	1			8 80					
	12	PAY ROLLS	1				250 00		331 20		

Fig. 284. General Expense Account, Form 154. Used for Keeping a Record of the Overhead Expense of Conducting Your Business.

EQUIPMENT AND DEPRECIATION RECORD

KIND OF EQUIPMENT	FORD TRUCK	PURCHASED FROM	FORD SALES Co.	SHEET NO.	1
				SERIAL NUMBER	12 34 56

DESCRIPTION | TON STAKE TRUCK

| DATE ACQUIRED | FEB. 1 | HOW ACQUIRED | NEW | ESTIMATED LIFE YEARS | 3 | DEPRECIATION YEARLY RATE | 33 1/3 % | DATE APPRAISED | MAR 1 |

APPRAISED VALUE $2,500.00

FORM 137 — FRANK R. WALKER CO., PUBLISHERS, CHICAGO

	MFD IN U S A	DATE Mo.	Day	Year	DESCRIPTION	Folio	ORIGINAL COST AND CAPITAL REPAIRS	DEPRECIATION PER YEAR	DEPRECIATION TOTAL TO DATE	PRESENT BOOK VALUE	OPERATING REPAIRS	RENTALS CHARGED OR RECEIVED	
1		1	2	1	MACHINE COST	1	2500 00	833 00					1
2		2			ADDITIONAL EQUIPMENT COST								2
3		3			FREIGHT, TRUCKING. ETC.								3
4		4			OTHER CHARGES								4
5		5			TOTAL ORIGINAL COST								5
6		6											6
7		7											7
8		8											8
9		9											9
10		10											10

Fig. 285. Equipment and Depreciation Record, Form 137. Used for Keeping Detailed Costs and Depreciation on Construction Tools and Equipment.

TRUCK & AUTOMOBILE EXPENSE

		DATE	ITEMS		GASOLINE DR.	OIL DR.	TIRES DR.	REPAIRS DR.		TOTAL DR.	
1		MAR 30	MARCH EXPENSE	1	4 20						1
2											2
3											3
4											4
5											5

Fig. 286. Columnar Sheet, Form 136. Used for Keeping Detailed Costs of Operating Your Automobiles and Trucks.

EQUIPMENT AND DEPRECIATION RECORD

KIND OF EQUIPMENT	FURNITURE & FIXTURES	PURCHASED FROM	H & H FURNITURE CO	SHEET NO.	1
				SERIAL NUMBER	

DESCRIPTION

| DATE ACQUIRED | MARCH 7 | HOW ACQUIRED | PURCHASE | ESTIMATED LIFE YEARS | 10 | DEPRECIATION YEARLY RATE | 10 % | DATE APPRAISED | MARCH 7 |

APPRAISED VALUE

FORM 137 — FRANK R. WALKER CO., PUBLISHERS, CHICAGO

	PRACTICAL MFD IN U S A	DATE Mo.	Day	Year	DESCRIPTION	Folio	ORIGINAL COST AND CAPITAL REPAIRS	DEPRECIATION PER YEAR	DEPRECIATION TOTAL TO DATE	PRESENT BOOK VALUE	OPERATING REPAIRS	RENTALS CHARGED OR RECEIVED	
1		1			MACHINE COST								1
2		2			ADDITIONAL EQUIPMENT COST								2
3		3			FREIGHT, TRUCKING. ETC.								3
4		4			OTHER CHARGES								4
5		5			TOTAL ORIGINAL COST								5
6		6	3	7	OFFICE FURNITURE	1	250 00	25 00					6
7		7											7
8		8											8
9		9											9
10		10											10

Fig. 287. Equipment and Depreciation Record, Form 137. Used for Keeping Detailed Cost Records and Depreciation on Office Furniture and Equipment.

GENERAL LEDGER
JOHN SMITH, PERSONAL DRAWING ACCOUNT

SHEET NO. 1

FORM 121 — FRANK R. WALKER CO., PUBLISHERS, CHICAGO

DATE	ITEMS	Folio	√	DEBITS	DATE	ITEMS	Folio	√	CREDITS	
MAR 4	CASH	1		100 00						

Fig. 288. Debit-Credit Ledger Sheet, Form 121. Used for Keeping Owner's or Partner's Personal Drawing Accounts.

use of same. This permits the various job cost accounts to show a larger profit but the "Tool and Equipment" account will show a loss at the end of each year.

The other method is to charge the original cost of each piece of equipment in the same manner as described above. However, using this method, each job is charged a regular weekly or monthly rental for all tools and equipment delivered and used on that job and the "Tool and Equipment" account is credited with the amount of such rentals. When using this method, the "Tool and Equipment" account will usually show a profit, while the various job cost accounts will show a smaller profit (but a more accurate cost) than where the first method is used.

Either of these methods will result in the same "Net Profit" for the business at the end of the year and it is merely a matter of individual preference as to the method to be used.

TRUCK AND AUTO EXPENSE. — This account enables you to keep an accurate cost record of operating your trucks and automobiles used in the business. A columnar form should be used where separate costs are desired for repairs, oil, gas, tires, etc., for both trucks and automobiles.

FURNITURE AND FIXTURES. — The office furniture and fixture account, should contain a record of all money invested in furniture, filing equipment, typewriters, adding and calculating machines, etc.

Strictly speaking this is an asset account upon which money may be realized or credit extended, but many concerns carry this equipment at a nominal sum, say $1.

A sheet similar to the Equipment and Depreciation Record may be used for keeping records of costs and depreciation of office furniture and equipment.

If sales of office furniture and equipment are made, this account should be credited.

DRAWING ACCOUNTS. — This account contains a record of all money withdrawn from the business for the personal use of the proprietor or partners. The amounts are entered in the Drawing Account column in the Cash-Journal and later transferred to the proper accounts in the ledger.

If the business is a corporation and the officers or active stockholders in the business draw a regular weekly or monthly salary from the business, these amounts may be first entered in the Cash-Journal under the column headed "General Expense-Salaries" where they are chargeable as a general expense of conducting the business. If any of the active stockholders are superintendents or foremen, their salaries should be charged direct to the jobs on which they are working.

TAX ACCOUNT. — The item of taxes is an extremely important one in every business because it is obligatory upon the employer to make deductions from all employees' salaries or wages for F.I.C.A., Income Withholding and (in some states) Unemployment Compensation Insurance taxes. These items must be deducted from each employee's pay and individual records kept of same in order that proper reports

TAX ACCOUNT

				F.I.C.A.		INCOME WITHHOLDING TAX		UNEMP. COMP. TAX			
				PAYMENTS DR.	DEDUCTIONS CR.	PAYMENTS DR.	DEDUCTIONS CR.	PAYMENTS DR.	DEDUCTIONS CR.		
1	FEB 28	DEDUCTIONS & PAYMENTS	1							1
2	MAR 31	" "	2		45 30		350 00			2
3	APR 15	" "	3	90 60		350 00		67 95		3
4										4
5										5

Left Hand Page   Fig. 289. Columnar Sheet, Form 134. Used for Keeping Tax Account.

TAX ACCOUNT

	SALES TAX		LICENSES, FEES, ETC.		MISC. TAXES				TOTALS		
	PAYMENTS DR.	CREDITS CR.	PAYMENTS DR.	CREDITS CR.	PAYMENTS DR.	CREDITS CR.			DR.	CR.	
1											1
2										395 30	2
3			15 00						523 55		3
4											4
5											5

Fig. 289. Columnar Sheet, Form 134. Used for Keeping Tax Account.   Right Hand Page

may be sent to the Department of Internal Revenue each Quarter, together with the Employer's contribution for F.I.C.A. and Unemployment Compensation Insurance taxes. This calls for accurate records.

A double page columnar sheet furnishes a simple and satisfactory method of keeping all Tax Accounts under one heading and on one sheet, carrying both Deduction and Payment columns for each class of taxes. The Debits and Credits for each column are totaled and transferred to the "TOTALS" column at the extreme right side of the sheet. This keeps all classes of taxes sub-divided for ready reference, while furnishing a total of all Taxes collected and paid.

The method of recording deductions for F.I.C.A. and Withholding taxes is illustrated on pages 50 to 56 and described on page 170, under "How to Handle Pay-Rolls."

F.I.C.A. and Unemployment Compensation taxes are handled in different ways by different contractors. Some prefer to charge the taxes direct to the various jobs on which incurred and others prefer to carry a "Tax Account" in the ledger and charge all classes of taxes to this account and write it off at the end of the year as one of the costs of doing business. This is the simplest method but it does not give the true cost of the job because the cost of F.I.C.A. and Unemployment Compensation Insurance should be estimated as a part of the cost of the job when the estimate is prepared.

Where F.I.C.A. and Unemployment Compensation Insurance is to be charged as a direct job cost, the "Tax Account" should be handled in the same manner as described above and at the end of each month or the completion of the job, the amount of tax chargeable to each job should be computed and charged direct to the "Job Cost Account" and the "Tax Account" in the ledger should be credited with the same amount.

INSURANCE. — Workmen's Compensation and Public Liability Insurance should be charged direct to the job on which applicable.

A contractor usually pays a minimum premium in advance and this should be carried in the "Insurance Account" in the ledger. At regular intervals the pay-rolls are audited by the insurance company and bills rendered according to amounts and labor classifications on each job. These amounts should be charged direct to the various "Job Cost Accounts" at the time the bills are received, as they are a direct job cost. Fire, Windstorm and all other classes of insurance covering the job during construction should be charged direct to the job on which incurred.

MISCELLANEOUS ACCOUNTS. — All miscellaneous ledger accounts that do not come under one of the special headings listed on the Cash-Journal sheet are carried under this heading, such as Capital In-

GENERAL LEDGER

JOHN SMITH, CAPITAL ACCOUNT   SHEET NO 1

DATE	ITEMS	Folio	✓	DEBITS	DATE	ITEMS	Folio	✓	CREDITS	
					MAR 1	BY CASH	1		10000 00	
					1	EQUIPMENT	1		2500 00	

FORM 121   FRANK R. WALKER CO. PUBLISHERS, CHICAGO

Fig. 290. Debit-Credit Ledger Sheet, Form 121. Used for Keeping Capital Account or Capital Stock Account, if a Corporation.

PERPETUAL STOCK RECORD

DESCRIPTION PORTLAND CEMENT STOCK ACCOUNT   SHEET NO 1

UNIT OF MEASURE BBL - 4 SACKS   PRICE 3.50 BBL   F.O.B YARD

FORM 156   FRANK R. WALKER CO., PUBLISHERS, CHICAGO

DATE	BOUGHT FROM	QUANTITY RECEIVED BBLS.	UNIT PRICE	AMOUNT	DATE	SOLD TO OR SENT TO JOB NO.	QUANTITY SOLD BBLS.	UNIT PRICE	AMOUNT	BALANCE IN STOCK	
MAR 1	UNIV P.C. Co	200	3 50	700 00	MAR 10	CASH SALES	50	4 50	225 00	1 50	
					10	HILLES JOB	50	4 50	225 00	1 00	

Fig. 291. Perpetual Stock Record, Form 156. Used for Keeping a Perpetual Inventory of Material Purchases and Sales.

DATE	NAME OF WORK	LOCATION	JOB NO.	TOTAL AMOUNT OF CONTRACT	ACTUAL COST OF CONTRACT	LOSS ON CONTRACT	PROFIT ON CONTRACT
	FRED H. HILLES RESIDENCE	176 WAYNE AVE.	120	4065 00	3620 00		445 00
	WM. SMITH ALTERATIONS	137 E. HARPER AVE.	121	758 00	630 50		127 50

JOB PROFIT AND LOSS ACCOUNT

FORM 210   FRANK R. WALKER CO., PUBLISHERS, CHICAGO

Fig. 292. Profit and Loss Account, Form 210. Used for Keeping a Record of all Profits and Losses.

vested or Capital Stock Account, if a corporation, also materials purchased for stock, cash sales of materials, etc.

The items are entered under Miscellaneous Accounts in the Cash-Journal and later transferred to the proper accounts in the ledger.

PROFIT AND LOSS ACCOUNT. — This account contains a record of the profits and losses incurred in the business. After a job has been completed and all charges and entries made against same, it will be necessary to make the closing entries in the accounts affected before they can be ruled up and the accounts closed.

As an example, assume you have a contract amounting to $2,973.00 and you have spent $2,540.00 for labor, material, sub-contracts and other miscellaneous job expenses in completing this contract. The profit on the job will be $433.00, the difference between the contract price and the cost of the job.

To make the closing entries in the ledger, the Job Cost account should be debited with $433.00 in the fifth column headed "Total Cost" and the Profit and Loss account in the ledger should be credited with the same amount.

The above entries should be made through the Cash-Journal and transferred to the proper ledger accounts at the end of each month.

If the job results in a loss instead of a profit, and the total cost of the job is more than the contract price, the Job Cost Account should be credited with the amount of the loss and the Profit and Loss account should be debited with the same amount.

The difference between the Debit and Credit column in the Profit and Loss Account should show the profit or loss resulting from the business.

The Monthly Trial Balance

At the end of each month when all invoices have been checked and entered in the Cash-Journal, and posted to their respective ledger accounts, a trial balance should be taken to show that the books are in balance. This consists of taking the Debit and Credit totals of each account or each control account and listing them on the Trial Balance sheet, as illustrated. When the entries are correctly made, the total of the Debit and Credit columns should be the same.

In order to illustrate clearly the method used in taking off a trial balance, it should be noted that the totals of the Debit and Credit entries in the Cash-Journal balance, as shown on page 172.

If the amounts have been correctly posted to the proper ledger accounts, the trial balance for the month should be the same as given in the Cash-Journal, although it is customary to carry the totals for the year in the various ledger accounts.

While there is only one entry for each Control Account listed on the Trial Balance sheet, there will probably be several individual accounts under each Control Account in the ledger. In instances of this kind, merely take the totals of the Debits and Credits of the different accounts and enter them as one total on the Trial Balance sheet. This will reduce the number of entries to a minimum and make the bookkeeping much easier.

HANDLING CONTROL ACCOUNTS IN THE LEDGER. — The various column headings in the Cash-Journal sheet, such as Cash Account, Bank Account, Accounts Payable, Contract Accounts, Sub-Contract Accounts, Job Cost Accounts, etc., are called "Control" accounts because all debit and credit entries applicable to that particular class of accounts are entered in this one double column.

For instance, under the heading "Accounts Payable," you may have accounts with 50 to 200 different

MONTHLY TRIAL BALANCE

SHEET NO.

FORM 122-L

FRANK R. WALKER CO. PUBLISHERS, CHICAGO

	DATE	TITLES OF ACCOUNTS	JANUARY Debit	JANUARY Credit	FEBRUARY Debit	FEBRUARY Credit	MARCH Debit	MARCH Credit	
1		CASH ACCOUNT					250 00	4 20	1
2		BANK ACCOUNT					14642 50	5748 26	2
3		PR DEDUCTIONS F.I.C.A.						45 30	3
4		" " WITHHOLDING						350 00	4
5		CONTRACT ACCOUNTS					4300 00	3650 00	5
6		SUB-CONTRACT "					956 25	1125 00	6
7		JOB COST "					4141 00	4300 00	7
8		ACCOUNTS PAYABLE					1476 00	1476 00	8
9		NOTES "					2125 00	2125 00	9
10		INTEREST & DISCOUNT					15 63	18 02	10
11		ACCOUNTS & NOTES REC.					250 00	250 00	11
12		CEMENT STOCK ACCOUNT					700 00	450 00	12
13		GENERAL EXPENSE "					331 20		13
14		TAXES							14
15		INSURANCE							15
16		WELFARE PAYMENTS							16
17		FURNITURE & FIXTURES					250 00		17
18		TOOLS & EQUIPMENT					250 00		18
19		TRUCK & AUTO EXPENSE					4 20		19
20		PERSONAL DRAWING ACCT.					100 00		20
21		CAPITAL ACCOUNT						1250 00	21
22									22
23									23
24									24
25									25
26									26
27									27
28									28
29								32041 78	32041 78	29

Fig. 293. Monthly Trial Balance, Form 122. Used for Taking Off and Recording the Monthly Trial Balance.

concerns but this one heading in the Cash-Journal carries all of the entries pertaining to this particular class of accounts.

In instances of this kind, it is advisable to carry a "Cap" sheet, which is the first sheet under the index heading "Accounts Payable" and the monthly totals of this account are posted from the Cash-Journal to the "Cap" sheet in the General Ledger. This sheet is used for taking off the trial balance and the various individual accounts under this heading must then balance with the "Cap" sheet.

Many firms carrying on an extensive business prefer to use a separate ledger for certain classes of account. For instance, a separate ledger would be used for Accounts Payable; a separate ledger for Sub-Contract Account (which is also an Accounts Payable account); a separate ledger for Contract Account (which is the Accounts Receivable account), and a separate ledger for Job Cost Accounts.

Where separate ledgers are used for these different classes of accounts, one sheet is carried in the General Ledger for Accounts Payable, Contract Accounts, Sub-Contract Accounts, Job Cost Accounts, etc., and the total for each class of accounts is posted from the Cash-Journal to the General Ledger accounts each month. The detailed entries pertaining to each class of accounts are then posted to their particular account in the Accounts Payable Ledger, Contract Accounts Ledger, Sub-Contract Accounts Ledger, Job Cost Account Ledger, etc. The Debit and Credit entries in each of these different ledgers must balance with the "Control" account sheet in the General Ledger.

Making Up the Statement of Accounts

At the end of each year it will be necessary to take the totals of all accounts listed on that portion of the sheet headed "Yearly Statement of Accounts." The Asset column should show everything you own and the

YEARLY STATEMENT AND RECAPITULATION

FORM 211 · FRANK R. WALKER CO., PUBLISHERS, CHICAGO

YEARLY STATEMENT OF ACCOUNTS

ASSETS (WHAT WE OWN)		LIABILITIES (WHAT WE OWE)	
ACCOUNT	AMOUNT	ACCOUNT	AMOUNT
Cash on Hand	21 20	Proprietor's Account	2950 00
Cash in Bank	1868 50		
Accounts Receivable		Accounts Payable	1575 00
Amount Due on Completed Contracts	4622 00	Notes Payable	3600 00
Plant and Equipment	1150 00	Other Loans	2000 00
Furniture and Fixtures	250 00	Mortgages, Etc.	3000 00
Automobiles and Trucks	1260 00	Other Liabilities:	324 00
Real Estate	5400 00		
Merchandise Inventory			
Other Assets: MORTGAGE BONDS	4000 00		
TOTAL	18571 70	TOTAL	13449 00

YEARLY INCOME RECAPITULATION

	AMOUNT	AMOUNT
TOTAL AMOUNT OF COMPLETED CONTRACTS FOR YEAR		32612 00
DEDUCT COST OF COMPLETED CONTRACTS:		
MATERIAL COST	12818 00	
LABOR COST	9416 00	
MISC. COSTS	3200 00	
TOTAL COST OF CONTRACTS		25434 00
GROSS PROFIT ON CONTRACTS		7178 00
DEDUCT:		
RENT	495 00	
LIGHT, HEAT AND POWER	73 60	
OFFICE SALARIES	720 00	
MISCELLANEOUS EXPENSES	326 00	
TRUCK AND AUTOMOBILE EXPENSES	415 00	
TOOLS AND EQUIPMENT DEPRECIATION	230 00	
TRUCK AND AUTOMOBILE DEPRECIATION	252 00	
FURNITURE AND FIXTURES DEPRECIATION	25 00	
LOSSES FROM BAD DEBTS – NONE		
INTEREST PAID ON BORROWED MONEY	112 00	
TAXES, INSURANCE, ETC.	57 30	
TOTAL	2705 90	2705 90
ADD OTHER INCOME: TOTAL BUSINESS INCOME		4472 10
FROM REAL ESTATE		240 00
INTEREST AND DISCOUNT EARNED		260 60
BONDS AND MORTGAGES		150 00
TOTAL YEARLY INCOME		5122 70

Fig. 294. Yearly Statement and Recapitulation, Form 211. Used for Making up Yearly Statement of Profit and Loss, also Yearly Income Tax Returns.

amount of same, while the "Liability" column furnishes a record of everything owed by you at the end of the year.

The difference between the "Asset" and "Liability" columns will give your net worth. Take your net worth for last year and deduct it from the net worth this year, and the difference will be your gain or loss for the year.

Yearly Income Recapitulation

This portion of the sheet furnishes the information from which your Government Income Tax Return should be made up. It furnishes a complete record of all business done; the amount, cost and profit on all your completed contracts.

It also furnishes a complete itemized list, together with the amounts of the different expenses of conducting your business.

The difference between the gross profit and the expense of conducting your business, together with any other items of Income, is your net income for the year, upon which your income tax return should be based.

The item of depreciation on tools and equipment, trucks and automobiles, etc., is a variable item as the Department of Internal Revenue issues a complete schedule giving the average life allowed for all classes of construction machinery and equipment. It is advisable to consult this schedule before closing your books or preparing your income tax return.

How to Close Your Books at the End of the Year

At the end of the year it will be necessary to close your books, showing the profits and losses accruing from your contracts, write off depreciation on your plant and equipment, trucks and automobiles, close out your expense accounts, etc., in order to arrive at the *Net Income* derived from your business. This is necessary before starting a new set of books at the beginning of the year and for making up your Income Tax Return.

The various ledger accounts will be taken in their order and instructions given as to the proper methods of handling them.

All closing entries MUST be made through the Cash-Journal and then posted to their respective Ledger Accounts.

ACCOUNTS PAYABLE. — Accounts with all concerns from whom you purchase materials and supplies are carried under Accounts Payable. Accounts with concerns or individuals to whom you owe money at the end of the year are carried forward into the next year's accounts just as they are. For instance, if you owe various concerns $3,500.00 at the end of the year, this amount should be carried forward into the next year's books.

If you do not carry any Accounts Payable in your books and enter invoices only at the time they are paid, then all unpaid invoices should be carried into the next year's business.

CASH ACCOUNT. — Any cash balance remaining in your cash account at the end of the year should be carried forward into the next year's business.

BANK ACCOUNT. — Any bank balance remaining at the end of the year should be carried forward into the next year's business.

CONTRACT ACCOUNTS. — All accounts with Owners and Others for whom you have done work during the year, where the jobs are completed and paid in full are closed. All uncompleted contracts or contracts that have not been paid in full are carried forward into the next year's business.

SUB-CONTRACT ACCOUNTS. — All accounts with Sub-Contractors where the jobs have been completed and the sub-contractor has been paid in full are closed.

All accounts with Sub-Contractors where the jobs have not been completed and where the sub-contractor has not been paid in full are carried forward into the next year's books.

JOB COST ACCOUNTS. — All uncompleted jobs or contracts are carried forward into the next year's business just as they are.

All jobs that have been completed during the current year are closed and the procedure is as follows: Suppose you have a contract amounting to $40,658.000. This amount should show in the Credit column of the Job Cost Account sheet in the ledger. Now assume the total of the four columns headed "Labor," "Material," "Sub-Contracts" and "Miscellaneous Expense" is $34,950.00.

The difference between the actual cost of the job and the amount of your contract is the profit or loss on the job. In this instance the difference between the Contract Amount and the actual cost of the job is $5,708.00, which is your profit on the job.

To close this account in the ledger, DEBIT this account in the fifth column headed "Total Cost" with $5,708.00. Now turn to the Profit and Loss Account sheet and CREDIT this account with $5,708.00. This transaction closes the Job Cost Account and transfers it to the Profit and Loss Account.

However, if the job results in a loss instead of a profit, then the Job Cost Account is CREDITED with the amount of the loss and the Profit and Loss Account is DEBITED with the amount of the loss.

As an example, assume the contract amounted to $40,658.00 as given above, and that the total of the four columns headed "Labor," "Material," "Sub-Contracts" and "Miscellaneous Expense" amounted to $46,050.00. The job would then show a $5,392.00 loss instead of a profit.

In this instance, enter $5,392.00 in the CREDIT column of the Job Cost Account sheet and enter the same amount in the Debit column of the Profit and Loss Account.

This same method should be used in closing all Job Cost Accounts in the ledger.

GENERAL EXPENSE. — This account should be closed out at the end of each year. If your general expense for the year, including rent, light, heat, office salaries, taxes and insurance, etc., amount to $1,671.90, the account should be closed and handled as follows: CREDIT the General Expense Account with $1,671.90 in the Credit column of this sheet and DEBIT the "Profit and Loss" Account with the same amount.

INTEREST AND DISCOUNT. — If you paid $112.00 interest charges during the year and collected $262.00 as interest due you and as discount earned, you have received $150.00 more than you paid out.

DEBIT this account with $150.00 and CREDIT the "Profit and Loss" Account with $150.00, as this is an income or profit item.

However, if you paid $250.00 interst charges during the year and collected only $125.00 as interest due you and as discount earned, you have paid out $125.00 more than you collected. CREDIT this account with $125.00 and DEBIT the "Profit and Loss" Account with $125.00, as this is then an expense item.

NOTES PAYABLE. — Any unpaid notes at the end of the year should be carried forward into the next year's books, otherwise the account should balance and be closed.

NOTES AND ACCOUNTS RECEIVABLE. — Any unpaid notes due you at the end of the year should be carried forward into the next year's books, otherwise the account should balance and be closed.

TAXES. — Taxes that have not been charged direct to the various jobs should be closed out as they are a direct expense of doing business.

For instance, if you have deducted $200.00 from your employees for F.I.C.A. taxes and paid $400.00 to the Government, credit this account with $200.00 and debit the Profit and Loss Account with the same amount.

Unemployment Compensation taxes that have not been charged direct to the various jobs on which incurred, should be handled in the same manner as described above and this same method applies to all classes of taxes that have not been charged as a direct cost of your various jobs.

The Income Withholding Tax account should balance, inasmuch as you make certain deductions from your employees' wages and turn around and pay this same amount to the Government, so there is no profit or loss involved in this account—other than your cost of keeping the records.

INSURANCE. — Insurance that has not been charged direct to the various jobs should be closed out, except where prepaid insurance carries forward into the following year. In such event, the amount chargeable to the current year should be charged off and balance carried forward into the next year's books.

TOOLS AND EQUIPMENT. — Suppose you have an investment of $2,530.00 in tools and equipment. It will be necessary to charge off a certain percentage for depreciation each year, based on the schedule prepared by the Department of Internal Revenue covering all classes of Construction Tools and Equipment.

Refer to your "Equipment and Depreciation Record" sheets and depreciate each piece of equipment according to schedule. The total depreciation shown on all of these sheets is your total depreciation for the year. Credit the "Equipment and Depreciation Record" with the amount of the depreciation and Debit "Profit and Loss" with the same amount.

TRUCK AND AUTOMOBILE ACCOUNT. — This account is handled in exactly the same manner as the "Tools and Equipment" Account, and the depreciation rate varies with the size of the truck or automobile, as follows:

Class	Year Life	Annual Depreciation
Automobiles, light	2	50 %
Medium	3	33⅓ %
Heavy	5	20 %
Trucks, ⅓ to ⅔ cu. yd, capacity	3	33⅓ %
1 to 1⅔ cu. yd. capacity	5	20 %
2 cu. yds. and over	8	12½ %

The entire cost of operating your trucks and automobiles should be charged off each year as this is entirely an expense item. Assuming the cost of gasoline, oil, tires, repairs, etc., at $415.00. CREDIT this account with $415.00 and DEBIT the "Profit and Loss" Account with $415.00.

FURNITURE AND FIXTURES. — This account is handled in exactly the same manner as the "Tools and Equipment" Account. Suppose you have an investment of $1,000.00 in office furniture and equipment and depreciate it at 10 percent a year. CREDIT this account with $100.00 and DEBIT the "Profit and Loss" Account with $100.00.

DRAWING ACCOUNTS. — This account cannot be written off because an individual must pay income tax on the entire NET PROFIT of the business, not including any money used for his personal expenses.

Refer to the yearly Income Recapitulation on Page 183. All of the legitimate expense of the busines may be deducted from the Gross Profit, but no personal expenses.

Here is the way the "Profit and Loss" Account in the Ledger should look:

Individual Profit and Loss Account

Gross Profits and Losses from the Job Profits and Loss Account Sheet		Debits	Credits
	Job Profits		$7,368.00
	Job Losses	$ 190.00	
Total Job Profits..			$7,178.00
DEDUCTIBLE EXPENSES			
General Expense—Rent...	$ 495.00		
Light, Heat and Power...	73.60		
Office Salaries...	720.00		
Miscellaneous Expenses..	326.00		
Taxes and Insurance...	57.30	$1,671.90	
Tools and Equipment—Depreciation........................		230.00	
Automobile and Trucks—Depreciation.....................		252.00	
Truck and Automobile—Expense..............................		415.00	
Furniture and Fixtures—Depreciation......................		25.00	
Interest Paid...		112.00	
Interest and Discount Earned..................................			262.00
TOTALS..		$2,705.90	$7,440.00
Net Income from Business..			$4,734.10

If the business is conducted by an individual or a partnership, the Net Profit of the business, $4,734.10, should be transferred from the "Profit and Loss" Account to the "Capital Account" as follows: DEBIT the "Profit and Loss" Account with $4,734.10 and CREDIT the "Capital Account" with $4,734.10. This entry shows that your Capital has been increased by $4,734.10 during the year.

However, if you have withdrawn $2,500.00 from the business for the personal use of the proprietor or partners, then your "Personal Drawing Account" in the ledger should be Credited with $2,500.00, which closes this account. The "Capital Account" should be DEBITED with $2,500.00, so that the increase in capital will be only $2,234.10 instead of $4,734.10, as originally entered.

If the business is a Corporation, the salaries of the officials charged as a direct business expense and the officials will be obliged to make up an Individual Income Tax Return, showing the amount of their earnings during the year. This is in addition to the Corporation Income Tax Return.

If the salaries of the officials, amounting to $2,500.00 are charged to the General Expense of conducting the business, then the "General Expense Account" in the ledger should be CREDITED with the Total of the "General Expense Account" and the "Profit and Loss" Account in the ledger should be debited with the same amount.

Here is the way the "Profit and Loss' Accont of the Corporation should look:

Corporation Profit and Loss Account

Gross Profits and Losses from the Job Profits and Loss Account Sheet		Debits	Credits
	Job Profits		$7,368.00
	Job Losses	$ 190.00	
Total Job Profits..			$7,178.00
DEDUCTIBLE EXPENSES			
General Expense—Rent...	$ 495.00		
Light, Heat and Power...	73.60		
Office Salaries...	720.00		
Officials Salaries...	2,500.00		

Miscellaneous Expenses...	326.00	
Taxes and Insurance..	57.30	$4,171.90
Tools and Equipment—Depreciation.............................		230.00
Automobile and Trucks—Depreciation.........................		252.00
Truck and Automobile Expense.....................................		415.00
Furniture and Fixtures—Depreciation..........................		25.00
Interest Paid..		112.00
Interest and Discount Earned.......................................		262.00
TOTALS...		$5,205.90 $7,440.00
Net Profits from Business...		$2,234.10

To close out this entry, DEBIT the "Profit and Loss" Account with $$2,234.10 and CREDIT the "Surplus Account" with $2,234.10. This entry shows that the business earned a surplus of $2,234.10, which is carried forward in the next year's books.

These entries close the books and you you are ready to start another year.

After transferring the balances from your present books, take off a new Trial Balance to be sure that all entries are correct and your books in balance for the beginning of a new year.

CHAPTER 16

ACCOUNTING METHODS

Cash Basis Method

The basic need among contractors is to employ an adequate accounting method to produce current and reliable cost and progress reports. Such reports will enable the contractor to recognize the progress his business is making and his financial position.

The accountant and the contractor should determine the accounting method best fitted for the contractor's need.

Small contractors favor a cash or a completed contract method as more conservative and it eliminates the laborious task for compiling the estimates of the percentage of completion method. The primary advantage of the cash basis method is its simplicity.

The cash basis method includes the income from contracts in the year when cash becomes available. There is the problem of bunching large amounts of income in a single taxable year and thereby becoming subject to higher taxes; excess profits in the case of a corporation or a graduated tax rate applicable to individual tax payers.

Job costs and expenses are entered when paid during the fiscal period. The net income can be controlled by timing of receipts and disbursements which determines the taxable income for the period. This will prove satisfactory if jobs are of a short duration. Gross income can be regarded for either short or long term contracts. A short term contract is one completed within one year. A long term contract is one completed in a period exceeding one year.

The cash basis method does not reflect the actual income earned in a fiscal period, the true income and expenses are not all recorded on the books. The actual financial condition, its assets and liabilities, are not always known.

Completed Contract Method

The completed contract method considers income only when a contract is completed or substantially completed. When this method is used, excess of accumulated costs over related billings should be indicated on the balance sheet "Excess of accumulated costs over related billings" a deferred charge under current assets. If accumulated billings exceed the related costs the amount should be shown as "Excess of accumulated billings over related costs" as deferred income under current liabilities. A careful evaluation of the contracts in progress are important to preclude over and undervaluing the amount of the uncompleted contracts. In cases where dependable cost figures are not available and an estimate of costs would be doubtful; the completed contract method of accounting would be preferable.

Percentage Completion Method

The normal practice is for the contractor to bill his customer for the work performed on the job site at regular intervals or at certain stages as the work progresses. But the billings usually do not coincide exactly with the related costs incurred. This creates an accounting problem peculiar to the construction business. Most projects extend over one or even several accounting periods making interim reports and financial

PERCENTAGE COMPLETION SCHEDULE

Amount of Contracts $	Total Costs $	% of Completion	Completed Costs $	Percent of Completion basis	
				Estimated Earnings $	Unbilled Accts. Rec. $

statements complex. Matching billings with related costs and constant checking is necessary to provide some equalization of this practice.

The percentage of completion method recognizes income on a contract as the work progresses. When properly applied this method provides a closer matching of income and related costs than other methods. Accounts receivable are recorded as earned and accounts payable are recorded as incurred. A comparative analysis of the various jobs under this method is attainable.

Under this method gross income on contracts is determined as work progresses. A percentage of completion is determined by the contract costs incurred to date, which is applied to the estimated total contract costs. Estimated earned income is ascertained in accordance with the stages of completion of each contract as determined by the superintendent, architect or engineer.

The first step in preparing a schedule of contract billings and related costs requires a revue of the jobs in progress to be made to determine the protion of the billable amount of the contract, then the related costs and the gross profit can be ascertained to be reported in the financial statements for the fiscal period. Subcontractors should inform the general contractor of their proportionate cost and completion on their jobs. Inventory of materials on the site to be used in future work are not to be included in costs only as an asset on the balance sheet.

Income should be in relation to the estimates of the percentage of the work completed. The percent of costs incurred to date to total estimated costs should be the basis for the accounting.

The unbilled accounts receivable is to be shown in the current assets section of the balance sheet as "Accounts receivable—unbilled" and in the statement of operations statement the projected income should be shown as "Excess of contract billings over costs. If the estimated costs exceed the estimated billings, the amount should appear as a deferred charge as "Excess of costs over contract billings."

The percentage completion method is endorsed because it recognizes income as it is earned with the expenses and costs of the project. Some opposition of this method is that it is primarily an estimate.

Any method of accounting should be consistent from year to year to comply with the regulations of the Internal Revenue Department. Any changes in the method must have the approval of the Internal Revenue Department.

Paper Closing Method

Some companies prefer to simplify their accounting by preparing a "paper closing" at the end of each month and formally entering all accruals on the books at the end of the taxable year.

A "Paper Closing" is accomplished by entering the accruals at the end of the interim month. After the trial balance of the books has been completed the following work sheet is prepared:

Trial Balance Per books $	Accruals end of the month $	New Balances $

A profit and loss statement and balance sheet can be made using the new balances which will show the current results at the end of a month and year to date balances. This precludes the work of reversing the accruals on the books each month. At the end of the taxable year, all accruals should be entered on the books and the year end profit and loss statement and balance sheet be prepared for the required income tax reports.

PROGRESS BILLING ON PERCENTAGE-OF-COMPLETION BASIS

Classification	Contract Amount	Percentage Completion	Earned Amount	Previously Billed	To be billed this period	Balance to complete
Clearing site	1600	100	1600	1000	600	—
Excavation	3200	100	3200	1500	1700	—
Foundation	2900	90	2610	1000	1610	290
Reinforcing	1800	80	1440		1440	360
Concrete, braces, tile	16000	50	8000	2000	6000	8000
Roofing	10500	—				10500
Plumbing	4100	25	1025	—	1025	3075
Electrical	5200	20	1040	—	1040	4160
Doors and windows	4700	10	470		470	4230
Finishing	1400	—	—			1400
Painting	3300	—	—			3300
Heating and Air Conditioning	4500	25	1125		1125	3375
Kitchen and Laundry equipment	1800	—	—			1800
Cleaning	700	—	—			700
	61700		20510	5500	15010	41190
Less 10% retention			2051	550	1501	
			18459	4950	13509	

"PRACTICAL" BOOKKEEPING AND ACCOUNTING SYSTEMS FOR SUB-CONTRACTORS

Air Conditioning Contractors
Carpenter Contractors
Cement Contractors
Excavating Contractors

Fire-proofing Contractors
Flooring Contractors
Glass and Glazing Contractors
Heating Contractors

Iron Contractors
Lathing Contractors
Marble Contractors
Mill Work Contractors

Painting Contractors
Plastering Contractors
Plumbing Contractors
Reinforcing Steel Contractors

Roofing Contractors
Sheet Metal Contractors
Steel Sash Contractors
Stone Contractors

Structural Steel Contractors
Sidewalk and Paving Contractors
Tile and Mosaic Contractors
Ventilating Contractors

"Practical" Bookkeeping and Accounting Systems for the different trades enumerated above, covering what are commonly known as Sub-Contractors are practically the same as the systems for contractors, illustrated and described on the previous pages, except they contain a few special sheets to meet the requirements of the sub-contractors' particular business.

For instance, the average sub-contractor receives contracts direct from the owner where there is no architect; direct from the owner through an architect, when separate contracts are let instead of a general contract, and from general contractors, where a general contract has been let covering the complete job and the general contractor sublets the different branches of work.

The sub-contractor does not usually sublet any of his work, so that the Sub-Contract ledger account sheets will not be required by most sub-contractors.

In the bookkeeping system illustrated and described on pages 137 to 161, the only difference between a general contractor's and a sub-contractor's system, would be the omission of the Sub-Contract Account sheet illustrated on page 151.

302

In the bookkeeping system illustrated and described on pages 162 to 185, there is a slight change in the short Cash-Journal sheet, between pages 165 and 169, as this short sheet does not contain the heading "Sub-Contract Accounts" but instead the last four columns on this sheet carry the heading "JOB COST ACCOUNTS—Labor, Material, Misc, Costs and Amount Complete" as illustrated, otherwise the Cash-Journal sheets are identical in both systems. Also the Sub-Contract Account sheets, illustrated on page 176, are not used in the sub-contractors bookkeeping system. Otherwise the systems are identical.

When Materials Are Sold In Connection With. the Contracting Business

Many sub-contractors sell building materials, such as Electrical and Plumbing supplies, Hardware, etc., in connection with their contracting business.

When a contractor conducts this type of business, the material purchases and sales should be handled as follows:

Insert a "short" sheet between the left and right hand Cash-Journal sheets, heading them to meet the requirements of the particular business, as illustrated.

When purchases are made, they should be entered in the proper column under the heading "Pipe and Fittings-Purchases-Dr."

When sales are made, they should be entered in the proper column under the heading, "Pipe and Fittings-Sales-Cr."

When materials are purchased for sale, the amount paid for same should be entered in the fourth column of the left hand Cash-Journal sheet, headed "Bank Account-Checks-Cr." and the same amount should be entered in the first column of the "short" sheet, headed "Pipe and Fittings-Purchases-Dr."

When sales are made for cash, the amount of the sale should be entered in the first column of the left-hand Cash-Journal sheet headed "Cash Account-Cash Received-Dr," and the same amount should be entered in the second column of the "short" sheet headed "Pipe and Fittings-Sales-Cr."

The difference between the "Purchase" column and the "Sales" column is the profit or loss on the sale of each particular item.

If it is not desired to keep separate costs on sales of different items, one column may be used headed "Material Purchases and Sales" and lump all items under one heading.

A Perpetual Stock Record sheet, as illustrated on page 181, furnishes an excellent record of all materials purchased for sale, one sheet being used for each class of material or if a record of each class of material is not desired, then one sheet may be used for the purchase and sale of all kinds of materials. This sheet may also be used for recording materials that are taken from stock and sent to any of the various jobs on which you are performing work.

If more convenient, sales tickets may be made out covering all sales made during each day and then one entry made at the close of each day covering all classes of sales. This reduces the number of entries considerably when a large number of sales are made.

ACCOUNTS PAYABLE		INTEREST AND DISCOUNT		NOTES PAYABLE			
Amount Paid DR.	Amount Owed CR.	Amount Paid DR.	Amount Received CR.	Amount Paid DR.	Amount Borrowed CR.		
							1
							2
							3
							4
							5

Left Hand Short Sheet   Fig. 295. Sub-Contractor's Cash-Journal Short Sheet, Form 224-SC.

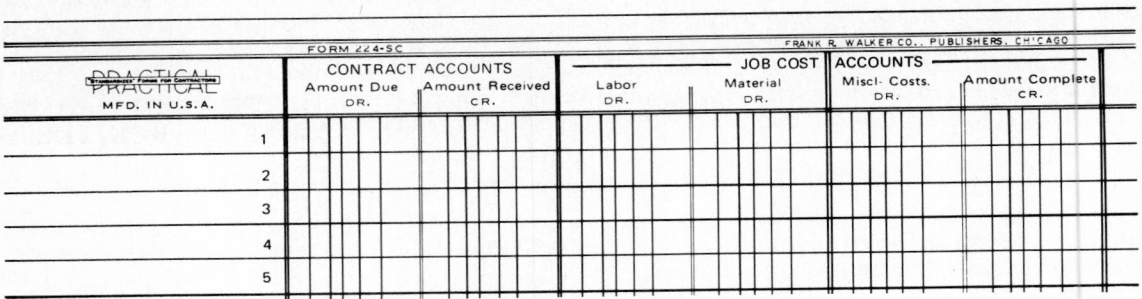

Fig. 295. Sub-Contractor's Cash-Journal Short Sheet, Form 224-SC.   Continued   **Right Hand Short Sheet**

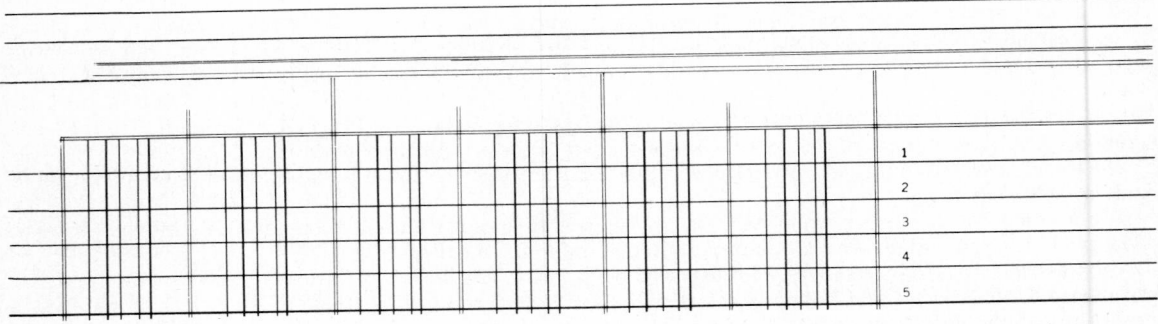

Left Hand Short Sheet   Fig. 296. Short Columnar Sheet, Form 134-S. Used for Special Classifications.

Fig. 296. Short Columnar Sheet, Form 134-S. Used for Special Classifications.   Continued   **Right Hand Short Sheet**

CHAPTER 18

THE "PRACTICAL" SELF-BALANCING BOOKKEEPING SYSTEM AND INCOME TAX RECORD FOR ARCHITECTS

This system of bookkeeping is the easiest any architect can possibly use, regardless of the size of the business. It is so simple that the architect who keeps his own books in spare time and doing a business of only a few thousand dollars a year, can handle it with ease.

It is so complete and efficient that the largest architects whose business runs into the hundreds of thousands will find it the most satisfactory system they have ever used. It furnishes both large and small architects more dependable, accurate information regarding every phase of their business than has ever been possible to obtain from any other accounting system.

The self-balancing Cash-Journal is the key to the entire system, and use of this one sheet will furnish all the information any architect requires to keep complete business records, including a monthly trial balance, if desired.

The various ledger sheets are used for keeping detailed accounts with persons or concerns for whom you are doing work; accounts with those from whom you purchase materials and supplies; detailed costs on your various jobs: accounts with all contractors doing work for you; also miscellaneous accounts, such as Capital Account, Profit and Loss, etc. If a smaller architect you may or may not use all of them, depending upon the amount of time at you disposal and the information you desire regarding the various classes of accounts. However, all of the accounts may be kept in detail by giving only a few hours to this book once or twice a month. The additional information furnished regarding your different jobs and the various expenses in connection with your business will more than repay you for the few hours spent.

Architects employing a bookkeeper will want complete ledger accounts and we believe that after you have given this system a fair trial, you will be surprised at the ease with which the accounts are kept and the wealth of information furnished you.

The Self-Balancing Cash-Journal

This sheet is the key to the entire system and furnishes complete records regarding every expense entering into your business.

It is divided into columns covering every class of expenditure entering into an architect's business. As an example of the ease with which these records are kept, assume you spend $4.20 for gasoline for your automobile. Refer to line 4 of this sheet. It shows you paid Nelson's garage $4.20 which is entered in the second column headed "Cash Account-Cash Paid Out-Cr."; then on the same line in the tenth column of the right hand page headed "Automobile Expense-Dr." the same amount is entered. This one simple entry gives the amount paid out and what it was spent for. Every other entry is made in exactly the same manner.

At the end of each month this sheet is totaled, and the total amount of all items entered in the columns headed "DR," signifying Debits, should balance with the total of all columns headed "CR," denoting Credits.

This sheet also eliminates the necessity of filling out check books stubs, as it furnishes a complete record of all checks written.

To obtain the bank balance at any time, subtract the total of the fourth column headed "Bank Account-Checks-CR." from the total of the third column headed "Bank Account-Deposits-Dr." The difference is your bank balance.

The correct method of handling all classes of accounts on this sheet is given on the following pages, showing actual entries, which are fully illustrated and decribed.

Control Accounts in the Cash-Journal

Each of the columns in the Cash-Journal headed "Cash Account," "Bank Account," "Accounts Payable," "Contract Accounts," "Job Cost Accounts," etc., are called Control Accounts, because they control the receipts and expenditures of each class of accounts in the business. Sufficient control accounts for practically any architect's business are carried in the Cash-Journal. However, additional control accounts or cost subdivisions may be carried in the Cash-Journal by merely inserting another "short" sheet between the left and right hand pages of the Cash-Journal. This "short" sheet uses the same descriptive column as the left hand Cash-Journal sheet and furnishes six additional "Debit-Credit" control accounts or twelve additional cost subdivisions. Any number of "short" sheets may be used.

The Self-Balancing Cash-Journal, together with the "short" sheets for additional control accounts, furnish records that are complete and flexible enough for any business.

How all Classes of Accounts Should be Handled in the "Practical" Self-Balancing Bookkeeping System for Architects

In order that all entries may be perfectly clear to users of this improved system of keeping architects' accounts, examples are given covering all classes of actual transactions, showing just what entries are necessary for complete records.

1   **How to Handle Capital or Money Invested in the Business**

Assume the proprietor invest $2,500.00 cash in the business.

How The Entries Should Be Made

Refer to line 1. Make entry as illustrated, entering $2,500.00 in the third column headed "Bank Account-Deposits-Dr."

Now refer to the fourteenth column of the right hand page headed "Miscellaneous Accounts-Cr." and enter $2,500.00 on line 1.

If the business is a partnership, separate Capital accounts should be kept for each partner or member of the firm, showing the amount of money invested by each.

If the business is a corporation, this amount should be carried in the ledger under the heading of "Capital Stock Account."

2   **Furniture, Typewriters, Drafting Room and Other Office Equipment**

Money expended for furniture, typewriters, adding machines and other items of permanent office or drafting room equipment should be charged to the Furniture and Fixture Account, as this is an asset of the business.

How The Entries Should Be Made

Assume you buy furniture amounting to $75.00 from the H. & H. Furniture Company. Refer to line 2. The amount of $75.00 should be entered in the fourth column headed "Bank Account-Checks-Cr." Now refer to line 2 in the ninth column of the right hand page headed "Tools and Equipment-Dr." and enter $75.00.

3   **How to Handle Petty Cash**

There are certain items of expense that will be paid in cash, such as postage, express, gasoline at filling stations, and other small expenses of this kind.

In order to have cash on hand to provide for these expenditures, assume $25.00 is withdrawn from the bank to take care of these items.

How The Entries Should Be Made

Refer to line 3. Currency check for $25.00 withdrawing cash from bank for petty cash expenditures. Notice $25.00 is entered in the fourth column headed "Bank Account-Checks-Cr." while the same amount is entered in the first column headed "Cash Account-Cash Received-Dr." This is merely transferring money from the bank to your pocket.

4   **How to Handle Small Expenditures Paid by Cash**

Assume you spent $4.20 for gasoline for the automobile used in your business.

How The Entries Should Be Made

Refer to line 4. The name Nelson's garage should be written in the descriptive column, then $4.20 entered in the second column headed "Cash Account-Cash Paid out-Cr." Now refer to line 4 in the tenth column of the right hand page headed "Automobile Expense-Dr." and the same amount is entered there.

5   **Drawing Account of Proprietor or Partners**

If the business is conducted by an individual or partners, an account should be carried for the proprietor or each partner, headed "Personal Account" or "Drawing Account."

MONTH OF _____ 19 ___ SHEET NO. ____

FORM 200   FRANK R. WALKER CO., PUBLISHERS, CHICAGO

	DATE	DESCRIPTION	Check Number	CASH ACCOUNT Cash Rec'd Dr.	Cash P'd Out Cr.	BANK ACCOUNT Deposits Dr.	Checks Cr.	PAY-ROLL DEDUCTIONS Federal Old Age Benefit Cr.	Income Tax Cr.	ACCOUNTS PAYABLE Amount Paid	Amount Owed Cr.	
1	MAR 1	CASH CAPITAL BY PROPRIETOR				2500 00						1
2	3	H & H FURN. CO.	1				75 00					2
3	10	CURRENCY FOR PETTY CASH	2	25 00			25 00					3
4	10	NELSON'S GARAGE			4 20							4
5	10	J. A. WILSON DRAWING ACCT.	3				75 00					5
6	10	WALKER'S STATIONERY	4				12 40					6
7	12	S. B. JONES, RENT	5				60 00					7
8	12	CITY POWER & LIGHT CO.	6				8 80					8
9	12	CASH EXPENSE - WILLIAMS	7				140 00					9
10	15	EUGENE DIETZGEN CO.									150 00	10
11	20	EUGENE DIETZGEN CO.	8				150 00			150 00		11
12	20	PAY ROLLS	9				434 40	10 60	85 00			12
13	21	FRED H. HILLES JOB ACCOUNT										13
14	21	FRED H. HILLES										14
15	22	GENERAL OFFICE EXPENSE										15
16	24	FRED H. HILLES				500 00						16
17	24	J. S. WILLIAMS + CO., JOB ACCT										17
18	25	J. S. WILLIAMS & CO.										18
19	25	NOTES RECEIVABLE										19
20	25	J. S. WILLIAMS & CO.				2525 00						20
21	25	NOTES RECEIVABLE										21
22	27	NOTES PAYABLE				990 00						22
23	28	FIRST NAT'L BANK - NOTES PAY										23
24	28	FIRST NAT'L BANK - NOTES PAY	10				1000 00					24
25												25
26												26
27												27
28												28
29				25 00	4 20	6515 00	1980 60	10 60	85 00	150 00	150 00	29

Left Hand Page   Fig. 297. The Self-Balancing Cash-Journal, Form 200.

JOB COST ACCOUNTS

		HILLES RES JOB		J.S. WILLIAMS JOB		JOB		JOB		
		Labor DR.	Other Costs DR.	Labor DR.	Other Costs DR.	Labor DR.	Other Costs DR.	Labor DR.	Other Costs DR.	
	1									1
	2									2
	3									3
	4									4
	5									5
	6									6
	7									7
	8									8
	9			T 96 00						9
	10			E 44 00						10
	11									11
	12	2 00 00		240 00	140 00					12
	13									13
	14									14
	15									15
	16									16
	17									17
	18									18
	19									19
	20									20
	21									21
	22									22
	23									23
	24									24
	25									25
	26									26
	27									27
	28									28
	29									29

FORM 201   FRANK R. WALKER COMPANY, PUBLISHERS, CHICAGO

THE PRACTICAL SELF BALANCING CASH JOURNAL   SHORT SHEET

Fig. 298. The Self-Balancing Cash-Journal Short Sheet, Form 201.   **Right Hand Short Sheet**

JOB COST ACCOUNTS

Left Hand Short Sheet   Fig. 298. The Self-Balancing Cash-Journal Short Sheet, Form 201.

If the business is a corporation, and each active officer or stock holder does not draw a regular salary, than a separate account should be carried for each active member of the corporation.

Assume the proprietor or one of the members of the firm withdraws $75.00 from the business for his personal use.

How the Entries Should Be Made

Refer to line 5. The amount withdrawn, $75.00, should be entered in the fourth column headed "Bank Account-Checks-Cr." Now refer to line 5 in the twelfth column of the right hand page headed "Personal Account-Amount Withdrawn from Business-Dr." and enter $75.00 in this column.

6   **Expenditures For Rent, Light And Heat, Stationery, Advertising And Other Items Of "Overhead" or General Expense of Conducting the Business**

In practically every business there will be expenditures for stationery and supplies, rent, light and heat, advertising, and other miscellaneous expenses necessary for the successful conduct of your business. This should be charged to Overhead or the General Expense of conducting your business.

Assume you purchase stationery and supplies from Walker's Stationery store amounting to $12.40.

WALKER'S "PRACTICAL" SELF-BALANCING CASH-JOURNAL

MONTH OF _____ 19___ SHEET NO. _____

FRANK R. WALKER CO., PUBLISHERS, CHICAGO

FORM 200

PRACTICAL MFD. IN U.S.A.

	CONTRACT ACCTS. Amount Due DR.	Am't Rec'd CR.	INTEREST & DISC'T Amount Paid DR.	Am't Rec'd CR.	Rent DR.	GENERAL EXPENSE Light, Heat and Power DR.	Salaries DR.	Misc. Exp. DR.	TOOLS & EQUIPM'T DR.	TRUCK & AUTO EXP. DR.	TAXES DR.	PERSONAL ACCT Amt. Withd'n from Business DR.	MISC. ACCOUNTS DR.	CR.	
1														2500 00	1
2									75 00						2
3															3
4										4 20					4
5												75 00			5
6								12 40							6
7					60 00										7
8						8 80									8
9															9
10									15 00						10
11															11
12							90 00								12
13	500 00													500 00	13
14	500 00														14
15														500 00	15
16		500 00													16
17	2500 00													2500 00	17
18		2500 00													18
19												2500 00			19
20															20
21				25 00										2500 00	21
22			10 00												22
23														100 00	23
24												100 00			24
25															25
26															26
27															27
28															28
29	3500 00	3000 00	10 00	25 00	60 00	8 80	90 00	12 40	225 00			75 00	3500 00	9500 00	29

Fig. 297. The Self-Balancing Cash-Journal, Form 200.

Right Hand Page

How The Entries Should Be Made

Refer to line 6. The amount of the check, $12.40, should be entered in the fourth column headed "Bank Account-Checks-Cr." Now refer to line 6 in the eighth column of the right hand page headed "General Expense-Misc. Expenses-Dr." and enter $12.40

The item of rent is handled in exactly the same manner. Refer to line 7 of the fourth column headed "Bank Account-Checks-Cr. and to the same line in the fifth column of the right hand "General Expenses-Rent-Dr." Note the amount of $60.00 entered in both places.

Electric light comes under the same heading. Refer to line 8 of the fourth column headed "Bank Account-Checks-Cr." and to the same line in the fourth column of the right hand page headed "General Expense-Light and Heat-Dr." Note the amount of $8.80 entered in both places.

7   Traveling And Entertaining Expense

An architect is often obliged to visit distant points in connection with his business, necessitating traveling expenses, hotel expense, etc. and is often called upon to entertain clients and prospective clients.

Expenditures of this kind should be charged under Business Expense.

Suppose you are called out of town in connection with a new job or a prospective job and your traveling and hotel expense amounted to $96.00 and you spent an additional $44.00 entertaining members of the building committee who are to select the architect.

How The Entries Should Be Made

Refer to line 9. The amount of the expense, $140.00, should be entered in the fourth column headed "Bank' Account-Checks-Cr."

Now refer to column thirteen of the right hand page, headed "Misc Accounts-Dr." and enter $140.00.

When the expense is chargeable to any particular job, then the amount should be entered under "Job Cost Accounts-Dr." as shown in column four of the right hand short sheet headed " J. S. Williams & Co., Job-Other Costs-Dr."

8   When Invoices are Received Covering Materials Purchased

When materials for use in the office or drafting room, furniture, etc. are purchased on open account, assume you purchase supplies amounting to $150.00, from the Eugene Dietzgen Co.

How the Entries Should Be Made

Refer to line 10. The amount of the invoice, $150.00, should be entered in the eighth column headed "Accounts Payable-Amount Owed," showing this amount of money is owed by the Eugene Dietzgen Co.

Now refer to column fo the right hand page headed "Tools and Equipment-Dr." and enter the same amount.

9   When You Pay Invoices Covering Materials Purchased

Assume the above invoice, totaling $150.00, is paid.

How the Entries Should Be Made

Refer to line 11. Make out a check in the amount of $150.00 This should be entered in the fourth column headed "Bank Account-Checks-Cr."

You will recollect $150.00 was entered in the eighth column of the left hand page headed "Accounts Payable-Amount Owed-Cr." before the invoice was paid. Now that the bill is páid, the same amount should be entered in the seventh column headed "Accounts Payable-Amount Paid-Dr." These two columns now balance, showing the bill is paid in full.

10   **Invoices that are Paid at the Time they are Entered in the Books**

There are frequently bills to be paid where an account is not carried in the ledger with the concern from whom materials or supplies were purchased. This occurs where purchases are made for such items as telephone, electric light, rent and other miscellaneous items or for any purchase where payment is made promptly.

In instances of this kind the only entry is made at the time the bill is paid and then it is charged direct to the proper account.

How the Entries Should Be Made

As an example of the correct method of handling accounts of this kind, refer to lines 6, 7 and 8. The amounts paid are all entered in the fourth column headed "Bank Account-Checks-Cr." and the same amount is charged direct to the proper account. The entry on line 6 shows expenditures for stationery and supplies amounting to $12.40. This amount is entered in the eighth column of the right hand page headed "General Expense-Misc. Expense-Dr."

11   **How to Handle Pay-Rolls**

The architect's office force, consisting of executives, draftsmen, stenographers, clerks, etc., together with the job superintendents are usually paid every week and may be paid either by cash or check.

When paid in cash one check is usually made out for the entire amount of the pay-roll but when paid by check, it is customary to make out a check for each person employed during the pay-roll period.

In the example given, assume the employees are paid in cash and only one entry is required for the entire amount of the week's pay-roll.

The pay-roll amounts to $530.00 divided as follows: Hilles' Residence job, $140.00 for drafting and $60.00 for specifications; J. S. Williams & Co., factory, $120.00 for drafting, and $120.00 for specifications, and the general office expense, such as stenographers, etc., amounts to $90.00, making a total of $530.00

How the Entries Should Be Made

Refer to line 12. The total of the pay-roll check (less deductions for F.I.C.A. and Withholding Tax) amounting to $434.40 should be entered in the fourth column headed "Bank Account-Checks-Cr." The amount of the job pay-rolls amounting to $440.00 should be entered in the first and third columns of right hand short sheet headed "Hilles Residence Job-Labor-Dr." and "J. S. Williams & Co., Job-Labor-Dr." as illustrated. The $90.00 chargeable to general office salaries should be entered in the seventh column of the right hand page headed "General Office Expenses-Salaries-Dr."

If you do not wish to keep separate labor costs on the various jobs in your office, it will not be necessary to use the short Job Cost Account sheet and the entire amount of the pay-roll can be entered in the seventh column of the right hand page headed "General Office Expense-Salaries-Dr."

12   **When You Send Owner or Client a Statement Covering Services Rendered**

The method of paying the architect for his services varies with the individual contract but it is customary for the owner to pay a certain percentage of the total when sketches are accepted, another percentage when working drawings have been completed and the percentage retained for supervision is paid as the work progresses.

As an example, assume you send Fred H. Hilles a statement in the amount of $500.00 for services rendered.

How the Entries Should Be Made

Refer to line 13. The owner is charged or debited with $500.00 in the first column of the right hand page headed "Contract Accounts-Amount due-Dr." and the job on which the work was performed should be credited with the same amount in the fourteenth column of the right hand page headed "Misc. Accounts-Cr."

An Alternate Method of Handling this Class of Accounts

The architect who does not wish to keep separate costs of drawing plans, writing specifications and superintending his various jobs, will require a different method of handling these accounts through the books.

Where separate costs are not kept on each job, all labor and supplies used in drawing plans, writing specifications, superintending, etc., are charged in the seventh and eighth columns of the right hand page headed "General Office Expense-Misc. Expense-Dr."

For this reason these same accounts should be credited when money is received from owners and clients.

Line 14 illustrates the method of charging or debiting the owner in the usual manner and General Office Expense should then be credited, as illustrated on line 15 of column 14, headed "Misc. Accounts-Cr."

13   When You Receive Payment from Owner or Client on Account of Services Rendered

Assume you receive a check from Fred H. Hilles, in the amount of $500.00, being the amount of your statement.

How the Entries Should Be Made

Refer to line 16. Enter $500.00 in the third column of the left hand page headed "Bank Account-Deposits-Dr." and enter the same amount in the second column of the right hand page headed "Contract Accounts-Amount Received-Cr."

14   When You Take a Promissory Note from Owner on Account of Services Rendered

On the J. S. Williams & Co. Factory Job, you request payment of $2,500.00 for services rendered. These entries are illustrated on line 17 and are made in exactly the same manner as described under Item 12, and illustrated on lines 13, 14 and 15.

Instead of paying this statement, J. S. Williams & Co., give you this promissory note for $2,500.00, running for 60 days at 6% interest.

How the Entries Should Be Made

Refer to line 18. The owner is given credit for $2,500.00 in the second column of the right hand page headed "Contract Accounts-Amount Received-Cr." and the same amount is entered under Notes Receivable in column thirteen of the right hand page headed "Miscellaneous Accounts-Dr."

15   When Owner's Note is Paid at Maturity

At the expiration of the 60-day period, J. S. Williams & Co., pay their note amounting to $2,500.00, plus $25.00 interest, making a total of $2,525.00.

How the Entries Should Be Made

Refer to line 20. The amount of the note plus interest, $2,525.00, is entered in the third column of the left hand page headed "Bank Account-Deposits-Dr." Now enter "Notes Receivable" in the Descriptive column and amount of the note, $2,500.00, in the fourteenth column of the right hand page headed "Miscellaneous Accounts-Cr."

The amount of the interest received, $25.00, should be entered in column four of the same page.

16   When You Borrow Money at the Bank

Suppose you borrow from your bank $1,000.00 for 60 days on your note. The bank deducts the interest amounting to $10.00, in advance, and credits your account with $990.00, for which you give your promissory note for $1,000.00.

How the Entries Should Be Made

Refer to line 22. Enter the details of the transaction in the Descriptive column and the amount of money credited to your account, $990.00, should be entered in the third column of the left hand page headed "Bank Account-Deposits-Dr."

Now refer to line 23 and enter the details of the transaction in the Descriptive column, and the amount of the note, $1,000.00 in the fourteenth column of the right hand page headed "Misc. Accounts-Cr." and the amount of the interest, $10.00, in the third column of the right hand page headed "Interest and Discount-Amount Paid-Dr."

17   ## When You Repay the Note at Maturity

At the expiration of the 60-day period it will be necessary to pay the bank the $1,000.00 borrowed.

How the Entries Should Be Made

Refer to line 24. Enter the amount of the note, $1,000.00, in the fourth column of the left hand page headed "Bank Account-Checks-Cr." Now refer to the right hand page and enter $1,000.00 in the fourteenth column headed "Misc. Account-Dr."

How to Take Care of all Classes of Miscellaneous Accounts

It will often be necessary to take care of miscellaneous cash receipts and expenditures, such as rents, interest on stocks, bonds and other securities, which will vary with the individual.

For handling accounts of this kind, it is advisable to use an additional short sheet having blank headings, which can be filled in to meet the individual requirements. In this manner any number of accounts can be handled in the Cash-Journal which will give you a daily picture of your business and finances.

How to Tell at the End of each Month Whether all Entries Have Been Correctly Made

At the top of each column of both the left and right hand pages, also the left and right short pages, there appears in small letters "DR" and "CR." The "DR" denotes Debits and the "CR" Credits. If you will refer back to the various examples given, you will note that for every entry in a "DR" column, there were also entries in the "CR" columns totaling the same amount. These entries when correctly made, keep the books in balance at all times.

At the end of each month all the columns on both pages should be added up and the total of each column written at the bottom of the page as shown in the illustrations.

After the columns have been totaled, the amounts of all columns having "DR" at the top should be listed and added together. When this done the totals of all columns having "CR" at the top should be listed and added in the same manner.

If all the entries have been correctly made and your additions are correct, *the total of the "DR" Columns Should Equal the Total of the "CR" Columns. You Then know Your Books are in Balance,* otherwise there has been a mistake in some of your entries.

The above statement furnishes a complete picture of your business each month, showing the amount of work completed; the amounts you have received on contracts and the amounts due; the cost of your various jobs; the amount of interest paid and earned during the month. It also shows the amount of money borrowed on notes, the amount paid on notes, etc., enabling you to tell the condition of your business at a glance.

This sheet also furnishes a complete trial balance of each month's business.

	Debits	Credits
Cash Account	$ 25.00	$ 4.20
Bank Account	6,515.00	1,980.60
Pay-Roll Deductions, F.I.C.A.		10.60
Withholding Tax		85.00
Accounts Payable	150.00	150.00
Contract Accounts	3,500.00	3,000.00
Job Cost Accounts, Hilles Residence	200.00	500.00
J. S. Williams & Co.	380.00	2,500.00
Interest and Discount	10.00	25.00
General Expenses, Rent	60.00	500.00
Light and Heat	8.80	
Salaries	90.00	
Misc. Expense	12.40	
Tools and Equipment	225.00	
Automobile Expense	4.20	
Personal Drawing Account	75.00	
Capital Account		2,500.00
Notes Receivable	2,500.00	2,500.00
Notes Payable	1,000.00	1,000.00
TOTAL	$14,755.40	$14,755.40

The Ledger in the "Practical" Self-Balancing Bookkeeping System

The General Ledger in this improved system is merely a summary of the accounts listed in the different columns of the Cash-Journal sheet, and may be kept in as much or as little detail as the individual architect desires.

There should be indexes separating the different classes of accounts listed on the Cash-Journal sheet, such as Cash Account, Bank Account, Accounts Payable, Contract Accounts, Job Cost Accounts, etc. Each class of accounts should be kept under this index heading, so when posting items from the Cash-Journal to the ledger accounts, all items entered under any particular column heading in the Cash-Journal should be entered under the same index heading in the ledger, For instance, under the heading "Accounts Payable" in the Cash-Journal, the totals of both columns are $150.00. Under the index heading "Accounts Payable" in the ledger you have an account with Eugene Dietzgen Co. The amounts of invoices and payments should be transferred from the Cash-Journal to the individual accounts of these firms, showing the dates and amounts of all transactions. These entries should then balance with the total of the "Accounts Payable" columns in the Cash-Journal. The method is simple and it requires very little time to keep your books in first-class condition at all times.

What Accounts are Necessary in the General Ledger

The ledger should contain just as few accounts as possible to furnish the desired information regarding your business and they should not be itemized in too much detail because every entry requires additional clerical work.

The following accounts will serve the purpose of practically every architect's business, but different individuals and concerns may desire different information, and in such instances additional ledger accounts may be necessary.

ACCOUNTS PAYABLE. — This account should contain accounts with all firms or individuals from whom you buy materials or supplies regularly on an open account basis. Each account should show the amounts owed and the amounts paid and where possible only one entry should be made for an entire month's business. For example, all of the invoices for any one concern should be totaled and only one entry made each month covering all of them. This also applies to payments made. This will greatly simplify your work and will be found much more satisfactory than attempting to enter each invoice.

If the invoices are paid at the time the accounts are made up and then posted through the books, an Accounts Payable account in the Ledger for that concern is not necessary.

CASH ACCOUNT. — This account contains a summary of the month's cash transactions. Only one entry is made each month, entering the totals of the Cash Received and Cash Paid Out columns in the Cash-Journal.

GENERAL LEDGER

NAME *EUGENE DIETZGEN CO.*   ADDRESS *215 W. MONROE ST.*   SHEET NO *1*

DATE		DESCRIPTION	Folio	DEBITS	√	CREDITS	√	Dr. or Cr.	BALANCE	√
MAR	15	DRAFTING ROOM EQUIPMENT	1			15000				
	20	BY CHECK	1	15000						

Fig. 299. Debit-Credit-Balance Ledger Sheet, Form 221. Used for Accounts Payable.

GENERAL LEDGER
CASH ACCOUNT   SHEET NO.

DATE		ITEMS	Folio	√	DEBITS	DATE		ITEMS	Folio	√	CREDITS	
MAR	31	CASH RECEIPTS	1		2500	MAR	31	CASH EXPENDITURES	1		420	

Fig. 300. Debit-Credit Ledger Sheet, Form 121. Used for Cash Account.

GENERAL LEDGER
FIRST NATIONAL BANK
BANK ACCOUNT   SHEET NO.

DATE		ITEMS	Folio	√	DEBITS	DATE		ITEMS	Folio	√	CREDITS	
MAR	31	DEPOSITS	1		651500	MAR	31	CHECKS	1		198060	

Fig. 301. Debit-Credit Ledger Sheet, Form 121. Used for Bank Account.

BANK ACCOUNT. — An account should be kept under this heading with each bank with whom money is deposited.

At the end of each month, the total of the Bank Account column in the Cash-Journal is posted to this account, showing the amount of Deposits and Checks. The difference is the bank balance at the first of each month.

CONTRACT ACCOUNTS. — This sheet is used for keeping accounts with Owners or others for whom you are doing work.

When a contract is received, an account is opened with the owner or client, stating the name and location of job, percentage of commission or fees, etc.

When the plans have been completed and bids received on the different branches of work included in the job, the amounts are entered in the first column headed "Contract and Extras."

Deductions or credits affecting the original contracts, due to work being omitted or changed, are entered in the second column headed "Credits to Contract."

The net amount or total cost of the job is obtained by subtracting the total amount of the "Credits to Contract" from the total amount of the column headed "Contract and Extras." The difference is the net amount of the contract.

When plans and specifications have been completed or when the architect is entitled to payment on account of plans and specifications furnished, according to his contract with the owner, the stipulated percentage of the total is entered in the fourth column headed "Amount Commission..........%.

This column shows what portion of your fees or commissions are earned at any date.

As payments are received from the owner or client on account of services rendered, the dates and amounts of all payments are entered on the right hand side of the ledger sheet in the columns headed "Date Paid" and "Amount Paid."

When the owner has paid the architect his fee or commission in full, the two columns headed "Amount Commission .%" and "Amount Paid" should balance.

The first three columns of this sheet headed "Contract and Extras," "Credits to Contract," and "Net Amount of Contract" are memorandum accounts and are used as a temporary record during the life of the contract. For this reason it is not necessary to make the entries through the Cash-Journal, as they are not used when taking off a trial balance.

As soon as the architect is entitled to payment according to the agreement with the owner, the owner is debited in the fourth column headed "Account Commission .%" and the Job Cost Account should be credited with the same amount. Both of these entries should be made through the Cash-Journal.

When taking off the trial balance, the total of the fourth column headed "Amount Commission..........%" forms the debit account and the last column headed "Amount Paid" forms the credit account.

JOB COST ACCOUNTS. — This Job Cost Account sheet is used for keeping an accurate record of the cost of preparing plans and specifications, superintendence, etc., of each job or contract.

As expenditures are made covering General Expenses, Designing and Drafting, Specifications, Superintendence, etc., they are entered in this sheet under the proper heading as illustrated.

The total of the four columns headed "General Expense," "Designing and Drafting," "Specifications" and "Superintendence" gives the total cost of preparing plans and superintending the job and enables you to tell the total amount of each class of expenditures.

GENERAL LEDGER

ACCOUNT WITH OWNER

NAME OF OWNER J. S. WILLIAMS & Co.   ADDRESS 212 S. FIFTH AVE.   SHEET NO. 1

NAME OF WORK J. S. WILLIAMS & Co. FACTORY   LOCATION 2715 W. 20th ST.   JOB NO. 102

ARCHITECT FORM 151   FRANK R. WALKER CO., PUBLISHERS, CHICAGO

	DATE	DESCRIPTION	Folio	√	CONTRACT AND EXTRAS	CREDITS TO CONTRACT	NET AMOUNT CONTRACT	AMOUNT COMMISSION 6 %	DATE PAID	Folio	√	AMOUNT PAID
	MAR 1	CONTRACT AMOUNT			8556000							
	10	EXTRA PLASTERING			56000				MAR 21			250000
	15	OMIT METAL LATH				44000	8568000					
	21	WORK COMPLETED						250000				

Fig. 302. Contract Account, Form 151. Used for Keeping Record of Account Between Architect and Owner.

GENERAL LEDGER

JOB COST ACCOUNT

NAME OF WORK J. S. WILLIAMS & Co., FACTORY   LOCATION 2715 W. 20th ST.   SHEET NO. 1

NAME OF OWNER J. S. WILLIAMS & Co.   ADDRESS 212 S. FIFTH AVE.   JOB NO. 102

ARCHITECT FORM 153   FRANK R. WALKER CO., PUBLISHERS, CHICAGO

DATE	DESCRIPTION	Folio	√	GENERAL EXPENSE	DESIGNING & DRAFTING	SPECIFICA-TIONS	SUPERINTEN-DENCE	TOTAL COST DR.	√	CREDITS CR.
MAR 12	TRAVEL EXPENSE	1		9600						250000
12	ENTERTAINMENT	1		4400						
12	PRELIM. SKETCHES			5000						
20	PAY ROLLS				20000	4000				

Fig. 303. Job Cost Account, Form 153. Used for Keeping Detailed Costs of Each Job.

Whenever invoices or applications for payment are made to the owner covering services rendered, the amount of each application or invoice should be entered on the right hand side of the sheet, in the column headed "Credits." This shows the amount of money to which you are entitled at any date.

When the job is completed, the total of the "Credits" columns should equal the total amount of commissions or fees due you on that job.

The profit or loss on the job is obtained by subtracting the total cost of the job as contained in the four columns headed "General Expense," "Designing and Drafting," "Specifications" and "Superintendence," from the total of the commissions or fees as given in the right hand column headed "Credits."

ARCHITECT'S COMBINATION CONTRACT ACCOUNT AND JOB COST ACCOUNT. — This sheet is a combination of the Contract Account, and the Job Account, as described above, and is used in exactly the same manner, the only difference being the two accounts are on one sheet—one on each side.

This sheet is intended principally for small jobs or contracts, where only a small number of entries are necessary and one sheet is sufficient for all records.

The Owner's side of the sheet contains a "Job Recapitulation" (as shown in the illustration), which states the total amount expended for "General Expense," "Designing and Drafting," "Specifications" and "Superintendence." These items added together give the total cost of the job.

The resulting profit or loss on the job is obtained by subtracting the total cost of the job from the amount of the commission or fees, as noted at the bottom of the sheet.

GENERAL EXPENSE ACCOUNT. — The General Expense sheet is used for keeping an accurate account of the Overhead or General Expense of conducting the business.

GENERAL LEDGER

JOB COST ACCOUNT

NAME OF WORK FRED H. HILLES RESIDENCE   LOCATION 176 WAYNE AVE.   SHEET NO. 1
NAME OF OWNER FRED H. HILLES   ADDRESS 476 WAYNE AVE   JOB NO. 101

ARCHITECT FORM 1513   FRANK R. WALKER CO., PUBLISHERS, CHICAGO

DATE	DESCRIPTION	Folio	√	GENERAL EXPENSE	DESIGNING & DRAFTING	SPECIFICA-TIONS	SUPERINTEN-DENCE	TOTAL COST DR.	√	CREDITS CR.	
FEB 15	EXPENSE - VISITING SITE			30 00				30 00			
MAR 20	PAY ROLL	1			100 00	50 00	50 00	200 00			
21	INVOICE RENDERED	1						230 00		500 00	
APR 4	PAY ROLL	2			250 00	75 00	50 00	375 00			

Left Hand Sheet

Fig. 304. Combination Contract-Job Cost Account, Form 1513.
Used on Small Jobs Where One Sheet is Sufficient for all Records. Used for Keeping Detailed Costs on Each Job.
Account with Owner is on Front of Sheet.

This includes such items as office rent, heat, light, stationery, postage, office supplies, telephone, telegraph, advertising, salaries of office employees, such as bookkeepers, stenographers, clerks, designers, engineers and draftsmen when on unproductive work.

As the various items are paid or invoices received covering same, they are entered in the proper column. This enables the architect or engineer to know exactly what it costs him to conduct his business.

CONTRACT ACCOUNTS WITH CONTRACTORS. — The Contract Accounts with Contractors sheet is used for keeping a record of all contracts let to general contractors and the various sub-contractors performing work under your direction.

When the Architect or Engineer lets a contract covering the General Contract or any Sub-contract trade, on any project, a memorandum account is opened in the Contract Account with Contractors.

The amount of the original contract and extras to same are entered in the first column headed "Contract and Extras."

Omissions or changes from the original contract which involve deductions or credits are entered in the second column headed "Credits to Contract."

The net amount of the contract is obtained by subtracting the amount of the "Credits to Contract" from the total amount of the "Contract and Extras" column.

At stated intervals or whenever invoices or applications for payment are received from the Contractor, the amounts of such invoices or applications are entered in the fourth column headed "Amount Completed." This column shows what proportion of the total contract has been completed from month to

GENERAL LEDGER

ACCOUNT WITH OWNER

NAME OF OWNER *FRED H. HILLES*   ADDRESS *476 WAYNE AVE.*   SHEET NO. *1*

NAME OF WORK *FRED H. HILLES RESIDENCE*   LOCATION *176 WAYNE AVE.*   JOB NO. *101*

ARCHITECT FORM 1513   FRANK R. WALKER CO., PUBLISHERS, CHICAGO

	DATE	DESCRIPTION	Folio	√	CONTRACT AND EXTRAS MEMO.	CREDITS TO CONTRACT MEMO.	NET AMOUNT CONTRACT MEMO.	AMOUNT COMMISSION 7 %	DATE PAID	Folio	√	AMOUNT PAID
	MAR 1	GENERAL CONTRACT	1		4050 00				MAR 21			500 00
	10	EXTRA PLASTER ATTIC	1		30 00							
	15	OMIT METAL LATH	1			147 00	4058 00					
	21	INVOICE RENDERED	1					500 00				

JOB RECAPITULATION

		AMOUNT	AMOUNT
	TOTAL AMOUNT OF COMMISSIONS AND FEES		2846 06
	ACTUAL COST GENERAL EXPENSE	125 00	
	ACTUAL COST OF DESIGNING AND DRAFTING	1200 00	
	ACTUAL COST OF SPECIFICATIONS	200 00	
	ACTUAL COST OF SUPERINTENDENCE	800 00	
	TOTAL COST OF JOB	2325 00	2325 00
	PROFIT LOSS ON CONTRACT		521 06

NOTE: Write Profits in Black Ink and Losses in Red Ink.

Fig. 304. Combination Contract-Job Cost Account, Form 1513. Used on Small Jobs Where One Sheet is Sufficient for All Records. Front of Sheet Contains a Record of Account Between Architect and Owner. (Job Cost Account on Back of Sheet.)

Right Hand Sheet

month during the progress of the work. When the work has been completed, the amount in the fourth column should be the same as the amount in the third column headed "Net Amount Contract."

As certificates for payment are issued by the architect on the owner authorizing payments to be made on contract, the dates and amounts of all certificates of payment are entered in columns headed "Date Paid" and "Amount Paid."

When the contractor has been paid in full, the totals of the three columns headed "Net Amount Contract," "Amount Completed" and "Amount Paid" should balance.

The Contract Accounts with Contractors are merely memorandum accounts, and as they are paid by the owner and not by the architect or engineer, they should not be entered in the Cash-Journal or used when taking off a trial balance.

INTEREST AND DISCOUNT. — This account contains the total of all money paid in interest and all money received as interest and all money saved by taking advantage of cash discounts. The total of the Interest and Discount in the Cash-Journal is posted to this account in the ledger at the end of each month.

NOTES PAYABLE. — This account contains a record of all notes given to banks or to individuals for money borrowed or in settlement of accounts.

These totals are merely transferred from the Notes Payable column in the Cash-Journal at the end of each month.

NOTES AND ACCOUNTS RECEIVABLE. — This account in the ledger contains a record of all money due you for which you hold notes or other accounts not covered by Contract.

BUSINESS EXPENSE. — This account is used for keeping a record of all expenditures made in connection with entertaining prospective clients, traveling expense in connection with new work, etc.

After the commission has been obtained, all traveling or entertaining expense, should be charged direct to that job.

AUTOMOBILE EXPENSE. — This account enables you to keep an accurate cost record of operating your automobiles used in the business. A columnar form should be used where separate costs are desired for repairs, oil, gas, tires, etc.

FURNITURE AND FIXTURES. — The office furniture and fixtures account should contain a record of all money invested in furniture, filing equipment, typewriters, adding and calculating machines, drafting room equipment, etc.

GENERAL LEDGER

GENERAL EXPENSE ACCOUNT

NAME J. A. WILSON, ARCHITECT   ADDRESS 222 WEST ADAMS ST.   SHEET NO. 1

FORM 154

	DATE		DESCRIPTION	Folio	√	RENT	LIGHT, HEAT AND POWER	OFFICE SALARIES	MISC. EXPENSE	TOTAL COST Dr.	√	CREDITS Cr.
	MAR	10	WALKER'S STAT. STORE	1					12 40			
		12	S. B. JONES, RENT	1		60 00						
		12	CITY POWER & LIGHT	1			8 80					
		20	PAY ROLLS	1				90 00		171 20		

Fig. 305. General Expense Account, Form 154. Used for Keeping a Record of the Overhead Expense of Conducting Your Business.

GENERAL LEDGER

CONTRACT ACCOUNT

NAME PIONEER CONSTRUCTION CO.   ADDRESS 316 N. MICHIGAN AVE.   SHEET NO. 1
NAME OF WORK J. S. WILLIAMS & CO., FACTORY   LOCATION 2715 WEST 20TH ST.   JOB NO. 102

FORM 142

	DATE		DESCRIPTION	Folio	√	CONTRACT AND EXTRAS	CREDITS TO CONTRACT	NET AMOUNT CONTRACT	AMOUNT COMPLETED Dr.	DATE PAID	Folio	AMOUNT PAID
	MAR	1	CONTRACT AMOUNT			85560 00				MAR		8500 00
		5	EXTRA PLASTERING			560 00						
		10	OMIT METAL LATH				440 00	85680 00				
		28	WORK COMPLETED						10000 00			

Fig. 306. Contract Account, Form 142. Used for keeping Account of Contract Between Owner and Contractor.

PRACTICAL

| Job No. 102 | | CERTIFICATE FOR PAYMENT TO CONTRACTOR | Certificate No. 1 |

Date March 31, 19   TO   J. S. WILLIAMS & COMPANY $ 8,500.00

STATEMENT		
Contract	$85,560.00	
Extras	560.00	
TOTAL	$86,120.00	
Deductions	440.00	
TOTAL	$85,680.00	
Total Comp. Wk.	8,500.00	
Less 0 Retention	-----	
Prev. Payments		- 0 -
AMOUNT DUE		$ 8,500.00

THIS IS TO CERTIFY, that

PIONEER CONSTRUCTION COMPANY

Contractor for   Factory Building at 2715 West 20th Street, Chicago, Illinois

is entitled to a   --- partial -----   payment of

---EIGHT THOUSAND FIVE HUNDRED ($8,500.00)------------ Dollars

under terms of this contract.

Architect

Received Amount of above Certificate.

Contractor

FORM 596   FRANK R. WALKER CO., PUBLISHERS, CHICAGO   MFD. IN U.S.A.

PRACTICAL

| Job No. | | CERTIFICATE FOR PAYMENT TO CONTRACTOR | Certificate No. |

Date   TO $

STATEMENT		
Contract	$	
Extras		
TOTAL		$
Deductions	$	
NET TOTAL		$
Prev. Certificates	$	
THIS CERTIFICATE TOTAL CERTIFIED		$
Balance on Contract NET TOTAL		$

THIS IS TO CERTIFY, that

Contractor for

is entitled to a   payment of

Dollars

under terms of this contract.

Received Amount of above Certificate.

DUPLICATE

Contractor

FORM 596   FRANK R. WALKER CO., PUBLISHERS, CHICAGO   MFD. IN U.S.A.

Fig. 307. Certificate for Payment to Contractor, Form 596. Certificate Issued by Architect to Contractor Covering Payment on Contract.

GENERAL LEDGER
INTEREST & DISCOUNT

SHEET NO. 1

PRACTICAL MFD IN U.S.A	DATE	ITEMS	Folio	✓	DEBITS	DATE	ITEMS	Folio	✓	CREDITS
	MAR 31	INTEREST PAID	1		10 00	MAR 31	INTEREST RECEIVED	1		25 00

FORM 121 — FRANK R. WALKER CO., PUBLISHERS, CHICAGO

Fig. 308. Debit-Credit Ledger Sheet, Form 121. Used for Interest and Discount.

GENERAL LEDGER
NOTES PAYABLE

SHEET NO.

PRACTICAL MFD IN U.S.A	DATE	ITEMS	Folio	✓	DEBITS	DATE	ITEMS	Folio	✓	CREDITS
	MAR 31	FIRST NATIONAL BANK	1		1000 00	MAR 31	FIRST NATIONAL BANK	1		1000 00

FORM 121 — FRANK R. WALKER CO., PUBLISHERS, CHICAGO

Fig. 309. Debit-Credit Ledger Sheet, Form 121. Used for Notes Payable.

GENERAL LEDGER
NOTES RECEIVABLE

SHEET NO.

PRACTICAL MFD IN U.S.A	DATE	ITEMS	Folio	✓	DEBITS	DATE	ITEMS	Folio	✓	CREDITS
	MAR 21	J. S. WILLIAMS & CO.	1		2500 00	MAR 21	J. S. WILLIAMS & CO.	1		2500 00

FORM 121 — FRANK R. WALKER CO., PUBLISHERS, CHICAGO

Fig. 310. Debit-Credit Ledger Sheet, Form 121. Used for Notes Receivable.

BUSINESS EXPENSE

				1 TRAVELING DR.	2 ENTERTAINMENT EXPENSE DR.	3	4	5	6	
1	MAR	CASH EXPENSE	1	96 00	44 00					1
2										2
3										3
4										4
5										5

Fig. 311. Columnar Sheet, Form 136. Used for Itemizing Business Expense.

AUTOMOBILE EXPENSE

					1 GASOLINE DR.	2 OIL DR.	3 TIRES DR.	4 REPAIRS DR.	5	6 TOTAL DR.	
1	MAR	10	NELSON'S GARAGE	1		4 20						1
2												2
3												3
4												4
5												5

Fig. 312. Columnar Sheet, Form 136. Used for Itemizing Automobile Expense.

EQUIPMENT AND DEPRECIATION RECORD

SHEET NO. 1

KIND OF EQUIPMENT OFFICE & DRAFTING   PURCHASED FROM   SERIAL NUMBER

DESCRIPTION ROOM FURNITURE AND FIXTURES   APPRAISED VALUE

DATE ACQUIRED   HOW ACQUIRED   ESTIMATED LIFE YEARS 10   DEPRECIATION YEARLY RATE 10%   DATE APPRAISED

FORM 137   FRANK R. WALKER CO., PUBLISHERS, CHICAGO

	DATE Mo. Day Year	DESCRIPTION	Folio	ORIGINAL COST AND CAPITAL REPAIRS	DEPRECIATION PER YEAR MEM'L	DEPRECIATION TOTAL TO DATE MEM'L	PRESENT BOOK VALUE MEM'L	OPERATING REPAIRS	RENTALS CHARGED OR RECEIVED	
1		BROUGHT FORWARD								1
2	3 3	H & H FURNITURE CO.	1	75 00	7 50					2
3	3 15	EUGENE DIETZGEN CO.	1	150 00	15 00					3
4										4
5										5

Fig. 313. Equipment and Depreciation Record, Form 137. Used for Keeping Detailed Cost Records and Depreciation on Office Furniture, Drafting Room Equipment, etc.

Strictly speaking this is an asset account upon which money may be realized or credit extended, but many concerns carry this equipment at a nominal sum, say $1.

The entries for all purchases of office furniture and equipment should be entered on the Equipment and Depreciation Record, and at the end of each year a certain percentage of the total cost should be charged off for depreciation. These items should be entered on the credit side of the sheet.

If sales of office furniture and equipment are made, this account should be credited.

DRAWING ACCOUNTS. — This account contains a record of all money withdrawn from the business for the personal use of the proprietor or partners. The amounts are entered in the Drawing Account column in the Cash-Journal and later transferred to the proper accounts in the ledger.

If the business is conducted as a corporation and the officers or active stockholders in the business draw a regular weekly or monthly salary from the business, these amounts may be first entered in the Cash-Journal under the column headed "General Expense-Salaries" where they are chargeable as a general expense of conducting the business.

MISCELLANEOUS ACCOUNTS. — It will often be necessary to take care of miscellaneous accounts in the ledger, such as rent, taxes, dividends on stocks, interest on bonds and mortgages, etc., which will vary with the individual.

Accounts of this kind should be carried under the Index Heading "Miscellaneous Accounts" in the ledger and posted from the Cash-Journal at the end of each month in the usual manner.

TAX ACCOUNT. — The item of taxes is an extremely important one in every business because it is obligatory upon the employer to make deductions from all employees' salaries or wages for F.I.C.A., Income Withholding and (in some states) Unemployment Compensation Insurance taxes. These items must be deducted from each employee's pay and individual records kept of same in order that proper reports may be sent to the Department of Internal Revenue each Quarter, together with the employer's contribution for F.I.C.A. and Unemployment Compensation Insurance taxes.

A double page columnar sheet furnishes a simple and satisfactory method of keeping all Tax accounts under one heading and on one sheet, carrying both Deduction and Payment columns for each class of taxes.

PROFIT AND LOSS ACCOUNT. — This account contains a record of the profits and losses incurred in the business. After a job has been completed and all charges and entries made against same, it will be nec-

GENERAL LEDGER

J.A. WILSON

PERSONAL DRAWING ACCOUNT

SHEET NO. 1

DATE	ITEMS	Folio	✓	DEBITS	DATE	ITEMS	Folio	✓	CREDITS
MAR 10	CASH	1		7500					

Fig. 314. Debit-Credit Ledger Sheet, Form 121. Used for Owner's Personal Drawing Account.

GENERAL LEDGER

J.A. WILSON, ARCHITECT

CAPITAL ACCOUNT

SHEET NO. 1

DATE	ITEMS	Folio	✓	DEBITS	DATE	ITEMS	Folio	✓	CREDITS
					MAR 1	CASH CAPITAL	1		250000

Fig. 315. Debit-Credit Ledger Sheet, Form 121. Used for Owner's Capital Account.

TAX ACCOUNT

	DATE	ITEMS			F.I.C.A. PAYMENTS DR.	DEDUCTIONS CR.	INCOME WITHHOLDING TAX PAYMENTS DR.	DEDUCTIONS CR.	UNEMP. COMP. TAX PAYMENTS DR.	DEDUCTIONS CR.		
1	MAR 31	TAXES	1			1060		8500				1
2	APR 30	"	2		2120		8500					2
3												3
4												4
5												5

Left Hand Page.

Fig. 316. Columnar Sheet, Form 134. Used for Tax Account.

TAX ACCOUNT

	SALES TAX PAYMENTS DR.	CREDITS CR.	LICENSES, FEES, ETC. PAYMENTS DR.	CREDITS CR.	MISC. TAXES PAYMENTS DR.	CREDITS CR.			TOTALS DR.	CR.	
1										9560	1
2									10620		2
3											3
4											4
5											5

Fig. 316. Columnar Sheet, Form 134. Used for Tax Account.   Right Hand Page.

essary to make the closing entries in the accounts affected before they can be ruled up and the accounts closed.

As an example, assume you have a contract amounting to $2,500.00, and you have spent $1,970.00 for designing and drafting, specifications and other miscellaneous expenses in completing this contract. The profit on the job will be $530.00, the difference between the contract price and the cost of the job.

To make the closing entries in the ledger, the Job Cost account should be debited with $530.00 in the first column headed "General Expense" and the Profit and Loss account in the ledger should be credited with the same amount.

The above entries should be made through the Cash-Journal and transferred to the proper ledger accounts at the end of each month.

If the job results in a loss instead of a profit, and the total cost of the job is more than the contract price, the Job Cost Account should be credited with the amount of the loss and the Profit and Loss account should be debited with the same amount.

The difference between the Debit and Credit column in the Profit and Loss Account should show the profit or loss resulting from the business.

JOB PROFIT AND LOSS ACCOUNT

FORM 210

FRANK R. WALKER CO., PUBLISHERS, CHICAGO

DATE	NAME OF WORK	LOCATION	JOB NO.	TOTAL AMOUNT OF CONTRACT	ACTUAL COST OF CONTRACT	LOSS ON CONTRACT	PROFIT ON CONTRACT
	HILLES RESIDENCE	176 WAYNE AVE.	101	2846 06	2325 00		521 06
	J. S. WILLIAMS & Co.	2715 W. 20TH ST.	102	5140 00	4260 00		880 00
			TOTAL				

Fig. 317. Job Profit and Loss Account, Form 210. Used for Keeping a Record of all Profits and Losses.

The Monthly Trial Balance

At the end of each month when all invoices have been checked and entered in the Cash-Journal, and posted to their respective ledger accounts, a trial balance should be taken off to show that the books are in balance. This consists of taking the Debit and Credit totals of each account or each control account and listing them on the Trial Balance sheet, as illustrated. When the entries are correctly made, the total of the Debit and Credit columns should be the same.

In order to illustrate clearly the method used in taking off a trial balance, it should be noted that the totals of the Debit and Credit entries in the Cash-Journal balance, as shown.

If the amounts have been correctly posted to the proper ledger accounts, the trial balance for the month should be the same as given in the Cash-Journal, although it is customary to carry the totals for the year in the various ledger accounts.

In the illustration of the Monthly Trial Balance, it will be noted that the totals of the Debits and Credits are the same as those appearing in the Cash-Journal.

While there is only one entry for each Control Account listed on the Trial Balance sheet, there will probably be several individual accounts under each Control Account in the ledger. In instances of this kind, merely take the totals of the Debits and Credits of the different accounts and enter them as one total on the Trial Balance sheet. This will reduce the number of entries to a minimum and make the bookkeeping much easier.

MONTHLY TRIAL BALANCE

SHEET NO.

	DATE	TITLES OF ACCOUNTS	JANUARY Debit	JANUARY Credit	FEBRUARY Debit	FEBRUARY Credit	MARCH Debit	MARCH Credit	
1		CASH ACCOUNT					25 00	4 20	1
2		BANK ACCOUNT					651 500	1980 60	2
3		ACCOUNTS PAYABLE					150 00	150 00	3
4		CONTRACT ACCOUNTS					3500 00	3000 00	4
5		JOB COST ACCOUNTS					5800 00	3000 00	5
6		INTEREST & DISCOUNT					10 00	25 00	6
7		GENERAL EXPENSE					171 20	500 00	7
8		NOTES PAYABLE					1000 00	1000 00	8
9		NOTES RECEIVABLE					2500 00	2500 00	9
10		FURNITURE & FIXTURES					225 00		10
11		TOOLS & EQUIPMENT							11
12		AUTOMOBILE EXPENSE					4 20		12
13		TAXES						95 60	13
14		INSURANCE							14
15		PERSONAL DRAWING ACCT.					75 00		15
16		CAPITAL ACCOUNT						2500 00	16
17		BUSINESS EXP. & ENT.							17
18									18
19									19
20									20
21									21
22									22
23									23
24									24
25									25
26									26
27									27
28									28
29								14755 40	14755 40	29

Fig. 318. Monthly Trial Balance, Form 122. Used for Taking Off and Recording the Monthly Trial Balance.

Making Up the Statement of Accounts

At the end of each year it will be necessary to take the totals of all the accounts listed on that portion of the sheet headed "Yearly Statement of Accounts." The Asset column should show everything you own and the amount of same, while the "Liability" column furnishes a record of everything owed by you at the end of the year.

The difference between the "Asset" and "Liability" columns will give your net worth. Take your net worth for last year and deduct it from the net worth this year, and the difference will be your gain or loss for the year.

Yearly Income Recapitulation

This portion of the sheet furnishes the information from which your Government Income Tax Return should be made up. It furnishes a complete record of all business done; the amount, cost and profit on all of your completed contracts.

It also furnishes a complete itemized list, together with the amounts of the different expenses of conducting your business.

YEARLY STATEMENT AND RECAPITULATION

FORM 211 — FRANK R. WALKER CO., PUBLISHERS, CHICAGO

YEARLY STATEMENT OF ACCOUNTS

ASSETS (WHAT WE OWN)	AMOUNT	LIABILITIES (WHAT WE OWE)	AMOUNT
Cash on Hand	21 20	Proprietor's Account	2950 00
Cash in Bank	1868 50		
Accounts Receivable		Accounts Payable	1575 00
Amount Due on Completed Contracts	4622 00	Notes Payable	3600 00
Plant and Equipment	1150 00	Other Loans	2000 00
Furniture and Fixtures	250 00	Mortgages, Etc.	3000 00
Automobiles and Trucks	1260 00	Other Liabilities:	324 00
Real Estate	5400 00		
Merchandise Inventory			
Other Assets:			
MORTGAGE BONDS	4000 00		
TOTAL	18571 70	TOTAL	13449 00

YEARLY INCOME RECAPITULATION

	AMOUNT	AMOUNT
TOTAL AMOUNT OF COMPLETED CONTRACTS FOR YEAR		32612 00
DEDUCT COST OF COMPLETED CONTRACTS:		
MATERIAL COST	12818 00	
LABOR COST	9416 00	
MISC. COSTS	3200 00	
TOTAL COST OF CONTRACTS		25434 00
GROSS PROFIT ON CONTRACTS		7178 00
DEDUCT:		
RENT	495 00	
LIGHT, HEAT AND POWER	73 60	
OFFICE SALARIES	720 00	
MISCELLANEOUS EXPENSES	326 00	
TRUCK AND AUTOMOBILE EXPENSES	415 00	
TOOLS AND EQUIPMENT DEPRECIATION	230 00	
TRUCK AND AUTOMOBILE DEPRECIATION	252 00	
FURNITURE AND FIXTURES DEPRECIATION	25 00	
LOSSES FROM BAD DEBTS — NONE		
INTEREST PAID ON BORROWED MONEY	112 00	
TAXES, INSURANCE, ETC.	57 30	
	2705 90	
TOTAL		2705 90
ADD OTHER INCOME: { TOTAL BUSINESS INCOME		4472 10
FROM REAL ESTATE		240 00
INTEREST AND DISCOUNT EARNED		260 60
BONDS AND MORTGAGES		150 00
TOTAL YEARLY INCOME		5122 70

Yearly Statement and Recapitulation, Form 211. Used for Making Up Yearly Statement of Profit and Loss, also Yearly Income Tax Returns.

The difference between the gross profit and the expense of conducting your business, together with any other items of income, is your net income for the year, upon which your income tax return should be based.

The item of depreciation on Furniture and Fixtures, Automobiles, etc., is a variable item, but ordinarily Furniture and Fixtures is figured at an annual depreciation of 10 per cent of the original cost and Automobiles at 20 to 25 per cent. Before doing anything with this item, it is advisable to consult the local income tax official regarding same.

CHAPTER 19

OVERHEAD EXPENSE

There are four classes of basic expenses which are included in the cost of construction. They are:

Direct Cost

The cost of materials used in the actual construction.

Direct Labor

All labor costs of employees who work directly on the construction. This does not include the salaries of supervisors and foremen but only those persons actually performing some operation directly on the specific construction.

Sub-Contracts

The work performed by outside contractors.

Overhead Expense

Overhead represents all costs except those of direct cost, sub-contracts and direct labor. The overhead account accumulates a number of diverse items of cost, such as depreciation, indirect labor, rent, automobile expense and other expenses not charegable to direct cost and direct labor.

There are basically two classes of overhead expense. They are:

Job overhead expense
General overhead expense

Job overhead expenses are those costs which are incurred for a particular job but do not physically become an integral part of the construction. They are, however, directly chargeable to the contract and thus must be separated in the accounting records from overhead expenses having a general nature. Expenditures which are directly chargeable to the job overhead category would include:

Permits
Bonds
Bidding expense

Job office expense:
    Office salaries
    Cost clerk
    Material clerk
    Timekeeper
    Watchman
    Payroll taxes
    Supplies—office
    Telephone
Working foremen
Construction insurance
Employees' insurance
Pensions
Rental of equipment for job
Job supplies and small tools
Electricity at job location
Water at job location
Temporary structures
Allocation of depreciation and expense of owners equipment

General overhead expenses are those costs incurred for purposes of general nature and not directly chargeable to any one job. Such expenditures would include:

General office expenses:
    Rent
    Telephone
    Electricity
    Water
    Office supplies and stationery
    Office salaries
Officers' salaries
Supervision and general foreman salaries
Advertising
Legal and audit expense
Insurance
Payroll taxes
Pensions
Automobile expense
Depreciation
Travel and entertainment
Dues and subscriptions

For the contractor to operate profitably he must be sure to have the total contract price cover not only the direct costs of material, labor and sub-contracts but also the job and general overhead expenses plus the profit that should be realized for investment and efforts.

When a job is estimated the estimator can readily determine the direct costs of material, sub-contractors and labor. Now he must add the costs of overhead. There are various procedures that may be followed.

Job overhead expenses can be estimated from prior experiences as to the expenses incurred on similar type jobs. The total estimated job overhead expenses should then be added to the job estimate.

General overhead expenses must also be allocated to each job. Ordinarily, estimators include a flat percentage of direct costs, excluding cost of sub-contracts, to cover general overhead expenses. This percentage may be determined by various methods:

(a) Direct costs and general overhead expenses during prior periods corrected for any anticipated changes.

(b) An estimate of general overhead expenses and direct costs for the next period.

Overhead expense can vary in different periods due to volume of business done.

A simple method of applying overhead for a small contractor who has five jobs in progress during a given month is shown in the following example:

DIRECT COSTS

Job	Labor	Material	Job Overhead Expense	Total	Percent To Total
1	475	530	30	1035	10.7
2	840	340	90	1270	13.2
3	1750	890	200	2840	29.4
4	400	380	50	830	8.6
5	2000	1030	650	3680	38.1
	5465	3170	1020	9655	100.0

GENERAL OVERHEAD EXPENSES

Office rent	300.00
Office salaries	1,000.00
Office supplies	40.00
Insurance	160.00
Payroll taxes	60.00
Other taxes	25.00
Depreciation	275.00
Auto and truck expense	80.00
Small tools	190.00
Other expenses	50.00
Telephone	30.00
Total	2,210.00

DISTRIBUTION OF GENERAL OVERHEAD TO JOBS

Job	%	Overhead
1	10.7	236.00
2	13.2	292.00
3	29.4	650.00
4	8.6	190.00
5	38.1	842.00
	100.0	2210.00

JOURNAL ENTRY DISTRIBUTING GENERAL OVERHEAD

Job 1	Cost	account	$236.00
2	"	"	292.00
3	"	"	650.00
4	"	"	190.00
5	"	"	842.00
General overhead expenses			$2,210.00

To distribute overhead for month of _____ .

Some companies charge a flat percentage of their gross billing to cover administrative overhead. A flat percentage can be based on prior year or months gross billings to total of administrative overhead expense.

A construction company which sub-contracts most of its work should apply overhead on the basis of direct costs, as sub-contract costs can vary widely in individual jobs. Distributing various types of overhead on different bases can pose allocation problems; also, varying the formula for each job would result in a serious distortion.

The construction industry seems to prefer total direct costs as a basis for overhead distribution. It is accurate enough to accomplish the need and is simple and easy to use.

Any method used to account for overhead costs should be consistent and comparable.

When an analysis of job cost during construction is required it is well to include overhead expense also. For example, if a job is 39% completed, then 39% of the estimated overhead should be considered.

A close scrutiny of overhead expenses is highly important; if too high the company will lose jobs and, if too low the bids may lose money on jobs.

CHAPTER 20

MISCELLANEOUS FORMS FOR CONTRACTORS

The miscellaneous forms illustrated and described on the following pages can be used by many contractors to advantage. While it is true that not all of the forms will be required by any one contractor, there is sufficient range to meet the requirement of any size business.

CASH STATEMENT

JOB 110 WEEK ENDING JAN 10, 19--

DATE	SUMMARY	ACCT. NO.	DEBIT		CREDIT	
1/10	CASH EXPENSE	AM-1	4	23		
"	" "	AM-21	300	00		
"	" "	AM-64	9	25		
"	" "	AM-67	20	60		
"	" "	CM-25	12	36		
"	" "	DM-23	11	33		
"	" "	FM-57	5	50		
1/5	CASH FROM OFFICE				325	00
1/7	" " "				100	00
	TOTAL		363	27	425	00
	CASH					
	BALANCE LAST STATEMENT		57	20		
	CASH RECEIVED THIS WEEK		425	00		
	TOTAL CASH		482	20		
	LESS CASH EXPENSE		363	27		
	CASH ON HAND		118	93		

O.K. BY Fred Smith, Supt.

FORM P-102 FRANK R. WALKER CO., PUBLISHERS, CHICAGO

Fig. 319. Cash Statement (Front), Form P-102. Used for Summarizing Cash Expenditures Made by Each Job.

CASH DISTRIBUTION

DATE	DESCRIPTION	ACCT. NO.	AMOUNT	
1/3	CARFARE	AM-1		80
"	PHONE CALL, LONG DISTANCE	"	1	13
1/4	SHOVELS, (INV. ENCL.)	AM-67	18	00
"	" , EXPRESS CHGES	"	2	60
"	TRUCKING, COL. CLIPS & SHORES	CM-25	12	36
"	REPAIRS FOR CONC. MIXER	AM-64	9	25
1/5	PHONE CALLS	AM-1		60
"	CARFARE	"		40
1/6	EXPRESS ON DAMPRFG. MTL.	FM-57	5	50
"	FREIGHT, REIN. ST. ACCES.	DM-23	11	33
"	CARFARE	AM-1		80
"	PHONE CALLS	"		50
"	S & W PLBG. CO., JOB OFFICE PLBG	AM-21	300	00
SIGNED		TOTAL	363	27

FORM P-102

Fig. 319. Cash Distribution (Back), Form P-102. Used for Keeping a Record Of Cash Expenditures Made by Each Job.

CASH STATEMENT

NAME OF WORK *CENTRAL HIGH SCHOOL*   JOB NO. *110*   CASH STATEMENT NO. *10*

REPORT OF RECEIPTS AND DISBURSEMENTS FOR PAYROLL PERIOD ENDING

DATE 19—		CASH RECEIVED FROM OR PAID TO	ACCOUNT TO BE CHARGED OR CREDITED	PAID BY CASH OR CHECK NO.	EXPENDITURES DR.	RECEIPTS CR.
		BROUGHT FORWARD				
JAN	3	CARFARE	AM-1	CASH	80	
"		PHONE CALL, LONG DISTANCE	AM-1	"	1 13	
	4	SHOVELS, INVOICE ATTACHED	AM-67	"	18 00	
"		" , EXPRESS CHARGES	AM-67	"	2 60	
"		TRUCKING, COLUMN CLAMPS & SHORES	CM-25	"	1 2 36	
"		REPAIRS FOR CONCRETE MIXER	AM-64	"	9 25	
	5	PHONE CALLS	AM-1	"	60	
"		CARFARE	AM-1	"	40	
"		CASH FROM OFFICE				325 00
	6	EXPRESS ON DAMPPROOFING MAT'L.	FM-57	"	5 50	
"		FREIGHT ON REIN. STL. ACCESS.	DM-23	"	1 1 33	
"		CARFARE	AM-1	"	80	
"		PHONE CALLS	AM-1	"	50	
"		S & W PLBG. CO. - JOB OFFICE PLBG.	AM-21	"	300 00	
	7	CASH FROM OFFICE				100 00
		TOTAL CASH RECEIPTS AND DISBURSEMENTS			363 27	425 00

CASH STATEMENT

O. K.	BALANCE LAST STATEMENT	57 20
Fred Smith	CASH RECEIVED THIS PERIOD	425 00
I HEREBY CERTIFY THE ABOVE TO BE CORRECT	TOTAL CASH	482 20
J. H. Williams	LESS CASH EXPENSE	363 27
(IN CHARGE)	CASH ON HAND	118 93

FORM 102 (THIS STATEMENT MUST BE FORWARDED TO MAIN OFFICE REGULARLY EACH PAYROLL PERIOD)

STANDARDIZED FORMS FOR CONTRACTORS PRACTICAL

FRANK R. WALKER CO., PUBLISHERS, CHICAGO

Fig. 320. Cash Statement, Form 102. Size 8½ x 11 Inches. Used for Keeping a Record and Summarizing Cash Expenditures Made by Each Job.

Cash Expense Sheets

On the jobs where the superintendent, foreman or timekeeper handle any cash, it is advisable to use a Cash Statement or expense sheet. This sheet should run from week to week and should be sent in with the pay-roll either weekly or semi-monthly, depending upon the system in use.

This sheet should contain a report of all cash expenses on the job, such as carfare, telephone, telegraph, cartage, freight charges, stationery, job office supplies, etc.

Cash statement sheets may be either small or pocket-size forms or they may be a large size sheet about letterhead size. The small sheets are convenient to carry in the pocket on the job but many contractors prefer the larger sheets for office use.

Figure 378 illustrates the back of the pocket-size form, showing just how the expenditures are listed. At the end of each pay-roll period, these items are totaled and a summary of the expenditures is made on the front of the form, Figure 378. A record of all cash receipts is also made, showing just what cash has been received by the job since the last statement.

The bottom of the sheet contains a complete statement, showing cash balance at time of last statement; cash received for current week, together with the total cash on hand. The amount of cash expenditures is deducted from the total cash on hand, leaving the balance or "Cash on Hand" at the time the statement is forwarded to the office.

If a large size sheet is desired, refer to Figure 379 which contains practically the same information as the smaller forms, except that more space is provided for listing the various items.

This sheet is especially valuable to contractors performing work away from the main office, as by sending in a cash statement each week the cash account is kept balanced at all times, and any mistakes or discrepancies may be rectified immediately.

Daily Equipment Use Report

The Daily Equipment Use reports inform the contractor what each piece of equipment did during the work day. Each operator fills in this report and turns it in at the close of the shift. (See illustration.)

This report contains space for Date, Shift, Name, Number and Location of Job, Name and Number of Equipment, together with ample space for describing the various items of work performed and the time required for each operation. Also contains space for listing cause and amount of delays and amount of idle time. Space is also provided for the Cost Engineer to enter account numbers or symbols for each classification.

Warehouse Requisition

The Warehouse Requisition is used to obtain materials from attic stock and tools and equipment from the yard. It may also be used on the job to control issuing tools and equipment to workmen.

As illustrated, the Warehouse Requisition contains space for Number, Name and Location of Job, Number of Pick-up Truck, Driver's Badge Number, together with ample space for description and quantity of items requested. Also contains space for entering account number, unit cost and amount.

The man in charge prepares the Warehouse Requisition in duplicate, retaining one copy for job records.

Voucher Checks are Valuable for the Contractor

A voucher check is a valuable asset to any contractor and if they were more generally used it would eliminate many disputes, arguments and even law suits.

A check that shows right on the face of it, the invoice paid, amount of same, amount of freight, and discounts or other deductions, forms a record of considerable value.

A check of this kind is especially valuable when making payments to sub-contractors on account, as illustrated by Figure 382. This gives the amount of the original contract, together with any credits or extras to same, amounts of previous payments, and amount of present payment, showing just how the account stands at any date. As the endorsement of the check constitutes a receipt, all chance of dispute is eliminated. Checks of this kind may be filled in on the typewriter or ruled for filling in with pen and ink.

DAILY EQUIPMENT USE REPORT

JOB NO. _122_
JOB _R. B. ADAMS Co. WAREHOUSE_ LOCATION _STERLING, WIS._
EQUIPMENT _22-B, BUCYRUS ERIE POWER HOE_

DATE _JULY 15, 19--_
SHIFT _8:00 - 4:30_
OPERATOR-BADGE NO. _162_
EQUIPMENT NO. _X-7_

DESCRIPTION OF WORK

OPERATION	MATERIAL	FROM	TO	QUANTITY	HOURS	ACCOUNT NO.
GEN'L. EXC.	SANDY CLAY	BOILER RM PIT	TRUCKS	360 C.Y.	4½	
TRENCH "	" "	FDTN. TRENCHES	CAST ON GRD.	120 CY	2	
" "	" "	UTILITY TRENCH	" " "	72 CY	1	
DELAYS	REPLACE BROKEN CABLE				½	

NOTE: HOURS OPERATING PLUS DELAYS PLUS IDLE TIME MUST EQUAL TOTAL SHIFT TIME. SHOW HOURS TO NEAREST QUARTER-HOUR ONLY.

IDLE TIME	
TOTAL SHIFT TIME	8

OPERATOR: ACCOUNT NUMBER COLUMN FOR OFFICE USE ONLY

MFD. IN U.S.A. FORM C-120   FRANK R. WALKER CO., PUBLISHERS, CHICAGO

Fig. 321. Daily Equipment Use Report, Form C-120. Size 4¼ x 6¾ Inches. Used for Keeping a Daily Record of Each Piece of Equipment.

WAREHOUSE REQUISITION

JOB NO. _117_
TRUCK NO. _3_
PLEASE DELIVER TO BEARER, BADGE NO. _162_
NAME OF WORK _NORTHWEST SHOPPING CENTER_ LOCATION _ARLINGTON, ILL._

DATE _JULY 9, 19--_
REQ. NO. _2_
SHEET NO. _1_ OF _1_
TO BE USED AT JOB NO. _117_

ACCT. NO.	DESCRIPTION	QUANTITY		UNIT COST		AMOUNT	
	10 LB. SLEDGE HAMMER	6	EA.	5	25	31	50
	#2 ROUND POINT, LONG HANDLE SHOVELS	12	EA.	3	75	45	00
	MATTOCKS	6	EA.	3	00	18	00
	PICKS	12	EA.	2	50	30	00
	3/4" WATER HOSE	200	L.F.		30	60	00
	ELECTRIC HAND SAWS	2	EA.	90	00	180	00
	½" ELECTRIC DRILL	1	EA.	75	00	75	00
	ELECTRIC EXTENSION CORD	200	L.F.		25	50	00
SIGNED _Harvey Anderson_				TOTAL		489	50

FORM P-139   MFD. IN U.S.A. FRANK R. WALKER CO., PUBLISHERS, CHICAGO

Fig. 322. Warehouse Requisition, Form P-139. Size 4¼ x 6¾ Inches. Used for Keeping a Record of Tools and Equipment Withdrawn from Warehouse or Materials Taken from Warehouse to Job.

	BOONE, IOWA. JUL 17 19___ No. 123A	
	PAY TO THE ORDER OF ___---------CENTRAL PLASTERING COMPANY--------- $**531.25**	

★★5₹T DOLS 2₹ CT

		DOLLARS
DATE	DESCRIPTION	AMOUNT

Payment on account of lathing and plastering on the Fred H. Hilles
Residence, 176 Wayne Avenue, Boone, Iowa.

Total Amount of Contract and Extras	$2,448.00	
Amount of this Request	625.00	
Less 15% retained percentage	93.75	
Amount of this payment	$ 531.25	$531.25

BY ENDORSEMENT, THIS CHECK IS ACCEPTED IN FULL PAYMENT OF THE ABOVE ACCOUNT. IF INCORRECT, PLEASE RETURN. NO RECEIPT NECESSARY.

TO THE

FIRST NATIONAL BANK
BOONE, IOWA

JOHN JONES & COMPANY
BY___SAMPLE ONLY SAMPLE

JOHN JONES & COMPANY
GENERAL CONTRACTORS

Fig. 323. Voucher Check

Copy of Freight Bill

For contractors performing work away from the home office where the different materials are shipped to the job on cars, it will be necessary for the job to take care of such items as freight, etc. The main office

COPY OF FREIGHT BILL

_____Railway

_____ Consignor _____Consignee

		DESCRIPTION OF ARTICLES	WEIGHT	RATE	AMOUNT
Car Number					
Car Initials					
No. of W. B.					
Date of W. B.					
Pro No.					
Shipped from					
Shipped to					
			Total Freight		

Original of this Bill sent to   Advance Charges
Date that it was sent   Cartage
Journal Page   Total Paid

Fig. 324. Copy of Freight Bill.

usually requires that all original bills and receipts covering cash expenditures be turned in each week with the pay-rolls and Cash Statement.

The "Copy of Freight Bill" illustrated in Figure 383 will prove useful in instances where it is desirable to retain copies of all paid freight bills on the job, as an exact copy of the original may be obtained by using this form.

A Job Estimate and Cost Record for the Builder Who Doesn't Keep Books!!

While we do not recommend that any contractor should not keep a complete set of books—there are apparently a lot of contractors who do not follow our recommendations.

However, for the contractor who wants a complete record of each house job on one sheet—and nothing more—here is a form that fills the bill.

It is an 11 x 17-inch sheet lithographed on heavy paper or index bristol, that folds to 8½ x 11-inches, so that it may be filed in a regular letter file or if left unfolded and holes punched at the top of the sheet, they may be filed in a 11 x 17-inch post binder.

The front of the sheet (8½ x 11-inches when folded), contains a complete description of the building, location, type of construction, number of rooms, number of baths, recreation room, garage, heating, air conditioning, landscaping, site improvements, square foot area of basement, first floor, second floor and total area, together with the number of cubic feet in the building.

PRACTICAL FORM 145	JOB NO. 176	JOB ESTIMATE AND COST RECORD	DATE MARCH 10, 19--
BUILDING MCLAIN RESIDENCE	LOCATION 1215 E. OAK DR., GLENLAKE, ILL.		BASEMENT AREA 1,910 S.F.
TYPE OF CONSTRUCTION 1 STORY & BASEMENT, FRAME			1ST FLOOR AREA 1,910 S.F.
NUMBER OF ROOMS 6	NUMBER OF BATHS 2	RECREATION ROOM NONE	2ND FLOOR AREA S.F.
GARAGE DOUBLE, ATTACHED	PORCH NONE		PORCH AREA S.F.
HEATING FORCED WARM AIR	AIR CONDITIONING NONE		TOTAL AREA 3,820 S.F.
LANDSCAPING ROUGH GRADING ONLY	SITE IMPROVEMENTS SIDEWALKS ONLY		CUBICAL CONTENTS 34,698 C.F.

SPECIFICATIONS	REMARKS
FOUNDATION: POURED CONCRETE, 1'-8" X 10" WALL FOOTINGS, 8" WALLS, EXT. FACE TO RECEIVE 1 COAT OF DAMPPROOF PAINT.	
BASEMENT FLOOR: 4" CONCRETE ON 4" PEA GRAVEL.	
GARAGE FLOOR: 4" CONCRETE ON 4" PEA GRAVEL, REINFORCED WITH 6" X 6" #6 X #6 WIRE MESH. DRAIN LINE FROM GARAGE TO SHALLOW DRY WELL.	
WALKS: 4" CONCRETE ON 4" PEA GRAVEL.	
1ST FL. FRAMING: 8" STEEL BEAMS ON 4" DIA. PIPE COLUMNS; 2" X 10" #1 FIR JOISTS, 16" ON CENTER; ¾" PLYWOOD SUB-FLOORING.	
EXTERIOR WALLS: 2" X 4" #1 FIR STUDS, 16" ON CENTER; 25/32" INSUL. SHEATHING; ¾" X 10" REDWOOD BEVEL SIDING; 2" ROCK WOOL BATT INSUL.	
ROOF FRAMING: TRUSSED RAFTERS, 2'-0" ON CENTER; ½" PLYWOOD DECKING; FULL-THICK ROCK WOOL BATT INSULATION.	
INTERIOR PARTITIONS: 2" X 4" #1 FIR STUDS, 16" ON CENTER.	
MASONRY: LANNON STONE ABOVE GRADE, CEMENT BLOCK BELOW GRADE	
MILLWORK: ALL TRIM #1 PONDEROSA PINE; EXTERIOR DOORS, 1¾" FLUSH, SOLID CORE, SELECT BIRCH; INTERIOR DOORS 1⅜" FLUSH, HOLLOW CORE, SELECT BIRCH; WINDOWS, 1⅜" DBL-HUNG, SPRING BALANCED, PONDEROSA PINE; ALUM. COMB. STORM & SCREEN DOORS; GARAGE DOOR, 16'-0" X 7'-0" OVERHEAD ACTING. KITCHEN CABINET ALLOWANCE #1,100.00 INSTALLED.	
SHEET METAL WORK: 26 GA. GALVANIZED IRON.	
ROOFING: 210-LB ASPHALT SHINGLES	
GLASS & GLAZING: ALL WINDOW GLASS, D.S.A.	
LATH & PLASTER: 2 COAT GYPSUM CEMENT PLASTER ON GYP. LATH.	
PAINTING & DECORATING: 2 COAT WORK.	
RESILIANT FLOORING: LINOLEUM OR VINYL TILE AS INDICATED ON DWGS.	
CERAMIC TILE: 4'-0" HIGH WAINSCOT IN BATHS, EXCEPT FULL HEIGHT AT TUBS.	
PLUMBING: AS INDICATED ON DRAWINGS.	
HEATING: AS INDICATED ON DRAWINGS.	
ELECTRICAL WORK: AS INDICATED ON DRAWINGS. FIXTURE ALLOW. $200.00	

Fig. 325. Job Estimate and Cost Record, Form 145. Back of Sheet.

FORM 145
NAME **Mc Lean Residence**   LOCATION 1215 E. Oak Dr., Glenlake, Ill.   JOB NO. **176**

JOB ESTIMATE AND COST RECORD

CLASSIFICATION	CONTRACTOR	ESTIMATE AMOUNT	CONTRACT AMOUNT	CHANGES AMOUNT	PAYMENTS TO SUB-CONTRACTORS						ACTUAL COST
					DATE	AMOUNT	DATE	AMOUNT	DATE	AMOUNT	
1. SURVEY	NORTHWEST SURVEYORS	50 00			4/10	50 00					50 00
2. PLANS & SPECIFICATIONS	ARNOLD LINSAY, AIA	275 00	275 00		5/10	150 00	6/10	125 00			275 00
3. PERMITS	VILLAGE OF GLENLAKE	60 00									54 75
4. EXCAVATION & GRADING	T. C. MORGAN, EXCAVATOR	625 00	590 00		5/10	500 00	11/2	90 00			590 00
5. FOUNDATIONS	ANDREWS CONST. CO.	2105 00									2201 50
6. DAMPPROOFING	" " "	20 00									18 25
7. CEMENT FLOORS & WALKS		788 00									772 40
8. STRUCTURAL STEEL	SCHRADER IRON WORKS	250 00	250 00		4/6	250 00					250 00
9. MISC. AND ORN. METAL											
10. MASONRY	WM. PURVIS & SON	860 00	850 00		7/10	400 00	8/8	450 00			850 00
11. CARPENTER LABOR-ROUGH	ANDREWS CONST. CO.	4209 00									4126 80
12. LUMBER - ROUGH	LORD LUMBER CO.	1811 00									1901 17
13. CARPENTER LABOR-FINISH	ANDREWS CONST. CO.	433 00									442 05
14. LUMBER - FINISH	LORD LUMBER CO.	346 00									338 62
15. DOOR & WINDOW FRAMES	ASHLEY MILLWORK CO	1325 00	1300 00		6/10	450 00	8/9	300 00	11/2	550 00	1300 00
16. DOORS AND SASH	INCL. IN #15										
17. DOOR & WINDOW SCREENS	" " "										
18. STORM DOORS & SASH	INLAND SUPPLY CO.	200 00	185 00		11/2	185 00					185 00
19. GARAGE DOORS	OVERHEAD DOOR CO.	230 00	230 00		10/9	230 00					230 00
20. FINISH WOOD FLOORING											
21. WOOD STAIRS	ROUGH ONLY- INCL IN #11										
22. CABINETS	MODERN KITCHENS, INC.	1100 00	1250 00	150 00	11/2	1250 00					1250 00
23. HARDWARE - ROUGH	BUILDERS SUPPLY CO.	100 00									117 26
24. HARDWARE - FINISH	LIND HARDWARE CO.	175 00	167 28		10/9	167 28					167 28
25. WEATHERSTRIPPING	ANDREWS CONST. CO.	25 00									22 10
26. CAULKING		35 00									37 18
27. SHEET METAL	BARTLETT SHEET METAL	150 00	150 00		7/10	100 00	10/9	50 00			150 00
28. ROOFING - MATERIAL	GLENLAKE MATERIALS	320 00									320 00
29. ROOFING - LABOR	ANDREWS CONST. CO.	256 00									248 40
30. GLASS AND GLAZING	HUNTLEY GLASS CO.	700 00	700 00		9/10	550 00	10/9	150 00			700 00
31. INSULATION	ANDREWS CONST. CO.	160 00									149 80
32. LATH AND PLASTER	ADAMS PLASTERING	1350 00	1350 00		9/10	1000 00	10/9	350 00			1350 00
33. PAINTING & DECORATING	CARLSON DECORATING	1250 00	1175 00		9/10	400 00	11/2	775 00			1175 00
34. RESILIENT FLOORING	NIELSEN FLOORS	280 00	280 00		11/2	280 00					280 00
35. CERAMIC TILE	ELGIN TILING	1050 00	1050 00		9/10	500 00	10/9	550 00			1050 00
36. SHADES AND BLINDS											
37. BATHROOM ACCESSORIES	INCL. IN #35										
38. MEDICINE CABINETS	SAMSON DIST.	110 00	110 00		11/2	110 00					110 00
39. PLUMBING	GERALD PLUMBING	2250 00	2200 00		6/10	300 00	7/10	650 00	11/2	1250 00	2200 00
40. SEWER WORK	TONY PELLA	150 00	150 00		6/10	150 00					150 00
41. HEATING	LARSEN HEATING	1150 00	1150 00		7/10	550 00	8/9	500 00	11/2	100 00	1150 00
42. AIR CONDITIONING											
43. ELECTRIC WORK	TRACY ELEC. CO.	1410 00	1400 00		8/9	500 00	9/10	650 00	11/2	250 00	1400 00
44. LIGHTING FIXTURES	" " - ALLOWANCE	200 00	276 00	76 00	11/2	276 00					276 00
45. DRIVEWAY											
46. LANDSCAPING											
47.											
48.											
49.											
50.											
51.											
52.											
53.											
54.											
55.											
56.											
57.											
58.											
59.											
60.											
61.											
62.											
63.											
64.											
65.											
66.											
67.											
68.											
69.											
70.											
71. SUPERVISION		500 00									561 25
72. TOOLS AND EQUIPMENT		250 00									250 00
73. RUBBISH REMOVAL		50 00									62 20
74. INSURANCE		250 00									231 85
75. SOCIAL SECURITY TAXES		300 00									292 20
76. TOTALS		27158 00	15138 28	226 00		8348 28		4640 00		2150 00	27290 56

77. ESTIMATED BUILDING COST	27158 00	ACTUAL BLDG. COST	27290 56
78. OVERHEAD AND PROFIT	2716 00	LOAN EXPENSES	300 00
79. BUILDING CONTRACT	29874 00	LOT COST	925 00
80. CHANGES IN CONTRACT	226 00	LEGAL EXPENSES	50 00
81. LOT	2100 00	SALES EXPENSES	730 00
82. LEGAL EXPENSES	50 00	TOTAL ACTUAL COST	29295 56
83. SALESMAN'S COMMISSION	705 00		
84. SELLING PRICE	32955 00	PROFIT OR LOSS	3659 44

PURCHASER MR & MRS ARTHUR H. McLEAN   DATE 3/10/--
ADDRESS 5922 N. KENDALL AVE.   CHICAGO, ILL.   ARDMORE   TEL. NO. Z-1655
PRICE $32,955.00   DOWN PAYMENT
LOAN BY GLENLAKE SAVINGS & LOAN ASSOC.

CASH RECEIVED

RECEIVED FROM	AMOUNT DUE	DATE	FIRST	DATE	SECOND	DATE	THIRD	DATE	FOURTH	DATE	FIFTH	TOTAL
OWNER MR & MRS. ARTHUR H. McLEAN	12955 00	4/3	955 00	6/15	4000 00	8/24	7000 00	10/26	1000 00			12955 00
LOAN CO. GLENLAKE SAVINGS & LOAN	20000 00							10/26	8000 00	11/30	12000 00	20000 00
TOTAL	32955 00		955 00		4000 00		7000 00		9000 00		12000 00	32955 00

MFD. IN U.S.A.
FRANK R. WALKER CO., PUBLISHERS, CHICAGO

Fig. 325. Job Estimate and Cost Record, Form 145. Front of Sheet.

ESTIMATE AND COST SUMMARY

PROJECT: STORE BUILDING   ESTIMATOR: F.W.   ESTIMATE NO. 429
LOCATION: 1292 MAIN   EXTENSIONS: J.Y.L.   SHEET NO. 2 OF 5
ARCHITECT ENGINEER: ANDREWS & SMITH   CHECKED: O.L.T.   DATE Nov. 4, 19--
CLASSIFICATION: GENERAL

| | | ESTIMATED COST | | | | | | | | | ACTUAL COST | | | | | | | |
| | | MATERIAL | | | | LABOR | | SUB-CONTRACTS OTHER COSTS | TOTAL ESTIMATE | % COMPLETE | MATERIAL | | | LABOR | | SUB-CONTRACTS OTHER COSTS | TOTAL COST | PROFIT OR (LOSS) |
CODE	DESCRIPTION	UNIT	QUANTITY	UNIT COST	AMOUNT	HOURS	AMOUNT				QUANTITY USED	UNIT COST	AMOUNT	HOURS	AMOUNT			
B-21	EXCAVATION	CY	371	1.27	472.00				472.00	100	320	1.27	406.00				406.00	66.00
22	GRADING					3	15.00		45.00	100				5	75.00		75.00	(30.00)
C-1-9	CONCRETE FOUNDATIONS				84.00	64	218.00		302.00	100			52.00	60	204.00		256.00	46.00
C-10-9	PLACING CONCRETE	CY	40	11.90	476.00	400	1640.00		2116.00	75	52	11.90	619.00	418	1713.80		2332.80	(216.00)

TOTALS

COMMENTS

MFG. IN U.S.A. FORM 550   FRANK R. WALKER CO., PUBLISHERS, CHICAGO

Fig. 326. Estimate and Cost Summary, Form 550, Size 17 x 11 inches

The front of the sheet also contains a space for a brief specification and any remarks regarding the building and its construction.

The inside of the sheet, 11 x 17-inches, contains a complete estimate and cost record of the job, giving the amount estimated for each branch of work, amount at which actual contracts were let, changes—extras and credits—together with three spaces showing dates and amounts of all payments to each sub-contractor or material supplier, also the total estimated and total actual cost of the building.

The sheet also gives the actual building cost, lot cost, loan expense, legal expense, sales expense, total actual cost complete, selling price and profit or loss on each job.

The bottom of the sheet contains a complete record of payments received by the contractor from the owner and loan company, with space for five payments on each job.

The back of the sheet contains a complete check list for house construction.

An excellent sheet for any home builder—and a MUST if you do not keep books.

Estimate and Cost Summary

Form 550 serves as a progress report as well as a summary of the final results of a project.

The form filled out frequently as the work progresses aids the contractor to detect immediately the areas in which the costs are exceeding estimate, enabling him to take remedial steps. the first half of the form provides for classification of the various operations of a job by code number and job description, the estimated quantities required and amount, estimated hours and labor, sub-contracts and the total of the estimates. The actual costs incurred are entered on the second half of the form. The total costs compared to the total estimates show the net results ending in either a profit or loss. Adjustments required for extra work and change orders should be shown as separate items correctly described, classified and coded.

The completed summary will be a valuable reference for similar jobs in the future.

Equipment Rental Forms

EQUIPMENT RENTAL									SHEET NO. ____ OF ____			

JOB _____
NAME _____　　　　　　　WEEK ENDING _____

DESCRIPTION OF EQUIPMENT	EQUIP. NO.								HOURS	RATE	AMOUNT
TOTALS											

FORM P-131

MFD. IN U.S.A.　　　　　　　FRANK R. WALKER CO., PUBLISHERS, CHICAGO

Fig. 327. Equipment Rental. Form P-131. Size 4¼ x 6¾ Inches.

MFD IN U.S.A

MONTHLY RENTAL EQUIPMENT SUMMARY
FOR THE MONTH OF _____ 19____

PROJECT
ADDRESS
CITY & STATE

EQUIPMENT ON PROJECT		1	2	3	4	5	6	7	8	9	10	11	12	13	14	15	16	17	18	19	20	21	22	23	24	25	26	27	28	29	30	31	TOTAL HOURS	RATE	AMOUNT
DESCRIPTION	SERIAL NO.																																			
TOTAL																																				

FORM 141

Fig. 328. Monthly Rental Equipment Summary. Form 141. Size 8½ x 14 Inches.